ENGINEERING MATHEMATICS

Volume 1

ENGINEERING MATHEMATICS

Volume 1

A. J. M. SPENCER
D. F. PARKER
D. S. BERRY
A. H. ENGLAND
T. R. FAULKNER
W. A. GREEN
J. T. HOLDEN
D. MIDDLETON
T. G. ROGERS

Department of Theoretical Mechanics
University of Nottingham

 VAN NOSTRAND REINHOLD COMPANY LIMITED

New York - Cincinnati - Toronto - London - Melbourne

© A. J. M. Spencer, D. F. Parker, D. S. Berry, A. H. England, T. R. Faulkner, W. A. Green, J. T. Holden, D. Middleton and T. G. Rogers, 1977

ISBN 0 442 30146 4 cloth
ISBN 0 442 30147 2 paper

Library of Congress Catalog Card No. 76—45663

Published by Van Nostrand Reinhold Company Ltd.,
Molly Millars Lane, Wokingham, Berkshire, England

Published in 1977 by Van Nostrand Reinhold Company
A Division of Litton Educational Publishing, Inc.,
450 West 33rd Street, New York, N.Y. 10001, U.S.A.

Van Nostrand Reinhold Limited
1410 Birchmount Road, Scarborough, Ontario, M1P 2E7

Van Nostrand Reinhold Australia Pty. Limited
17 Queen Street, Mitcham, Victoria 3132, Australia

Library of Congress Cataloguing in Publication Data
Main entry under title:
Engineering mathematics.
    Includes bibliographies and index.
    1. Engineering mathematics.   I. Spencer,
Anthony James Merrill.
TA330.E53   515'.14   76—45663

ISBN 0-442-30146-4
ISBN 0-442-30147-2 pbk.

Typeset in Great Britain by Preface Ltd., Salisbury
Printed in Great Britain by Biddles Ltd, Guildford, Surrey

Preface

This book is the first volume of a two-volume text on mathematics for engineering students in universities and polytechnics, for use in the second and subsequent years of a first degree course. The text is primarily designed to assist engineering undergraduates and their teachers, but we hope it may also prove of value to students of other disciplines that employ mathematics as a tool, to mathematicians who are interested in applications of their subject, and as a reference book for practising engineers and others. Volume 1 covers mathematical topics which most engineering students are required to study; Volume 2 deals with more advanced subjects which are often available as options in the later stages of an undergraduate course.

The text is based on courses in mathematics given by the authors to the engineering students of the University of Nottingham. These courses have evolved over the last sixteen years, and have been developed in close consultation with our fellow teachers in the engineering departments of the University. In preparing the text, we have kept in mind the constraints imposed by the normal three or four year undergraduate course, and we believe that the choice of material in the two volumes is realistic in that respect. For completeness, some topics are pursued a little further than an engineering mathematics lecture course would normally take them, but all the material and examples should be within the grasp of a competent engineering undergraduate student. The greater part of Chapters 1–4 and 7–12 of Volume 1 forms a core of subjects which are included in most engineering courses. The remaining chapters of Volume 1, and those of Volume 2, are more often studied as optional subjects. At Nottingham, almost all of the material in both volumes is taught to engineering students, although no single student studies all of the topics included. In our experience, this pattern of a core syllabus supplemented by a range of optional courses has proved to be a satisfactory way of meeting the varying needs of engineering students and their departments.

We have tried to give equal emphasis to both the analytical and the numerical aspects of engineering mathematics, so that the reader is encouraged to make use of whatever mathematical tool is best for the problem he has in hand. Until quite recently, engineering mathematics courses mainly comprised analysis. Most of this traditionally taught material is still essential, and it is not neglected in this text. However, recent trends have increased the importance of algebraic and numerical methods relative to analytical methods, and this is reflected in the list of contents of both volumes. Statistics, also, assumes an ever-increasing importance in engineering, and is the subject of a chapter in each volume. A feature of Volume 2 is the inclusion of two chapters on optimization methods, which are now used extensively in engineering practice. Computer programming as such is not included because we feel that the teaching of this subject should be related to the computing facilities available to the student, and these vary greatly from one institution to another.

As far as possible within the space available, we have related the mathematics to its applications in engineering through illustrative examples and problems. The various topics have been approached in ways which we hope are relevant and useful to engineers. Since this is a book on the use of mathematics, we have made frequent use of intuitive arguments and have not attempted a standard of rigour which would be expected in a book designed for mathematics specialists. Nevertheless, we have tried to make our mathematical arguments accurate and precise. We have not hesitated to quote useful results without proof when we consider the proofs to be too difficult or too time-consuming for engineering undergraduates, but a short bibliography is appended to each chapter to assist the reader who wishes to pursue any topic further. At all stages the mathematical arguments are given in sufficient detail for the reader to be able to follow them with a minimum of filling-in of intermediate steps, and we expect a student working on his own to be quite capable of following them.

The text contains a large number of worked examples, many of which relate to engineering applications. A good selection of exercises on specific topics is given at the ends of sections. Each chapter concludes with a set of miscellaneous problems. These exercises and problems form an essential part of the text, and answers to them are given at the end of each volume. Many of the problems are taken from examination papers set for second and third year engineering students of the University of Nottingham in the period 1960–76, and we acknowledge the University's permission to make use of these questions.

Each chapter was first drafted by one or two of the authors, read and checked by several others, and then discussed and amended until a mutually agreed version was produced. The text is therefore a truly collaborative effort; no part of it is the sole work of any individual , and we share responsibility for the whole . Of course, this will not inhibit us from blaming each other for the slips and errors which, despite all our efforts to eliminate them, no doubt still remain.

Among many who helped with the preparation of the manuscript, we particularly thank Mrs. Judy Hind who, as well as typing several chapters, gave us a great deal of assistance with the preparation of the final draft, dealing with correspondence, and in many other ways.

Finally, the rest of us gladly acknowledge our gratitude to David Parker who, in addition to his share of the writing, acted as our 'liaison officer' with the publishers, compelled us to (nearly) meet our deadlines, and generally organized and coordinated our activities. Without his strenuous and time-consuming efforts this book, if it had come into existence at all, would be much less consistent than it is.

Department of Theoretical Mechanics   A.J.M.S.   W.A.G.
University of Nottingham   D.F.P.   J.T.H.
June 1976   D.S.B.   D.M.
                                             A.H.E.   T.G.R.
                                             T.R.F.

The Greek Alphabet

α	A	alpha		ν	N	nu
β	B	beta		ξ	Ξ	xi
γ	Γ	gamma		o	O	omicron
δ	Δ	delta		π	Π	pi
ϵ	E	epsilon		ρ	P	rho
ζ	Z	zeta		σ	Σ	sigma
η	H	eta		τ	T	tau
θ	Θ	theta		υ	Υ	upsilon
ι	I	iota		ϕ	Φ	phi
κ	K	kappa		χ	X	chi
λ	Λ	lambda		ψ	Ψ	psi
μ	M	mu		ω	Ω	omega

Contents

CONTENTS OF VOLUME 2

CHAPTER 1

Ordinary Differential Equations

1.1 INTRODUCTION

Any equation whose terms contain differential coefficients (or derivatives) of an unknown function is a differential equation. A very large proportion, probably the majority, of the analytical problems that an engineer is likely to meet involve the solution of differential equations. They arise so frequently in practice because most of the physical laws that control the environment in which an engineer has to work are most conveniently expressed in terms of differential equations. To give a simple example, one of the most important laws in mechanics is Newton's second law, which states that the rate of change of momentum of a body is proportional to the force applied to it. For motion in a straight line, the mathematical statement of this law is

$$\frac{\mathrm{d}}{\mathrm{d}t}(mv) = F,$$

where m is mass, v is speed, t is time, and F is force. Direct measurement of speed is difficult, but measurement of distance is easy, so we are more likely to use the equation in the form

$$\frac{\mathrm{d}}{\mathrm{d}t}\left(m\frac{\mathrm{d}x}{\mathrm{d}t}\right) = F,$$

where x denotes distance along the line from some origin on it. If the force F is given as a function of time t, then x, the distance travelled, can be calculated by solving the differential equation. Two other items of information, for example the position from which the body starts, and its initial speed, will also be required.

Many other physical systems with which engineers have to deal are most easily described by means of differential equations. Some examples are the equations of electromagnetism, of fluid mechanics, of elasticity theory, of heat and mass transfer, of electrical circuit theory, of chemical reactions, and of nuclear reactions. Some of these will be used as illustrations later in this chapter and in subsequent chapters.

An engineer requiring an answer to a problem which can be expressed in terms of one or more differential equations has (a) to formulate the correct equations and (b) to extract the information he requires from these equations. Usually step (b) involves solving the equations in order to obtain numerical values of the dependent variable, although often useful qualitative information about the solution can be obtained without actually solving the equations (see Chapter 6 of Volume 2).

This chapter and others will deal with analytical and numerical methods of solution; that is, with step (b). However, (a) is just as important. It is assumed that the reader will meet elsewhere many problems which lead to the formulation of differential equations. Often the engineer has to deal with a standard problem such as the calculation of the deflection of a beam, or finding the current in an electrical circuit. In such cases, the appropriate equations are well known and will be found in any suitable textbook. It should be borne in mind, though, that the engineer engaged in research or advanced development work may well encounter situations in which he has to formulate differential equations as well as to solve them.

Classification of Differential Equations

The subject of differential equations is vast, and the first task is to break it down into more manageable parts. The major division is into *ordinary differential equations*, which involve only *ordinary* derivatives of a function of a single independent variable, and *partial differential equations*, which involve *partial* derivatives of a function of more than one independent variable. The other main classification is by *order*; the order of a differential equation is the order of the highest order differential coefficient occurring in the equation. A differential equation is *linear* if it is of first degree in the dependent variable and its derivatives; otherwise it is non-linear.

In the remainder of this chapter, methods of solution of some of the simple, but important, ordinary differential equations which are amenable to analytical solution are described. An analytical, as distinct from a numerical or graphical, solution is one which can be derived by using the methods of calculus. It can usually be expressed in terms of familiar functions such as polynomials, trigonometrical functions (sines, tangents, etc.), exponentials, and so on. Some important partial differential equations are the subject of Chapter 7. Further theory of ordinary differential equations will be presented in Chapter 6 of Volume 2. Several other chapters also have a bearing on the problem of solution of differential equations by analytical methods.

An analytical solution of a differential equation has several advantages over a numerical solution. First there is an obvious saving in computing time and cost. Second and more important, an analytical solution, if it is not too complicated, will show clearly the effect on the solution of the various constants (usually called *parameters*) which appear in the equation. In a practical problem these parameters will represent physical quantities, such as the resistance of a circuit or the viscosity of a fluid, and it is often important for a designer to be able to assess the effect of varying such quantities. This information is often clearly shown by an analytical solution but is laborious to obtain in a numerical one, particularly if several parameters are involved. Another advantage of an analytical solution is that it may yield qualitative information about the solution, such as whether it is oscillatory or non-oscillatory, how it behaves when the independent variable is very large or very small, and the existence of maxima, minima and infinities. Such information may not be evident from a numerical solution which is necessarily restricted to a limited range of the independent variable. For these reasons it is always advisable, when confronted by a differential equation, first to investigate the possibility of obtaining an analytical solution. However, although analytical solutions are available for many important differential equations, there are many more equations whose solutions cannot be expressed in a simple analytical form. To solve such equations there is often no alternative but to use numerical methods, and numerical methods of solution of differential equations are the subject of Chapter 7 of Volume 2.

1.2 GEOMETRICAL INTERPRETATION OF SOLUTIONS OF ORDINARY DIFFERENTIAL EQUATIONS

The reader will be familiar with the idea that an equation relating two variables x and y can be represented by a curve in the x, y plane. This idea is a useful one. If the curve is drawn accurately, then corresponding values of x and y can be read off from it, and the equation is solved graphically. A rough sketch of the curve may yield valuable qualitative information, for example about the existence of maxima and minima of y, the behaviour of y when x becomes very large, and so on. It is therefore natural to enquire if solutions of differential equations can also be represented graphically.

First-order Equations

A first-order differential equation, with y as dependent variable and x as independent variable, can be expressed in the form

$$\frac{dy}{dx} = f(x, y), \tag{1}$$

where $f(x, y)$ is a known function. For simplicity suppose that $f(x, y)$ is a single-valued function of x and y which is defined for $-\infty < x < \infty$, $-\infty < y < \infty$. The arguments need be modified only slightly if $f(x, y)$ is defined for limited ranges of the values of x and y.

Choose *any* pair of values (x_0, y_0) of x and y. These correspond to the point $P_0(x_0, y_0)$ in the x, y plane, shown in Fig. 1.1(a). Substituting these values in the right-hand side of equation (1) gives a value of dy/dx corresponding to (x_0, y_0). The derivative dy/dx represents the slope of a curve, so a line $P_0 P_1$, with slope $f(x_0, y_0)$, is drawn through P_0. A short distance along this line, at P_1, x and y have the values x_1, y_1, and a new value of $dy/dx = f(x_1, y_1)$ can be calculated. Then the process can be repeated by drawing a new line $P_1 P_2$ through P_1 with slope $f(x_1, y_1)$ and so on. In this way we arrive at the series of straight-line segments $P_0 P_1 P_2 P_3 P_4 \ldots$ illustrated in Fig. 1.1(a), which have the property that the relation between the coordinates of a typical point P_r and the slope of the line segment starting at P_r satisfies the equation (1).

If the distance between successive points $P_0, P_1, P_2 \ldots$ is made smaller, the series of line segments resembles more and more a smooth continuous curve through P_0. In the limit when the distance between successive points tends to zero, the smooth curve through P_0 illustrated in Fig. 1.1(b) is obtained. This curve has the property that

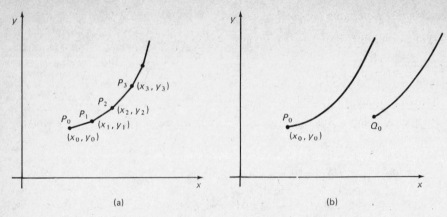

Fig. 1.1   Graphical solution of first-order equation

equation (1) is satisfied by the coordinates and slope at any point on the curve. It may therefore be said that the curve represents equation (1).

In this construction the point P_0 was chosen at random; we could equally well have started at the point Q_0, say, and obtained the curve through Q_0 shown in Fig. 1.1(b), which represents equation (1) just as well as the curve through P_0. The same holds for any other point which does not lie on the curve through P_0, so that there is an infinite number (a *family*) of curves which represent equation (1). Thus a differential equation corresponds not to a single curve, but to a *family of curves*. This is not really surprising, because solving a differential equation involves integration, which introduces a constant of integration. The different curves of the family correspond to the different values the constant of integration may take. As a very simple example, the differential equation

$$\frac{dy}{dx} = 3x^2 \tag{2}$$

has the solution

$$y = x^3 + C, \tag{3}$$

and the family of curves representing equation (2) is the family which is obtained by taking all possible values for the integration constant C in equation (3).

In a practical problem it will usually be necessary to pick out one particular curve from the family. In order to do this, it is necessary to have some additional information, called an *initial condition* or a *boundary condition*. For example, equation (1) may be given together with the information that $y = 1$ when $x = 1$. Then the required curve must pass through $(1, 1)$, so P_0 may be chosen to be the point $(1, 1)$, and the curve is then fixed. If the condition $y = 1$ when $x = 1$ is given with equation (2) and its solution (3), then $C = 0$, and we have the unambiguous solution $y = x^3$.

Geometrical properties of solutions of first-order equations are discussed in more detail in Chapter 6 of Volume 2.

Second-order Equations

A second-order differential equation can be expressed in the form

$$\frac{d^2y}{dx^2} = f(x, y, dy/dx). \tag{4}$$

In dealing with second-order differential equations, it is often helpful to introduce an additional variable $p = dy/dx$. Equation (4) is then replaced by the pair of first-order equations

$$\frac{dy}{dx} = p, \quad \frac{dp}{dx} = f(x, y, p). \tag{5}$$

Since equation (4) follows from equations (5) by eliminating p, equations (4) and (5) are equivalent to one another.

   To construct a graphical solution, we work simultaneously in the x, y and x, p planes illustrated in Fig. 1.2(a). Choose arbitrarily the values x_0, y_0, p_0; these correspond to the points P_0 and P_0' respectively. Then the line segments P_0P_1 and

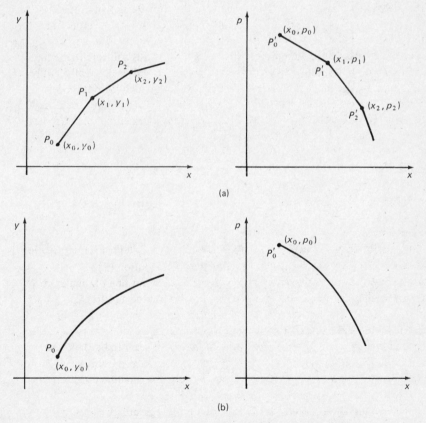

Fig. 1.2   Graphical solution of second-order equation

$P_0' P_1'$ are constructed with slopes p_0 and $f(x_0, y_0, p_0)$ respectively. On these lines points P_1 and P_1' with the same value x_1 of the x-coordinate are chosen, and the process is repeated so that the series of straight-line segments shown in Fig. 1.2(a) is obtained. In the limit when the difference between successive values of x tends to zero, we obtain the smooth curves shown in Fig. 1.2(b), which represent a solution of equations (5) or, equivalently, of equation (4).

In this construction both P_0 and P_0' were chosen arbitrarily, and a different pair of curves results for each choice of this pair of points. Two additional pieces of information are required to select a particular pair of curves; for example, it might be specified that $y = 0$ and $dy/dx = 1$, when $x = 0$.

The need for two conditions corresponds to the fact that the solution of a second-order differential equation in effect involves two integrations, and so two constants of integration arise. In general, the solution of an nth order differential equation contains n constants of integration, and n additional conditions are required to determine a particular solution.

The constructions described above are the basis of several methods of numerical solution of differential equations, which will be described in Chapter 7 of Volume 2.

Differential Equation of a Family of Curves

It has been shown that the differential equation (1) can be represented by a family of curves. Conversely, to a family of curves there corresponds a differential equation. Suppose the family of curves is represented by the equation

$$g(x, y, a) = 0, \tag{6}$$

where a is a parameter whose different values determine the different curves of the family. To find the differential equation of the family, equation (6) is differentiated with respect to x, and a is eliminated from the resulting equation and equation (6). As an example, consider the equation

$$x^2 - 2ax + y^2 = 0, \tag{7}$$

which represents a circle of radius a, with its centre at $(a, 0)$. The different curves of the family are obtained by varying a. By differentiating equation (7) with respect to x, we obtain

$$2x - 2a + 2y \frac{dy}{dx} = 0, \tag{8}$$

and eliminating a from (7) and (8) gives

$$\frac{dy}{dx} = \frac{y^2 - x^2}{2xy}, \tag{9}$$

which is the differential equation of the family of circles described above. It will be shown in §1.3 that equation (7) can be recovered by integrating the differential equation (9).

Exercises

1. A third-order differential equation can be expressed in the form

$$\frac{d^3y}{dx^3} = f\left(x, y, \frac{dy}{dx}, \frac{d^2y}{dx^2}\right).$$

Verify that this is equivalent to the set of three first-order equations

$$\frac{dy}{dx} = p, \quad \frac{dp}{dx} = q, \quad \frac{dq}{dx} = f(x, y, p, q),$$

and outline a graphical scheme for solving these equations.

2. Find the differential equations of the following families of curves:

(a) $y^2 = 4ax$, (b) $y = a\exp(x^2)$. (c) $y = \sin ax$.

1.3 FIRST-ORDER EQUATIONS

The first-order ordinary differential equation (1) may be multiplied by any function $N(x, y)$, and then takes the form

$$M(x, y) + N(x, y)\frac{dy}{dx} = 0, \tag{10}$$

where $M(x, y) = -N(x, y)f(x, y)$. It is sometimes convenient to introduce the *differentials* dx and dy, and write equation (10) as

$$M(x, y)dx + N(x, y)dy = 0.$$

However, the use of differentials can be confusing, and they will not be employed in this chapter.

There is no general method of analytical solution of equations of the form (10), but there are a number of special types of first-order equation for which standard methods of solution are available. The most important of these will be described.

(a) *Equations with the Variables Separable*

If equation (10) can be arranged so that M is a function of x only, and N is a function of y only, it is said that the variables are *separable*. The equation then becomes

$$M(x) + N(y)\frac{dy}{dx} = 0. \tag{11}$$

To solve, integrate equation (11) throughout with respect to x; thus

$$\int M(x)\,dx + \int N(y)\frac{dy}{dx}dx = C,$$

or

$$\int M(x)\, dx + \int N(y)\, dy = C,$$

where C is a constant of integration. The solution therefore reduces to the integration of the functions $M(x)$ and $N(y)$.

EXAMPLE 1

$$2 - x \tanh y \frac{dy}{dx} = 0.$$

This is not of the form (11) as it stands, but becomes of this form on division by x. Thus

$$\frac{2}{x} - \tanh y \frac{dy}{dx} = 0,$$

$$\int \frac{2}{x}\, dx - \int \tanh y\, dy = C,$$

$$\log x^2 - \log \cosh y = C.$$

This solution can be expressed in a neater form by choosing a new constant C_1 such that $C = \log C_1$. We then have

$$\log x^2 = \log(C_1 \cosh y), \quad \text{or} \quad x^2 = C_1 \cosh y.$$

(b) *Homogeneous Equations*

These are equations which can be expressed in the form

$$\frac{dy}{dx} = f\left(\frac{y}{x}\right), \tag{12}$$

in which x and y appear only in the ratio y/x. The function f is said to be a *homogeneous function* of degree zero in x and y. A homogeneous function of degree zero can easily be recognized, because if $g(x, y)$ is such a function, then for any multiplier λ we have $g(x, y) = g(\lambda x, \lambda y)$. Thus to check if $g(x, y)$ is homogeneous of degree zero, simply replace x and y by λx and λy, and observe whether or not this changes the function.

A homogeneous equation can always be converted to an equation with separable variables by making the substitution $y = xv$, and eliminating y in favour of the new variable v. Then

$$y = xv, \quad \frac{dy}{dx} = v + x \frac{dv}{dx}, \quad f\left(\frac{y}{x}\right) = f(v), \tag{13}$$

and equation (12) becomes

$$v + x\frac{dv}{dx} = f(v), \quad \text{or} \quad \frac{1}{x} + \frac{1}{v - f(v)}\frac{dv}{dx} = 0$$

which is separable.

EXAMPLE 2

$$\frac{dy}{dx} = \frac{y^2 - x^2}{2xy}.$$

This equation was obtained in §1.2 as the equation (9) of the family of curves (7). The right-hand side is a homogeneous function, because it can be written as $\frac{1}{2}\{(y/x) - (y/x)^{-1}\}$ which depends only on y/x. Alternatively, we have

$$\frac{(\lambda y)^2 - (\lambda x)^2}{2(\lambda x)(\lambda y)} = \frac{\lambda^2(y^2 - x^2)}{2\lambda^2 xy} = \frac{y^2 - x^2}{2xy}.$$

The substitution (13) transforms the equation to

$$v + x\frac{dv}{dx} = \frac{v^2 x^2 - x^2}{2vx^2} = \frac{v^2 - 1}{2v},$$

or, after rearrangement,

$$x\frac{dv}{dx} + \frac{v^2 + 1}{2v} = 0.$$

Separating variables and integrating now gives

$$\int \frac{2v\,dv}{v^2 + 1} + \int \frac{dx}{x} = 0, \quad \text{so that} \quad \log(v^2 + 1) + \log x = \log 2a,$$

or

$$x(v^2 + 1) = 2a,$$

where the constant of integration has been expressed as $\log 2a$. To complete the solution now substitute back y/x for v to obtain, after a little rearrangement,

$$y^2 - 2ax + x^2 = 0.$$

Thus equation (7) is recovered as the solution of equation (9).

(c) *Equations Reducible to Homogeneous Form*

The equation

$$\frac{dy}{dx} = \frac{a_1 x + b_1 y + c_1}{a_2 x + b_2 y + c_2}, \tag{14}$$

where $a_1, b_1, c_1, a_2, b_2, c_2$ are constants, is not homogeneous, but provided

$a_1 b_2 \neq a_2 b_1$ it can be made homogeneous by the substitution

$$x = X + \alpha, \quad y = Y + \beta, \tag{15}$$

where α and β are constants to be chosen later. Since

$$\frac{dy}{dx} = \frac{dy}{dY} \frac{dY}{dX} \frac{dX}{dx}, \quad \text{and} \quad \frac{dx}{dX} = 1, \quad \frac{dy}{dY} = 1,$$

it follows that $dy/dx = dY/dX$. Hence, substituting equations (15) into equation (14) gives

$$\frac{dY}{dX} = \frac{a_1 X + b_1 Y + a_1 \alpha + b_1 \beta + c_1}{a_2 X + b_2 Y + a_2 \alpha + b_2 \beta + c_2}. \tag{16}$$

This reduces to the homogeneous equation

$$\frac{dY}{dX} = \frac{a_1 X + b_1 Y}{a_2 X + b_2 Y}$$

if α and β (which are still at our disposal) are chosen to satisfy the equations

$$a_1 \alpha + b_1 \beta + c_1 = 0, \quad a_2 \alpha + b_2 \beta + c_2 = 0. \tag{17}$$

Provided that $a_1 b_2 \neq a_2 b_1$, equations (17) have a unique solution for α and β. The exceptional case $a_1 b_2 = a_2 b_1$ is discussed in (d) below.

EXAMPLE 3

$$\frac{dy}{dx} = \frac{x + y + 3}{x - y + 1}.$$

This equation is of the form (14). The substitution (15) converts it to

$$\frac{dY}{dX} = \frac{X + Y + \alpha + \beta + 3}{X - Y + \alpha - \beta + 1},$$

so α and β are chosen so that

$$\alpha + \beta + 3 = 0, \quad \alpha - \beta + 1 = 0.$$

The solution of these is $\alpha = -2, \beta = -1$, so that $x = X - 2, y = Y - 1$, and now

$$\frac{dY}{dX} = \frac{X + Y}{X - Y}.$$

Since this is homogeneous, substitute $Y = vX$ to obtain

$$v + X \frac{dv}{dX} = \frac{1 + v}{1 - v}, \quad X \frac{dv}{dX} = \frac{1 + v^2}{1 - v},$$

and hence

$$\int \frac{1 - v}{1 + v^2} \, dv = \int \frac{dX}{X} + C.$$

After the integration, this becomes

$$\tan^{-1} v - \tfrac{1}{2} \log(1 + v^2) = \log X + C,$$

or

$$\tan^{-1} v - \tfrac{1}{2} \log\{X^2(1 + v^2)\} = C.$$

On substituting back $v = Y/X = (y + 1)/(x + 2)$, $X = x + 2$, we obtain

$$\tan^{-1}\left(\frac{y + 1}{x + 2}\right) - \tfrac{1}{2} \log\{(x + 2)^2 + (y + 1)^2\} = C.$$

(d) *The Case of Equation (14) with* $a_1 b_2 = a_2 b_1$

In this exceptional case the method of (c) cannot be applied. However, now $a_1/a_2 = b_1/b_2$ and $a_2 x + b_2 y$ is a multiple of $a_1 x + b_1 y$. Consequently the equation becomes separable by making the substitution $z = a_1 x + b_1 y$, and eliminating y in favour of z. The following example illustrates the method.

EXAMPLE 4

$$\frac{dy}{dx} = \frac{2x + y + 1}{4x + 2y + 3}.$$

It is easily verified that $a_1 b_2 - a_2 b_1 = 0$. Hence substitute

$$z = 2x + y, \qquad \frac{dz}{dx} = 2 + \frac{dy}{dx}$$

and the equation becomes

$$\frac{dz}{dx} - 2 = \frac{z + 1}{2z + 3}, \qquad \text{or} \qquad \frac{dz}{dx} = \frac{5z + 7}{2z + 3}.$$

The equation is now separable. The integration is straightforward and is left as an exercise.

(e) *The Linear First-order Equation*

This equation can be expressed in the form

$$\frac{dy}{dx} + P(x)y = Q(x), \tag{18}$$

where $P(x)$ and $Q(x)$ are given functions of x. The characteristic feature of this equation is that it is linear in y and dy/dx. Equations of this kind occur frequently in applications, and this is probably the most important type of first-order differential equation. The method of solution is to multiply by the *integrating factor*

$\exp(\int P(x)\,dx)$, whereupon the equation becomes

$$\frac{dy}{dx} \exp(\int P(x)\,dx) + P(x)y \exp(\int P(x)\,dx) = Q(x) \exp(\int P(x)\,dx),$$

which may be written

$$\frac{d}{dx}\{y \exp(\int P(x)\,dx)\} = Q(x) \exp(\int P(x)\,dx).$$

The solution follows by integrating both sides with respect to x, and is illustrated by the following example.

EXAMPLE 5

$$\frac{dy}{dx} - 2y \cot x = 2 \sin^3 x \cos x.$$

In this example $P(x) = -2 \cot x$ (note that the minus sign must be included in $P(x)$). Hence

$$\int P(x)\,dx = -2 \int \cot x \, dx = -2 \log \sin x.$$

There is no need to include the constant of integration, although it will do no harm if inserted. The integrating factor is therefore

$$\exp(-2 \log \sin x) = \frac{1}{\sin^2 x}.$$

On multiplying by this integrating factor, the equation becomes

$$\frac{1}{\sin^2 x} \frac{dy}{dx} - \frac{2 \cos x}{\sin^3 x} y = 2 \sin x \cos x.$$

If the integrating factor has been correctly calculated, the left-hand side will now be

$$\frac{d}{dx}\{y \times \text{integrating factor}\},$$

and it is always advisable to take this opportunity to check the integrating factor. In this case

$$\frac{d}{dx}\left(\frac{y}{\sin^2 x}\right) = \frac{1}{\sin^2 x}\frac{dy}{dx} - \frac{2 \cos x}{\sin^3 x} y,$$

as required. Hence the equation may be written

$$\frac{d}{dx}\left(\frac{y}{\sin^2 x}\right) = 2 \sin x \cos x.$$

Now integrate with respect to x, to obtain

$$\frac{y}{\sin^2 x} = \sin^2 x + C, \quad \text{or} \quad y = \sin^4 x + C \sin^2 x,$$

where C is an integration constant.

One occasionally encounters *Bernoulli's equation*, which has the form

$$\frac{dy}{dx} + P(x)y = Q(x)y^n. \tag{19}$$

This reduces to the first-order linear equation by the substitution $z = 1/y^{n-1}$.

(f) *Exact Equations*

For these equations some knowledge of the elementary properties of partial derivatives is required. The reader who is not familiar with partial derivatives should first read §4.1.

Consider the equation (not a differential equation)

$$F(x, y) = C \tag{20}$$

where C is constant. Differentiating equation (20) totally with respect to x gives

$$\frac{\partial F(x, y)}{\partial x} + \frac{\partial F(x, y)}{\partial y} \frac{dy}{dx} = 0. \tag{21}$$

This has the form of equation (10), namely

$$M(x, y) + N(x, y) \frac{dy}{dx} = 0, \tag{10}$$

with

$$M(x, y) = \partial F(x, y)/\partial x, \quad N(x, y) = \partial F(x, y)/\partial y. \tag{22}$$

Conversely, suppose an equation of the form (10) is given. Then if there can be found a function $F(x, y)$ such that $M(x, y)$ and $N(x, y)$ satisfy equations (22), the equation takes the form of equation (21) and its solution is equation (20). In this case the original differential equation is said to be an *exact equation*.

EXAMPLE 6

$y + x \, dy/dx = 0$.

Here $M = y$, $N = x$, and choosing $F = xy$ gives $M = \partial F/\partial x$, $N = \partial F/\partial y$, and the solution is $xy = C$, as may easily be seen by inspection. (The equation is also separable, homogeneous and linear, so it may be solved in a variety of ways.)

EXAMPLE 7

$-y + x \, dy/dx = 0$.

Here $M = -y$, $N = x$, and there is no $F(x, y)$ such that $M = \partial F/\partial x$, $N = \partial F/\partial y$.

However, on dividing the equation by x^2 it becomes the exact equation

$$-\frac{y}{x^2} + \frac{1}{x}\frac{dy}{dx} = 0, \quad \text{or} \quad \frac{d}{dx}\left(\frac{y}{x}\right) = 0$$

with the solution $y/x = C$. This equation also can be solved in several other ways.

It is not *generally* true that, given $M(x,y)$ and $N(x,y)$, there exists an $F(x,y)$ which satisfies equations (22). Consequently exact equations are the exception rather than the rule, and a test by which they can be identified is required. The test is that *equation (10) is exact if and only if*

$$\partial M/\partial y = \partial N/\partial x. \tag{23}$$

To prove that the condition (23) is a *necessary* one for the equation to be exact, assume that equation (10) is exact. Then there is an $F(x,y)$ such that $M = \partial F/\partial x$, $N = \partial F/\partial y$. Consequently $\partial M/\partial y = \partial^2 F/\partial y \partial x$, $\partial N/\partial x = \partial^2 F/\partial x \partial y$, and so $\partial M/\partial y = \partial N/\partial x$ as required.

The proof that equation (23) is also a *sufficient* condition for the equation to be exact (that is, that if equation (23) is satisfied, then the equation is exact) is straightforward but a little longer. The proof will be found in most introductory texts on ordinary differential equations, for example Rainville and Bedient [1].

When the above test establishes that an equation is exact, the solution is found by constructing the function $F(x,y)$, as in the following example.

EXAMPLE 8

$$e^y + \cos(x+y) + 2x + \{xe^y + \cos(x+y) - 1\}\frac{dy}{dx} = 0.$$

Here

$$M = e^y + \cos(x+y) + 2x, \quad \partial M/\partial y = e^y - \sin(x+y),$$
$$N = xe^y + \cos(x+y) - 1, \quad \partial N/\partial x = e^y - \sin(x+y).$$

Hence $\partial M/\partial y = \partial N/\partial x$, the equation is exact, so we proceed to find $F(x,y)$, which is given by

$$\frac{\partial F}{\partial x} = M = e^y + \cos(x+y) + 2x, \quad \frac{\partial F}{\partial y} = N = xe^y + \cos(x+y) - 1. \tag{24}$$

Integrating the first of these (see the subsection on partial differential equations in §4.5) gives

$$F = xe^y + \sin(x+y) + x^2 + \phi(y),$$

which determines F except for the arbitrary function $\phi(y)$, which arises in the integration because the partial derivative with respect to x of any function of y is zero. To determine $\phi(y)$, differentiate the above expression for F partially with respect to y.

This gives

$$\frac{\partial F}{\partial y} = xe^y + \cos(x + y) + \phi'(y),$$

which agrees with the second of equations (24) only when

$$\phi'(y) = -1, \quad \text{or} \quad \phi(y) = -y.$$

It is unnecessary to include a constant of integration in $\phi(y)$. $F(x, y)$ is now completely determined and the solution is $F(x, y) = C$, that is

$$xe^y + \sin(x + y) + x^2 - y = C.$$

Most first-order equations are not exact, but some may be converted into exact equations by multiplication by a suitable integrating factor. For instance, the integrating factor x^{-2} was used to make exact the equation solved in example 7 above. It may be shown that every first-order equation has an integrating factor which will make it an exact equation. However, there is no systematic way to find such integrating factors, so the knowledge that they exist is of little practical use.

Discussion of First-order Equations

The reader is strongly advised to equip himself with a mental list of the types of first-order equation discussed in this section. If an equation can be identified as being of one of the types (a) to (f) described in this section, then one of the routine procedures for solution outlined above can be applied. A major part of the solution process lies in recognizing the type of equation.

If a first-order equation is encountered which does not belong to any of these standard types, then it may be possible to spot an integrating factor which will make the equation exact, or to find a substitution which will reduce the equation to a standard type. When analytical methods fail, a numerical solution is usually possible (see Chapter 7 of Volume 2).

EXAMPLE 9

$$\frac{dy}{dx} + (x + 8y)^3 = 0.$$

This is not an equation of a standard type. However, it is natural to substitute

$$z = x + 8y, \quad \frac{dz}{dx} = 1 + 8\frac{dy}{dx}.$$

On eliminating y and dy/dx, the equation becomes

$$\frac{dz}{dx} + 8z^3 - 1 = 0,$$

which is separable. The completion of the solution is left to the reader.

Exercises

1. Solve the following separable differential equations:

   (a) $\tan x \dfrac{dy}{dx} = \cot y$,

   (b) $\dfrac{dT}{dt} = K(T_0^4 - T^4)$ (K and T_0 constant).

2. Solve the following homogeneous differential equations:

   (a) $(x^3 - y^3)\dfrac{dy}{dx} = x^2 y$,   (b) $\dfrac{dy}{dx} = \tan\left(\dfrac{y}{x}\right) + \dfrac{y}{x}$.

3. Reduce the following equations to homogeneous form, and solve:

   (a) $\dfrac{dy}{dx} = \dfrac{x + y}{2x - y - 1}$,   (b) $\dfrac{dy}{dx} = \dfrac{x - y + 3}{x + y - 1}$.

4. Solve the following differential equation (the exceptional case (d) of this section):

   $$\dfrac{dy}{dx} = \dfrac{x + 2y + 1}{2x + 4y + 3}.$$

5. Solve the following linear differential equations:

   (a) $\dfrac{dy}{dx} + 2y \tan x = \sin x$,   (b) $\dfrac{dy}{dx} - 2y \tan x = \sin x$.

6. Show that the following equations are exact, and solve them:

   (a) $(x^2 + y) + (y^2 + x)\dfrac{dy}{dx} = 0$,

   (b) $(1 + y \cos xy) + x \cos xy \dfrac{dy}{dx} = 0$.

7. The following equations each belong to one of the standard types discussed in this section. For each equation, identify the type, and solve.

   (a) $\dfrac{dy}{dx} - y = xe^x$,   (b) $\dfrac{dy}{dx} = \dfrac{(x + y)}{(x - y)}$,

   (c) $\dfrac{dy}{dx} = \dfrac{y + 1}{x + y}$,   (d) $e^y \left\{ \dfrac{1}{1 + x} + \dfrac{dy}{dx} \log(1 + x) \right\} = 1$.

8. Solve the following equations:

   (a) $2\dfrac{dy}{dx} + y = xy^3$ (*Hint:* Bernoulli's equation),

(b) $\dfrac{dy}{dx} + (x+y)^4 = 0$ (*Hint:* make a substitution),

(c) $\dfrac{1}{y}\left(\dfrac{\sin x}{x} - \cos y\right)\dfrac{dy}{dx} - \dfrac{1}{x}\left(\dfrac{\sin y}{y} - \cos x\right) = 0$

(*Hint:* find an integrating factor).

1.4 LINEAR ORDINARY DIFFERENTIAL EQUATIONS WITH CONSTANT COEFFICIENTS. D OPERATOR NOTATION

An equation of the form

$$a_0 \frac{d^n y}{dx^n} + a_1 \frac{d^{n-1}y}{dx^{n-1}} + a_2 \frac{d^{n-2}y}{dx^{n-2}} + \ldots + a_{n-1}\frac{dy}{dx} + a_n y = f(x), \tag{25}$$

where $a_0, a_1, \ldots, a_{n-1}, a_n$ are constants with $a_0 \neq 0$, and $f(x)$ is a given function of x, is an *nth order linear differential equation with constant coefficients*. We shall be mainly concerned with the *second-order* equation

$$a \frac{d^2 y}{dx^2} + b \frac{dy}{dx} + cy = f(x), \tag{26}$$

where a, b, c are constants and $a \neq 0$. If desired, the equation may be divided through by a (or a_0), so there is no loss of generality in taking $a = 1$ or $a_0 = 1$.

Equation (25) is probably the most important single type of ordinary differential equation. Among other things, it is the governing equation for vibration phenomena, whether they are mechanical, electrical, acoustical or any other; examples of this application will be given in §1.6 and §1.8. An important special case of equation (26) is the equation of *simple harmonic motion*

$$\frac{d^2 y}{dx^2} + \omega^2 y = 0.$$

Notation

Use will often be made of the 'prime' notation for derivatives, in which equation (26) is written in the form

$$ay''(x) + by'(x) + cy(x) = f(x), \tag{27}$$

or, for greater brevity,

$$ay'' + by' + cy = f(x). \tag{28}$$

Another notation which is sometimes convenient is to write Dy for dy/dx, D^2y for d^2y/dx^2, and so on, so that equation (26) becomes

$$aD^2 y + bDy + cy = f(x). \tag{29}$$

This is 'factorized' and written as

$$(a\mathrm{D}^2 + b\mathrm{D} + c)y = f(x). \tag{30}$$

Equations (29) and (30) are merely alternative ways of writing equation (26). The symbols D, D^2 and $a\mathrm{D}^2 + b\mathrm{D} + c$ represent examples of *linear operators*; D performs the operation of differentiation with respect to x on any variable which follows it (in the usual algebraic sense, using brackets) in an equation. Similarly D^2 performs the operation of forming the second derivative, and $(a\mathrm{D}^2 + b\mathrm{D} + c)$ performs the operation of adding c times the variable to b times its first derivative and a times its second derivative.

Properties of the Operator D

If u and v are functions of x, and c, α and β are constants, the following properties are easily verified by replacing D by d/dx.

(a) $\mathrm{D}(u + v) = \mathrm{D}u + \mathrm{D}v$,

(b) $\mathrm{D}(cu) = c\mathrm{D}u$,

(c) $\mathrm{D}^m \mathrm{D}^n u = \mathrm{D}^{m+n} u$,

(d) $\mathrm{D}(uv) = u\mathrm{D}v + v\mathrm{D}u$,

(e) $(\mathrm{D} + \alpha)(\mathrm{D} + \beta)u = (\mathrm{D} + \beta)(\mathrm{D} + \alpha)u = \{\mathrm{D}^2 + (\alpha + \beta)\mathrm{D} + \alpha\beta\}u$.

Property (e) shows that it is legitimate to factorize expressions such as $a\mathrm{D}^2 + b\mathrm{D} + c$, provided that a, b and c are constants. Note that D obeys most of the laws of ordinary algebra, but D must always come before a function on which it operates — it is not permissible to replace $\mathrm{D}u$ by $u\mathrm{D}$.

1.5 SOLUTION OF HOMOGENEOUS LINEAR EQUATIONS WITH CONSTANT COEFFICIENTS

If the term $f(x)$ on the right-hand side of equation (25) or (26) is zero, the equation is said to be *homogeneous*. If $f(x) \neq 0$, the equation is *inhomogeneous*. In this section homogeneous equations are considered. The word 'homogeneous' is overworked in mathematics — in this section it has a different meaning from that in which it was used in §1.3. This is unfortunate, but both usages are too well established for it to be possible for us to change them.

It is convenient to begin with the first-order equation, because this gives a clue to the form of solution of higher order equations. Consider

$$\frac{dy}{dx} + cy = 0,$$

where c is constant. This may be solved in many ways; the solution is $y = A\mathrm{e}^{-cx}$, where A is a constant of integration. Now consider the second-order equation

$$a\frac{d^2y}{dx^2} + b\frac{dy}{dx} + cy = 0. \tag{31}$$

The previous result suggests looking for trial solutions of the form

$$y = Ae^{mx}, \tag{32}$$

where A is constant and m is not yet known. Substituting for y from equation (32) into equation (31) gives

$$aAm^2e^{mx} + bAme^{mx} + cAe^{mx} = 0,$$

that is $Ae^{mx}(am^2 + bm + c) = 0$.

Thus the trial solution (32) satisfies equation (31) if either $A = 0$ or $am^2 + bm + c = 0$. If $A = 0$ then $y = 0$; this is certainly a solution of equation (31) but it is of limited interest (it is termed the *trivial solution*). The solution of greater interest arises when

$$am^2 + bm + c = 0. \tag{33}$$

This is a quadratic equation for m, with two roots, say m_1 and m_2. Equation (31) is satisfied by the expression (32), for any value of A, if $m = m_1$ or $m = m_2$. Thus two independent solutions of equation (31) are

$$y = A\,\exp(m_1x), \quad y = B\,\exp(m_2x).$$

It is readily verified that the sum of these two solutions, namely

$$y = A\,\exp(m_1x) + B\,\exp(m_2x), \tag{34}$$

also satisfies equation (31), for all values of A and B. A and B are called *arbitrary constants*. From the discussion of §1.2 it is to be expected that the solution of a second-order equation will involve two arbitrary constants. The solution (34) is called the *general solution*. *Particular solutions* are obtained from equation (34) by giving particular values to A and B.

Equation (33), which gives m_1 and m_2, is called the *auxiliary equation*. Note how it is formed. The auxiliary equation for

$$a\frac{d^2y}{dx^2} + b\frac{dy}{dx} + cy = 0, \quad \text{or} \quad (aD^2 + bD + c)y = 0,$$

is

$$am^2 + bm + c = 0.$$

For a linear second-order differential equation with real constant coefficients, the following possibilities exist for the roots m_1 and m_2 of the auxiliary equation.

(a) The roots m_1 and m_2 are real and distinct. The solution (34) then requires no further discussion.

(b) The roots m_1 and m_2 are complex conjugate numbers, say $m_1 = \alpha + i\beta$, $m_2 = \alpha - i\beta$, where α and β are real. Then equation (34) becomes

$$y = Ae^{(\alpha+i\beta)x} + Be^{(\alpha-i\beta)x} = e^{\alpha x}(Ae^{i\beta x} + Be^{-i\beta x}). \tag{35}$$

Although it is mathematically correct, equation (35) gives the solution in a form which is not usually convenient to use. Preferable and equivalent forms of the solution are

$$y = e^{\alpha x}(C \cos \beta x + E \sin \beta x), \tag{36}$$

$$y = F e^{\alpha x} \cos(\beta x - \epsilon), \tag{37}$$

$$y = F e^{\alpha x} \sin(\beta x - \delta), \tag{38}$$

where C, E, F, ϵ and δ are arbitrary constants. To show the equivalence of the solutions (35) and (36), note that

$$e^{i\beta x} = \cos \beta x + i \sin \beta x, \quad e^{-i\beta x} = \cos \beta x - i \sin \beta x.$$

Hence equation (35) can be written as

$$y = e^{\alpha x}\{(A + B)\cos \beta x + i(A - B)\sin \beta x\},$$

and equation (36) follows if we choose $A + B = C$, $i(A - B) = E$. Since A and B are arbitrary, so are C and E. Note that there is no mathematical requirement for A and B, or C and E, to be real numbers; they may be complex constants. However, a practical problem will usually yield real values for y, and this is ensured if C and E are real numbers. If A and B are real numbers, then y is complex, whereas complex values of A and B are required to produce real values of y. This is a reason why the form (36) is usually preferred to the form (35).

To obtain the form (37) of the solution, in equation (36) let

$$F = \sqrt{(C^2 + E^2)}, \quad \epsilon = \tan^{-1}(E/C).$$

Since C and E are arbitrary, so are F and ϵ. Now equation (36) can be written as

$$y = \sqrt{(C^2 + E^2)} e^{\alpha x} \left\{ \frac{C}{\sqrt{(C^2 + E^2)}} \cos \beta x + \frac{E}{\sqrt{(C^2 + E^2)}} \sin \beta x \right\}$$

$$= F e^{\alpha x}\{\cos \epsilon \cos \beta x + \sin \epsilon \sin \beta x\} = F e^{\alpha x} \cos(\beta x - \epsilon).$$

For real values of y, both F and ϵ must be real constants. The final form (38) of the solution is derived by setting $\epsilon = \delta + \frac{1}{2}\pi$ in equation (37).

(c) The roots m_1 and m_2 are pure imaginary numbers, equal in magnitude but opposite in sign, say $m_1 = i\beta$, $m_2 = -i\beta$. This is the case of simple harmonic motion, in which in equation (31) $b = 0$, and c/a is positive and equal to β^2. It is the special case of (b) above in which $\alpha = 0$, and so equivalent forms of the solution are obtained from equations (36), (37) and (38) by setting $\alpha = 0$, which gives the solution in the various forms

$$y = C \cos \beta x + D \sin \beta x = F \cos(\beta x - \epsilon) = F \sin(\beta x - \delta).$$

(d) The roots m_1 and m_2 are real and equal, $m_1 = m_2$. In this case $b^2 = 4ac$ and equation (34) becomes

$$y = (A + B)\exp(m_1 x)$$

which is only a single solution, because it involves only the single arbitrary constant

$A + B$. It can easily be verified that the second independent solution is

$$y = Bx \exp(m_1 x),$$

and so the general solution has the form

$$y = (A + Bx)\exp(m_1 x). \tag{39}$$

EXAMPLE 1

$$\frac{d^2y}{dx^2} - \frac{dy}{dx} - 6y = 0.$$

The auxiliary equation is $m^2 - m - 6 = 0$, or $(m - 3)(m + 2) = 0$, with roots $m = 3$ and $m = -2$. Hence the general solution is

$$y = Ae^{3x} + Be^{-2x}.$$

EXAMPLE 2

$$\frac{d^2y}{dx^2} + 4y = 0 \quad \text{(simple harmonic motion)}.$$

The auxiliary equation is $m^2 + 4 = 0$, with roots $m = \pm 2i$. Hence

$$y = C \cos 2x + E \sin 2x = F \cos(2x - \epsilon) = F \sin(2x - \delta).$$

EXAMPLE 3

$$(4D^2 + 4D + 17)y = 0.$$

The auxiliary equation is $4m^2 + 4m + 17 = 0$, with roots $m = -\frac{1}{2} \pm 2i$. Hence the solution of the differential equation is

$$y = e^{-x/2}(C \cos 2x + E \sin 2x) = Fe^{-x/2} \cos(2x - \epsilon) = Fe^{-x/2} \sin(2x - \delta).$$

EXAMPLE 4

$$y'' + 4y' + 4y = 0.$$

The auxiliary equation is $m^2 + 4m + 4 = 0$, or $(m + 2)^2 = 0$, and has the double root $m = -2$. Hence the general solution is

$$y = (A + Bx)e^{-2x}.$$

The solutions to examples 1–4 may be checked by substitution in the equations.

Equations of Higher Order

The method of seeking solutions of the form $y = Ae^{mx}$ is also applicable to the nth order homogeneous equation given by equation (25) with $f(x) = 0$. For example, to solve the third-order equation

$$a\frac{d^3y}{dx^3}+b\frac{d^2y}{dx^2}+c\frac{dy}{dx}+ey=0, \qquad (a,b,c,e \text{ constants})$$

form the auxiliary equation

$$am^3+bm^2+cm+e=0.$$

This is a cubic equation for m, with three roots (some of which may be complex) say m_1, m_2, m_3. If the three roots are all distinct, the general solution is

$$y = A\exp(m_1 x)+B\exp(m_2 x)+C\exp(m_3 x).$$

Various possibilities can arise, as the following examples illustrate. Remember that a cubic equation with real coefficients always has either three real roots (of which two or three may be coincident) or one real root and two complex conjugate roots (which may be purely imaginary).

EXAMPLE 5

$$(D^3+6D^2+11D+6)y=0.$$

The auxiliary equation is $m^3+6m^2+11m+6=0$, or $(m+1)(m+2)(m+3)=0$, so that $m=-1,-2,-3$, and the solution is

$$y=Ae^{-x}+Be^{-2x}+Ce^{-3x}.$$

EXAMPLE 6

$$2y'''-8y''+3y'+13y=0.$$

The auxiliary equation is $2m^3-8m^2+3m+13=0$, or $(m+1)(2m^2-10m+13)=0$, which gives $m=-1, m=\frac{5}{2}\pm\frac{1}{2}i$. Hence the solution is

$$y=A\exp(-x)+B\exp\{(\tfrac{5}{2}+\tfrac{1}{2}i)x\}+C\exp\{(\tfrac{5}{2}-\tfrac{1}{2}i)x\}$$

$$=Ae^{-x}+e^{5x/2}(E\cos\tfrac{1}{2}x+F\sin\tfrac{1}{2}x).$$

EXAMPLE 7

$$(D^3-3D^2+4)y=0.$$

The auxiliary equation is $m^3-3m^2+4=0$, or $(m+1)(m-2)^2=0$, which gives $m=-1,2,2$. In this case there is a repeated root, so the solution is

$$y=Ae^{-x}+(B+Cx)e^{2x}.$$

EXAMPLE 8

$$y'''+3y''+3y'+y=0.$$

The auxiliary equation is $m^3+3m^2+3m+1=(m+1)^3=0$, which has the triple root $m=-1$. The solution is

$$y=(A+Bx+Cx^2)e^{-x}.$$

Equations of fourth and higher orders are treated in the same way.

Exercises

1. Solve the following differential equations:

(a) $\dfrac{d^2y}{dx^2} - 9y = 0,$ (b) $\dfrac{d^2y}{dx^2} + 9y = 0,$

(c) $(D^2 + 8D + 15)y = 0,$ (d) $(D^2 + 6D + 13)y = 0,$

(e) $y'' - 6y' + 9y = 0,$ (f) $y'' - 3y' = 0,$

(g) $\dfrac{d^3y}{dx^3} - \dfrac{d^2y}{dx^2} + 4\dfrac{dy}{dx} - 4y = 0,$ (h) $(D^4 + 1)y = 0,$

(i) $(D^4 + 2D^2 + 1)y = 0,$ (j) $(D + 1)^4 y = 0.$

1.6 THEORY OF DAMPED FREE VIBRATIONS

The nature (real or complex) of the roots of the auxiliary equation is often important in physical problems. For example consider the equation of motion of a mass oscillating on a spring in a resisting medium, illustrated in Fig. 1.3. Let y denote the downward displacement of the mass m from its equilibrium position. The spring exerts a *downward* force $-ky$ on the mass, and the medium produces a resisting force (represented by a dashpot) opposing the motion and proportional to the speed of the mass. In this section we set the applied force $F(t) = 0$, so that the equation of motion of the mass is

$$m\frac{d^2y}{dt^2} = -ky - h\frac{dy}{dt}, \quad \text{or} \quad m\frac{d^2y}{dt^2} + h\frac{dy}{dt} + ky = 0.$$

For physical reasons, m, h and k are positive in this problem. To simplify the algebra

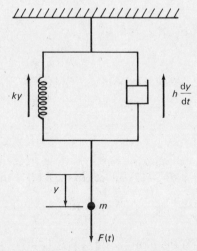

Fig. 1.3 Oscillations of a mass suspended from a spring in a resisting medium

which follows, denote

$$k/m = \omega^2, \quad h/m = 2\alpha \quad (\alpha > 0).$$

The equation of motion then becomes

$$\frac{d^2y}{dt^2} + 2\alpha \frac{dy}{dt} + \omega^2 y = 0, \tag{40}$$

whose auxiliary equation has roots $-\alpha \pm \sqrt{(\alpha^2 - \omega^2)}$. The solution of equation (40) is therefore

$$y = e^{-\alpha t}\{Ae^{t\sqrt{(\alpha^2-\omega^2)}} + Be^{-t\sqrt{(\alpha^2-\omega^2)}}\} \quad \text{for } \alpha \neq \omega, \tag{41}$$

where A and B are arbitrary constants.

There are three cases to consider, namely

(a) $\alpha^2 - \omega^2 > 0$,   (b) $\alpha^2 - \omega^2 < 0$,   (c) $\alpha^2 - \omega^2 = 0$.

(a) $\alpha^2 - \omega^2 > 0$. *Heavy Damping*

In this case $h^2 > 4mk$. Then the damping effect determined by h predominates over the spring force determined by k. Let $\alpha^2 - \omega^2 = \lambda^2$, and note that this implies $\alpha > \lambda$. Then equation (41) becomes

$$y = Ae^{-(\alpha-\lambda)t} + Be^{-(\alpha+\lambda)t}. \tag{42}$$

Since $\alpha > \lambda$, the solution consists of the sum of two exponentially decreasing terms. Hence $y \to 0$ as $t \to \infty$, whatever the values of A and B.

To be specific, suppose that the mass is displaced downwards through a distance a and then released from rest at $t = 0$, which gives the *initial conditions*

$$y = a, \quad dy/dt = 0, \quad \text{when } t = 0, \tag{43}$$

(initial conditions in general will be discussed in §1.7). Putting $y = a$ and $t = 0$ in equation (42) gives

$$a = A + B. \tag{44}$$

Also from equation (42)

$$\frac{dy}{dt} = -A(\alpha - \lambda)e^{-(\alpha-\lambda)t} - B(\alpha + \lambda)e^{-(\alpha+\lambda)t}$$

so, since $dy/dt = 0$ when $t = 0$,

$$0 = A(\alpha - \lambda) + B(\alpha + \lambda). \tag{45}$$

Equations (44) and (45) determine the constants A and B, and give $A = a(\alpha + \lambda)/2\lambda$, $B = -a(\alpha - \lambda)/2\lambda$, so the solution (42) subject to the initial conditions (43) is

$$y = \frac{a}{2\lambda}\{(\alpha + \lambda)e^{-(\alpha-\lambda)t} - (\alpha - \lambda)e^{-(\alpha+\lambda)t}\}.$$

The graph of y against t is of the form shown in Fig. 1.4(a). Other initial conditions

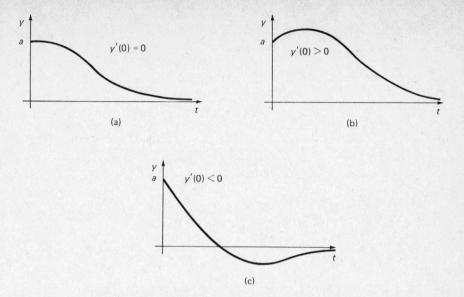

Fig. 1.4   Damped free vibrations. Heavy damping

would give different values of A and B and graphs of the forms illustrated in Figs 1.4(b) and 1.4(c). In each case $y \to 0$ as $t \to \infty$, and the mass passes its equilibrium position $y = 0$ at most once before coming eventually to rest in this position. The motion is *non-oscillatory*. This of course is what one would expect to happen if the experiment illustrated in Fig. 1.3 were carried out in a medium, such as a viscous oil, which exerts a large resistance to the motion.

(b) $\alpha^2 - \omega^2 < 0$. *Light Damping*

In this case $4mk > h^2$, and the spring force predominates. Let $\alpha^2 - \omega^2 = -\beta^2$, so that the solution (41) becomes

$$y = Fe^{-\alpha t} \cos(\beta t - \epsilon), \tag{46}$$

where F and ϵ are now the arbitrary constants. Since $\alpha > 0$, $y \to 0$ as $t \to \infty$ for all values of F and ϵ, but the way in which y approaches zero is different from that of heavy damping.

With the same initial conditions (43) as before, the solution (46) becomes

$$y = \frac{a}{\cos \epsilon} \, e^{-\alpha t} \cos(\beta t - \epsilon), \quad \text{where } \epsilon = \tan^{-1}(\alpha/\beta).$$

Since $|\cos(\beta t - \epsilon)| \leqslant 1$, y always lies between the upper and lower curves shown in Fig. 1.5, and the cosine term ensures that y oscillates between these curves as shown. Thus $y \to 0$ through an infinite succession of oscillations, each of smaller amplitude than the one before; the mass executes *damped oscillations*. This is the expected

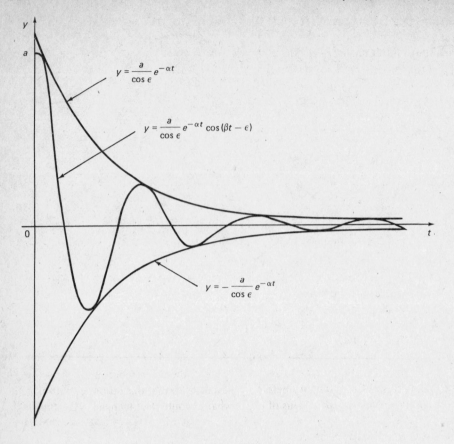

$$y = \frac{a}{\cos \epsilon} e^{-\alpha t}$$

$$y = \frac{a}{\cos \epsilon} e^{-\alpha t} \cos(\beta t - \epsilon)$$

$$y = -\frac{a}{\cos \epsilon} e^{-\alpha t}$$

Fig. 1.5   Damped free vibrations. Light damping

behaviour of the system illustrated in Fig. 1.3 when the medium is one such as air which exerts only a slight damping force.

(c) $\alpha^2 = \omega^2$. *Critical Damping*

If $\alpha = \omega$, equation (40) becomes

$$\frac{d^2 y}{dt^2} + 2\alpha \frac{dy}{dt} + \alpha^2 y = 0.$$

The auxiliary equation has equal roots $-\alpha, -\alpha$, so (see §1.5) the solution is

$$y = (A + Bt)e^{-\alpha t},$$

and again $y \to 0$ as $t \to \infty$ for any values of A and B. With the initial conditions (43), the solution becomes

$$y = a(1 + \alpha t)e^{-\alpha t}.$$

The graph of y against t is qualitatively similar to that for heavy damping which is illustrated in Fig. 1.4(a).

Although it is a special case, critical damping is of practical importance in that $\alpha = \omega$, or $h^2 = 4mk$, gives the smallest value of the damping coefficient h which produces non-oscillatory motion. It is important in the design of instruments. In a car speedometer, for example, it is desirable to record the present speed rather than the speed at some time in the past, so the damping should not be heavy. However if the damping is light, the recording needle will oscillate about the true reading. To avoid undesirable extremes, the designer of a speedometer will aim to achieve critical damping, or something close to it.

Discharge of a Capacitor

Many other physical systems lead to equations of the form (40). Other problems in mechanics governed by this equation are the small oscillations of a simple pendulum in a resisting medium, torsional oscillations of a shaft, and so on. The same equation arises in electrical circuit theory and elsewhere. Consider for example the problem of discharge of a capacitor with capacitance C through a circuit with resistance R and self-inductance L, as illustrated in Fig. 1.6. If the charge on the capacitor at time t is Q, the governing equation is

$$L\frac{d^2Q}{dt^2} + R\frac{dQ}{dt} + \frac{Q}{C} = 0.$$

Suppose that at $t = 0$ the capacitor has charge $Q = Q_0$, and no current is flowing, so that $dQ/dt = 0$. If the substitutions

$$2\alpha = R/L, \quad \omega^2 = 1/LC, \quad Q = y, \quad Q_0 = a$$

are made, then equation (40) and the initial conditions (43) are recovered. Thus mathematically this problem is identical to the one discussed already, and its solution is obtained from the previous solution simply by re-interpreting α, ω, y and a. The case of heavy damping ($\alpha^2 - \omega^2 > 0$) now corresponds to $R^2 > 4L/C$; in this case the charge Q decays steadily to zero. For $R^2 < 4L/C$ there is light damping and a decaying alternating current is set up in the circuit. The intermediate case $R^2 = 4L/C$ represents critical damping.

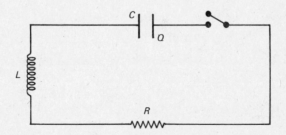

Fig. 1.6   Discharge of capacitor through L, R, C circuit

1.7 INHOMOGENEOUS SECOND-ORDER EQUATIONS WITH CONSTANT COEFFICIENTS

The equations considered in §§1.5–1.6 were homogeneous linear ordinary differential equations with constant coefficients in which the function $f(x)$ in equation (25) or (26) is identically zero. We now turn to the inhomogeneous equation, in which $f(x) \neq 0$.

Consider first the particular example

$$\frac{d^2y}{dx^2} - \frac{dy}{dx} - 6y = -6x^2 - 14x + 18. \tag{47}$$

It can be verified that a solution of this equation is $y = x^2 + 2x - 3$ (how this solution is arrived at is described below). Since this solution contains no arbitrary constants, it cannot be the general solution. A special solution of this kind is called a *particular integral*.

Now let $y = u + x^2 + 2x - 3$, and eliminate y from the equation in favour of the new variable u. Then

$$\frac{dy}{dx} = \frac{du}{dx} + 2x + 2, \qquad \frac{d^2y}{dx^2} = \frac{d^2u}{dx^2} + 2$$

and the equation becomes

$$\frac{d^2u}{dx^2} - \frac{du}{dx} - 6u = 0.$$

Thus u satisfies the homogeneous equation whose solution was shown in §1.5, example 1, to be $u = Ae^{3x} + Be^{-2x}$. Hence

$$y = Ae^{3x} + Be^{-2x} + x^2 + 2x - 3.$$

This includes the two arbitrary constants A and B, and is the general solution of equation (47).

In general, suppose that $y = v(x)$ is a particular integral of

$$a\frac{d^2y}{dx^2} + b\frac{dy}{dx} + cy = f(x), \tag{26}$$

so that

$$a\frac{d^2v}{dx^2} + b\frac{dv}{dx} + cv = f(x).$$

Substitute $y = u(x) + v(x)$ in equation (26), which then becomes

$$a\frac{d^2u}{dx^2} + b\frac{du}{dx} + cu = 0.$$

This is the homogeneous form of equation (26), and can be solved by the methods of

§1.5. The solution for $u(x)$ is

$$u(x) = A \exp(m_1 x) + B \exp(m_2 x)$$

where m_1 and m_2 are the roots of the auxiliary equation $am^2 + bm + c = 0$. Hence the solution of equation (26) reduces to the problem of finding a particular integral $v(x)$.

The function $u(x)$ (which contains the arbitrary constants A and B) is called the *complementary function* for equation (26), and is the solution of the homogeneous equation which is obtained by setting $f(x) = 0$ in equation (26). Then

GENERAL SOLUTION = COMPLEMENTARY FUNCTION + PARTICULAR INTEGRAL

The problem of finding the complementary function was solved in §1.5. The remaining problem is to find a particular integral of (26) for a given function $f(x)$. There is an infinite number of particular integrals, because a particular integral is obtained by taking the general solution and giving any definite values to the constants A and B. Any of these particular integrals is as good as any other for our purposes; it is necessary only to find one of them.

There are various ways of finding particular integrals. One general method (solution in terms of integrals) is given later in this section. A very powerful method is that of Laplace Transforms, which is described in Chapter 3. For the simplest and most commonly occurring functions $f(x)$, however, the easiest and quickest method is, in effect, to guess the answer (this is usually called solution by inspection). The guessing must of course be done systematically; the following examples illustrate the procedure.

EXAMPLE 1

$$\frac{d^2 y}{dx^2} - \frac{dy}{dx} - 6y = -6x^2 - 14x + 18. \tag{47}$$

For reasons which will become apparent later it is always best to find the complementary function first. The auxiliary equation is $m^2 - m - 6 = 0$, with solutions $m = 3, -2$, and the complementary function is

$$u = Ae^{3x} + Be^{-2x}.$$

To find a particular integral, we enquire what form $v(x)$ must have in order that $v'' - v' - 6v$ shall equal the polynomial $-6x^2 - 14x + 18$. Since polynomials are derivatives of other polynomials, in this example it is reasonable to look for a solution in which $v(x)$ is itself a polynomial. As the right-hand side of equation (47) is of degree two, $v(x)$ must also be of degree two, so we try $v = fx^2 + gx + h$, where f, g, h are constants to be determined. Then

$$v'' - v' - 6v = 2f - (2fx + g) - 6(fx^2 + gx + h)$$

$$= -6fx^2 + (-2f - 6g)x + (2f - g - 6h).$$

This must equal $-6x^2 - 14x + 18$, and so we choose

$$-6f = -6, \quad -2f - 6g = -14, \quad 2f - g - 6h = 18.$$

These are three equations for f, g and h, whose solution is $f = 1, g = 2, h = -3$. Thus a particular integral is $v = x^2 + 2x - 3$, and the general solution is

$$y = u + v = Ae^{3x} + Be^{-2x} + x^2 + 2x - 3.$$

This solution can be verified by substitution in the original equation.

In general, if $f(x)$ is a polynomial of degree n, the trial particular integral is also a polynomial of degree n.

EXAMPLE 2

$$\frac{d^2y}{dx^2} - \frac{dy}{dx} - 6y = 7e^{5x}.$$

As in example 1, the complementary function is $u = Ae^{3x} + Be^{-2x}$. To find a particular integral we enquire what function can be twice differentiated and appropriately combined with its derivatives to produce $7e^{5x}$. Since differentiating e^{5x} any number of times yields a multiple of e^{5x}, a particular integral of the form ge^{5x} is suggested. Substituting this in the left-hand side of the equation gives $g(25 - 5 - 6)e^{5x} = 14ge^{5x}$. This is equal to the right-hand side if $14g = 7$, giving $g = \frac{1}{2}$. Hence a particular integral is $\frac{1}{2}e^{5x}$, and the general solution is

$$y = Ae^{3x} + Be^{-2x} + \frac{1}{2}e^{5x}.$$

The reader should verify this by substitution in the equation.

In general, if $f(x) = pe^{\alpha x}$, the trial particular integral is of the form $v = ge^{\alpha x}$, but it should be noted that this choice fails in a case described later.

EXAMPLE 3

$$\frac{d^2y}{dx^2} - \frac{dy}{dx} - 6y = 13 \cos 2x.$$

As before, the complementary function is $u = Ae^{3x} + Be^{-2x}$. For the particular integral, we give two alternative methods, of which the second is to be preferred.

(1) Write $\cos 2x = \frac{1}{2}(e^{2ix} + e^{-2ix})$, and, following the arguments of example 2, look for a particular integral of the form $ge^{2ix} + he^{-2ix}$.

(2) The functions which when differentiated once or twice produce multiples of $\cos 2x$ are multiples of $\cos 2x$ and $\sin 2x$. Hence the trial particular integral is chosen to be of the form

$$v = g \cos 2x + h \sin 2x,$$

so that

$$v' = 2h \cos 2x - 2g \sin 2x,$$

and

$$v'' = -4g \cos 2x - 4h \sin 2x.$$

Then

$$v'' - v' - 6v = (-4g - 2h - 6g)\cos 2x + (-4h + 2g - 6h)\sin 2x$$

$$= (-10g - 2h)\cos 2x + (2g - 10h)\sin 2x.$$

In order to satisfy the equation this expression must be equal to $13 \cos 2x$, so it is necessary that g and h satisfy the equations

$$-10g - 2h = 13, \quad 2g - 10h = 0,$$

which have the solution $g = -\tfrac{5}{4}, h = -\tfrac{1}{4}$. Hence $v = -\tfrac{1}{4}(5 \cos 2x + \sin 2x)$, and the general solution is

$$y = Ae^{3x} + Be^{-2x} - \tfrac{1}{4}(5 \cos 2x + \sin 2x).$$

In general, if $f(x) = p \cos \beta x$ or $f(x) = p \sin \beta x$, where p is constant, then the trial particular integral is of the form $v = g \cos \beta x + h \sin \beta x$. Again there is an exceptional case (discussed below) in which this fails to give a solution.

Similar arguments can be used in the more complicated case in which $f(x)$ is a product formed from polynomials, exponentials, cosines and sines. For example, if $f(x) = xe^{-x}$, the trial particular integral is of the form $(g + hx)e^{-x}$. The various cases are tabulated in table 1.1. Note that the trial particular integrals listed in table 1.1 will fail in certain exceptional cases described below.

In table 1.1, $P_n(x)$, $Q_n(x)$ and $R_n(x)$ denote polynomials of degree n, and p, g and h are constants.

If $f(x)$ is a sum of two or more terms, then the part of the particular integral which corresponds to each term can be found separately, and these parts added. For example, consider the equation

$$\frac{d^2y}{dx^2} - \frac{dy}{dx} - 6y = 7e^{5x} + 13 \cos 2x.$$

Combining the results of examples 2 and 3 gives the particular integral

$$v = \tfrac{1}{2}e^{5x} - \tfrac{1}{4}(5 \cos 2x + \sin 2x).$$

TABLE 1.1   Particular Integrals — Normal Case

Form of $f(x)$	Form of particular integral
$P_n(x)$	$Q_n(x)$
$pe^{\alpha x}$	$ge^{\alpha x}$
$p \cos \beta x, p \sin \beta x$	$g \cos \beta x + h \sin \beta x$
$pe^{\alpha x} \cos \beta x, pe^{\alpha x} \sin \beta x$	$e^{\alpha x}(g \cos \beta x + h \sin \beta x)$
$P_n(x)e^{\alpha x}$	$Q_n(x)e^{\alpha x}$
$P_n(x)\cos \beta x, P_n(x)\sin \beta x$	$Q_n(x)\cos \beta x + R_n(x)\sin \beta x$
$P_n(x)e^{\alpha x} \cos \beta x, P_n(x)e^{\alpha x} \sin \beta x$	$e^{\alpha x}\{Q_n(x)\cos \beta x + R_n(x)\sin \beta x\}$

The Exceptional Cases

Consider the equation

$$\frac{d^2y}{dx^2} - \frac{dy}{dx} - 6y = 2e^{3x}.$$

As before the complementary function is $u = Ae^{3x} + Be^{-2x}$. The arguments used in example 2 suggest a trial particular integral of the form $v = ge^{3x}$. Then

$$v'' - v' - 6v = (9 - 3 - 6)ge^{3x} = 0ge^{3x}.$$

Since the right-hand side above is zero, there is no value of g such that $v'' - v' - 6v = 2e^{3x}$, and the method fails. On reflection this is not surprising, since $y = Ae^{3x}$ already appears in the solution as part of the complementary function, and A is arbitrary. It follows that nothing can be gained by including a fixed multiple of e^{3x} in the particular integral part of the solution as well. Consequently it is necessary to try a different form for the particular integral. The required form is $v = gxe^{3x}$, for then

$$v' = (3x + 1)ge^{3x}$$
$$v'' = (9x + 6)ge^{3x}$$
$$v'' - v' - 6v = |(9x| + 6 - 3x - 1 - 6x)ge^{3x} = 5ge^{3x}.$$

Note that the terms in xe^{3x} in the above expression cancel, and this is why the new trial form is successful. It is now necessary to choose g so that $5ge^{3x} = 2e^{3x}$. Thus $g = \frac{2}{5}$, and the particular integral is

$$v = \frac{2}{5}xe^{3x}.$$

In general, difficulties will arise whenever $f(x)$ is a multiple of $e^{\alpha x}$, if the complementary function contains a term $Ae^{\alpha x}$. In this case the new trial particular integral is of the form $v = gxe^{\alpha x}$. If the complementary function also contains a term $Bxe^{\alpha x}$ (as it will if α is a double root of the auxiliary equation) then the trial particular integral is of the form $gx^2e^{\alpha x}$. If $f(x)$ is of the form $P_n(x)e^{\alpha x}$, where $P_n(x)$ is a polynomial in x of degree n, and $Ae^{\alpha x}$ appears in the complementary function, then (unless the auxiliary equation has a repeated root) the trial particular integral is of the form $xQ_n(x)e^{\alpha x}$, where $Q_n(x)$ is another polynomial of degree n.

Similar problems occur in various other cases. For second-order equations these cases and the corresponding forms of the trial particular integrals are tabulated in table 1.2. The general rule is that if the initial trial form of the particular integral suggested by table 1.1 fails to give an answer, then this form should be multiplied by the independent variable x.

The methods described above for second-order equations extend in a straightforward way to equations of higher order.

Solution in Terms of Integrals

The methods for finding particular integrals that have been described so far can be applied only when $f(x)$ has a fairly simple form; essentially it must consist of products

TABLE 1.2 Particular Integrals for Second-order Equations – Exceptional Cases

Complementary function	Form of $f(x)$	Form of particular integral
$Ae^{\alpha x} + Be^{\beta x}$	$pe^{\alpha x}$ or $pe^{\beta x}$	$gxe^{\alpha x}$ or $hxe^{\beta x}$
	$P_n(x)e^{\alpha x}$ or $P_n(x)e^{\beta x}$	$xQ_n(x)e^{\alpha x}$ or $xQ_n(x)e^{\beta x}$
$A\cos\beta x + B\sin\beta x$	$p\cos\beta x$ or $p\sin\beta x$	$gx\cos\beta x + hx\sin\beta x$
	$P_n(x)\cos\beta x$ or $P_n(x)\sin\beta x$	$xQ_n(x)\cos\beta x + xR_n(x)\sin\beta x$
$e^{\alpha x}(A\cos\beta x + B\sin\beta x)$	$pe^{\alpha x}\cos\beta x$ or $pe^{\alpha x}\sin\beta x$	$gxe^{\alpha x}\cos\beta x + hxe^{\alpha x}\sin\beta x$
	$P_n(x)e^{\alpha x}\cos\beta x$ or $P_n(x)e^{\alpha x}\sin\beta x$	$xQ_n(x)e^{\alpha x}\cos\beta x + xR_n(x)e^{\alpha x}\sin\beta x$
$(A + Bx)e^{\alpha x}$	$e^{\alpha x}$	$gx^2 e^{\alpha x}$
	$P_n(x)e^{\alpha x}$	$x^2 Q_n(x)e^{\alpha x}$

and sums of polynomials, exponential functions, and sine and cosine functions. We now give a method which can in principle be used for any $f(x)$. Equation (26) is written in the factorized D operator form (see §1.4)

$$(D + \alpha)(D + \beta)y = f(x). \tag{48}$$

It is supposed that $\alpha \neq \beta$, so that α and β are either distinct real numbers or conjugate complex numbers. Define a new variable

$$z = (D + \beta)y = \frac{dy}{dx} + \beta y, \tag{49}$$

and equation (48) becomes

$$(D + \alpha)z = f(x), \quad \text{or} \quad \frac{dz}{dx} + \alpha z = f(x). \tag{50}$$

Equation (50) is a first-order linear equation for z (§1.3(e)), with integrating factor $e^{\alpha x}$. Its solution is

$$z = \frac{dy}{dx} + \beta y = e^{-\alpha x} \int e^{\alpha x} f(x)\, dx + A' e^{-\alpha x}, \tag{51}$$

where A' is a constant of integration.

Now equation (51) is a first-order linear equation for y, which can be solved on multiplying by the integrating factor $e^{\beta x}$. It is, however, easier to use the following short cut. Since $(D + \alpha)(D + \beta)y = (D + \beta)(D + \alpha)y$, we could equally well have chosen $z = (D + \alpha)y$. The only difference would then be that α and β were interchanged, so that in place of equation (51) there would be obtained

$$\frac{dy}{dx} + \alpha y = e^{-\beta x} \int e^{\beta x} f(x)\, dx + B' e^{-\beta x}. \tag{52}$$

Subtracting equation (52) from equation (51) gives

$$y = \frac{1}{\beta - \alpha} \left\{ e^{-\alpha x} \int e^{\alpha x} f(x)\, dx - e^{-\beta x} \int e^{\beta x} f(x)\, dx \right\} + A e^{-\alpha x} + B e^{-\beta x}. \tag{53}$$

where $A = A'/(\beta - \alpha)$ and $B = -B'/(\beta - \alpha)$. Now equation (53) is the general solution of equation (48), because $A e^{-\alpha x} + B e^{-\beta x}$ is the complementary function. The remaining terms on the right of equation (53) are a particular integral. It remains only to evaluate the integrals; if analytical integration is not possible the integrals can be evaluated numerically.

In practice the formula (53) is used infrequently because, in cases where the simpler inspection method cannot be employed, it is usually easier to use the Laplace Transform method described in Chapter 3.

Boundary and Initial Conditions

As has been emphasized, the general solution of a second-order differential equation contains two arbitrary constants. In a practical problem it is usually necessary to pick out a particular solution which represents the solution of a specific physical problem. In order to select this particular solution it is necessary to assign particular values to the arbitrary constants. To do this, two additional items of information are required. An example was given in the problem of damped motion of a mass on a spring discussed in §1.6, in which the displacement and speed of the mass were specified at time $t = 0$. This information proved to be sufficient to determine the arbitrary constants.

The extra given information may take several forms. To illustrate some of the main ones consider the equation

$$(D^2 - D - 2)y = 4e^{-2x}, \tag{54}$$

which has the general solution

$$y = Ae^{2x} + Be^{-x} + e^{-2x}. \tag{55}$$

(a) *Initial value problems*   In this case y and dy/dx are given at some value of x. This value is usually, though not always, $x = 0$; it can always be made to be $x = 0$ by suitably defining the independent variable x. Suppose there is given

$$y = a, \quad dy/dx = V, \quad \text{when } x = 0. \tag{56}$$

Then inserting $y = a$ and $x = 0$ in equation (55) gives

$$a = A + B + 1. \tag{57}$$

Also from equation (55)

$$\frac{dy}{dx} = 2Ae^{2x} - Be^{-x} - 2e^{-2x}, \tag{58}$$

and inserting $dy/dx = V$ and $x = 0$ gives

$$V = 2A - B - 2. \tag{59}$$

We can now solve equations (57) and (59) for A and B, to obtain

$$A = \tfrac{1}{3}(a + V + 1), \quad B = \tfrac{1}{3}(2a - V - 4).$$

Hence the solution of equation (54) subject to the conditions (56) is

$$y = \tfrac{1}{3}\{(a + V + 1)e^{2x} + (2a - V - 4)e^{-x}\} + e^{-2x}.$$

(b) *Two-point boundary value problems*   In these, one item of information (usually a value of y or dy/dx) is given at one value of x, say $x = x_1$, and a second item at another value $x = x_2$.

EXAMPLE 4
Solve equation (54) subject to the conditions $y(0) = 1, y(1) = 4$.

In the general solution (55) substitute $x = 0, y = 1$, and then $x = 1, y = 4$, to obtain

$$1 = A + B + 1, \quad 4 = Ae^2 + Be^{-1} + e^{-2}.$$

These give $A = -B = (4 - e^{-2})/(e^2 - e^{-1})$. The solution follows by inserting these values in equation (55).

EXAMPLE 5

Solve equation (54) subject to the conditions $y(0) = 1$, $y'(1) = 0$.

Substitute $x = 0$, $y = 1$ in equation (55), and $x = 1$, $dy/dx = 0$ in equation (58), which gives

$$1 = A + B + 1', \quad 0 = 2Ae^2 - Be^{-1} - 2e^{-2}.$$

Hence $A = -B = 2e^{-2}/(2e^2 + e^{-1})$ and the solution follows by inserting these values in equation (55).

(c) *Conditions as $x \to \pm \infty$*   Often one of the conditions specifies the behaviour of y as $x \to \infty$ or as $x \to -\infty$. In practice such conditions will arise from knowledge of the physical behaviour of the system described by the equation, which may, for example, tell us that the variable tends to zero as $x \to \infty$.

EXAMPLE 6

Solve equation (54) subject to the conditions $y = 0$ when $x = 0$, $y \to 0$ as $x \to \infty$.

Consider the second condition. As $x \to \infty$, $e^{2x} \to \infty$, $e^{-x} \to 0$, $e^{-2x} \to 0$. Hence, from equation (55), y will tend to $\pm \infty$ (depending on the sign of A) for all values of A except $A = 0$. Hence to satisfy the condition it is necessary to set $A = 0$. The first condition then gives $B = 1$, and the required solution is

$$y = -e^{-x} + e^{-2x}.$$

These ideas extend straightforwardly to equations of higher order. The general solution of an nth-order equation contains n arbitrary constants, and n conditions are required to fix the values of the constants.

Exercises

1. Find the general solutions of the following differential equations:

    (a) $y'' - 2y' + 2y = 2e^x$,

    (b) $y'' - 13y' + 12y = 24$,

    (c) $y'' - 3y' + 2y = x^3 - x^2 + x - 1$,

    (d) $y'' - 4y' + 3y = 3 \cos x - 4 \sin x$,

    (e) $y'' - 16y = 32e^{4x}$,

    (f) $y'' - 16y = 32xe^{4x}$,

    (g) $\dfrac{d^2y}{dx^2} - p^2y = a \sinh px$,

    (h) $(D^3 + D^2 - 4D - 4)y = 6e^{-x}$,

    (i) $(D^2 + 2D + 2)y = e^x \sin x$,

    (j) $(D^2 + 2D + 5)y = e^{-x} \sin 2x$.

2. Solve the following:

    (a) $\dfrac{d^2s}{dt^2} + 4\dfrac{ds}{dt} + 13s = 0$,   given that $s = 0$ and $ds/dt = V$, when $t = 0$.

    (b) $\dfrac{d^2y}{dt^2} - y + 2 \sin \pi t = 0$,   given that $y(0) = 0$, $y(\frac{1}{2}) = 1$.

(c) $\dfrac{d^2y}{dt^2} + \dfrac{dy}{dt} - 12y = 0$, given that $y = 1$ when $t = 0$, and $y \to 0$ as $t \to \infty$.

3. $EI\dfrac{d^4y}{dx^4} - \dfrac{w\Omega^2}{g}y = w$, $(E, I, w, \Omega, g$ constants) is the equation for the deflection of a rotating shaft. Find the general solution and also the solutions subject to the conditions

(a) simply supported ends: $y = 0$, $d^2y/dx^2 = 0$ at $x = \pm l$,

(b) built-in ends: $y = 0$, $dy/dx = 0$ at $x = \pm l$.

1.8 THEORY OF FORCED VIBRATIONS

Consider again the problem, which was discussed in §1.6 and illustrated in Fig. 1.3, of a mass vibrating on a spring. However, now suppose that in addition to the spring force $-ky$ and damping force $-hdy/dt$, the variable downward force $F(t)$ is applied to the mass by some external agency, so that the equation of motion becomes

$$m\frac{d^2y}{dt^2} + h\frac{dy}{dt} + ky = F(t). \tag{60}$$

Again suppose that an e.m.f. $E(t)$ is introduced in the electrical circuit discussed in §1.6, and illustrated in Fig. 1.6. The equation for the current I in this circuit is then

$$L\frac{d^2I}{dt^2} + R\frac{dI}{dt} + \frac{I}{C} = \frac{dE(t)}{dt}. \tag{61}$$

Of particular importance are the cases in which $F(t)$ and $E(t)$ are *periodic* functions, whose values repeat themselves at constant intervals. In the electrical example, this corresponds to an alternating current. In mechanics, periodic forces are common; for example the forces applied by an internal combustion or steam engine running at constant speed are periodic. Periodic functions in general are discussed in Chapter 2. At present it is sufficient to note that the simplest and most important periodic functions are sine and cosine functions. In Chapter 2 it will be shown that most periodic functions encountered in practice can be expressed as infinite sums of sine and cosine functions. Hence we consider the cases

$$F(t) = F_0 \cos pt, \quad E(t) = E_0 \sin pt,$$

so that equations (60) and (61) become respectively

$$m\frac{d^2y}{dt^2} + h\frac{dy}{dt} + ky = F_0 \cos pt, \tag{62}$$

$$L\frac{d^2I}{dt^2} + R\frac{dI}{dt} + \frac{I}{C} = pE_0 \cos pt. \tag{63}$$

Following and extending the notation of §1.6, in equation (62) denote

$$h/m = 2\alpha, \quad k/m = \omega^2, \quad F_0/m = f_0 \tag{64}$$

and in equation (63) denote

$$I = y, \quad R/L = 2\alpha, \quad 1/CL = \omega^2, \quad pE_0/L = f_0. \tag{65}$$

Then equations (62) and (63) both take the form

$$\frac{d^2y}{dt^2} + 2\alpha \frac{dy}{dt} + \omega^2 y = f_0 \cos pt. \tag{66}$$

Thus mathematically the two problems are identical, and both may be dealt with at the same time.

We consider the case of light damping, $\alpha^2 - \omega^2 = -\beta^2 < 0$. The complementary function is the solution of the homogeneous equation (40) and is given by (46) as

$$u(t) = A e^{-\alpha t} \cos(\beta t - \epsilon), \tag{67}$$

where A and ϵ are arbitrary constants. This part of the solution represents *free vibrations*; it depends only on the properties of the system (that is, on m, h and k in the spring problem) and not on the applied force or e.m.f. Because of the factor $e^{-\alpha t}$, the amplitude of the free vibrations tends to zero as $t \to \infty$, whatever the initial conditions. For this reason the free vibrations are often called *transients*.

From §1.7, a particular integral of equation (66) is of the form

$$v(t) = g \cos pt + h \sin pt. \tag{68}$$

By substitution, we find that $y = v(t)$ satisfies equation (66) if

$$(-p^2 + \omega^2)g + 2\alpha p h = f_0, \quad -2\alpha p g + (-p^2 + \omega^2)h = 0,$$

which determine g and h to be

$$g = \frac{(\omega^2 - p^2)f_0}{(\omega^2 - p^2)^2 + 4\alpha^2 p^2}, \quad h = \frac{2\alpha p f_0}{(\omega^2 - p^2)^2 + 4\alpha^2 p^2}.$$

It is convenient to introduce the angle γ defined by

$$\tan \gamma = \frac{2\alpha p}{\omega^2 - p^2}. \tag{69}$$

Then

$$g = \frac{f_0 \cos \gamma}{\sqrt{\{(\omega^2 - p^2)^2 + 4\alpha^2 p^2\}}}, \quad h = \frac{f_0 \sin \gamma}{\sqrt{\{(\omega^2 - p^2)^2 + 4\alpha^2 p^2\}}}$$

and, from equation (68), a particular integral of equation (66) is

$$v(t) = \frac{f_0(\cos pt \cos \gamma + \sin pt \sin \gamma)}{\sqrt{\{(\omega^2 - p^2)^2 + 4\alpha^2 p^2\}}} = \frac{f_0 \cos(pt - \gamma)}{\sqrt{\{(\omega^2 - p^2)^2 + 4\alpha^2 p^2\}}}. \tag{70}$$

The general solution is obtained by adding the complementary function (67) to the particular integral (70).

The particular integral depends on f_0 and p, and so on the applied force or e.m.f. It represents a periodic displacement or current which has the same period $2\pi/p$ as the applied force or e.m.f., but is not in phase with it. This part of the solution represents *forced vibrations.* Unlike the free vibrations, the forced vibrations do not tend to zero as $t \to \infty$. Hence, whatever the initial conditions, for sufficiently large t the forced vibrations will predominate over the free vibrations.

The amplitude $\hat{v}$ of the forced vibrations is, from equation (70)

$$\hat{v} = \frac{f_0}{\sqrt{\{(\omega^2 - p^2)^2 + 4\alpha^2 p^2\}}} \,.$$

The variation of $\hat{v}$ with p for fixed values of f_0, α and ω is shown in Fig. 1.7. If f_0, α and ω are fixed, $\hat{v}$ has its maximum value when $(\omega^2 - p^2)^2 + 4\alpha^2 p^2$ has its minimum value as p varies. This minimum occurs when $p^2 = \omega^2 - 2\alpha^2 = \beta^2 - \alpha^2$. The corresponding maximum value of $\hat{v}$ is

$$\hat{v} = \frac{f_0}{2\alpha\beta} \,. \tag{71}$$

If α is very small compared to ω so that there is very little damping effect, then $\omega \simeq \beta$. Then the maximum amplitude of $\hat{v}$ occurs when $p \simeq \beta$ and the frequency $2\pi/p$ of the forced vibrations is close to the frequency $2\pi/\beta$ of the free vibrations. Moreover when α is small, Fig. 1.7 and equation (71) show that this maximum is large, and the peak of

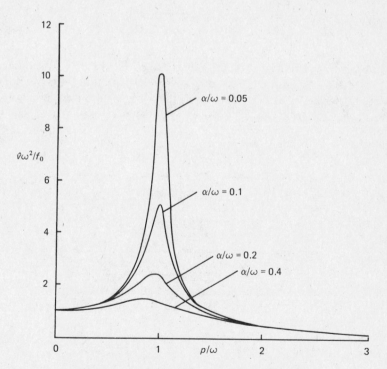

Fig. 1.7 Variation of $\hat{v}$ with p, illustrating resonance

the curve is a sharp one. This is the phenomenon of *resonance*, whereby forced vibrations are greatly magnified if their period is close to the period of the free vibrations of the system. In mechanical systems resonance is usually undesirable, and a designer will try to prevent it occurring. In electrical systems, resonance is essential for the working of devices such as amplifiers.

1.9 SIMULTANEOUS LINEAR DIFFERENTIAL EQUATIONS WITH CONSTANT COEFFICIENTS

Many engineering problems give rise to systems of ordinary differential equations. These involve two or more dependent variables and their derivatives with respect to a single independent variable. For example, Fig. 1.8 shows a circuit diagram for a simplified transformer. The primary circuit has current I_1, capacitance C_1, self-inductance L_1 and applied e.m.f. $E \sin pt$, the secondary circuit has current I_2, capacitance C_2 and self-inductance L_2, and the mutual inductance is M. Resistances are neglected, but could have been included at the expense of some additional complexity. The equations which govern the currents I_1 and I_2 as functions of time t are

$$L_1 \frac{d^2 I_1}{dt^2} + M \frac{d^2 I_2}{dt^2} + \frac{I_1}{C_1} = Ep \cos pt,$$

$$L_2 \frac{d^2 I_2}{dt^2} + M \frac{d^2 I_1}{dt^2} + \frac{I_2}{C_2} = 0.$$

(72)

These are a pair of simultaneous linear differential equations for I_1 and I_2; since L_1, L_2, C_1, C_2 and M are constants, the equations have constant coefficients. We return to equations (72) later in this section. It is evident that more complicated electrical circuits or mechanical systems will give rise to larger systems of differential equations.

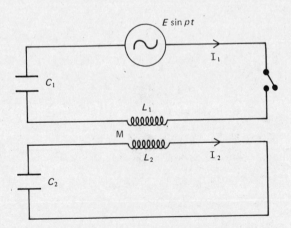

Fig. 1.8   Circuit diagram for simplified transformer

The simplest procedure is often to use the D operator (§1.4) (an alternative approach which is preferable for certain types of problem will be introduced in §8.8). A D operator can be applied to every term of an equation without violating the equality, so D can be treated in almost the same way as an algebraic quantity. This makes it possible to use the elimination method of solution in essentially the same manner as in solving linear algebraic equations, except that it must be remembered that D has always to appear to the left of quantities on which it operates.

EXAMPLE 1
Solve the simultaneous differential equations

$$(5D - 1)y - (2D - 1)z = 4e^{-2x},$$
$$(D + 7)y \qquad - 3z = 12e^{-2x},$$

where D denotes d/dx.

To eliminate z, multiply the first equation by 3, operate on the second by $(2D - 1)$, and subtract the second equation from the first. This gives

$$\{3(5D - 1) - (2D - 1)(D + 7)\}y = 12e^{-2x} - 12(2D - 1)e^{-2x}.$$

On the left we simplify the expression in braces, and on the right use

$$De^{-2x} = d(e^{-2x})/dx = -2e^{-2x},$$

to obtain

$$(-2D^2 + 2D + 4)y = 72e^{-2x}, \quad \text{or} \quad (D^2 - D - 2)y = -36e^{-2x}.$$

This is now a second-order equation for y. By the methods of §1.5 and §1.7 it is straightforward to obtain its solution as

$$y = Ae^{2x} + Be^{-x} - 9e^{-2x}. \tag{73}$$

One way to determine z is to eliminate y from the original equations and proceed as before. However, it is easier in this example to substitute for y from equation (73) into the second of the original equations, which gives

$$z = \tfrac{1}{3}(D + 7)y - 4e^{-2x} = \tfrac{1}{3}(Dy + 7y) - 4e^{-2x}$$
$$= \tfrac{1}{3}\{2Ae^{2x} - Be^{-x} + 18e^{-2x} + 7Ae^{2x} + 7Be^{-x} - 63e^{-2x}\} - 4e^{-2x}$$
$$= 3Ae^{2x} + 2Be^{-x} - 19e^{-2x}. \tag{74}$$

The solution (73) and (74) is readily checked by substitution in the first of the original equations.

EXAMPLE 2
Solve the simultaneous differential equations

$$(3D + 7)y + (3D + 5)z = 0,$$
$$(4D + 11)y - (D + 5)z = 0. \tag{75}$$

First eliminate z by operating on the first equation by $(D + 5)$, on the second by

(3D + 5), and adding. This gives

$$\{(D + 5)(3D + 7) + (3D + 5)(4D + 11)\}y = 0,$$

from which

$$(15D^2 + 75D + 90)y = 0, \quad \text{or} \quad (D^2 + 5D + 6)y = 0,$$

which has the general solution

$$y = Ae^{-2x} + Be^{-3x}. \tag{76}$$

In this case it is not possible to find z directly by substituting for y in one of the original equations. A suitable procedure is to return to the original equations and eliminate y by operating on the first equation by $(4D + 11)$, on the second by $(3D + 7)$ and subtracting. After simplification, this gives

$$(D^2 + 5D + 6)z = 0.$$

Hence z satisfies the same equation as y (for homogeneous equations this is true in general, and is not just a special feature of this example). This does *not* mean that $z = y$, because the arbitrary constants in the solution for z are generally different from those in the solution for y. Hence

$$z = Ce^{-2x} + Ee^{-3x}. \tag{77}$$

Now equations (76) and (77) together contain the four arbitrary constants A, B, C, E, although we expect the general solution of two first-order equations (75) to contain two constants. In fact, A, B, C, E are related. To show this, substitute equations (76) and (77) back into the first of equations (75), which gives

$$-6Ae^{-2x} - 9Be^{-3x} + 7Ae^{-2x} + 7Be^{-3x} - 6Ce^{-2x} - 9Ee^{-3x} + 5Ce^{-2x}$$

$$+ 5Ee^{-3x} = 0,$$

or

$$(A - C)e^{-2x} + (-2B - 4E)e^{-3x} = 0.$$

Hence the first of equations (75) is satisfied only if $C = A$ and $E = -\tfrac{1}{2}B$. It can be verified that no further conditions are required in order to satisfy the second of equations (75), and so the general solution of the simultaneous equations is

$$y = Ae^{-2x} + Be^{-3x}, \quad z = Ae^{-2x} - \tfrac{1}{2}Be^{-3x}.$$

Equations of a Transformer

Equations (72) govern the currents I_1 and I_2 in the circuit illustrated in Fig. 1.8. When they are expressed in D operator notation (with D denoting the operation d/dt), these equations become

$$\left(L_1 D^2 + \frac{1}{C_1}\right) I_1 + MD^2 I_2 = Ep \cos pt,$$

$$MD^2 I_1 + \left(L_2 D^2 + \frac{1}{C_2}\right) I_2 = 0.$$

Eliminating I_1 gives, after simplification,

$$\{C_1 C_2 (L_1 L_2 - M^2) D^4 + (L_1 C_1 + L_2 C_2) D^2 + 1\} I_2 = MEC_1 C_2 p^3 \cos pt.$$

This is a fourth-order inhomogeneous equation for I_2, whose solution by the methods of §1.7 is straightforward. For physical reasons $L_1 L_2 - M^2 > 0$, and using this it can be shown that the four roots of the auxiliary equation are all purely imaginary. The solution is

$$I_2 = A \cos \beta_1 t + B \sin \beta_1 t + C \cos \beta_2 t + F \sin \beta_2 t$$

$$+ \frac{MEp^3 C_1 C_2 \cos pt}{C_1 C_2 (L_1 L_2 - M^2) p^4 - (L_1 C_1 + L_2 C_2) p^2 + 1},$$

where $m = \pm i\beta_1, \pm i\beta_2$ are the roots of

$$C_1 C_2 (L_1 L_2 - M^2) m^4 - (L_1 C_1 + L_2 C_2) m^2 + 1 = 0,$$

and A, B, C and F are arbitrary constants. It is left to the reader to find I_1.

Exercises

1. Solve the following pairs of differential equations:

    (a) $\dfrac{dy}{dt} + 3y = z + e^t$, $\dfrac{dz}{dt} + 2z = y + e^t$.

    (b) $(2D^2 - 6D + 4)y + (D^2 - D - 2)z = 0$,

           $(D^2 + D - 2)y + (2D^2 + 6D + 4)z = 0$,

where D denotes the operation d/dx.

2. The coordinates of a charged particle moving in a certain electric and magnetic field satisfy

$$M \frac{d^2 x}{dt^2} + He \frac{dy}{dt} = Ve,$$

$$He \frac{dx}{dt} - M \frac{d^2 y}{dt^2} = 0,$$

where M, H, e and V are constants. If $x = y = dx/dt = dy/dt = 0$ when $t = 0$, show that the particle describes a cycloid, and find its equation.

1.10 EULER'S EQUATION

The equation

$$a_0 x^n \frac{d^n y}{dx^n} + a_1 x^{n-1} \frac{d^{n-1} y}{dx^{n-1}} + \ldots + a_{n-1} x \frac{dy}{dx} + a_n y = f(x), \tag{78}$$

where $a_0, a_1, \ldots, a_n$ are constants, is often called Euler's equation. Two methods of solution will be described.

First method   Euler's equation (78) can always be reduced to a linear equation with constant coefficients by the substitution $x = e^t$. Then $dx/dt = e^t$ and

$$x \frac{d}{dx} = e^t \frac{dt}{dx} \frac{d}{dt} = e^t e^{-t} \frac{d}{dt} = \frac{d}{dt} . \tag{79}$$

Thus

$$x \frac{dy}{dx} = \frac{dy}{dt} ,$$

$$\tag{80}$$

$$x^2 \frac{d^2 y}{dx^2} = x \frac{d}{dx} \left(x \frac{dy}{dx} \right) - x \frac{dy}{dx} = \frac{d^2 y}{dt^2} - \frac{dy}{dt} ,$$

and so on for higher derivatives. Equation (78) becomes a linear equation with constant coefficients on making the substitutions (80).

EXAMPLE 1

$$x^2 \frac{d^2 y}{dx^2} + 3x \frac{dy}{dx} - 3y = 2x^2 .$$

Substitute for $x^2 \dfrac{d^2 y}{dx^2}$ and $x \dfrac{dy}{dx}$ from equations (80) and set $x = e^t$ on the right-hand side. This gives

$$\left(\frac{d^2 y}{dt^2} - \frac{dy}{dt} \right) + 3 \frac{dy}{dt} - 3y = 2e^{2t},$$

$$\frac{d^2 y}{dt^2} + 2 \frac{dy}{dt} - 3y = 2e^{2t}.$$

This is now a linear equation with constant coefficients whose general solution is easily found by the methods of §1.5 and §1.7 to be

$$y = Ae^t + Be^{-3t} + \tfrac{2}{5} e^{2t} = Ax + Bx^{-3} + \tfrac{2}{5} x^2 .$$

Second method   For the homogeneous Euler's equation, with $f(x) = 0$, this is usually the easier method to apply. Inspection of equation (78), with $f(x) = 0$, suggests seeking trial solutions of the form $y = Ax^q$, which gives

$$x \frac{dy}{dx} = Aqx^q, \quad x^2 \frac{d^2 y}{dx^2} = Aq(q-1)x^q, \quad \text{and so on.}$$

On substituting these expressions, the equation reduces to an algebraic equation for q, as in the following example.

EXAMPLE 2

$$x^2 \frac{d^2y}{dx^2} + 7x \frac{dy}{dx} + 8y = 0.$$

The trial solution $y = Ax^q$ satisfies the equation if

$$A\{q(q-1) + 7q + 8\}x^q = 0,$$

that is $q^2 + 6q + 8 = 0$, so that $q = -2$ or $q = -4$. Hence two solutions are $y = Ax^{-2}$ and $y = Bx^{-4}$, and the general solution is

$$y = Ax^{-2} + Bx^{-4}.$$

This method fails to give two independent solutions if the equation for q has equal roots, but in such a case the first method can still be used. It will then be found that the auxiliary equation has equal roots, and the solution for y will include terms which involve $\log x$.

Exercises

1. Solve the differential equations:

(a) $\quad x^2 \dfrac{d^2y}{dx^2} + x \dfrac{dy}{dx} - n^2 y = 0 \quad$ (n constant),

(b) $\quad x^2 \dfrac{d^2y}{dx^2} + 6x \dfrac{dy}{dx} + 4y = 2 \log x,$

(c) $\quad (x-2)^2 \dfrac{d^2y}{dx^2} + 4(x-2)\dfrac{dy}{dx} + 2y = 0.$

PROBLEMS

1. Solve the differential equations:

(a) $\quad \dfrac{dy}{dx} = \dfrac{y}{x} + \sec\left(\dfrac{y}{x}\right),$ $\qquad$ (b) $\quad \cos x \dfrac{dy}{dx} - 2y \sin x = 4 \sin x.$

2. Solve the following differential equations:

(a) $\quad \dfrac{dy}{dx} = \dfrac{x^2 + 2xy + 2y^2}{xy},$ $\qquad$ (b) $\quad \dfrac{dy}{dx} + y \cot x = 1,$

(c) $\quad (2xe^x \log y + x^2 e^x \log y + y) + \left(\dfrac{1}{y} x^2 e^x + x\right)\dfrac{dy}{dx} = 0.$

3. Determine which of the following equations is exact and solve it:

(a) $e^x(x^2 + y^2 + 2x)dx + 2ye^x \, dy = 0,$

(b) $e^x(x^2 + y^2 + 2x)dx - 2ye^x \, dy = 0.$

4. (a)   Solve the equation

$$4\frac{d^2y}{dt^2} + 4a\frac{dy}{dt} + 25y = 0,$$

where a is a constant. Distinguish between the cases $a > 5, 0 < a < 5, a = 5$.

(b)   Solve the equation

$$4\frac{d^2y}{dt^2} + 12\frac{dy}{dt} + 25y = 73 \cos 2t,$$

given that $y = dy/dt = 0$ when $t = 0$.

5. Find the general solution of the equation

$$\frac{d^3y}{dx^3} - 3\frac{dy}{dx} + 2y = 3e^{-2x}.$$

Hence derive the solution such that $y = 1$ at $x = 0$, and $y \to 0$ as $x \to \infty$.

6. Determine the solutions of the following differential equations subject to the boundary conditions stated:

(a) $(D^3 - 3D^2 + D + 5)y = 3(1 + x)e^{2x},$

subject to $y(0) = 0, y'(0) = 0$ and $y(-\infty) = 0.$

(b) $(D^3 - 3D^2 + D + 5)y = 20(1 + x)e^{-x},$

subject to $y(0) = 0$ and $y(\infty) = 0.$

7. Obtain the general solutions to the following differential equations:

(a) $x\dfrac{dy}{dx} + 2y = e^x,$ (b) $\dfrac{d^2y}{dx^2} - 2\dfrac{dy}{dx} + y = e^x.$

8. Solve the following differential equations:

(a) $\dfrac{dy}{dx} + \dfrac{x^2 - a^2}{x(x^2 + a^2)}y = \dfrac{x}{x^2 + a^2}$ where a is constant,

(b) $\dfrac{d^2y}{dx^2} + 4\dfrac{dy}{dx} + 13y = 40 \cos x,$

(c) $\dfrac{d^2y}{dx^2} + 2\dfrac{dy}{dx} + y = e^{-x}.$

9. Find the general solutions of the following differential equations:

(a) $\dfrac{dy}{dx} + \left(2x + \dfrac{1}{x}\right)y = 1,$

(b) $\dfrac{d^2y}{dx^2} + 3\dfrac{dy}{dx} + 2y = 10\cos x,$

(c) $\dfrac{d^2y}{dx^2} + 3\dfrac{dy}{dx} + 2y = 2xe^{-x}.$

10. Solve the simultaneous differential equations

$$\dfrac{dx}{dt} = y, \quad \dfrac{dy}{dt} = z, \quad \dfrac{dz}{dt} = x,$$

given that $x = 1$, $y = 1$ and $z = 1$ when $t = 0$.

11. Solve the simultaneous differential equations

$$\dfrac{dx}{dt} + x + y = e^t, \quad \dfrac{dy}{dt} - y - 2x = te^{-t}.$$

12. Find the general solution of the simultaneous equations

$$\dfrac{d^2x}{dt^2} - 4\dfrac{dx}{dt} + 4x = y,$$

$$\dfrac{d^2y}{dt^2} + 4\dfrac{dy}{dt} + 4y = 25x + 16e^{-t},$$

and hence the solution such that $y = -4$ at $t = 0$ and $x, y \to 0$ as $t \to \infty$.

13. A particle moves in a plane so that its coordinates at time t satisfy the simultaneous differential equations

$$\dfrac{d^2x}{dt^2} - 2y = 0, \quad \dfrac{d^2y}{dt^2} + 2x = 0.$$

If, at time $t = 0$, the particle is at the point $x = 1$, $y = 0$, and has velocity components $dx/dt = -1$, $dy/dt = 1$, show that the particle describes the logarithmic spiral $r = e^{-\theta}$ ($x = r\cos\theta$, $y = r\sin\theta$). Find the velocity of the particle at time t.

14. A particle moves in a plane so that its coordinates at time t satisfy the simultaneous differential equations

$$\dfrac{d^2x}{dt^2} + k\dfrac{dy}{dt} + 2k^2x = 0,$$

$$\dfrac{d^2y}{dt^2} - k\dfrac{dx}{dt} + 2k^2y = 0,$$

where k is a constant. If, at time $t = 0$, the particle is at the point $x = 1$, $y = 0$ and has velocity components $dx/dt = 0$, $dy/dt = 2k$, show that it moves in a circle with angular velocity $2k$.

15. Solve the equation

$$t^2 \frac{d^2y}{dt^2} + 9t \frac{dy}{dt} + 25y = 0,$$

given that $y = 1$ when $t = 1$ and when $t = e^{\pi/6}$.

16. Solve the differential equation

$$x^2 \frac{d^2y}{dx^2} + x \frac{dy}{dx} + 4y = \sin(\log x) + \sin(2 \log x).$$

17. Find the solution of the simultaneous differential equations

$$t \frac{dx}{dt} + y = 0, \qquad t \frac{dy}{dt} + x = 0,$$

such that $x = 1$ and $y = -1$ when $t = 1$.

BIBLIOGRAPHY

[1]   Rainville, E. D., and P. E. Bedient. *Elementary Differential Equations*, 5th edition, Macmillan, New York (1974).
[2]   Bickley, W. G. and A. Talbot. *An Introduction to the Theory of Vibrating Systems*, Clarendon Press, Oxford (1961).
See also the bibliography to Chapter 6 of Volume 2.

CHAPTER 2

Fourier Series

2.1 INTRODUCTION

Many simple physical models used by engineers and scientists can be described mathematically by an inhomogeneous linear differential equation such as

$$a \frac{d^2y}{dt^2} + b \frac{dy}{dt} + cy = f(t), \tag{1}$$

where $f(t)$ is a forcing or exciting function which is usually periodic, and a, b and c are constants (see §1.8).

Methods of solving equation (1) for certain simple functions $f(t)$ have been considered in §1.7. In particular, when $f(t)$ is a sine or cosine function, equation (1) is very easily solved. Let $y = u_m(t)$ and $y = v_n(t)$, where m and n are integers, be solutions of the equations

$$a \frac{d^2y}{dt^2} + b \frac{dy}{dt} + cy = \cos mt \quad \text{and} \quad a \frac{d^2y}{dt^2} + b \frac{dy}{dt} + cy = \sin nt \tag{2}$$

respectively, then $y = Au_m(t) + Bv_n(t)$ is the solution of the equation

$$a \frac{d^2y}{dt^2} + b \frac{dy}{dt} + cy = A \cos mt + B \sin nt.$$

This method of solution can be extended to include the more general case in which $f(t)$ is *any* sum of sines and cosines. Thus, if $f(t)$ is the finite trigonometric series

$$f(t) = \sum_{m=1}^{M} a_m \cos mt + \sum_{n=1}^{N} b_n \sin nt, \tag{3}$$

the solution of equation (1) is

$$y = \sum_{m=1}^{M} a_m u_m(t) + \sum_{n=1}^{N} b_n v_n(t).$$

In practice however, the functions $f(t)$ are rarely sines and cosines or finite trigonometric series. Then the problem of solving equation (1) can be extremely difficult. However, if it were possible to represent or expand $f(t)$ as a trigonometric series of the form (3) *with M and N possibly infinite*, then equation (1) could still be solved by the method outlined above. These infinite series representations are called *Fourier series* after *J. B. Fourier* (1768–1830), who in the course of investigating a heat conduction problem, showed that certain functions could indeed be expressed as infinite trigonometric series.

The idea of series representation of functions is quite common in mathematics; for instance, many functions can be expressed as power series. For example, $\exp x$ can be expressed as

$$\exp x = 1 + x + \frac{x^2}{2!} + \ldots + \frac{x^n}{n!} + \ldots$$

This kind of series representation is called a *Taylor series*. A series representation of a function can be regarded as a resolution of the function into components which have known simple properties. In the case of a Taylor series the resolved components are the polynomials $1, x, \ldots, x^n, \ldots$, whereas in the case of a Fourier series the resolved components are sines and cosines. A difficult problem such as equation (1) can be solved easily when $f(t)$ is expressed as a Fourier series because the problem is broken down into a set of simple problems of the type (2). The above procedure can have wide application because very many functions which are of physical interest can be expressed as Fourier series. A particular example of equation (1) is solved using Fourier series in §2.6, and other types of equation amenable to solution by Fourier series methods are discussed in Chapter 7.

2.2 DERIVATION OF THE FOURIER SERIES

Preliminaries

The terms of a Fourier series are sines and cosines and therefore it will be useful to state those properties of $\sin nx$ and $\cos nx$, where n is an integer, which will be used in the subsequent analysis.

The functions $\sin mx$ and $\cos nx$ are defined and continuous in $-\infty < x < \infty$ and, if m and n are integers, satisfy the relations (see example 1 of this section),

$$\left.\begin{array}{l} \displaystyle\int_{-\pi}^{\pi} \sin mx \cos nx \, \mathrm{d}x = \int_{-\pi}^{\pi} \sin mx \, \mathrm{d}x = \int_{-\pi}^{\pi} \cos mx \, \mathrm{d}x = 0, \\[3mm] \displaystyle\int_{-\pi}^{\pi} \cos mx \cos nx \, \mathrm{d}x = \int_{-\pi}^{\pi} \sin mx \sin nx \, \mathrm{d}x = \begin{cases} 0 & \text{when } m \neq n \\ \pi & \text{when } m = n. \end{cases} \end{array}\right\} \quad (4)$$

Here we make use of the following definitions:

DEFINITION   A function $f(x)$ is continuous at $x = x_0$ if $f(x_0^+) = f(x_0^-) = f(x_0)$ where $f(x_0^+) = \lim_{x \to x_0^+} f(x)$ is the limit as $x \to x_0$ from values of $x > x_0$, and $f(x_0^-) = \lim_{x \to x_0^-} f(x)$ is the limit as $x \to x_0$ from values of $x < x_0$.

DEFINITION   A function is *continuous* in the interval $a < x < b$ if it is continuous at every point of $a < x < b$.

DEFINITION   A function $f(x)$ is *periodic* if it is defined for all real x and if there is some positive number p which is independent of x, such that $f(x + p) = f(x)$ for all x. The number p is called a *period* of $f(x)$.

The number $2p$ is also a period of $f(x)$ since

$$f(x + 2p) = f([x + p] + p) = f(x + p) = f(x),$$

and similarly the number rp is a period for all integers r.

DEFINITION   The *fundamental period* of $f(x)$ is the least positive period of $f(x)$.

A periodic function is repetitive in cycles of equal duration, as shown by the graph in Fig. 2.1. The fundamental period of $\cos x$ and $\sin x$ is 2π and the numbers $2r\pi$, where r is an integer, are also periods. The fundamental period of $\cos nx$ and $\sin nx$ is $2\pi/n$ and the numbers $2r\pi/n$ are also periods. For example, $\sin 3x$ has fundamental period $\frac{2}{3}\pi$ and also has periods $4\pi/3, 2\pi, \ldots, 2r\pi/3, \ldots$.

A constant function (e.g. $f(x) = 2$, for all x) satisfies the definition of a periodic function for any period p, and therefore will be regarded as a periodic function.

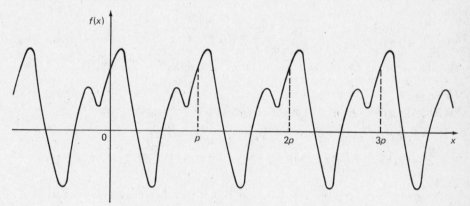

Fig. 2.1   A periodic function with fundamental period p

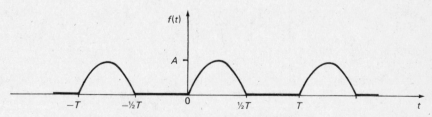

Fig. 2.2   The output $f(t)$ of a half-wave rectifier

$$f(t) = \begin{cases} 0 & \text{for } -T/2 \leqslant t < 0 \\ A \sin(2\pi t/T) & \text{for } 0 \leqslant t < T/2 \end{cases} \quad \text{and } f(t + T) = f(t)$$

Examples of periodic functions which arise in engineering problems are the e.m.f. in an a.c. circuit, the output of a half-wave rectifier (see Fig. 2.2), the thrust on the piston and the displacement of the piston in a piston engine, the rise and fall of the tide, and the beating of a heart. These are all functions which are periodic in time. The sag of a telephone cable which is suspended from regularly spaced poles, is a function which is periodic in the distance along the cable.

EXAMPLE 1

If m and n are integers prove that

$$\int_{-\pi}^{\pi} \sin mx \sin nx \, dx = \begin{cases} 0 \text{ when } m \neq n \\ \pi \text{ when } m = n. \end{cases}$$

The integrand may be written as $\frac{1}{2}[\cos(m-n)x - \cos(m+n)x]$ and therefore if $m = n$

$$\int_{-\pi}^{\pi} \sin nx \sin nx \, dx = \frac{1}{2}\int_{-\pi}^{\pi}(1 - \cos 2nx)\, dx = \frac{1}{2}\left[x - \frac{\sin 2nx}{2n}\right]_{-\pi}^{\pi} = \pi,$$

whilst if $m \neq n$

$$\int_{-\pi}^{\pi} \sin mx \sin nx \, dx = \frac{1}{2}\left[\frac{\sin(m-n)x}{m-n} - \frac{\sin(m+n)x}{m+n}\right]_{-\pi}^{\pi} = 0.$$

The other relations (4) can be proved in a similar fashion.

EXAMPLE 2

Sketch the graph of the function defined as

$$f(x) = x^2 \quad \text{for} \quad 1 \leqslant x < 5 \quad \text{and} \quad f(x+4) = f(x).$$

State an expression for $f(x)$ when (a) $21 \leqslant x < 25$, (b) $3 \leqslant x < 7$.

The graph of $f(x)$ is given in Fig. 2.3. In $21 \leqslant x < 25$ the function is given by

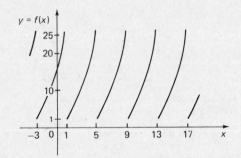

Fig. 2.3   The graph of $y = f(x)$ defined in example 2

the expression

$$f(x) = (x - 20)^2.$$

In $3 \leqslant x < 7$ the function is given by the expressions

$$f(x) = x^2 \qquad \text{when } 3 \leqslant x < 5$$

and

$$f(x) = (x - 4)^2 \quad \text{when } 5 \leqslant x < 7.$$

The Fourier Coefficients

Consider a function $f(x)$ which is periodic with fundamental period 2π, and suppose that it can be represented in $-\pi \leqslant x \leqslant \pi$ by the infinite trigonometric series

$$f(x) = \tfrac{1}{2}a_0 + \sum_{n=1}^{\infty} (a_n \cdot \cos nx + b_n \sin nx), \tag{5}$$

where a_0, a_n, b_n, for $n = 1, 2, \ldots$ are constants. For an arbitrary periodic function $f(x)$ these constants are as yet unknown but obviously will depend on the precise form of $f(x)$. The constant a_0 is given the coefficient $\tfrac{1}{2}$ for convenience, as will be seen in equations (10).

In order to calculate a_0, we assume that $f(x)$ is integrable and then both sides of equation (5) may be integrated between $-\pi$ and π giving

$$\int_{-\pi}^{\pi} f(x)dx = \int_{-\pi}^{\pi} \left(\tfrac{1}{2}a_0 + \sum_{n=1}^{\infty} (a_n \cos nx + b_n \sin nx) \right) dx. \tag{6a}$$

If it is now assumed that the right-hand side of equation (6a) can be integrated term by term, the equation

$$\int_{-\pi}^{\pi} f(x)dx = \tfrac{1}{2}a_0 \int_{-\pi}^{\pi} dx + \sum_{n=1}^{\infty} \left(a_n \int_{-\pi}^{\pi} \cos nx \, dx + b_n \int_{-\pi}^{\pi} \sin nx \, dx \right) \tag{6b}$$

is obtained. It can be seen from equations (4) that the terms under the summation sign are all zero so that equation (6b) reduces to

$$\int_{-\pi}^{\pi} f(x)dx = \pi a_0, \quad \text{that is} \quad a_0 = \frac{1}{\pi} \int_{-\pi}^{\pi} f(x)dx.$$

Thus $\tfrac{1}{2}a_0$ is the mean value of $f(x)$ in the interval $-\pi \leqslant x \leqslant \pi$.

The coefficient a_1 may be calculated by multiplying equation (5) by $\cos x$ and then integrating both sides of the equation between $-\pi$ and π. This gives the equation

$$\int_{-\pi}^{\pi} f(x)\cos x \, dx = \int_{-\pi}^{\pi} \left(\tfrac{1}{2}a_0 + \sum_{n=1}^{\infty} (a_n \cos nx + b_n \sin nx) \right) \cos x \, dx. \tag{7a}$$

After term by term integration, equation (7a) becomes

$$\int_{-\pi}^{\pi} f(x)\cos x \, dx = \tfrac{1}{2}a_0 \int_{-\pi}^{\pi} \cos x \, dx$$

$$+ \sum_{n=1}^{\infty} \left(a_n \int_{-\pi}^{\pi} \cos nx \cos x \, dx + b_n \int_{-\pi}^{\pi} \sin nx \cos x \, dx \right).$$

(7b)

We see from equations (4), with $m = 1$, that the only non-zero term on the right-hand side of equation (7b) is πa_1 and hence equation (7b) gives the result

$$a_1 = \frac{1}{\pi} \int_{-\pi}^{\pi} f(x)\cos x \, dx.$$

The coefficient a_2 can be found in a similar fashion by multiplying equation (5) by $\cos 2x$ and integrating both sides of the resulting equation between $-\pi$ and π. This gives the formula

$$a_2 = \frac{1}{\pi} \int_{-\pi}^{\pi} f(x)\cos 2x \, dx.$$

The procedure for calculating a_1 and a_2 can easily be generalized to provide a method of calculating a_m, where m is any positive integer. Equation (5) is multiplied by $\cos mx$ where m is a fixed positive integer, and both sides of the resulting equation are integrated between $-\pi$ and π. This gives the equation

$$\int_{-\pi}^{\pi} f(x)\cos mx \, dx = \int_{-\pi}^{\pi} \left(\tfrac{1}{2}a_0 + \sum_{n=1}^{\infty} (a_n \cos nx + b_n \sin nx) \right) \cos mx \, dx, \quad (8a)$$

where m is fixed and the summation is over values of n. Integrating term by term as before, equation (8a) becomes

$$\int_{-\pi}^{\pi} f(x)\cos mx \, dx = \tfrac{1}{2}a_0 \int_{-\pi}^{\pi} \cos mx \, dx$$

$$+ \sum_{n=1}^{\infty} \left(a_n \int_{-\pi}^{\pi} \cos nx \cos mx \, dx + b_n \int_{-\pi}^{\pi} \sin nx \cos mx \, dx \right).$$

(8b)

The relations given in equations (4) can be used again to show that the only non-zero term on the right-hand side of equation (8b) is πa_m. Hence for each m,

$$a_m = \frac{1}{\pi} \int_{-\pi}^{\pi} f(x)\cos mx \, dx.$$

The coefficients b_m can be calculated using a modification of the method given above for calculating a_m. Equation (5) is now multiplied by sin mx where m is a fixed positive integer, and both sides of the resulting equation are integrated between $-\pi$ and π. This gives the equation

$$\int_{-\pi}^{\pi} f(x)\sin mx \, dx = \int_{-\pi}^{\pi} \left(\tfrac{1}{2}a_0 + \sum_{n=1}^{\infty} (a_n \cos nx + b_n \sin nx) \right) \sin mx \, dx, \qquad (9)$$

where m is fixed and the summation is over n. Equation (9) is then integrated term by term and with the aid of equations (4) the result

$$b_m = \frac{1}{\pi} \int_{-\pi}^{\pi} f(x)\sin mx \, dx$$

for each m is obtained.

Thus the coefficients a_0, a_n, b_n for $n = 1, 2, \ldots$ are given by

$$a_0 = \frac{1}{\pi} \int_{-\pi}^{\pi} f(x)dx,$$

$$a_n = \frac{1}{\pi} \int_{-\pi}^{\pi} f(x)\cos nx \, dx, \qquad\qquad (10)$$

$$b_n = \frac{1}{\pi} \int_{-\pi}^{\pi} f(x)\sin nx \, dx.$$

It can now be seen that the coefficient $\tfrac{1}{2}$ in equation (5) ensures that the formula for a_0 is a special case of the formula for a_n.

The formulae (10) are called *Euler formulae* and the constants a_0, a_n, b_n defined by (10) are called the *Fourier coefficients* of $f(x)$. When a_0, a_n, b_n for $n = 1, 2, \ldots$ are defined by the formulae (10) the series (5) is called the *Fourier series* representation of $f(x)$.

EXAMPLE 3

Find the Fourier coefficients of the periodic function defined by

$$f(x) = x \quad \text{for } -\pi \leqslant x < \pi \quad \text{and} \quad f(x + 2\pi) = f(x).$$

The graph of $f(x)$ is given in Fig. 2.4. Using the Euler formulae (10) gives

$$a_0 = \frac{1}{\pi} \int_{-\pi}^{\pi} x \, dx = \frac{1}{\pi} \left[\frac{x^2}{2} \right]_{-\pi}^{\pi} = 0,$$

$$a_n = \frac{1}{\pi} \int_{-\pi}^{\pi} x \cos nx \, dx$$

$$= \frac{1}{\pi} \left[\frac{x \sin nx}{n} \right]_{-\pi}^{\pi} - \frac{1}{\pi} \int_{-\pi}^{\pi} \frac{\sin nx}{n} \, dx = \frac{1}{\pi} \left[\frac{\cos nx}{n^2} \right]_{-\pi}^{\pi} = 0,$$

since $\sin n\pi = \sin(-n\pi) = 0$ and $\cos n\pi = \cos(-n\pi) = (-1)^n$. Also

$$b_n = \frac{1}{\pi} \int_{-\pi}^{\pi} x \sin nx \, dx$$

$$= \frac{1}{\pi} \left[\frac{-x \cos nx}{n} \right]_{-\pi}^{\pi} + \frac{1}{\pi} \int_{-\pi}^{\pi} \frac{\cos nx}{n} \, dx = \frac{2(-1)^{n+1}}{n}.$$

The Fourier series for the function $f(x) = x$ in the range $-\pi \leqslant x \leqslant \pi$ is therefore

$$2 \left(\sin x - \frac{\sin 2x}{2} + \frac{\sin 3x}{3} - \frac{\sin 4x}{4} + \ldots \right).$$

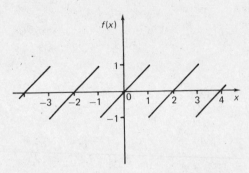

Fig. 2.4   The graph of the function defined in example 3

The Euler formulae may be used to calculate a set of Fourier coefficients for any function $f(x)$ provided only that it is integrable. However there is no guarantee that the Fourier series (5) formed with these particular coefficients will be convergent, or that the term-by-term integration of the series in equations (6a), (7a), (8a) and (9a) is allowed. Both of these questions are crucial to the whole theory. The convergence of Fourier series will be discussed in §2.3 and their integration will be justified in §2.5.

Fourier Series Representations in Other Intervals

The theory so far has been concerned with Fourier series representations in the interval $-\pi \leqslant x \leqslant \pi$ of functions with period 2π. However, in most problems it is necessary or desirable to find representations in other intervals.

(1) *Representations in $p \leqslant x \leqslant p + 2\pi$ where p is any real number*
An inspection of the formulae (10) shows that the integrands are periodic with period 2π, and therefore the range of integration may be replaced by the range $\pi \leqslant x \leqslant 3\pi$ or $\frac{1}{2}\pi \leqslant x \leqslant 5\pi/2$ or in general by $p \leqslant x \leqslant p + 2\pi$, where p is any real number (see example 4 and exercise 6 of this section). This implies that the Fourier coefficients and therefore the Fourier series representation of a function of period 2π are the same for any interval of length 2π.

EXAMPLE 4

Find the Fourier coefficients in the interval $0 \leqslant x \leqslant 2\pi$ of the periodic function defined as $f(x) = x$ for $-\pi \leqslant x < \pi$ and $f(x + 2\pi) = f(x)$.

The graph of the function is given in Fig. 2.4. In the interval $0 \leqslant x \leqslant 2\pi$ the function is given by the formulae

$$f(x) = \begin{cases} x & \text{for } 0 \leqslant x < \pi \\ x - 2\pi & \text{for } \pi \leqslant x \leqslant 2\pi \end{cases}$$

therefore

$$a_0 = \frac{1}{\pi} \int_0^\pi x \, dx + \frac{1}{\pi} \int_\pi^{2\pi} (x - 2\pi) \, dx = 0,$$

$$a_n = \frac{1}{\pi} \int_0^\pi x \cos nx \, dx + \frac{1}{\pi} \int_\pi^{2\pi} (x - 2\pi) \cos nx \, dx = 0,$$

$$b_n = \frac{1}{\pi} \int_0^\pi x \sin nx \, dx + \frac{1}{\pi} \int_\pi^{2\pi} (x - 2\pi) \sin nx \, dx = \frac{2(-1)^{n+1}}{n}.$$

Thus a_0, a_n, b_n are identical with those calculated in the previous example for the interval $-\pi \leqslant x \leqslant \pi$.

(2) *Representation of a function with period 2L in the interval $-L \leqslant x \leqslant L$.*
Consider a function $f(x)$ which has period $2L$, that is

$$f(x + 2L) = f(x).$$

If the new variable $y = \pi x / L$ is substituted into this equation we obtain

$$f\left(\frac{L}{\pi}\{y + 2\pi\}\right) = f\left(\frac{Ly}{\pi}\right),$$

that is, the function $f(Ly/\pi)$ has period 2π in the new variable y. The function $f(Ly/\pi)$ therefore has the Fourier series representation in $-\pi \leqslant y \leqslant \pi$ given in terms of y by

$$\tfrac{1}{2}a_0 + \sum_{n=1}^\infty (a_n \cos ny + b_n \sin ny),$$

where

$$a_0 = \frac{1}{\pi} \int_{-\pi}^\pi f\left(\frac{Ly}{\pi}\right) dy, \quad a_n = \frac{1}{\pi} \int_{-\pi}^\pi f\left(\frac{Ly}{\pi}\right) \cos ny \, dy,$$

$$b_n = \frac{1}{\pi} \int_{-\pi}^\pi f\left(\frac{Ly}{\pi}\right) \sin ny \, dy.$$

Substituting $y = \pi x / L$ in these equations we obtain the Fourier series expressed in terms of the variable x. That is, $f(x)$ is represented in the interval $-L \leqslant x \leqslant L$ by the

Fourier series

$$\tfrac{1}{2}a_0 + \sum_{n=1}^{\infty} \left[a_n \cos\left(\frac{n\pi x}{L}\right) + b_n \sin\left(\frac{n\pi x}{L}\right) \right],$$ (11)

where

$$a_0 = \frac{1}{L}\int_{-L}^{L} f(x)\,dx, \quad a_n = \frac{1}{L}\int_{-L}^{L} f(x)\cos\left(\frac{n\pi x}{L}\right) dx,$$

$$b_n = \frac{1}{L}\int_{-L}^{L} f(x)\sin\left(\frac{n\pi x}{L}\right) dx.$$ (12)

EXAMPLE 5

Find the Fourier coefficients of the function defined as

$$g(x) = x^2 \quad \text{for} \quad -L \leqslant x < L \quad \text{and} \quad g(x+2L) = g(x).$$

From equations (12) we obtain

$$a_0 = \frac{1}{L}\int_{-L}^{L} x^2\,dx = \left[\frac{x^3}{3L}\right]_{-L}^{L} = \frac{2}{3}L^2,$$

$$a_n = \frac{1}{L}\int_{-L}^{L} x^2 \cos\left(\frac{n\pi x}{L}\right) dx$$

$$= \frac{1}{L}\left[\frac{Lx^2}{n\pi}\sin\left(\frac{n\pi x}{L}\right)\right]_{-L}^{L} - \frac{1}{n\pi}\int_{-L}^{L} 2x\sin\left(\frac{n\pi x}{L}\right) dx$$

$$= \frac{-2}{n\pi}\left[\frac{-Lx}{n\pi}\cos\left(\frac{n\pi x}{L}\right)\right]_{-L}^{L} - \frac{2L}{n^2\pi^2}\int_{-L}^{L}\cos\left(\frac{n\pi x}{L}\right) dx = \frac{4L^2(-1)^n}{n^2\pi^2},$$

$$b_n = \frac{1}{L}\int_{-L}^{L} x^2\sin\left(\frac{n\pi x}{L}\right) dx = 0.$$

The Fourier series for $g(x)$ is therefore

$$\tfrac{1}{3}L^2 + \frac{4L^2}{\pi^2}\sum_{n=1}^{\infty}\frac{(-1)^n}{n^2}\cos\left(\frac{n\pi x}{L}\right).$$

Equations (11) and (12) give the Fourier representation for *any* periodic function $f(x)$, where the period is $2L$, and will clearly have wider application than the Fourier series over an interval of 2π (see equations (5) and (10)). Furthermore, the integration from $x = -L$ to $x = L$ may be replaced by integration over any interval of length $2L$ (see example 4 and exercise 6 of this section).

The Fourier Series Representation of $f(x) + g(x)$

If $f(x)$ and $g(x)$ are periodic with period 2π then $F(x) = f(x) + g(x)$ is also periodic with period 2π. Let a_0, a_n, b_n be the Fourier coefficients of $f(x)$ and $a_0', a_n', b_n',$ be the Fourier coefficients of $g(x)$, then the Fourier coefficients of $F(x)$ are $A_0 = a_0 + a_0', A_n = a_n + a_n', B_n = b_n + b_n'$. These results follow from elementary theorems on integrals, since, for example,

$$A_n = \frac{1}{\pi} \int_{-\pi}^{\pi} F(x) \cos nx \, dx = \frac{1}{\pi} \int_{-\pi}^{\pi} f(x) \cos nx \, dx + \frac{1}{\pi} \int_{-\pi}^{\pi} g(x) \cos nx \, dx$$

$$= a_n + a_n'.$$

EXAMPLE 6
Find the Fourier coefficients of $F(x)$ defined as

$$F(x) = x + x^2 \quad \text{in} \quad -\pi \leqslant x < \pi \quad \text{and} \quad F(x + 2\pi) = F(x).$$

Let $f(x) = x$ and $g(x) = x^2$, so that $F(x) = f(x) + g(x)$ in $-\pi \leqslant x < \pi$. The Fourier coefficients of $f(x)$ are, from example 3,

$$a_0 = 0, \quad a_n = 0, \quad b_n = \frac{2(-1)^{n+1}}{n} \quad \text{for } n = 1, 2, \ldots,$$

and the Fourier coefficients of $g(x)$ are, from example 5 with $L = \pi$,

$$a_0' = \frac{2\pi^2}{3}, \quad a_n' = \frac{4(-1)^n}{n^2}, \quad b_n' = 0 \quad \text{for } n = 1, 2, \ldots$$

The Fourier coefficients of $F(x)$ are therefore

$$A_0 = \frac{2\pi^2}{3}, \quad A_n = \frac{4(-1)^n}{n^2}, \quad B_n = \frac{2(-1)^{n+1}}{n} \quad \text{for } n = 1, 2, \ldots,$$

so that the Fourier series for $F(x) = x + x^2$ in $-\pi \leqslant x < \pi$ is

$$\frac{\pi^2}{3} + \sum_{n=1}^{\infty} \left(\frac{4(-1)^n \cos nx}{n^2} + \frac{2(-1)^{n+1} \sin nx}{n} \right).$$

Exercises

1. Find the fundamental period of the following functions $\cos 2x$, $2 \cos x$, $\sin(x/5)$, $\cos 2lx$, $\sin(2\pi x/L)$, $\cos(\omega x + \epsilon)$, $\sin \omega(x + \epsilon)$, $3 \sin x + 2 \cos x$, $\sin x + \sin(x/3)$, $\cos x \sin 2x$.

2. If $f(x) = e^x$ for $-\pi \leqslant x < \pi$ and $f(x + 2\pi) = f(x)$, sketch $f(x)$ and find a formula for $f(x)$ in terms of the exponential function when

(a) $\pi \leqslant x < 3\pi$,
(b) $p\pi \leqslant x < (p + 2)\pi$, where p is an integer.

3. If $f(x)$ is periodic with period 2π, sketch $f(x)$ and use the Euler formulae to find the Fourier coefficients when

(a) $f(x) = \begin{cases} -1 & \text{for } -\pi \leqslant x < 0 \\ 1 & \text{for } 0 \leqslant x < \pi \end{cases}$

(b) $f(x) = \begin{cases} 0 & \text{for } -\pi \leqslant x < 0, \\ x & \text{for } 0 \leqslant x < \pi. \end{cases}$

4. Find the Fourier series of the function defined as

$$f(x) = \begin{cases} x - 1 & \text{for } -\pi \leqslant x < 0 \\ x + 1 & \text{for } \ \ 0 \leqslant x < \pi \end{cases} \quad \text{and} \quad f(x + 2\pi) = f(x).$$

5. Find the Fourier series of the function $f(x)$ defined as

$$f(x) = \begin{cases} 0 & \text{for } -L \leqslant x < 0 \\ x^2 & \text{for } \ \ 0 \leqslant x < L \end{cases} \quad \text{and} \quad f(x + 2L) = f(x).$$

6. A periodic function $F(x)$ is defined as $F(x) = f(x)$ for $-\pi \leqslant x < \pi$ and $F(x + 2\pi) = F(x)$. Show that the Fourier coefficients in the interval $p \leqslant x \leqslant p + 2\pi$, where p is any real number, are the same as those calculated in the interval $-\pi \leqslant x \leqslant \pi$.

2.3 CONVERGENCE OF FOURIER SERIES

In the previous section the Fourier coefficients of a given function $f(x)$ were evaluated using the Euler formulae (10) or (12). It still remains to consider whether the Fourier series formed with these coefficients is convergent, and if it is convergent whether it converges to $f(x)$. Consider the following examples.

EXAMPLE 1
Find the Fourier series of the function defined as

$$f(x) = \begin{cases} 0 & \text{for } -\pi \leqslant x < 0 \\ 1 & \text{for } \ \ 0 \leqslant x < \pi \end{cases} \quad \text{and} \quad f(x + 2\pi) = f(x).$$

Using the Euler formulae (10) we obtain

$$a_0 = \frac{1}{\pi} \int_0^\pi dx = 1, \quad a_n = \frac{1}{\pi} \int_0^\pi \cos nx \ dx = \left[\frac{\sin nx}{n\pi} \right]_0^\pi = 0,$$

$$b_n = \frac{1}{\pi} \int_0^\pi \sin nx \ dx = \left[-\frac{\cos nx}{n\pi} \right]_0^\pi = \frac{(1 - (-1)^n)}{n\pi} = \begin{cases} 0 & \text{for } n \text{ even} \\ 2/n\pi & \text{for } n \text{ odd}. \end{cases}$$

The Fourier series for $f(x)$ is therefore

$$\frac{1}{2} + \frac{2}{\pi} \sin x + \frac{2}{3\pi} \sin 3x + \frac{2}{5\pi} \sin 5x + \ldots,$$

that is

$$\frac{1}{2} + \frac{2}{\pi} \sum_{r=1}^\infty \frac{\sin(2r - 1)x}{(2r - 1)}.$$

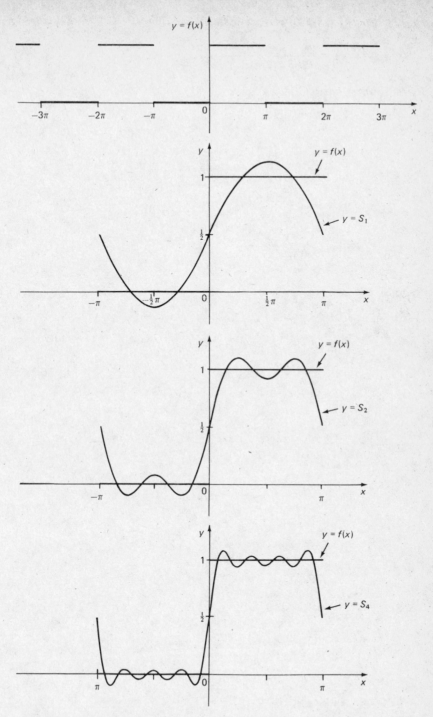

Fig. 2.5   The graphs of $y = f(x)$, $y = S_1$, $y = S_2$ and $y = S_4$ defined in example 1

Let S_p be the sum of the first $(p + 1)$ terms of the above Fourier series, that is

$$S_p = \frac{1}{2} + \frac{2}{\pi} \sum_{r=1}^{p} \frac{\sin(2r - 1)x}{(2r - 1)}.$$

S_p is called the pth partial sum of the series and in particular

$$S_1 = \frac{1}{2} + \frac{2 \sin x}{\pi}, \qquad S_2 = S_1 + \frac{2 \sin 3x}{3\pi},$$

$$S_3 = S_2 + \frac{2 \sin 5x}{5\pi}, \qquad S_4 = S_3 + \frac{2 \sin 7x}{7\pi}.$$

The graphs of the partial sums are shown in Fig. 2.5.

EXAMPLE 2

Find the Fourier series of the function defined as

$$g(x) = \begin{cases} x + \pi & \text{for } 0 \leqslant x < \pi \\ -x - \pi & \text{for } -\pi \leqslant x < 0 \end{cases} \qquad \text{and} \qquad g(x + 2\pi) = g(x),$$

and shown in Fig. 2.6(a).

The Fourier coefficients are

$$a_0 = \frac{1}{\pi} \int_{-\pi}^{'} -(x + \pi) dx + \frac{1}{\pi} \int_{0}^{\pi} (x + \pi) dx = \frac{2}{\pi} \int_{0}^{\pi} x \, dx = \left[\frac{2x^2}{2\pi} \right]_{0}^{\pi} = \pi,$$

$$a_n = \frac{1}{\pi} \int_{-\pi}^{0} -(x + \pi) \cos nx \, dx + \frac{1}{\pi} \int_{0}^{\pi} (x + \pi) \cos nx \, dx = \frac{2}{\pi} \int_{0}^{\pi} x \cos nx \, dx$$

$$= \left[\frac{2x \sin nx}{n\pi} \right]_{0}^{\pi} - \int_{0}^{\pi} \frac{\sin nx}{n\pi} \, dx = \left[\frac{2 \cos nx}{n^2 \pi} \right]_{0}^{\pi}$$

$$= \frac{2[(-1)^n - 1]}{n^2 \pi} = \begin{cases} 0 & \text{for } n \text{ even,} \\ -4/\pi n^2 & \text{for } n \text{ odd,} \end{cases}$$

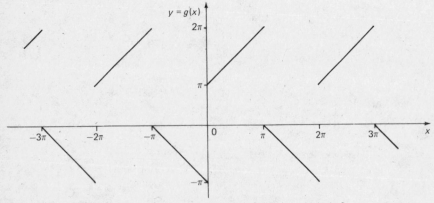

Fig. 2.6(a)   The graph of $y = g(x)$ defined in example 2.

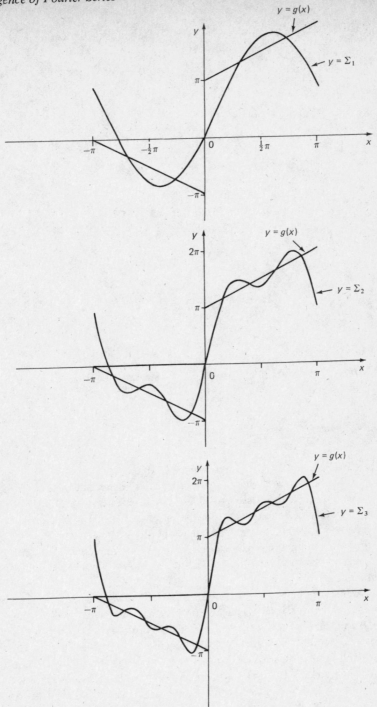

Fig. 2.6(b)   The graphs of $y = \Sigma_1$, $y = \Sigma_2$ and $y = \Sigma_3$ defined in example 2

$$b_n = \frac{1}{\pi} \int_{-\pi}^{0} -(x+\pi)\sin nx \, dx + \frac{1}{\pi} \int_{0}^{\pi} (\pi+x)\sin nx \, dx = \frac{2}{\pi} \int_{0}^{\pi} \pi \sin nx \, dx$$

$$= \left[-\frac{2\cos nx}{n} \right]_{0}^{\pi} = \frac{2}{n}[1-(-1)^n] = \begin{cases} 0 & \text{for } n \text{ even,} \\ 4/n & \text{for } n \text{ odd.} \end{cases}$$

The Fourier series for $g(x)$ is therefore

$$\frac{\pi}{2} - \frac{4}{\pi}\left(\cos x + \frac{\cos 3x}{9} + \frac{\cos 5x}{25} + \cdots\right) + 4\left(\sin x + \frac{\sin 3x}{3} + \frac{\sin 5x}{5} + \cdots\right),$$

that is

$$\frac{\pi}{2} + 4\sum_{r=1}^{\infty}\left(\frac{\sin(2r-1)x}{(2r-1)} - \frac{\cos(2r-1)x}{\pi(2r-1)^2}\right).$$

Let Σ_p be defined as

$$\Sigma_p = \frac{\pi}{2} + 4\sum_{r=1}^{p}\left(\frac{\sin(2r-1)x}{(2r-1)} - \frac{\cos(2r-1)x}{\pi(2r-1)^2}\right);$$

then

$$\Sigma_1 = \frac{\pi}{2} + 4\sin x - \frac{4}{\pi}\cos x, \quad \Sigma_2 = \Sigma_1 + \frac{4\sin 3x}{3} - \frac{4\cos 3x}{9\pi},$$

$$\Sigma_3 = \Sigma_2 + \frac{4\sin 5x}{5} - \frac{4\cos 5x}{25\pi}.$$

The graphs of Σ_1, Σ_2 and Σ_3 are given in Fig. 2.6(b).

In these examples relatively few terms of the series are needed to demonstrate that S_p is approaching $f(x)$ and Σ_p is approaching $g(x)$ except near the points $\pm\pi$ and 0. Therefore, although the series are apparently converging for all x, they do not appear to converge to $f(x)$ and $g(x)$ respectively at the points $x = \pm\pi, 0$, which are points of discontinuity of the functions. This suggests that in any analytical treatment of convergence, special attention must be given to the points where the function is discontinuous.

The convergence of a trigonometric series is nearly always difficult to establish, and as the functions which arise in physical problems may have several discontinuities (jumps), the problem of the convergence of their Fourier series is likely to be particularly difficult. However, the convergence of any particular Fourier series will clearly depend on the values of the Fourier coefficients a_n and b_n, which in turn depend on the precise form of $f(x)$. It seems reasonable therefore to ask whether it is possible to find a set of conditions which, when satisfied by $f(x)$, will ensure convergence of its Fourier series. Such conditions exist and are stated without proof in the following theorem.

FOURIER'S THEOREM   If the function $f(x)$ is such that

(1)   it is periodic with period 2π,
(2)   it is *piecewise continuous* in $-\pi \leqslant x \leqslant \pi$,
(3)   for each x in $-\pi < x < \pi$ it has left- and right-hand derivatives,

then the corresponding Fourier series (5) with coefficients (10) is convergent. Its sum is $f(x)$ at points where $f(x)$ is continuous and at a point of discontinuity x_0 the sum is

$$\tfrac{1}{2}[f(x_0^+) + f(x_0^-)].$$

At the end points $x = \pm\pi$ of the interval $-\pi \leqslant x \leqslant \pi$, the sum is

$$\tfrac{1}{2}[f(\pi^-) + f(-\pi^+)].$$

DEFINITION   A function $f(x)$ is said to be *piecewise continuous* in an interval if it is defined and has at most a finite number of finite discontinuities in the interval.

DEFINITION   The *left-hand derivative* of $f(x)$ is defined as

$$f'(x_0^-) = \lim_{x \to x_0^-} \left[\frac{f(x) - f(x_0)}{x - x_0} \right] \quad \text{if the limit exists.}$$

The *right-hand derivative* of $f(x)$ is defined as

$$f'(x_0^+) = \lim_{x \to x_0^+} \left[\frac{f(x) - f(x_0)}{x - x_0} \right] \quad \text{if the limit exists.}$$

The function $f(x)$ is *differentiable* at $x = x_0$ if $f'(x_0^+) = f'(x_0^-)$.

It is important to note that the conditions on $f(x)$ in Fourier's theorem are *sufficient* to ensure the convergence of the Fourier series, but they are not *necessary*. That is, functions which satisfy these conditions will have convergent Fourier series, but functions exist which do not satisfy the conditions but which do have convergent Fourier series. However, nearly all functions which are of physical interest satisfy the conditions of the theorem and therefore the convergence of their Fourier series is assured. It should be emphasized that the Fourier series of a function $f(x)$ which satisfies the conditions of Fourier's theorem will converge to $f(x)$ only at points where $f(x)$ is continuous. At a discontinuity of $f(x)$, the Fourier series converges to the mean of the values of $f(x)$ on either side of the discontinuity (see Figs. 2.5 and 2.6).

EXAMPLE 3

The Fourier series of the function $f(x)$ defined as

$$f(x) = \begin{cases} 0 & \text{for } -\pi \leqslant x < 0 \\ 1 & \text{for } 0 \leqslant x < \pi \end{cases} \quad \text{and} \quad f(x + 2\pi) = f(x),$$

was found in example 1 of this section to be

$$\frac{1}{2} + \frac{2}{\pi} \sum_{r=1}^{\infty} \frac{1}{2r-1} \sin(2r-1)x.$$

The function $f(x)$ satisfies the conditions of Fourier's theorem and therefore the series is convergent.

The function $f(x)$ has finite discontinuities at $x = 0, \pm\pi, \pm 2\pi, \ldots$, that is at $x_n = n\pi$ where n is an integer; therefore at $x = x_n$ the Fourier series converges to

$$\tfrac{1}{2}[f(x_n^+) + f(x_n^-)] = \tfrac{1}{2}$$

for all integers n. At all other points the series converges to $f(x)$. In particular at $x = \pi/2$ the series converges to $f(\pi/2) = 1$, hence

$$1 = \frac{1}{2} + \frac{2}{\pi}\left(1 + \frac{(-1)}{3} + \frac{1}{5} + \frac{(-1)}{7} \cdots \right),$$

from which we obtain the result

$$\sum_{r=1}^{\infty} \frac{(-1)^{r+1}}{(2r-1)} = \frac{\pi}{4}.$$

EXAMPLE 4

The function $g(x)$ defined as

$$g(x) = \begin{cases} -(x+\pi) & \text{for } -\pi \leqslant x < 0 \\ (x+\pi) & \text{for } 0 \leqslant x < \pi \end{cases} \quad \text{and} \quad g(x + 2\pi) = g(x),$$

satisfies the conditions of Fourier's theorem and therefore its Fourier series is convergent. The Fourier series for $g(x)$ was found in example 2 of this section to be

$$\frac{\pi}{2} + 4 \sum_{r=1}^{\infty} \left(\frac{\sin(2r-1)x}{2r-1} - \frac{\cos(2r-1)x}{\pi(2r-1)^2}\right),$$

and $g(x)$ has discontinuities at $x = 0, \pm\pi, \pm 2\pi, \ldots$, that is at $x = n\pi$ where n is an integer. At $x = 0$, for example, the series converges to

$$\tfrac{1}{2}[g(0^-) + g(0^+)] = 0,$$

therefore

$$0 = \frac{\pi}{2} - \left| \frac{4}{\pi} \sum_{r=1}^{\infty} \frac{1}{(2r-1)^2}, \right.$$

from which we obtain the result

$$\sum_{r=1}^{\infty} \frac{1}{(2r-1)^2} = \frac{\pi^2}{8}.$$

At all points $x' \neq n\pi$, where n is an integer, the Fourier series converges to $g(x')$.

Examples 3 and 4 demonstrate how the sums of various infinite series may be obtained by evaluating Fourier series at particular points.

Exercises

1. Find the points of discontinuity, if any, of the functions defined as

    (a) $f(x) = x^2$ for $-\pi \leqslant x < \pi$ and $f(x + 2\pi) = f(x)$,

    (b) $f(x) = \begin{cases} 0 & \text{for } 0 \leqslant x < L \\ x - L & \text{for } L \leqslant x < 2L \end{cases}$ and $f(x + 2L) = f(x)$.

2. Find $f(\pi^+), f(\pi^-), f'(\pi^+)$, when $f(x)$ is defined as

    (a) $f(x) = e^x$ for $-\pi \leqslant x < \pi$ and $f(x + 2\pi) = f(x)$,

    (b) $f(x) = \begin{cases} \pi \, | & \text{for } -\pi \leqslant x < 0 \\ \pi \cos x & \text{for } 0 \leqslant x < \pi \end{cases}$ and $f(x + 2\pi) = f(x)$.

3. Show that the functions defined in exercises 1 and 2 satisfy the conditions of Fourier's theorem.

4. Find the Fourier series for $f(x)$ defined as $f(x) = x^2$ for $-\pi \leqslant x < \pi$ and $f(x + 2\pi) = f(x)$, and hence show that for $-\pi \leqslant x \leqslant \pi$

$$x^2 = \frac{\pi^2}{3} + 4 \sum_{n=1}^{\infty} \frac{(-1)^n}{n^2} \cos nx.$$

By substituting a specific value for x show that

$$\sum_{n=1}^{\infty} \frac{(-1)^{n+1}}{n^2} = \frac{\pi^2}{12}.$$

2.4 FOURIER SINE AND COSINE SERIES

The Fourier series found in examples 3 and 5 of §2.2 turned out to be particularly simple. In example 3 the coefficients a_0, a_n were zero because $f(x)$ was an *odd function*. Therefore the Fourier series for $f(x)$ was a series of sines only. In example 5 the coefficients b_n were zero because $g(x)$ was an *even function*. The Fourier series for $g(x)$ was then a series of cosines together with a constant term.

DEFINITION   An *even function* $y = g(x)$ is such that $g(-x) = g(x)$ for all values of x.

The graph of an even function (see Fig. 2.7) is symmetric about the y axis, with

$$\int_{-a}^{a} g(x)\,dx = 2\int_{0}^{a} g(x)\,dx.$$

Examples of even functions are $\cos nx$, x^2 and x^4.

DEFINITION   An *odd function* $y = f(x)$ is such that $f(-x) = -f(x)$ for all values of x.

The graph of an odd function (see Fig. 2.7) is antisymmetric about the y axis, with

$$\int_{-a}^{a} f(x)\,dx = 0.$$

Examples of odd functions are $\sin nx$, x and x^3.

EXAMPLE 1
If $h(x) = g(x)f(x)$, show that

(1) $h(x)$ is odd when $g(x)$ is odd and $f(x)$ is even,
(2) $h(x)$ is even when $g(x)$ and $f(x)$ are either both even or both odd.

Replacing x by $-x$ we have

$$h(-x) = g(-x)f(-x) = \begin{cases} -g(x)f(x) = -h(x) & \text{in case (1)}, \\ g(x)f(x) = h(x) & \text{in case (2)}. \end{cases}$$

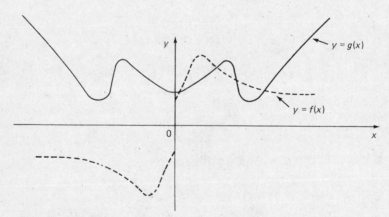

Fig. 2.7   The graph of an even function $y = g(x)$ and an odd function $y = f(x)$

We see, therefore, that if $g(x)$ is an even function then $g(x)\cos nx$ is even and $g(x)\sin nx$ is odd. Consequently, if $g(x)$ is even and periodic with period 2π, its Fourier coefficients are found from the Euler formulae (10) to be

$$a_0 = \frac{1}{\pi}\int_{-\pi}^{\pi} g(x)\,dx = \frac{2}{\pi}\int_{0}^{\pi} g(x)\,dx, \quad a_n = \frac{1}{\pi}\int_{-\pi}^{\pi} g(x)\cos nx \, dx = \frac{2}{\pi}\int_{0}^{\pi} g(x)\cos nx \, dx,$$

and

$$b_n = \frac{1}{\pi}\int_{-\pi}^{\pi} g(x)\sin nx \, dx = 0.$$

The Fourier series for $g(x)$ then takes the form

$$\tfrac{1}{2}a_0 + \sum_{n=1}^{\infty} a_n \cos nx, \tag{13}$$

where

$$a_0 = \frac{2}{\pi}\int_{0}^{\pi} g(x)\,dx \quad \text{and} \quad a_n = \frac{2}{\pi}\int_{0}^{\pi} g(x)\cos nx \, dx. \tag{14}$$

This representation is called a *Fourier cosine series*.

If $f(x)$ is an odd function with period 2π, then $f(x)\cos nx$ is odd and $f(x)\sin nx$ is even. In this case, equations (10) give

$$a_0 = \frac{1}{\pi}\int_{-\pi}^{\pi} f(x)\,dx = 0, \quad a_n = \frac{1}{\pi}\int_{-\pi}^{\pi} f(x)\cos nx \, dx = 0$$

and

$$b_n = \frac{1}{\pi}\int_{-\pi}^{\pi} f(x)\sin nx \, dx = \frac{2}{\pi}\int_{0}^{\pi} f(x)\sin nx \, dx.$$

The Fourier series of the odd periodic function $f(x)$ is therefore

$$\sum_{n=1}^{\infty} b_n \sin nx, \tag{15}$$

where

$$b_n = \frac{2}{\pi}\int_{0}^{\pi} f(x)\sin nx \, dx. \tag{16}$$

This representation is called a *Fourier sine series*.

EXAMPLE 2
Find the Fourier series of $f(x)$ where $f(x + 2\pi) = f(x)$ and

$$f(x) = \begin{cases} \pi + x & \text{for } -\pi \leqslant x < 0, \\ \pi - x & \text{for } 0 \leqslant x < \pi. \end{cases}$$

Since $f(x) = f(-x)$, the function $f(x)$ is even as well as being periodic with period 2π. The Fourier coefficients are, from equations (14),

$$a_0 = \pi, \quad b_n = 0,$$

$$a_n = \frac{2}{\pi} \int_0^\pi (\pi - x)\cos nx \, dx = \frac{2}{\pi n^2}(1 - \cos n\pi) = \begin{cases} 0 & \text{for } n \text{ even} \\ 4/\pi n^2 & \text{for } n \text{ odd.} \end{cases}$$

Therefore the Fourier series of $f(x)$ is

$$\frac{\pi}{2} + \frac{4}{\pi} \sum_{r=1}^\infty \frac{1}{(2r-1)^2} \cos(2r-1)x,$$

where n has been replaced by $2r - 1$.

EXAMPLE 3
Find the Fourier series of $g(x)$ where $g(x + 2\pi) = g(x)$ and

$$g(x) = \begin{cases} -\sin x & \text{for } -\pi \leqslant x < \pi/2 \\ \sin x & \text{for } -\pi/2 \leqslant x \leqslant \pi/2 \\ -\sin x & \text{for } \pi/2 < x < \pi. \end{cases}$$

The function $g(x)$ is an odd function, as demonstrated in Fig. 2.8. Consequently $a_0 = a_n = 0$ and

$$b_n = \frac{2}{\pi} \int_0^{\pi/2} \sin x \sin nx \, dx - \frac{2}{\pi} \int_{\pi/2}^\pi \sin x \sin nx \, dx.$$

Evaluation of these integrals gives the result

$$b_1 = 0 \quad \text{and} \quad b_n = -\frac{4n \cos(\frac{1}{2}n\pi)}{\pi(n^2 - 1)} \quad \text{for } n = 2, 3, 4, \ldots.$$

The coefficient b_n is non-zero only when n is even; therefore we can write $n = 2r$ for $r = 1, 2, \ldots$ and the Fourier series for $g(x)$ defined above is

$$\sum_{r=1}^\infty \frac{8r(-1)^{r+1}}{\pi(4r^2 - 1)} \sin 2rx.$$

Periodic Extensions

One of the conditions of Fourier's theorem (see §2.3) is that the function should be

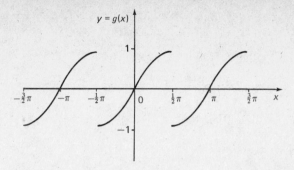

Fig. 2.8 The graph of $y = g(x)$ defined in example 3

periodic, which implies that it is defined for all x. However the theory may be extended to include *functions defined only in a finite interval.*

Consider a function $f(x)$ which is defined only in the interval $0 \leqslant x \leqslant l$ and satisfies conditions (2) and (3) of Fourier's theorem. If a new function $H(x)$ defined for all x is constructed so that it is identical to $f(x)$ in $0 \leqslant x \leqslant l$ and is periodic, then $H(x)$ is called a *periodic extension of* $f(x)$. The simplest periodic extension of $f(x)$ is obtained by defining $H(x)$ to be

$$H(x) = f(x) \quad \text{for } 0 \leqslant x < l \quad \text{and} \quad H(x + l) = H(x)$$

(see Fig. 2.9).

Half-range Series

Since a certain amount of choice can be exercised in the definition of a periodic extension, we might as well construct it so that the problem of finding its Fourier series is as simple as possible. It is customary, therefore, to construct $H(x)$ so that it is either an even function, which has a Fourier cosine series, or an odd function, which has a Fourier sine series. For example, if $H(x)$ is chosen to be the function $F(x)$, defined as

$$F(x) = \begin{cases} -f(-x) & \text{for } -l \leqslant x < 0 \\ f(x) & \text{for } 0 \leqslant x < l \end{cases} \quad \text{and} \quad F(x + 2l) = F(x),$$

then $F(x)$ is an odd function (see Fig. 2.9) and is an *odd periodic extension of* $f(x)$. The Fourier series of $F(x)$ is

$$\sum_{n=1}^{\infty} b_n \sin\left(\frac{n\pi x}{l}\right), \tag{17}$$

where

$$b_n = \frac{2}{l} \int_0^l f(x) \sin\left(\frac{n\pi x}{l}\right) dx, \tag{18}$$

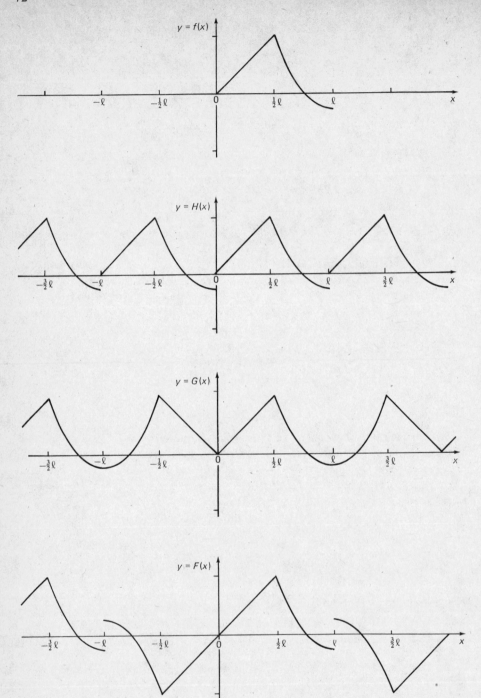

Fig. 2.9 The graph of $f(x)$ and the graphs of $H(x)$, $G(x)$ and $F(x)$, the periodic extensions of $f(x)$

and this series will represent $f(x)$ in $0 \leqslant x \leqslant l$. We could also construct a function $G(x)$ by the equations

$$G(x) = \begin{cases} f(-x) & \text{for } -l \leqslant x < 0 \\ f(x) & \text{for } 0 \leqslant x < l \end{cases} \qquad \text{and} \qquad G(x + 2l) = G(x).$$

The function $G(x)$ is even and so is an *even periodic extension* of $f(x)$ (see Fig. 2.9). Its Fourier series is

$$\tfrac{1}{2}a_0 + \sum_{n=1}^{\infty} a_n \cos\left(\frac{n\pi x}{l}\right), \tag{19}$$

where

$$a_0 = \frac{2}{l}\int_0^l f(x)\,dx \quad \text{and} \quad a_n = \frac{2}{l}\int_0^l f(x)\cos\left(\frac{n\pi x}{l}\right) dx. \tag{20}$$

This series will also represent $f(x)$ in $0 \leqslant x \leqslant l$.

The length l of the interval $0 \leqslant x \leqslant l$ is half of the period of the extended functions $F(x)$ and $G(x)$. Consequently series (17) and (19), with the coefficients defined by equations (18) and (20), are called *half-range series*.

EXAMPLE 4
Find the half-range series of $f(x)$ defined as $f(x) = x(\pi - x)$ for $0 \leqslant x \leqslant \pi$.

(a) Let $F(x)$ be the odd periodic extension of $f(x)$, that is,

$$F(x) = \begin{cases} x(\pi - x) & \text{for } 0 \leqslant x < \pi \\ x(\pi + x) & \text{for } -\pi \leqslant x < 0 \end{cases} \qquad \text{and} \qquad F(x + 2\pi) = F(x).$$

The Fourier series for $F(x)$ is a sine series, and so

$$a_0 = 0, \quad a_n = 0,$$

$$b_n = \frac{2}{\pi}\int_0^{\pi} x(\pi - x)\sin nx \, dx = \frac{4(1-(-1)^n)}{\pi n^3} = \begin{cases} 0 & \text{when } n \text{ is even} \\ 8/\pi n^3 & \text{when } n \text{ is odd.} \end{cases}$$

The Fourier series for $F(x)$ is therefore

$$\sum_{r=1}^{\infty} \frac{8}{\pi(2r-1)^3} \sin(2r-1)x.$$

(b) Let $G(x)$ be the even periodic extension of $f(x)$, that is,

$$G(x) = \begin{cases} x(\pi - x) & \text{for } 0 \leqslant x < \pi \\ -x(\pi + x) & \text{for } -\pi \leqslant x < 0 \end{cases} \qquad \text{and} \qquad G(x + 2\pi) = G(x).$$

The Fourier series for $G(x)$ is a cosine series, with coefficients

$$b'_n = 0, \quad a'_0 = \frac{2}{\pi}\int_0^\pi x(\pi - x)dx = \frac{\pi^2}{3},$$

$$a'_n = \frac{2}{\pi}\int_0^\pi x(\pi - x)\cos nx \; dx = \begin{cases} -4/n^2 & \text{when } n \text{ is even} \\ 0 & \text{when } n \text{ is odd.} \end{cases}$$

The Fourier series for $G(x)$ is therefore

$$\frac{\pi^2}{6} - \sum_{r=1}^\infty \frac{\cos 2rx}{r^2}.$$

The functions $F(x)$ and $G(x)$ are continuous for all x, therefore

$$F(x) = \sum_{r=1}^\infty \frac{8 \sin(2r-1)x}{\pi(2r-1)^3} \quad \text{and} \quad G(x) = \frac{\pi^2}{6} - \sum_{r=1}^\infty \frac{\cos 2rx}{r^2}.$$

From the definitions of $F(x)$ and $G(x)$, $F(\pi/2) = \pi^2/4$ and $G(0) = 0$, and the results

$$\sum_{r=1}^\infty \frac{(-1)^{r+1}}{(2r-1)^3} = \frac{\pi^3}{32} \quad \text{and} \quad \sum_{r=1}^\infty \frac{1}{r^2} = \frac{\pi^2}{6}$$

follow.

Exercises

1. State which of the following functions is even, which is odd and which is neither even nor odd.

(a) $f(x) = \begin{cases} -x^2 & \text{for} \quad -\pi < x < 0 \\ x^2 & \text{for} \quad 0 \leqslant x < \pi \end{cases}$ with $f(-\pi) = 0$ and $f(x + 2\pi) = f(x)$.

(b) $f(x) = \sin x$ for $0 \leqslant x < \pi$ and $f(x + \pi) = f(x)$.

(c) $f(x) = e^x$ for $-L \leqslant x < L$ and $f(x + 2L) = f(x)$.

(d) $f(x) = |x| + x$ for all x.

(e) $f(x) = e^{|x|}$ for all x.

(f) $f(x) = \tan x$ for all x.

2. Find the Fourier series of $f(x)$ defined as

$$f(x) = \begin{cases} x^2 - 1 & \text{for} \quad -\pi \leqslant x < 0 \\ 0 & \text{for} \quad x = 0 \\ x^2 + 1 & \text{for} \quad 0 < x < \pi \end{cases} \quad \text{and} \quad f(x + 2\pi) = f(x).$$

3. Find the Fourier sine series for the function $g(x)$ defined as $g(x) = \cos x$ for $0 \leqslant x \leqslant \pi$. Sketch the graph of the corresponding periodic extension of $g(x)$.

4. The function $f(x)$ is defined as $f(x) = x + 2L$ for $0 \leqslant x \leqslant L$. Define and sketch the odd periodic extension of $f(x)$ and the even periodic extension of $f(x)$. Find (a) the Fourier sine series, and (b) the Fourier cosine series of $f(x)$.

5. Show that an arbitrary function $f(x)$ can be written as $f(x) = g(x) + h(x)$ where $g(x)$ is an even function and $h(x)$ is an odd function.

2.5 INTEGRATION AND DIFFERENTIATION OF FOURIER SERIES

The processes of integration and differentiation occur so frequently in mathematics that it is highly likely that at some stage in the application of Fourier series the integral or the derivative of the series will be required.

Integration

The problem of integrating a Fourier series was encountered in §2.2 where it was assumed that the series could be integrated term by term. That is, if $f(x)$ can be represented by the Fourier series

$$f(x) = \tfrac{1}{2}a_0 + \sum_{n=1}^{\infty} (a_n \cos nx + b_n \sin nx),\tag{21}$$

where the Fourier coefficients a_0, a_n, b_n are given by equations (10), then

$$\int_{-\pi}^{t} f(x)\,dx = \tfrac{1}{2}a_0(t + \pi) + \sum_{n=1}^{\infty} \left(\frac{1}{n}a_n \sin nt - \frac{1}{n}b_n(\cos nt - \cos n\pi) \right),$$

or after rearranging

$$\int_{-\pi}^{t} f(x)\,dx - \tfrac{1}{2}a_0 t = \left(\tfrac{1}{2}a_0\pi + \sum_{n=1}^{\infty} \frac{1}{n}b_n \cos n\pi \right)$$

$$+ \sum_{n=1}^{\infty} \left(-\frac{1}{n}b_n \cos nt + \frac{1}{n}a_n \sin nt \right).\tag{22}$$

The first sum $\displaystyle\sum_{n=1}^{\infty} \frac{1}{n}b_n \cos n\pi$ gives rise to a constant; therefore the right-hand side of equation (22) has the form of a Fourier series. Hence, if the function

$$F(t) = \int_{-\pi}^{t} f(x)\,dx - \tfrac{1}{2}a_0 t$$

has a Fourier series which can be found directly and which is identical to the right-hand side of equation (22), we can conclude that term-by-term integration of equation (21) is permissible.

If $f(x)$ satisfies the conditions of Fourier's theorem then $F(t)$ will satisfy the conditions also, and therefore $F(t)$ can be represented by a Fourier series. Let the Fourier coefficients of $F(t)$ be A_0, A_n, B_n, defined as

$$A_0 = \frac{1}{\pi} \int_{-\pi}^{\pi} F(t)dt, \quad A_n = \frac{1}{\pi} \int_{-\pi}^{\pi} F(t)\cos nt \, dt \quad \text{and} \quad B_n = \frac{1}{\pi} \int_{-\pi}^{\pi} F(t)\sin nt \, dt$$

(23)

for $n = 1, 2, \ldots$. Now $F'(t) = f(t) - \frac{1}{2}a_0$ and $F(\pi) = F(-\pi) = \frac{1}{2}a_0\pi$, therefore integrating equations (23) by parts gives

$$A_n = \frac{1}{\pi} \left[\frac{F(t)\sin nt}{n} \right]_{-\pi}^{\pi} - \int_{-\pi}^{\pi} \frac{F'(t)\sin nt}{\pi n} \, dt = -\frac{1}{\pi n} \int_{-\pi}^{\pi} \{f(t) - \frac{1}{2}a_0\}\sin nt \, dt$$

$$= -\frac{b_n}{n} + \frac{a_0}{2\pi} \int_{-\pi}^{\pi} \sin nt \, dt = -\frac{b_n}{n},$$

and similarly $B_n = \frac{a_n}{n}$.

The Fourier series of $F(t)$ is therefore

$$\frac{1}{2}A_0 + \sum_{n=1}^{\infty} \left(\frac{-b_n}{n} \cos nt + \frac{a_n}{n} \sin nt \right).$$

(24)

At $t = \pi$, the series (24) converges to

$$\frac{1}{2}[F(-\pi^+) + F(\pi^-)] = \frac{1}{2}a_0\pi;$$

therefore

$$\frac{1}{2}a_0\pi = \frac{1}{2}A_0 - \sum_{n=1}^{\infty} \frac{b_n}{n} \cos n\pi,$$

which gives

$$\frac{1}{2}A_0 = \frac{1}{2}a_0\pi + \sum_{n=1}^{\infty} \frac{b_n}{n} \cos n\pi.$$

(25)

Substituting $\frac{1}{2}A_0$ given by equation (25) into the series (24) gives the Fourier series for $F(t)$ as

$$\frac{1}{2}a_0\pi + \sum_{n=1}^{\infty} \left(\frac{a_n}{n} \sin nt - \frac{b_n}{n} (\cos nt - \cos n\pi) \right),$$

which is the right-hand side of equation (22). Hence the Fourier series for $f(x)$ may be integrated term by term. The resulting series will not itself be a Fourier series unless $a_0 = 0$, that is unless the mean value of $f(x)$ in $-\pi \leqslant x \leqslant \pi$ is zero (see the definition of a_0). The result may be stated formally as

THEOREM   If $f(x)$ satisfies the conditions of Fourier's theorem in $-\pi \leqslant x \leqslant \pi$ and if a_0, a_n, b_n are the Fourier coefficients of $f(x)$, then

$$\int_\xi^t f(x)\,dx = \tfrac{1}{2}a_0(t - \xi) + \sum_{n=1}^\infty \left(\frac{b_n}{n}(\cos n\xi - \cos nt) + \frac{a_n}{n}(\sin nt - \sin n\xi) \right)$$

(26)

when $-\pi \leqslant \xi < t \leqslant \pi$.

The Fourier coefficients in equation (26) are $-b_n/n$ and a_n/n, so that the series for $\int f(x)\,dx$ converges more rapidly than the Fourier series for $f(x)$.

EXAMPLE 1
The Fourier series of the function defined as

$$f(x) = x^2 \quad \text{for } -\pi \leqslant x < \pi \quad \text{and} \quad f(x + 2\pi) = f(x)$$

is

$$x^2 = \frac{\pi^2}{3} + 4 \sum_{n=1}^\infty \frac{(-1)^n \cos nx}{n^2} \quad \text{in } -\pi \leqslant x \leqslant \pi \text{ (see example 6 of §2.2)}.$$

(27)

Integrating equation (27) term by term between the limits 0 and t gives

$$\frac{t^3}{3} = \frac{\pi^2 t}{3} + 4 \sum_{n=1}^\infty \frac{(-1)^n}{n^3} \sin nt.$$

(28)

The right-hand side of equation (28) is not a Fourier series because of the term $\pi^2 t/3$. However, rearranging equation (28) we obtain

$$\frac{t(t^2 - \pi^2)}{12} = \sum_{n=1}^\infty \frac{(-1)^n}{n^3} \sin nt.$$

(29)

The right-hand side of equation (29) is a Fourier series and therefore the Fourier series representation of $F(t)$ defined as

$$F(t) = t(t^2 - \pi^2)/12 \quad \text{for } -\pi \leqslant t < \pi \quad \text{and} \quad F(t + 2\pi) = F(t)$$

is

$$\sum_{n=1}^\infty \frac{(-1)^n}{n^3} \sin nt.$$

Differentiation

If $f(x)$ has a derivative $f'(x)$ which satisfies the conditions of Fourier's theorem, then $f'(x)$ can be represented by a Fourier series. Let the Fourier coefficients of $f'(x)$ be

A'_0, A'_n, B'_n defined by

$$A'_0 = \frac{1}{\pi} \int_{-\pi}^{\pi} f'(x)\,dx, \qquad A'_n = \frac{1}{\pi} \int_{-\pi}^{\pi} f'(x)\cos nx\,dx,$$

(30)

$$B'_n = \frac{1}{\pi} \int_{-\pi}^{\pi} f'(x)\sin nx\,dx.$$

By evaluating the integrals (30) it is found that

$$A'_0 = \frac{1}{\pi}\,[f(\pi^-) - f(-\pi^+)], \qquad A'_n = (-1)^n A'_0 + nb_n \quad \text{and} \quad B'_n = -na_n, \qquad (31)$$

where a_n and b_n are the Fourier coefficients of $f(x)$.
   If $f(\pi^-) = f(-\pi^+)$, equations (31) reduce to

$$A'_0 = 0, \quad A'_n = nb_n, \quad B'_n = nb_n,$$

and the Fourier series for $f'(x)$ is then

$$\sum_{n=1}^{\infty} n(b_n \cos nx - a_n \sin nx), \qquad (32)$$

which is the series obtained from term-by-term differentiation of equation (21), the Fourier series for $f(x)$. This result may be stated formally:

THEOREM   If $f(x)$ is continuous in the interval $-\pi \leqslant x \leqslant \pi$ and satisfies the condition $f(\pi^-) = f(-\pi^+)$ at the end points of the interval, and if the derivative $f'(x)$ satisfies the conditions of Fourier's theorem, then the Fourier series representation of $f'(x)$ is

$$\sum_{n=1}^{\infty} n(-a_n \sin nx + b_n \cos nx), \qquad (33)$$

where a_n and b_n are the Fourier coefficients of $f(x)$.

The condition $f(\pi^-) = f(-\pi^+)$ states that the periodic extension of $f(x)$ is continuous everywhere. This condition is very restrictive, and the Fourier series of many commonly occurring functions, for example

$$f(x) = x \quad \text{for } -\pi \leqslant x < \pi, \quad \text{and} \quad f(x + 2\pi) = f(x),$$

cannot be differentiated term by term. Great care must therefore be taken to ensure that differentiation of a Fourier series is permissible. This situation contrasts strongly with that of integration of a Fourier series, which is almost always allowed.
   The Fourier coefficients in series (33) are $-na_n$ and nb_n, so that for large n the terms of series (33) tend to zero more slowly than the terms of series (21). That is, the Fourier series for $f'(x)$ converges more slowly than the Fourier series for $f(x)$.

EXAMPLE 2
The function defined as

$$f(x) = x^2 \quad \text{for } -\pi \leqslant x < \pi \quad \text{and} \quad f(x + 2\pi) = f(x),$$

is continuous at $x = \pm\pi$ and therefore its Fourier series can be differentiated term by term to obtain the Fourier series of $f'(x)$. The Fourier series for $f(x)$ is given by equation (27) and if we differentiate this equation we obtain

$$2x = 4 \sum_{n=1}^{\infty} \frac{(-1)^{n+1}}{n} \sin nx \quad \text{in } -\pi < x < \pi.$$

Therefore if $g(x)$ is defined as

$$g(x) = x \quad \text{for } -\pi \leqslant x < \pi \quad \text{and} \quad g(x + 2\pi) = g(x),$$

the Fourier series for $g(x)$ is

$$2 \sum_{n=1}^{\infty} \frac{(-1)^{n+1}}{n} \sin nx.$$

This result was obtained in example 3 of §2.2.

EXAMPLE 3
The Fourier series of the function defined as

$$f(x) = x + x^2 \quad \text{for } -\pi \leqslant x < \pi \quad \text{and} \quad f(x + 2\pi) = f(x),$$

was found in example 6 of §2.2 to be

$$\frac{\pi^2}{3} + \sum_{n=1}^{\infty} \left(\frac{4(-1)^n}{n^2} \cos nx + \frac{2(-1)^{n+1}}{n} \sin nx \right).$$

The derivative of this Fourier series of $f(x)$ is

$$\sum_{n=1}^{\infty} (-1)^{n+1} \left(\frac{4}{n} \sin nx + 2 \cos nx \right).$$

However, this result is *not* the Fourier series of $f'(x)$, since $f(x)$ is discontinuous at $x = \pm\pi$. In this case we must use equations (31) to find the Fourier coefficients of $f'(x)$. From equations (31),

$$A_0' = 2, \quad A_n' = 2(-1)^n + 2(-1)^{n+1} = 0 \quad \text{and} \quad B_n' = 4(-1)^{n+1}/n.$$

This result, which differs from the derivative of the Fourier series of $f(x)$, can be checked by finding the Fourier series of $f'(x) = 1 + 2x$ in $-\pi < x < \pi$.

Exercises

1. Find the Fourier series in $-L \leqslant t \leqslant L$ for $f(t)$ defined as

$$f(t) = \begin{cases} -1 & \text{for } -L \leqslant t < 0 \\ 1 & \text{for } 0 \leqslant t < L \end{cases} \quad \text{and} \quad f(t+2L) = f(t).$$

Hence find the Fourier series in $-L \leqslant x \leqslant L$ for $g(x)$ defined as

$$g(x) = |x| \quad \text{for } -L \leqslant x < L \quad \text{and} \quad g(x+2L) = g(x).$$

2. Find the Fourier series for $f(x)$ defined as

$$f(x) = x \sin x \quad \text{for } -\pi \leqslant x < \pi \quad \text{and} \quad f(x+2\pi) = f(x).$$

Hence find the Fourier series for $g(x)$ defined as

$$g(x) = x \cos x \quad \text{for } -\pi \leqslant x < \pi \quad \text{and} \quad g(x+2\pi) = g(x).$$

2.6 APPLICATION OF FOURIER SERIES

The theory of Fourier series was motivated in §2.1 by the need to find a method for solving the inhomogeneous ordinary differential equation

$$a \frac{d^2 y}{dt^2} + b \frac{dy}{dt} + cy = f(t),$$

where a, b and c are constants and $f(t)$ represents a periodic forcing function. It seems appropriate therefore to conclude this chapter on Fourier series by applying the theory to the solution of a particular example of the above equation. The important application of the theory to problems involving partial differential equations will be considered in Chapter 7.

EXAMPLE 1

A body of mass 1 kg is attached to a rigid support by a spring of modulus 36 kg/s^2 and to a dashpot, which is equivalent to a resistive medium, with damping constant 0.05 kg/s, in a configuration given in Fig. 1.3. The system is kept in motion by an external force $f(t)$ newtons which is periodic with period $2T$ and is given by

$$f(t) = \begin{cases} c(t+T) & \text{in } -T \leqslant t < 0 \\ ct & \text{in } 0 \leqslant t < T \end{cases} \quad \text{and} \quad f(t+2T) = f(t).$$

Find the *steady-state solution*.

The oscillations of the system are governed by the equation

$$\frac{d^2 y}{dt^2} + 0.05 \frac{dy}{dt} + 36y = f(t), \tag{34}$$

where $y(t)$ metres is the displacement of the body from the static equilibrium position (see §1.8).

The complementary function $u(t)$ is given by (see §1.6)

$$u(t) = e^{-0.025t}(A \cos \omega t + B \sin \omega t),$$

where $\omega = \sqrt{\{36 - (0.025)^2\}} \approx 6$, and A and B are constants which can be determined by the initial conditions. Thus $u(t)$ represents damped free oscillations of angular frequency approximately 6 rad s^{-1} which, after a sufficiently long time, tend to zero. Hence it is sufficient to look for the periodic particular integral of equation (34) and designate this to be $v(t)$, the steady-state solution.

The Fourier series representation of $f(t)$ may be written as

$$\tfrac{1}{2}cT + \sum_{n=1}^{\infty} b_n \sin npt, \tag{35a}$$

where $p = \pi/T$ is the angular frequency of the fundamental component of $f(t)$ and

$$b_n = \begin{cases} -(2cT/n\pi) & \text{when } n \text{ is even} \\ 0 & \text{when } n \text{ is odd.} \end{cases} \tag{35b}$$

If this representation for $f(t)$ is substituted into equation (34), which is a linear equation, $v(t)$ will be the superposition of solutions of the equations

$$\frac{d^2y}{dt^2} + 0.05 \frac{dy}{dt} + 36y = \tfrac{1}{2}cT, \tag{36a}$$

and

$$\frac{d^2y}{dt^2} + 0.05 \frac{dy}{dt} + 36y = b_n \sin npt \quad \text{for } n = 1, 2, \ldots . \tag{36b}$$

A particular integral of equation (36a) is $\bar{v}(t) = cT/72$, and the particular integral of equation (36b) is of the form (see §1.8)

$$v_6(t) = A_n \cos npt + B_n \sin npt \quad \text{for } n = 1, 2, \ldots,$$

where A_n and B_n are constants which must be determined for each integer n. The steady state solution is therefore of the form

$$v(t) = \frac{cT}{72} + \sum_{n=1}^{\infty} (A_n \cos npt + B_n \sin npt).$$

An alternative approach to the solution of equation (34) is to observe that $v(t)$ will be a continuous periodic function and such that $v(t)$ and its derivatives $\dot{v}(t)$ and $\ddot{v}(t)$ each possesses a Fourier series representation. Therefore, if we let the Fourier series representation of $v(t)$ be

$$v(t) = \tfrac{1}{2}A_0 + \sum_{n=1}^{\infty} (A_n \cos npt + B_n \sin npt), \tag{37}$$

and substitute equations (35) and (37) into equation (34), we obtain the equation

$$-n^2 p^2 A_n \cos npt - n^2 p^2 B_n \sin npt + 0.05(-npA_n \sin npt + npB_n \cos npt)$$

$$+ 36(\tfrac{1}{2} A_0 + A_n \cos npt + B_n \sin npt) = \tfrac{1}{2} cT + b_n \sin npt \quad \text{for } n = 1, 2, \ldots,$$

$$\tag{38}$$

where b_n is given by equation (35b).

Equating coefficients of the constant terms, of sin npt and of cos npt in equation (38) gives

$$\left. \begin{array}{l} 18A_0 = \tfrac{1}{2} cT \\[4pt] -n^2 p^2 A_n + 0.05\, npB_n + 36A_n = 0 \\[4pt] -n^2 p^2 B_n - 0.05\, npA_n + 36B_n = b_n \end{array} \right\} \quad \text{for } n = 1, 2, \ldots .$$

For each $n \neq 0$ these give two simultaneous equations for A_n and B_n, which may be solved by elimination to give

$$A_0 = \frac{cT}{36}, \quad A_n = \frac{-0.05 npb_n}{(n^2 p^2 - 36)^2 + (0.05np)^2},$$

$$\tag{39}$$

$$B_n = \frac{-(n^2 p^2 - 36)b_n}{(n^2 p^2 - 36)^2 + (0.05np)^2}.$$

Equations (37) and (39) give the steady-state solution.

Equation (37) can be written as (see §1.5)

$$v(t) = \tfrac{1}{2} A_0 + \sum_{n=1}^{\infty} (A_n^2 + B_n^2)^{1/2} \left(\frac{A_n \cos npt}{(A_n^2 + B_n^2)^{1/2}} + \frac{B_n \sin npt}{(A_n^2 + B_n^2)^{1/2}} \right)$$

$$= \tfrac{1}{2} A_0 + \sum_{n=1}^{\infty} Y_n \cos(npt - \epsilon_n) \tag{40}$$

where

$$Y_n = (A_n^2 + B_n^2)^{1/2} \quad \text{and} \quad \epsilon_n = \tan^{-1} \left(\frac{B_n}{A_n} \right).$$

We see from equation (40) that, apart from a constant displacement, $v(t)$ is a superposition of sinusoidal or harmonic oscillations which have the frequency of $f(t)$ and multiples of this frequency. The amplitude of the nth term (or harmonic) is Y_n which is given by

$$Y_n = \frac{b_n}{[(n^2 p^2 - 36)^2 + (0.05np)^2]^{1/2}} \quad \text{for all } n.$$

This, like equations (39), exhibits the dependence of the amplitudes of the various harmonics on the frequency p of the external force. It shows that for values n satisfying $np \simeq 6$, the term $[(n^2 p^2 - 36)^2 + (0.05np)^2]^{1/2}$ is small and the ratio $Y_n : b_n$ is large, so that the corresponding harmonics of $v(t)$ are liable to be dominant.

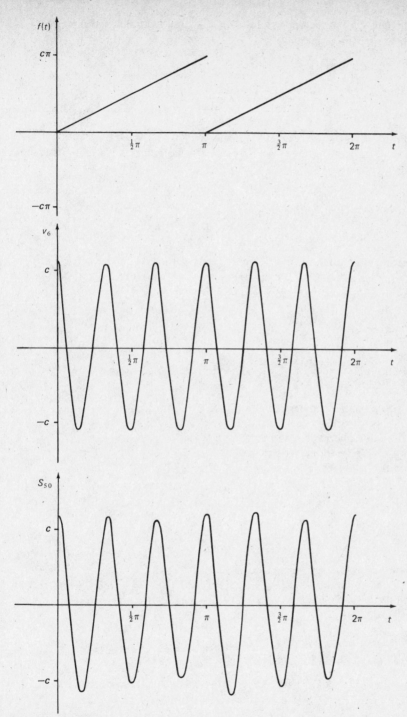

Fig. 2.10   The graphs of $y = f(t)$, $y = v_6$ and $y = S_{50}$ defined in example 1, in the case of $T = \pi$

For example, when $T = \pi$ so that $p = 1$, the term is small when $n = 6$, and therefore Y_6 is large and the dominant harmonic is

$$v_6(t) = Y_6 \cos(6t - \epsilon_6).$$

Now $B_6 = 0$, therefore $Y_6 = A_6$ and $\epsilon_6 = 0$, hence

$$v_6(t) = A_6 \cos 6t.$$

The function $v_6(t)$ is plotted in Fig. 2.10. Y_n will be relatively small for all other values of n and therefore the steady state solution is *almost* a harmonic oscillation. The graph of S_{50}, defined as

$$S_{50} = \tfrac{1}{2}A_0 + \sum_{n=1}^{50} Y_n \cos(nt - \epsilon_n),$$

is plotted in Fig. 2.10.

It is interesting to note that $v_6(t)$ has the frequency of the undamped free oscillations of the system, that is $v_6(t)$ has the frequency of the free oscillations when the coefficient of dy/dt in equation (34) is zero.

PROBLEMS

1. If the functions $f(x)$ and $g(x)$ are periodic with period L, and α and β are constants, show that

    (a) $h = \alpha f$ is periodic with period L,
    (b) $h = \alpha f + \beta g$ is periodic with period L,
    (c) $h(x) = f(\alpha x)$ is periodic with period L/α,
    (d) $h(x) = f(x/\beta)$ is periodic with period βL,
    (e) $h = fg$ is periodic with period L.

2. If

$$f(t + 2\pi) = f(t) \quad \text{and} \quad a_0 = \frac{1}{\pi} \int_{-\pi}^{\pi} f(t)\,dt,$$

show that

$$F(t) = \int_0^t f(x)\,dx - \tfrac{1}{2}a_0 t$$

is periodic with period 2π.

3. Sketch the function $f(x)$ defined as

$$f(x) = \begin{cases} -x & \text{for } -\pi \leqslant x < 0 \\ x & \text{for } 0 \leqslant x < \pi \end{cases} \quad \text{and} \quad f(x + 2\pi) = f(x),$$

and find the Fourier series for $f(x)$ in $-\pi \leqslant x \leqslant \pi$.

4. Find the Fourier series of the function defined as

$$f(x) = \begin{cases} \pi & \text{for } -L \leqslant x < 0 \\ \pi + x & \text{for } 0 \leqslant x < L \end{cases} \quad \text{and} \quad f(x + 2L) = f(x).$$

5. Find the Fourier series of the function $f(x)$ defined as

$$f(x) = \begin{cases} -x^3 + 1 & \text{for } -\pi/2 \leqslant x < 0 \\ x^3 + 1 & \text{for } 0 \leqslant x < \pi/2 \end{cases} \quad \text{and} \quad f(x + \pi) = f(x).$$

6. Find the Fourier series of the function defined as $f(x) = e^x$ for $-\pi \leqslant x < \pi$, and $f(x + 2\pi) = f(x)$. Hence show that

$$\sum_{n=1}^{\infty} \frac{1}{1 + n^2} = \tfrac{1}{2}(\pi \coth \pi - 1).$$

7. Find the Fourier series of the function defined as

$$f(x) = \begin{cases} -x + e^x & \text{for } -\pi \leqslant x < 0 \\ x + e^x & \text{for } 0 \leqslant x < \pi \end{cases} \quad \text{and} \quad f(x + 2\pi) = f(x).$$

8. From the Fourier series of the function defined as

$$f(x) = \begin{cases} -1 & \text{for } -\pi \leqslant x < 0 \\ 1 & \text{for } 0 \leqslant x < \pi \end{cases} \quad \text{and} \quad f(x + 2\pi) = f(x),$$

show that

$$\frac{\pi}{4} = \sum_{r=1}^{\infty} \frac{(-1)^{r+1}}{2r - 1}.$$

9. Find (a) the Fourier sine series (b) the Fourier cosine series to represent $f(x)$ defined as

$$f(x) = x \quad \text{for } 0 \leqslant x < \tfrac{1}{3}l \quad \text{and} \quad f(x) = \tfrac{1}{2}(l - x) \quad \text{for } \tfrac{1}{3}l \leqslant x \leqslant l.$$

Show by sketches the functions which the series represents outside the range $0 \leqslant x \leqslant l$.

10. Find both half range series representing the function $g(x)$ defined as $g(x) = e^x$ for $0 \leqslant x \leqslant L$. Sketch the graphs of the corresponding periodic extensions of $g(x)$.

11. Use the substitution $t = \pi x/L$ in equation (29) to find the Fourier series of $f(x)$ defined as

$$f(x) = x^3 - L^2 x \quad \text{for } -L \leqslant y < L \quad \text{and} \quad f(x + 2L) = f(x).$$

Hence find the Fourier series of $g(y)$ defined as

$$g(y) = (y^2 - L^2)^2 \quad \text{for } -L \leqslant y < L \quad \text{and} \quad g(y + 2L) = g(y).$$

12. Find the Fourier series for $f(x)$ defined as

$$f(x) = \begin{cases} -x^2/2 & \text{for } -\pi \leqslant x < 0 \\ x^2/2 & \text{for } 0 \leqslant x < \pi \end{cases} \qquad \text{and} \qquad f(x + 2\pi) = f(x).$$

Differentiate the Fourier series for $f(x)$ term by term and explain why the resulting series is *not* the Fourier series for $g(x)$ defined as

$$g(x) = \begin{cases} -x & \text{for } -\pi \leqslant x < 0 \\ x & \text{for } 0 \leqslant x < \pi \end{cases} \qquad \text{and} \qquad g(x + 2\pi) = g(x).$$

13. Given the Fourier series

$$f(x) = 1.5707 - 1.2732(\cos x + \tfrac{1}{9}\cos 3x + \tfrac{1}{25}\cos 5x + \ldots),$$

determine the nature of the function $f(x)$ by answering the following questions. What is the period of the series? Is it an odd or even function? By approximately evaluating the sum of the series at convenient points, draw a rough sketch of $f(x)$. Guess a form for $f(x)$ and compare this with the function of problem 3.

14. Find the steady-state solution of the equation

$$\frac{d^2y}{dt^2} + 0.03\frac{dy}{dt} + 25y = f(t)$$

where $f(t)$ is defined as

$$f(t) = \begin{cases} t + \pi/2\omega & \text{for } -\pi \leqslant \omega t < 0 \\ -t + \pi/2\omega & \text{for } 0 \leqslant \omega t < \pi \end{cases} \qquad \text{and} \qquad f(t + 2\pi/\omega) = f(t).$$

Find the dominant term in the solution, when $\omega = 1$.

15. A damped linear system satisfies the equation

$$y''(t) + ky'(t) + c^2 y(t) = r(t)$$

where $r(t)$ is defined as

$$r(t) = \frac{t}{12}(\pi^2 - t^2) \qquad \text{for } -\pi \leqslant t < \pi \qquad \text{and} \qquad r(t + 2\pi) = r(t).$$

Determine the response of the system by using a Fourier series expansion for $r(t)$. If $k \ll 1$ find the values of c for which there is a dominant term in the solution.

16. A function $f(t)$ is said to be *anti-periodic* if it has the property $f(t + T) = -f(t)$.

Show that

(a) $f(t)$ is periodic with period $2T$,

(b) $f(t)$ has a Fourier series of the form

$$\sum_{r=1}^{\infty}\left[a_{2r-1}\cos\{(2r-1)\pi t/T\}+b_{2r-1}\sin\{(2r-1)\pi t/T\}\right].$$

(c) Verify results (a) and (b) when $f(t)$ is defined as

$$f(t)=t \quad \text{for } 0\leqslant t<T \quad \text{and} \quad f(t+T)=-f(t).$$

CHAPTER 3

Laplace Transforms

3.1 INTRODUCTION

Many mathematical problems encountered in engineering may be successfully tackled by using the method of *integral transforms*. The most widely used of these is the *Laplace transform* and this chapter shows how its properties may be used in the solution of ordinary differential equations and of difference and integral equations. Some of its more difficult aspects are not considered until Volume 2, where some other transforms are introduced and the solution of partial differential equations by means of integral transforms is studied.

Definition and Notation

If $f(t)$ is uniquely defined for all t in $0 \leqslant t < \infty$, then

$$\mathscr{L}\{f(t)\} \equiv \int_0^\infty e^{-st}f(t)\mathrm{d}t \tag{1}$$

is the Laplace transform of $f(t)$. If the integral converges for a sufficiently large value of s, a function $\bar{f}(s)$ is defined by the equation

$$\bar{f}(s) = \mathscr{L}\{f(t)\}$$

and the Laplace transform is said to *exist*. The symbol $\mathscr{L}$ in equation (1) may be interpreted as the *operation* of multiplying $f(t)$ by e^{-st} and integrating the product over $0 \leqslant t < \infty$. The operation transforms a function of t into a function of s in a way which takes account of the behaviour of $f(t)$ over its complete range of definition. For example,

$$\mathscr{L}\{e^{kt}\} \equiv \int_0^\infty e^{-st}e^{kt}\,\mathrm{d}t = \int_0^\infty e^{-(s-k)t}\mathrm{d}t.$$

The integral is convergent for $s > k$. Hence the transform exists and

$$\mathscr{L}\{e^{kt}\} = \left[-\frac{1}{s-k}e^{-(s-k)t}\right]_0^\infty = \frac{1}{s-k}.$$

Putting $k = 0$ gives the result

$$\mathscr{L}\{1\} = \frac{1}{s}.$$

The two functions $f(t)$ and $\bar{f}(s)$ are often called a *transform pair* and it is sometimes convenient to denote their relation by the *inverse* operator $\mathscr{L}^{-1}$, defined by the equation

$$f(t) = \mathscr{L}^{-1}\{\bar{f}(s)\}.$$

Thus the relation between e^{kt} and its transform may be expressed by either of the equations

$$\mathscr{L}\{e^{kt}\} = \frac{1}{s-k}, \quad \mathscr{L}^{-1}\left\{\frac{1}{s-k}\right\} = e^{kt}. \tag{2}$$

The most frequent variation from the notation of equation (1) is the use of p instead of s. Sometimes the Laplace transform of $f(t)$ is defined by

$$p\int_0^\infty e^{-pt} f(t)\,dt,$$

the 'p-multiplied transform' (or *Heaviside* transform), which has the slight advantage of preserving some symmetry between $f(t)$ and its transform, seen at its simplest in the p-multiplied transform of 1, which is also 1. When tables of transforms are consulted, inspection of the transform of 1, or some other simple function, is sufficient to indicate which definition has been used. The distinction between a function and its transform is sometimes made by changing from small to capital letters, or vice versa, thus:

$$F(s) = \mathscr{L}\{f(t)\} \quad \text{or} \quad f(s) = \mathscr{L}\{F(t)\}.$$

Existence and Uniqueness

Consider the three integrals

$$\text{(a)} \int_0^\infty \frac{e^{-st}}{t}\,dt, \quad \text{(b)} \int_0^\infty e^{-st} e^{t^2}\,dt, \quad \text{(c)} \int_0^\infty \frac{e^{-st}}{(t-c)^2}\,dt \quad (c>0).$$

It is not difficult to show that none of them is convergent. Integral (a) does not converge at $t = 0$, integral (b) does not converge as $t \to \infty$, while integral (c) is divergent at $t = c$ where there is an infinite discontinuity. It follows that none of the transforms

$$\mathscr{L}\{t^{-1}\}, \quad \mathscr{L}\{\exp(t^2)\}, \quad \mathscr{L}\{(t-c)^{-2}\}$$

can exist. In practice, most of the transforms which one seeks do exist, but a formal set of conditions for existence is useful and it is convenient to arrange them according to the behaviour of $f(t)$ for (a) t small, (b) t large and (c) t finite but non-zero, as in the next paragraph.

If the following conditions are satisfied:

(a) $|f(t)| < Mt^{a-1}$ for $0 \leqslant t \leqslant t_0$ where M, a and t_0 are some positive numbers,

(b) $f(t)$ is of exponential order α as $t \to \infty$ (that is, $|f(t)| < Ne^{\alpha t}$ for $t > T$ where N and T are positive numbers), where α is any real number, and

(c) $f(t)$ is continuous or piecewise continuous (that is, it has a finite number of finite discontinuities) in every interval $t_0 \leqslant t \leqslant T$, where $t_0 > 0$,

then $\bar{f}(s)$ *exists* for all $s > \alpha$. This restriction on s does not limit the use of the transform and may be ignored at present. These are *sufficient* conditions and (c), in particular, is stronger than necessary, as is shown by the function

$$f(t) = \begin{cases} 0, & t < c, \\ (t-c)^{-\frac{1}{2}}, & t > c, \end{cases} \quad (c > 0)$$

which has a Laplace transform despite the infinite discontinuity at $t = c$.

It follows from the definition of the Laplace transform as an integral that if the Laplace transform of a function exists it is *unique* and, for practical purposes, the same is true of the inverse transform.

Another fundamental property of the Laplace transform is its *linearity*. It is obvious that, if c_1 and c_2 are any constants,

$$\mathscr{L}\{c_1 f_1(t) + c_2 f_2(t)\} = c_1 \mathscr{L}\{f_1(t)\} + c_2 \mathscr{L}\{f_2(t)\}. \tag{3}$$

This result may clearly be generalized to any finite number of terms and may be extended to an infinite number if the sum is convergent.

Many engineering problems are adequately modelled mathematically by linear systems and it is among these that the Laplace transform finds its applications. In this chapter we shall be particularly concerned with linear ordinary differential equations (chiefly those with constant coefficients) and linear difference and integral equations.

Since the Laplace transform does not take account of values of $f(t)$ for $t < 0$, it is not suitable for problems in which the values of functions for $t < 0$ are relevant. It is most often useful where the data include the values of the unknown function $f(t)$ and some of its derivatives at $t = 0$, and it is frequently applied to *initial value* problems, in which t usually represents time. It also provides an effective method of dealing with some *boundary value* problems, in which the independent variable may be a space coordinate x.

The first essential is to determine the Laplace transforms of all functions that occur in the given problem. Many common functions are easily transformed by means of elementary techniques such as integration by parts, as in examples 1 and 2 below. In each example of this and subsequent sections, the integral defining the transform exists for sufficiently large s.

EXAMPLE 1

Show that $\mathscr{L}\{\sin kt\} = \dfrac{k}{s^2 + k^2}$.

$$\int_0^\infty e^{-st} \sin kt \, dt = [-s^{-1} e^{-st} \sin kt]_0^\infty + ks^{-1} \int_0^\infty e^{-st} \cos kt \, dt$$

$$= -ks^{-2} [e^{-st} \cos kt]_0^\infty - k^2 s^{-2} \int_0^\infty e^{-st} \sin kt \, dt$$

$$= \frac{k}{s^2} - \frac{k^2}{s^2} \mathscr{L}\{\sin kt\}.$$

Then

$$\left(1 + \frac{k^2}{s^2}\right) \mathcal{L}\{\sin kt\} = \frac{k}{s^2}$$

and the result follows.

EXAMPLE 2

Show that $\mathcal{L}\{t\} = s^{-2}$.

$$\int_0^\infty te^{-st} \, dt = [-ts^{-1}e^{-st}]_0^\infty + s^{-1}\int_0^\infty e^{-st} \, dt = s^{-2}.$$

The transform of t^n, where n is any positive integer, may be calculated by n successive integrations by parts.

Other results may be found by applying the linearity property to known transforms, as in the following example, in which the previously calculated transform of e^{kt} is used.

EXAMPLE 3

Show that $\mathcal{L}\{\sinh kt\} = \dfrac{k}{s^2 - k^2}$.

$$\mathcal{L}\{\sinh kt\} = \mathcal{L}\{\tfrac{1}{2}(e^{kt} - e^{-kt})\} = \tfrac{1}{2}\mathcal{L}\{e^{kt}\} - \tfrac{1}{2}\mathcal{L}\{e^{-kt}\}$$

$$= \tfrac{1}{2}(s - k)^{-1} - \tfrac{1}{2}(s + k)^{-1} = k(s^2 - k^2)^{-1}.$$

In addition, some of the properties given in §3.4 are helpful in deducing transforms from those already known. However, the most effective assistance comes from a sufficiently comprehensive table of transforms (see Bibliography). A short list of properties and transform pairs is given in Table A1 in the Appendix. It should be noted that some of the functions which appear there are not defined until Volume 2.

When a problem is being solved by Laplace transform methods it is necessary at some stage to invert a function $\bar{f}(s)$ which has been derived. It may be possible to do this at once by consulting a table of transforms. Sometimes, however, the function must be rearranged as a sum of functions, each of which may be inverted by means of a table, possibly with the help of the properties given in §3.4. There is an *inversion formula* valid for any tranform $\bar{f}(s)$, but it is not considered until Volume 2, Chapter 5 for two reasons: first, it is not necessary for the types of problems of this chapter and, secondly, it depends upon topics in complex variable theory which are discussed in Volume 2, Chapter 4.

When $\bar{f}(s)$ is a *rational* function (that is, a quotient of two polynomials) it is usually necessary to decompose it into *partial fractions.* Since the solution of a linear ordinary differential equation is almost always found as the inverse of a rational function, familiarity with partial fractions is essential.

EXAMPLE 4

Find $f(t)$ when $\bar{f}(s) = \dfrac{6s^2 + 10s + 2}{s(s^2 + 3s + 2)}$.

The denominator is $s(s + 1)(s + 2)$, so write

$$\bar{f}(s) = \frac{A}{s} + \frac{B}{s+1} + \frac{C}{s+2}$$

and determine A, B and C by one of the well-known methods. Then, on substitution,

$$\bar{f}(s) = \frac{1}{s} + \frac{2}{s+1} + \frac{3}{s+2} \, ,$$

and so, by the linearity property, equation (3),

$$f(t) = \mathscr{L}^{-1}\left\{\frac{1}{s}\right\} + 2\mathscr{L}^{-1}\left\{\frac{1}{s+1}\right\} + 3\mathscr{L}^{-1}\left\{\frac{1}{s+2}\right\}.$$

Finally, from equation (2) with $k = 0, -1, -2$ in succession,

$$f(t) = 1 + 2e^{-t} + 3e^{-2t}.$$

Although complex variable theory is not used in this chapter, it is sometimes convenient to use *complex numbers* in problems involving *real variables*. Both the theory and the properties of the transform are essentially unchanged by the introduction of complex parameters, although simple modification to conditions of existence may be required. When s is considered as a complex variable, condition (c) for the existence of a transform becomes Re $s > \alpha$. The original variable t is always considered to be real.

EXAMPLE 5
By expressing $\cos \omega t$ as a sum of imaginary exponentials, find its Laplace transform.

$$\cos \omega t = \tfrac{1}{2}(e^{i\omega t} + e^{-i\omega t}),$$

and so by equation (3)

$$\mathscr{L}\{\cos \omega t\} = \tfrac{1}{2}\mathscr{L}\{e^{i\omega t}\} + \tfrac{1}{2}\mathscr{L}\{e^{-i\omega t}\}.$$

Both of the integrals $\mathscr{L}\{e^{i\omega t}\}$ and $\mathscr{L}\{e^{-i\omega t}\}$ converge for all $s > 0$ and so define Laplace transforms. Then, by equation (2)

$$\mathscr{L}\{\cos \omega t\} = \tfrac{1}{2}\left(\frac{1}{s - i\omega} + \frac{1}{s + i\omega}\right) = \frac{s}{s^2 + \omega^2}.$$

Exercises

1. Find the Laplace transforms of (a) t^2, (b) t^n (n any positive integer).

2. Find the Laplace transform of cosh kt by

   (a)   expressing it as a sum of exponentials,
   (b)   using the relation cosh $kt = \cos(ikt)$ in the result of example 5.

3. Find the Laplace transform of (a) $\cos \omega t$ by the method of example 1, (b) $\sin \omega t$ by the method of example 5.

4. Find the inverse Laplace transforms of

(a) s^{-4},   (b) $(s-3)^{-1}$,   (c) $(s^2-4)^{-1}$,

(d) $\dfrac{2}{s(s-2)}$,   (e) $\dfrac{2s^2+s+1}{(s^2+1)(s+1)}$.

3.2 TRANSFORMS OF DERIVATIVES

Convenient expressions for the Laplace transforms of derivatives are required for use in solving differential equations. By definition,

$$\mathcal{L}\{f'(t)\} = \int_0^\infty e^{-st}f'(t)\,dt.$$

Integration by parts gives

$$\mathcal{L}\{f'(t)\} = [e^{-st}f(t)]_0^\infty + s\int_0^\infty e^{-st}f(t)\,dt$$

$$= s\bar{f}(s) - f(0), \tag{4}$$

provided that $f(t)$ is continuous for $0 \leqslant t < \infty$ and is of exponential order as $t \to \infty$, and that $f'(t)$ is piecewise continuous for $0 \leqslant t < \infty$.

If $f(t)$ and $f'(t)$ are continuous for $0 \leqslant t < \infty$ and of exponential order as $t \to \infty$, while $f''(t)$ is piecewise continuous for $0 \leqslant t < \infty$, then

$$\int_0^\infty e^{-st}f''(t)\,dt = [e^{-st}f'(t)]_0^\infty + s\int_0^\infty e^{-st}f'(t)\,dt$$

$$= s\mathcal{L}\{f'(t)\} - f'(0),$$

and so, with the help of equation (4),

$$\mathcal{L}\{f''(t)\} = s^2\bar{f}(s) - sf(0) - f'(0). \tag{5}$$

Continuation of this process yields the general result: if $f(t)$ and its first $n-1$ derivatives are continuous for $0 \leqslant t < \infty$ and of exponential order as $t \to \infty$, while $f^{(n)}(t)$ is piecewise continuous for $0 \leqslant t < \infty$, then

$$\mathcal{L}\{f^{(n)}(t)\} = s^n\bar{f}(s) - s^{n-1}f(0) - s^{n-2}f'(0) - \dots$$

$$- sf^{(n-2)}(0) - f^{(n-1)}(0)$$

$$= s^n\bar{f}(s) - \sum_{r=1}^n s^{n-r}f^{(r-1)}(0). \tag{6}$$

Note that, since the values of $f(t)$ for $t < 0$ are irrelevant, $f(0)$ and $f^{(r)}(0)$ should be interpreted as the *limits* of $f(t)$ and $f^{(r)}(t)$, respectively, as $t \to 0$ through positive values.

It is possible that the solution $f(t)$ of a given differential equation does not satisfy the conditions specified above and so it seems that a solution would then be unobtainable by the use of the derivative formula. However, this apparent difficulty is easily surmounted, as later examples show.

The derivative formulae (4), (5) and (6) are required in the solution of differential equations but they may also be used to obtain certain transforms from known transforms when direct calculation is difficult. Consider, as a simple example, the calculation of $\mathscr{L}\{\cos kt\}$, given the transform of $\sin kt$ derived in §3.1.

$$\mathscr{L}\{k \cos kt\} = \mathscr{L}\left\{\frac{d}{dt} \sin kt\right\} = s\mathscr{L}\{\sin kt\} - \sin 0 = \frac{sk}{s^2 + k^2}$$

and so

$$\mathscr{L}\{\cos kt\} = \frac{s}{s^2 + k^2}. \tag{7}$$

Linear Ordinary Differential Equations

A thorough treatment of the application of the Laplace transform to linear ordinary differential equations is given in §3.5, after the derivation, in §3.4, of various useful properties. Here, we merely illustrate the principles by means of simple examples.

EXAMPLE 1
Solve the equation

$$\frac{d^2 y}{dt^2} - y = 1 \tag{8}$$

for $y(t)$ with the *initial conditions*

$$y(0) = 0, \quad y'(0) = 1. \tag{9}$$

Multiply both sides of equation (8) by e^{-st} and integrate over $0 \leqslant t < \infty$. The linearity property, embodied in equation (3) of §3.1, implies that this operation is equivalent to replacing each term of equation (8) by its Laplace transform:

$$\mathscr{L}\left\{\frac{d^2 y}{dt^2}\right\} - \mathscr{L}\{y\} = \mathscr{L}\{1\}. \tag{10}$$

But, by equation (5),

$$\mathscr{L}\left\{\frac{d^2 y}{dt^2}\right\} = s^2 \bar{y}(s) - sy(0) - y'(0) = s^2 \bar{y}(s) - 1 \tag{11}$$

where we have used the conditions (9). Also

$$\mathscr{L}\{1\} = \int_0^\infty e^{-st} dt = s^{-1}$$

and substitution of this and equation (11) into equation (10) gives the *algebraic* equation

$$s^2 \bar{y}(s) - 1 - \bar{y}(s) = s^{-1},$$

from which

$$\bar{y}(s) = \frac{s^{-1} + 1}{s^2 - 1} = \frac{1}{s(s-1)}. \tag{12}$$

The solution for $\bar{y}(s)$ must now be *inverted* to yield $y(t)$. The first step is to resolve the right side of equation (12) into partial fractions as:

$$\bar{y}(s) = \frac{1}{s-1} - \frac{1}{s}.$$

Then, by equations (2) and (3),

$$y(t) = e^t - 1. \tag{13}$$

It is good practice to verify solutions of differential equations. In this case, it is easy to show that solution (13) satisfies equation (8) and the initial conditions (9).

In the above example the method of solution has been explained at length, but all of the steps are simple and can be carried out quite quickly.

EXAMPLE 2
Solve

$$\frac{d^2 y}{dt^2} + y = \cos 2t, \quad y'(0) = 0, \quad y'(\tfrac{1}{2}\pi) = 0. \tag{14}$$

Proceeding as in example 1 and using the result given by equation (7), we obtain the *transformed equation*

$$s^2 \bar{y} - sy(0) + \bar{y} = \frac{s}{s^2 + 4}. \tag{15}$$

Notice that, because only one *initial* value has been given, the other, $y(0)$, remains undetermined in the equation for $\bar{y}(s)$. The condition on y at $t = \frac{1}{2}\pi$ cannot be used at this stage, but we proceed giving $y(0)$ the unknown constant value y_0. The solution of equation (15) is then

$$\bar{y}(s) = \frac{y_0 s}{s^2 + 1} + \frac{s}{(s^2 + 1)(s^2 + 4)} = \left(y_0 + \frac{1}{3}\right)\frac{s}{s^2 + 1} - \frac{1}{3}\frac{s}{s^2 + 4},$$

and hence

$$y(t) = (y_0 + \tfrac{1}{3})\cos t - \tfrac{1}{3}\cos 2t. \tag{16}$$

Differentiation gives

$$y'(t) = -(y_0 + \tfrac{1}{3})\sin t + \tfrac{2}{3}\sin 2t.$$

The condition $y'(0) = 0$ is clearly satisfied, while $y'(\tfrac{1}{2}\pi) = 0$ is satisfied if $y_0 = -\tfrac{1}{3}$. Substitution in equation (16) gives the solution of equation (14) under the given conditions:

$$y(t) = -\tfrac{1}{3}\cos 2t,$$

which is easily verified.

Exercises

1. Use the relation $d(te^t)/dt = (t + 1)e^t$ and the derivative formula (4) to find $\mathcal{L}\{te^t\}$.

2. Calculate $d^2(t^2 e^t)/dt^2$ and use the formula (5) with the result from exercise 1 to find $\mathcal{L}\{t^2 e^t\}$.

3. Find the Laplace transform of each of the following functions $y(t)$ and use the derivative formulae (4) and (5) to calculate $\mathcal{L}\{y'(t)\}$ and $\mathcal{L}\{y''(t)\}$:

   (a) $e^t - e^{-2t}$,   (b) $e^{-t}\cosh 2t$,   (c) $t \sin t$.

4. Show that, if

$$\mathcal{L}\{f^{(n-1)}(t)\} = s^{n-1}\bar{f}(s) - \sum_{r=1}^{n-1} s^{n-1-r} f^{(r-1)}(0),$$

then

$$\mathcal{L}\{f^{(n)}(t)\} = s^n \bar{f}(s) - \sum_{r=1}^{n} s^{n-r} f^{(r-1)}(0),$$

so long as $f^{(n)}(t)$ is piecewise continuous for $0 \leqslant t < \infty$ and $f^{(n-1)}(t)$ is continuous for $0 \leqslant t < \infty$ and of exponential order as $t \to \infty$. Hence, by induction, prove equation (6).

5. Solve the equation

$$y''(t) - 2y(t) = \cos t, \quad y(0) = 1, \quad y'(0) = 0.$$

3.3 STEP FUNCTION AND DELTA FUNCTION

Two functions which are often used in connexion with Laplace transforms are the *Heaviside step function* $H(t)$ and the *Dirac delta function* $\delta(t)$. Other names for these functions are, respectively, the *unit function* and the *unit impulse function*.

The *Heaviside step function* (see Fig. 3.1) is defined thus:

$$H(t - t_0) = \begin{cases} 0, & t < t_0, \\ 1, & t \geqslant t_0. \end{cases} \tag{17}$$

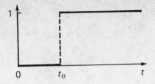

Fig. 3.1   Heaviside step function, $H(t - t_0)$

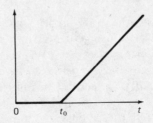

Fig. 3.2   Graph of $(t - t_0) H(t - t_0)$

It allows us to express in compact form functions that are zero whenever t is less than some value t_0. Thus for any function $f(t)$

$$f(t)H(t - t_0) = \begin{cases} 0, & t < t_0, \\ f(t), & t \geq t_0. \end{cases}$$

An example is the function

$$(t - t_0)H(t - t_0) = \begin{cases} 0, & t < t_0, \\ t - t_0, & t \geq t_0, \end{cases}$$

shown in Fig. 3.2. Periodic functions may be represented by a series of terms involving step functions; for example

$$\sum_{n=0}^{\infty} \{H(t - 2n) - H(t - 2n - 1)\} \equiv H(t) - H(t - 1) + H(t - 2) - \ldots$$

is the function indicated in Fig. 3.3.

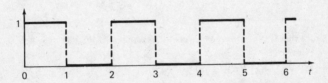

Fig. 3.3   Graph of $H(t) - H(t - 1) + H(t - 2) - H(t - 3) + \ldots$

The Laplace transform of the step function is easily calculated as follows:

$$\mathscr{L}\{H(t - t_0)\} = \int_0^\infty e^{-st} H(t - t_0)\,dt = \int_{t_0}^\infty e^{-st}\,dt$$

$$= -s^{-1}[e^{-st}]_{t_0}^\infty = s^{-1}\exp(-t_0 s), \tag{18}$$

if $t_0 \geqslant 0$.

The Dirac Delta Function

In various physical contexts, there arises the problem of describing an entity which has very small extent in either space or time, but nevertheless has a significant 'total' value. Some obvious examples are a force applied over a very small area on the surface of a solid, the electric charge on a very small particle and an acoustic pulse of very short duration. The first two, which may conveniently be called a 'point force' and a 'point charge', respectively, are each distributed over a very small region in space and, apart from the approximate position in space, the important quantities are merely the *resultant* force or the total charge. Similarly, the precise distribution in time of a very short pulse, or *impulse*, is much less important than its 'total' value, measured by its integral over time. Moreover, it is usually much easier to measure this total value than to determine the distribution in space or time. Such a distribution is idealized in the Dirac delta function, which concentrates the total value at one point. It is defined by

$$\delta(t) = 0, \quad \text{for } t \neq 0,$$

$$\int_{-\infty}^\infty \delta(t)\,dt = 1. \tag{19}$$

The definition implies that $\delta(t)$ is infinite at $t = 0$ although it is zero elsewhere. Clearly, $\delta(t)$ is not a function in the usual sense but the following construction may make it more comprehensible. Consider the function $\delta_\epsilon(t)$ illustrated in Fig. 3.4 and defined as

$$\delta_\epsilon(t) = \begin{cases} 0 & \text{for } -\infty < t < 0, \\ \epsilon^{-1} & \text{for } 0 < t < \epsilon, \\ 0 & \text{for } \epsilon < t < \infty. \end{cases} \tag{20}$$

Now

$$\int_{-\infty}^\infty \delta_\epsilon(t)\,dt = \int_0^\epsilon \epsilon^{-1}\,dt = [\epsilon^{-1}t]_0^\epsilon = 1,$$

so that $\lim_{\epsilon \to 0} \delta_\epsilon(t)$ has the properties given by equation (19) and may be identified with $\delta(t)$. This is the simplest of many ways of constructing a function with the required properties.

The Dirac delta function has the important property that, given a function $f(t)$,

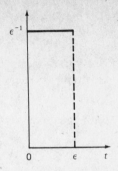

Fig. 3.4 Graph of $\delta_\epsilon(t)$ as defined by equation (24)

continuous at $t = a$,

$$\int_{-\infty}^{\infty} \delta(t - a)f(t)\mathrm{d}t = f(a). \tag{21}$$

This *sifting property* will not be proved here. Notice that, by putting $a = 0$ and $f(t) \equiv 1$, we obtain the second of equations (19). It is convenient, for theoretical reasons, to have infinite limits in the integrals in equations (19) and (21), but finite limits can usually be substituted. Thus a result equivalent to equation (21) is

$$\int_{a-\eta}^{a+\eta} \delta(t - a)f(t)\mathrm{d}t = f(a)$$

where η is any positive number.

Although $\delta(t)$ is not a 'proper' function, used with care in appropriate problems it leads to physically significant solutions which would be difficult, if not impossible, to find otherwise.

The Heaviside step function may be expressed in terms of the delta function by the equation

$$H(t - t_0) = \int_{-\infty}^{t} \delta(\tau - t_0)\mathrm{d}\tau \tag{22}$$

since the interval of integration contains t_0 if $t > t_0$, but not if $t < t_0$. The converse of equation (22) is

$$\delta(t - t_0) = H'(t - t_0),$$

which expresses the fact that $H'(t - t_0)$ is zero everywhere except at $t = t_0$ where the jump in $H(t - t_0)$ occurs.

Formally, if $t_0 \geq 0$, the Laplace transform of $\delta(t - t_0)$ is

$$\mathscr{L}\{\delta(t - t_0)\} = \int_{0}^{\infty} e^{-st}\delta(t - t_0)\mathrm{d}t = \exp(-t_0 s). \tag{23}$$

Notice that, when $t_0 = 0$, we have

$$\mathscr{L}^{-1}\{1\} = \delta(t).$$

This result, with that of exercise 1 of §3.1, gives us $\mathscr{L}^{-1}\{s^{-n}\}$ for $n = 0, 1, 2, 3, \ldots$, whilst for *non*-integer $n \, \mathscr{L}^{-1}\{s^{-n}\}$ is given in Volume 2.

EXAMPLE 1
Obtain the Laplace transform of $\delta_\epsilon(t)$, the function given by equation (20).

$$\mathscr{L}\{\delta_\epsilon(t)\} = \mathscr{L}\{\epsilon^{-1}[H(t) - H(t - \epsilon)]\} = \epsilon^{-1}[s^{-1} - s^{-1}e^{-\epsilon s}]$$

$$= (\epsilon s)^{-1}(1 - e^{-\epsilon s}).$$

We note that this can be written as

$$\mathscr{L}\{\delta_\epsilon(t)\} = 1 - \tfrac{1}{2}\epsilon s + \tfrac{1}{6}\epsilon^2 s^2 - \ldots$$

and, by taking the limit as $\epsilon \to 0$, we verify that $\mathscr{L}\{\delta(t)\} = 1$.

EXAMPLE 2
Find the velocity $v(t)$ of a particle of mass m accelerated in the x direction by a force $F(t)$ if (a) $v(0) = 0$ and $F(t)$ is a constant force P applied for all $t \geqslant 0$, (b) $v(0) = v_0$ and $F(t)$ is an impulse Q applied at $t = t_0$.

The equation of motion in each case is

$$mv'(t) = F(t).$$

From equation (4), the transformed equation is

$$m[s\bar{v} - v(0)] = \mathscr{L}\{F(t)\} = \bar{F}(s),$$

from which

$$m\bar{v}(s) = \frac{mv(0)}{s} + \frac{\bar{F}(s)}{s}.$$

(a) $F(t) = PH(t)$, $\mathscr{L}\{F(t)\} = P/s$, and since $v(0) = 0$

$$m\bar{v}(s) = \frac{P}{s^2},$$

with inverse transform

$$mv(t) = Pt.$$

(b)   In mechanics, the words *impulse* and *impulsive force* are sometimes used interchangeably, but it may be useful to distinguish between them. If a force $F(t)$ acts during the interval $t_0 < t < t_1$, its *impulse* is defined as the integral

$$I = \int_{t_0}^{t_1} F(t)\,dt,$$

and is equal to the change of momentum produced. If the interval becomes infinitesimally small, but I remains finite, we call the force an *impulsive force* with impulse I. If $F(t) = Q/\epsilon$ and acts for $0 \leqslant t \leqslant \epsilon$, we can use the notation of equation (20) to put $F(t) = Q\delta_\epsilon(t)$. The impulse of this force is

$$\int_0^\epsilon \frac{Q}{\epsilon} dt = Q.$$

Now let $\epsilon \to 0$, so that $\delta_\epsilon(t) \to \delta(t)$. The impulse Q is independent of ϵ and so $Q\delta(t)$ represents an impulsive force of impulse Q acting at $t = 0$. In the present case, since the force is applied at $t = t_0$, $F(t) = Q\delta(t - t_0)$ and $\mathscr{L}\{F(t)\} = Q\exp(-t_0 s)$. Then, with $v(0) = v_0$,

$$m\bar{v}(s) = \frac{mv_0}{s} + \frac{Q\exp(-t_0 s)}{s}$$

which inverts to give

$$mv(t) = mv_0 + QH(t - t_0). \tag{24}$$

Notice that, for any $t_1 > t_0$, the change of momentum given by this equation is, as expected,

$$mv(t_1) - mv_0 = Q.$$

Equation (24) gives the correct solution of the impulse problem although $v(t)$ does not satisfy the continuity condition for the derivative formula (4). This example shows how the theoretical limitations on the use of the derivative formulae may be surmounted by means of the delta function and step function.

Exercises

1. Express in terms of step functions the 'saw-tooth' function $f(t)$ such that $f(t) = 0$ for $t \leqslant 0$ and $f(t) = t/a - n$ for $n \leqslant t/a < n + 1$, where $n = 0, 1, 2, 3, \ldots$.

2. Express in terms of step functions the 'triangle' function $f_\epsilon(t)$ such that

$$f_\epsilon(t) = \begin{cases} \epsilon^{-2}(t - t_0 + \epsilon) & \text{for } t_0 - \epsilon \leqslant t \leqslant t_0, \\ \epsilon^{-2}(-t + t_0 + \epsilon) & \text{for } t_0 \leqslant t \leqslant t_0 + \epsilon, \end{cases}$$

but $f_\epsilon(t) = 0$ elsewhere. Sketch the graph of the function and, by considering

$\int_{-\infty}^{\infty} f_\epsilon(t)dt$, show that $\lim_{\epsilon \to 0} f_\epsilon(t)$ has the properties of the Dirac delta function $\delta(t - t_0)$.

3. Show that, for $t_0 > \epsilon$, the Laplace transform of $f_\epsilon(t)$, defined in exercise 2, is

$$\bar{f}_\epsilon(s) \doteq 4(\epsilon s)^{-2} \exp(-t_0 s) \sinh^2(\tfrac{1}{2}\epsilon s)$$

and hence that $\lim_{\epsilon \to 0} \bar{f}_\epsilon(s) = \exp(-t_0 s)$.

3.4 PROPERTIES OF THE LAPLACE TRANSFORM

There are a number of properties of the Laplace transform which are useful in its application to the solution of differential equations and other problems. Here we state each property with an outline of its proof and one or two examples. The examples show how the properties may be used to deduce further transform pairs; their use in the solution of problems is illustrated in later sections. Wherever it occurs in the following, n is a non-negative integer but a is any real number unless otherwise prescribed.

(a) *First Shift Property*

$$\mathscr{L}\{e^{at}f(t)\} = \bar{f}(s-a) \quad \text{where} \quad \bar{f}(s) = \mathscr{L}\{f(t)\}. \tag{25}$$

Proof:

$$\int_0^\infty e^{-st}e^{at}f(t)\,dt = \int_0^\infty e^{-(s-a)t}f(t)\,dt = \bar{f}(s-a).$$

EXAMPLE 1

Since $\mathscr{L}\{\sin kt\} = \dfrac{k}{s^2 + k^2}$ and $\mathscr{L}\{t^n\} = \dfrac{n!}{s^{n+1}}$,

it follows that

$$\mathscr{L}\{e^{at}\sin kt\} = \frac{k}{(s-a)^2 + k^2} \quad \text{and} \quad \mathscr{L}\{e^{at}t^n\} = \frac{n!}{(s-a)^{n+1}}.$$

(b) *Second Shift Property*

$$\mathscr{L}\{f(t-a)H(t-a)\} = e^{-as}\bar{f}(s), \quad a > 0. \tag{26}$$

Proof:

$$\mathscr{L}\{f(t-a)H(t-a)\} = \int_0^\infty e^{-st}f(t-a)H(t-a)\,dt$$

$$= \int_a^\infty e^{-st}f(t-a)\,dt.$$

Make the substitution $\tau = t - a$. Then

$$\mathscr{L}\{f(t-a)H(t-a)\} = \int_0^\infty e^{-s(\tau+a)}f(\tau)\,d\tau$$

$$= e^{-as}\int_0^\infty e^{-s\tau}f(\tau)\,d\tau = e^{-as}\bar{f}(s).$$

EXAMPLE 2

$$\mathcal{L}\{(t - t_0)^n H(t - t_0)\} = \frac{\exp(-t_0 s)n!}{s^{n+1}}, \quad t_0 > 0.$$

(c) *Transform of Integral*

$$\mathcal{L}\left\{\int_0^t f(\tau)d\tau\right\} = \frac{1}{s}\bar{f}(s). \tag{27}$$

Proof: Put

$$F(t) = \int_0^t f(\tau)d\tau.$$

Then $F(0) = 0$, $F'(t) = f(t)$ and, from equation (4),

$$\bar{f}(s) = \mathcal{L}\{F'(t)\} = s\mathcal{L}\{F(t)\} - F(0) = s\,\mathcal{L}\left\{\int_0^t f(\tau)d\tau\right\}.$$

The result follows at once. In terms of the inverse operator $\mathcal{L}^{-1}$, the property becomes

$$\mathcal{L}^{-1}\left\{\frac{1}{s}\bar{f}(s)\right\} = \int_0^t f(\tau)d\tau. \tag{28}$$

EXAMPLE 3
Since

$$\mathcal{L}^{-1}\left\{\frac{k}{s^2 + k^2}\right\} = \sin kt,$$

$$\mathcal{L}^{-1}\left\{\frac{k}{s(s^2 + k^2)}\right\} = \int_0^t \sin k\tau\, d\tau = \frac{1}{k}(1 - \cos kt). \tag{29}$$

Problem 4 shows how the result may be extended to repeated integrals.

(d) *Derivative of Transform*

$$\mathcal{L}\{t^n f(t)\} = (-1)^n \frac{d^n \bar{f}(s)}{ds^n}. \tag{30}$$

This is proved by repeated differentiation of $\mathcal{L}\{f(t)\}$ with respect to s under the integral sign.

EXAMPLE 4

$$\mathcal{L}\{t \sin kt\} = -\frac{d}{ds}\left(\frac{k}{s^2 + k^2}\right) = \frac{2ks}{(s^2 + k^2)^2},$$

$$\mathcal{L}\{t^2 \sin kt\} = \frac{d^2}{ds^2}\left(\frac{k}{s^2 + k^2}\right) = -\frac{d}{ds}\left(\frac{2ks}{(s^2 + k^2)^2}\right) = \frac{2k(3s^2 - k^2)}{(s^2 + k^2)^3}.$$

(e) *Integral of Transform*

$$\mathscr{L}\{t^{-1}f(t)\} = \int_s^\infty \bar{f}(\sigma)d\sigma \tag{31}$$

provided the integral converges. The proof will not be given here. The result can be generalized to repeated integrals.

EXAMPLE 5

$$\mathscr{L}\left\{\frac{\sin kt}{t}\right\} = \int_s^\infty \frac{k}{\sigma^2 + k^2}d\sigma = \left[\tan^{-1}\frac{\sigma}{k}\right]_s^\infty = \frac{\pi}{2} - \tan^{-1}\frac{s}{k} = \tan^{-1}\frac{k}{s} .$$

(f) *Periodic Functions*

If $f(t + nT) = f(t)$ for all integers n, then

$$\mathscr{L}\{f(t)\} = \frac{1}{1 - e^{-Ts}} \int_0^T e^{-su}f(u)du. \tag{32}$$

Proof: Write $\mathscr{L}\{f(t)\}$ as an infinite sum of integrals over intervals of length T and substitute in each integral $u = t - nT$, $n = 0, 1, 2, 3, \ldots$. The·

$$\mathscr{L}\{f(t)\} = \sum_{n=0}^\infty \int_{nT}^{(n+1)T} e^{-st}f(t)dt = \sum_{n=0}^\infty \int_0^T e^{-s(u+nT)}f(u + nT)du$$

$$= \sum_{n=0}^\infty e^{-snT} \int_0^T e^{-su}f(u)du.$$

This is a geometric series with first term $\int_0^T e^{-su}f(u)du$ and common ratio e^{-sT} so that its sum is the right side of equation (32).

EXAMPLE 6

The *square wave* function $f(t)$ (Fig. 3.5), such that

$$f(t) = \begin{cases} 1, & 2n \leqslant t < 2n + 1, \\ -1, & 2n + 1 \leqslant t < 2n + 2, \end{cases} \quad n = 0, 1, 2, 3, \ldots ,$$

has period $T = 2$ and so from equation (32)

$$\mathscr{L}\{f(t)\} = \frac{1}{1 - e^{-2s}} \left\{ \int_0^1 e^{-st} dt - \int_1^2 e^{-st} dt \right\}$$

$$= \frac{1}{1 - e^{-2s}} \left\{ \frac{1 - e^{-s}}{s} - \frac{e^{-s} - e^{-2s}}{s} \right\}$$

$$= \frac{(1 - e^{-s})^2}{s(1 - e^{-s})(1 + e^{-s})} = \frac{1 - e^{-s}}{s(1 + e^{-s})} = \frac{e^{\frac{1}{2}s} - e^{-\frac{1}{2}s}}{s(e^{\frac{1}{2}s} + e^{-\frac{1}{2}s})}$$

$$= \frac{\tanh \frac{1}{2}s}{s} .$$

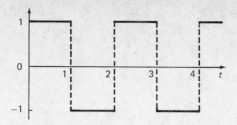

Fig. 3.5   Square wave function

(g) *Convolution Property*

If $\bar{f}(s) = \mathscr{L}\{f(t)\}$ and $\bar{g}(s) = \mathscr{L}\{g(t)\}$, then

$$\mathscr{L}\left\{\int_0^t f(\tau)g(t-\tau)\mathrm{d}\tau\right\} = \bar{f}(s)\bar{g}(s). \tag{33}$$

The proof of this result is given as example 9 of §5.2. We use the notation

$$f(t) * g(t) = \int_0^t f(\tau)g(t-\tau)\mathrm{d}\tau$$

and call this function of t the *convolution* of $f(t)$ and $g(t)$. By the change of variable $\tau' = t - \tau$, the convolution becomes

$$f(t) * g(t) = \int_0^t g(\tau')f(t-\tau')\mathrm{d}\tau' = g(t) * f(t).$$

As will be seen in §3.7, convolutions have important physical significance in some contexts.

EXAMPLE 7

$$\mathscr{L}^{-1}\left\{\frac{1}{s^2}\frac{k}{s^2+k^2}\right\} = \mathscr{L}^{-1}\left\{\frac{1}{s^2}\right\} * \mathscr{L}^{-1}\left\{\frac{k}{s^2+k^2}\right\} = \int_0^t \tau \sin\{k(t-\tau)\}\,\mathrm{d}\tau$$

$$= \frac{1}{k}\left[\tau\cos\{k(t-\tau)\}\right]_0^t - \frac{1}{k}\int_0^t \cos\{k(t-\tau)\}\,\mathrm{d}\tau$$

$$= \frac{1}{k^2}(kt - \sin kt).$$

Exercises

1. Given that $\mathscr{L}\{t^{-1}\sin t\} = \tan^{-1}(s^{-1})$, use properties (a) and (b) to find the Laplace transforms of, respectively,

    (a) $e^{-2t}t^{-1}\sin t$,   (b) $-(t-\tfrac{1}{2}\pi)^{-1}\cos t\,H(t-\tfrac{1}{2}\pi)$.

2. Given that $\mathcal{L}^{-1}\{(s^2+1)^{-2}\} = \frac{1}{2}(\sin t - t\cos t)$, use properties (a) and (b) to find the inverse Laplace transforms of, respectively,

(a) $\{(s+1)^2+1\}^{-2}$,   (b) $e^{-\pi s}(s^2+1)^{-2}$.

3. Given that $\mathcal{L}^{-1}\{s^{-n}\} = t^{n-1}/(n-1)!$ use property (c) to show that $\mathcal{L}^{-1}\{s^{-n-1}\} = t^n/n!$

4. Use property (d) to find the transforms of $t\cos 2t$ and $t^2\cos 2t$, given that $\mathcal{L}\{\cos kt\} = s(s^2+k^2)^{-1}$.

5. Use property (e) to show that

$$\mathcal{L}\{t^{-1}(e^{-at} - e^{-bt})\} = \log\frac{s+b}{s+a}$$

and hence find $\mathcal{L}\{t^{-1}\sinh t\}$.

6. Find the Laplace transform of the periodic function with period 1 which equals t when $0 \leqslant t < 1$.

7. Use the convolution property to find

$$\mathcal{L}^{-1}\left\{\frac{s}{(s^2+1)(s^2+4)}\right\}.$$

As a check, take the Laplace transform of your answer.

8. Show that $\mathcal{L}\{f(at)\} = a^{-1}\bar{f}(s/a)$ when $a > 0$ ('Change of scale' property.) Use this result with the data of exercises 1 and 2 to find

(a) $\mathcal{L}\{t^{-1}\sin 3t\}$,   (b) $\mathcal{L}^{-1}\{[(4s+1)^2+1]^{-2}\}$.

3.5 LINEAR ORDINARY DIFFERENTIAL EQUATIONS

Some of the properties described in the previous sections of this chapter are now used in the solution of a number of ordinary differential equations. As shown in §3.2, equations with constant coefficients can be transformed into algebraic equations which may then be solved for the transform of the unknown function. This process is particularly easy if the conditions of the problem are all *initial* conditions. The method is equally applicable to *simultaneous* equations with constant coefficients. For the possibility of applying the Laplace transform to certain equations with variable coefficients, see problem 11.

(a) Equations with Constant Coefficients

Consider the general second-order equation

$$y''(t) + ay'(t) + by(t) = f(t) \tag{34}$$

with initial conditions

$$y(0) = y_0, \quad y'(0) = y_1.$$

This may be transformed with the aid of equations (4) and (5) with the result

$$s^2 \bar{y} - sy_0 - y_1 + a(s\bar{y} - y_0) + b\bar{y} = \bar{f}(s), \tag{35}$$

where

$$\bar{y}(s) = \int_0^\infty e^{-st} y(t) \, dt, \quad \bar{f}(s) = \int_0^\infty e^{-st} f(t) \, dt.$$

Rearranging equation (35), we have

$$(s^2 + as + b)\bar{y} = \bar{f}(s) + (s + a)y_0 + y_1$$

and hence

$$\bar{y}(s) = \frac{\bar{f}(s) + (s + a)y_0 + y_1}{s^2 + as + b}. \tag{36}$$

Notice the connexion between the denominator on the right side of this equation and the auxiliary equation used in Chapter 1 in the solution of an equation with constant coefficients. Upon inversion the term involving $\bar{f}(s)$ leads to a *particular integral* of the equation, while the terms involving y_0 and y_1 give the *complementary function*. The procedure with higher order equations is the same in principle.

EXAMPLE 1
Solve

$$\frac{d^2 y}{dt^2} + \frac{dy}{dt} - 2y = 9e^t, \quad y(0) = 3, \quad y'(0) = 0.$$

The transformed equation is

$$s^2 \bar{y} - 3s + s\bar{y} - 3 - 2\bar{y} = \frac{9}{s - 1},$$

from which

$$(s^2 + s - 2)\bar{y} = 3(s + 1) + \frac{9}{s - 1},$$

and hence

$$\bar{y} = \frac{3(s^2 - 1) + 9}{(s - 1)^2 (s + 2)} = \frac{3}{(s - 1)^2} + \frac{1}{s - 1} + \frac{2}{s + 2}.$$

The first term is inverted with the aid of the *first shift property*, equation (25), and the solution is

$$y = (3t + 1)e^t + 2e^{-2t}.$$

EXAMPLE 2
Solve

$$\frac{d^2y}{dt^2} + y = f(t), \quad t \geqslant 0, \quad y(0) = y\left(\frac{3\pi}{2}\right) = 1$$

where $f(t)$ is the function (see Fig. 3.6) given by

$$f(t) = \begin{cases} \sin t, & 0 \leqslant t \leqslant \pi, \\ 0, & t > \pi. \end{cases}$$

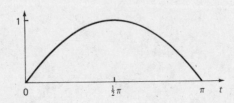

Fig. 3.6   Sine pulse, given as $f(t)$ in example 2

The condition at $t = 3\pi/2$ cannot be used yet and it is necessary to proceed with an unknown value for $y'(0)$, say y_1. In order to use the second shift property, as expressed in equation (26), write $f(t)$ in the form

$$f(t) = \sin t \ [1 - H(t - \pi)] = \sin t + \sin(t - \pi) \quad H(t - \pi),$$

and then the transformed equation is

$$s^2\bar{y} - s - y_1 + \bar{y} = \frac{1 + e^{-\pi s}}{s^2 + 1},$$

so that

$$\bar{y} = \frac{1}{(s^2 + 1)^2} + \frac{e^{-\pi s}}{(s^2 + 1)^2} + \frac{s}{s^2 + 1} + \frac{y_1}{s^2 + 1}. \tag{37}$$

Now

$$\mathscr{L}^{-1}\left\{\frac{1}{s^2 + 1}\right\} = \sin t$$

and so, by the convolution property, equation (33),

$$\mathscr{L}^{-1}\left\{\frac{1}{(s^2 + 1)^2}\right\} = \sin t * \sin t = \int_0^t \sin \tau \sin(t - \tau)d\tau$$

$$= \frac{1}{2}\int_0^t \{\cos(2\tau - t) - \cos t\}d\tau = \frac{1}{2}(\sin t - t \cos t). \tag{38}$$

With the aid of this result and of the second shift property, equation (37) can be inverted term by term to give the result

$$y(t) = \tfrac{1}{2}(\sin t - t \cos t) + \tfrac{1}{2}[\sin(t - \pi) - (t - \pi)\cos(t - \pi)] H(t - \pi)$$

$$+ \cos t + y_1 \sin t.$$

Use of the condition $y(3\pi/2) = 1$ shows that $y_1 = -1$. The solution of the problem may then be put in the form

$$y(t) = \begin{cases} (1 - \tfrac{1}{2}t)\cos t - \tfrac{1}{2} \sin t, & 0 \le t \le \pi, \\ (1 - \pi/2)\cos t - \sin t, & t \ge \pi. \end{cases}$$

EXAMPLE 3
Solve

$$\frac{d^3y}{dt^3} - \frac{d^2y}{dt^2} + \frac{dy}{dt} - y = \cos t + \sin t - 1,$$

$$y(0) = y''(0) = 0, \quad y'(0) = 1.$$

The transform of this equation (with the initial conditions) is

$$s^3\bar{y} - s - (s^2\bar{y} - 1) + s\bar{y} - \bar{y} = \frac{s+1}{s^2+1} - \frac{1}{s},$$

from which

$$(s^3 - s^2 + s - 1)\bar{y} = \frac{s+1}{s^2+1} - \frac{1}{s} + s - 1,$$

so that

$$(s^2 + 1)(s - 1)\bar{y} = \frac{s-1}{s(s^2+1)} + s - 1,$$

and

$$\bar{y} = \frac{1}{s(s^2+1)^2} + \frac{1}{s^2+1}.$$

The inverse of the first term on the right may be calculated from equation (38), with the aid of property (c) as given by equation (28), as follows:

$$\mathcal{L}^{-1}\left\{ \frac{1}{s(s^2+1)^2} \right\} = \int_0^t \tfrac{1}{2}(\sin \tau - \tau \cos \tau) d\tau$$

$$= -[\cos \tau + \tfrac{1}{2}\tau \sin \tau]_0^t = 1 - \cos t - \tfrac{1}{2}t \sin t.$$

The complete solution is then

$$y = 1 - \cos t + (1 - \tfrac{1}{2}t)\sin t.$$

(b) *Simultaneous Equations with Constant Coefficients*

Application of the Laplace transform yields algebraic equations which are solved for
the transformed variables. The process is usually much easier than that of direct
elimination of unknowns from the original equations.

EXAMPLE 4

$$\frac{dy}{dt} - \frac{dz}{dt} - 2y + 2z = 1 - 2t, \qquad \frac{d^2y}{dt^2} + 2\frac{dz}{dt} + y = 0,$$

$$y(0) = y'(0) = z(0) = 0.$$

The transformed equations are

$$(s-2)\bar{y} - (s-2)\bar{z} = \frac{1}{s} - \frac{2}{s^2}, \tag{39}$$

$$(s^2 + 1)\bar{y} + 2s\bar{z} = 0, \tag{40}$$

from which $\bar{z}$ is easily eliminated to yield

$$\bar{y} = \frac{2}{s(s+1)^2}.$$

Now $\mathcal{L}^{-1}\{s^{-2}\} = t$ and so, by the first shift property, equation (25),

$$\mathcal{L}^{-1}\{(s+1)^{-2}\} = te^{-t}.$$

Then, by property (c), equation (28),

$$y = 2\int_0^t \tau e^{-\tau} \, d\tau = 2 - 2e^{-t}(1+t).$$

From equation (40),

$$\bar{z} = -\frac{s^2+1}{2s}\bar{y} = -\frac{s^2+1}{s^2(s+1)^2} = \frac{2}{s(s+1)^2} - \frac{1}{s^2} = \bar{y} - \frac{1}{s^2}$$

and so $z = 2 - 2e^{-t}(1+t) - t$. It is easy to check that the solution satisfies the
equations and initial conditions.

Exercises

1. Solve the following differential equations, under the stated conditions:

   (a) $\dfrac{d^2y}{dt^2} - 2a\dfrac{dy}{dt} + (a^2 + b^2)y = 0, \quad y(0) = 0, \quad y'(0) = 1.$

   (b) $\dfrac{d^2y}{dt^2} + 2\dfrac{dy}{dt} + 2y = 5 \sin t, \quad y(0) = y'(0) = 0.$

(c) $\dfrac{d^3y}{dt^3} + 2\dfrac{d^2y}{dt^2} - 4\dfrac{dy}{dt} - 8y = 8e^{2t}, \quad y''(0) = 0, \quad y'(0) = 1, \quad y(0) = 0.$

(d) $\dfrac{d^2y}{dt^2} + 3\dfrac{dy}{dt} + 2y = te^{-2t}, \quad y(0) = y(1) = 0.$

(e) $\dfrac{d^2y}{dt^2} + 4y = \cos t\,\{1 - H(t - \tfrac{1}{2}\pi)\}, \quad y(0) = y'(0) = 0.$

2. Solve the simultaneous differential equations

$$\frac{d^2x}{dt^2} + 8x + 2y = 24\cos 4t, \qquad \frac{d^2y}{dt^2} + 2x + 5y = 0,$$

where $x = y = \dfrac{dx}{dt} = \dfrac{dy}{dt} = 0$ at $t = 0$.

3. Solve the simultaneous differential equations

$$4\frac{d^2y}{dt^2} = x - \frac{d^2x}{dt^2}, \qquad x = \frac{d^2y}{dt^2} - y,$$

where $x(0) = x'(0) = y'(0) = 0$ and $y(0) = 1$.

4. Use the Laplace transform method to solve the equations given in exercise 2 of §1.7.

3.6 DIFFERENCE AND INTEGRAL EQUATIONS

The Laplace transform is useful in solving certain kinds of linear difference and integral equations, as shown below. The inclusion in such equations of terms involving derivatives of the unknown function, to form *differential-difference* equations and *integro-differential* equations, adds no major difficulties (see exercises 4 and 6).

(a) *Linear Difference Equations with Constant Coefficients*

A difference equation relates the values of an unknown function $y(t)$ at several equally spaced values of t and may be either inhomogeneous or homogeneous (that is, either with or without a term not involving y). The value of $y(t)$ over an initial interval $-\infty < t < t_0$ ($t_0 \geqslant 0$) must be prescribed.

EXAMPLE 1

Given that $y(t) = 0$ for $t \leqslant 0$, solve the inhomogeneous equation

$$3y(t) - 5y(t - 1) + 2y(t - 2) = t^2 H(t). \tag{41}$$

By the second shift property, the transform of this equation is

$$3\bar{y}(s) - 5e^{-s}\bar{y}(s) + 2e^{-2s}\bar{y}(s) = 2s^{-3},$$

and hence

$$\bar{y}(s) = \frac{2s^{-3}}{3 - 5e^{-s} + 2e^{-2s}}.$$

To invert this expression, we observe that its denominator is quadratic in e^{-s} and so can be written in factorized form as $(1 - e^{-s})(3 - 2e^{-s})$. Then, by using the technique of partial fractions we express $\bar{y}(s)$ as a sum of two terms, each of which can be expanded as a geometric series, as follows.

$$\bar{y}(s) = \frac{2}{s^3}\left\{ \frac{1}{1 - e^{-s}} - \frac{2}{3}\frac{1}{1 - \frac{2}{3}e^{-s}} \right\}$$

$$= \frac{2}{s^3}\left\{ \sum_{n=0}^{\infty} (e^{-s})^n - \frac{2}{3}\sum_{n=0}^{\infty} (\frac{2}{3}e^{-s})^n \right\}$$

$$= \frac{2}{s^3} \sum_{n=0}^{\infty} \left\{ 1 - (\frac{2}{3})^{n+1} \right\} e^{-ns}$$

when $e^{-s} < 1$, that is, when $s > 0$.

Inversion by the second shift formula gives the solution

$$y(t) = \sum_{n=0}^{\infty} \left\{ 1 - (\frac{2}{3})^{n+1} \right\} (t - n)^2 H(t - n). \tag{42}$$

Notice that the step functions ensure that, for any finite t, the series has only a *finite* number of terms. Figure 3.7 shows how successive terms take effect at $t = 1, 2, 3, \ldots$.

Equation (41) is typical of many equations whose solution involves the inversion of terms of the form

$$\bar{f}(s) = \frac{\bar{g}(s)}{1 - \bar{r}(s)e^{-as}}, \quad a > 0. \tag{43}$$

For s such that $\bar{r}(s) < e^{as}$, $\bar{f}(s)$ is the sum of the series

$$\bar{f}(s) = \sum_{n=0}^{\infty} \bar{g}(s)[\bar{r}(s)]^n e^{-nas}.$$

Then, if the inverse functions

$$f_n(t) \equiv \mathscr{L}^{-1}\{\bar{g}(s)[\bar{r}(s)]^n\}$$

can be found, the inverse of equation (43) is, by the second shift property,

$$f(t) = \sum_{n=0}^{\infty} a_n(t - na) H(t - na).$$

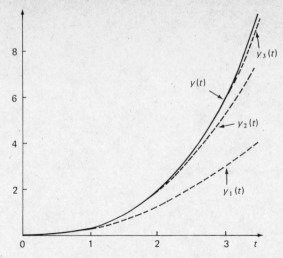

Fig. 3.7 Graph of $y(t)$ given by equation (42); $y_r(t)$ denotes the sum of the first r terms

With the aid of the *entier function* $[u]$, which denotes the greatest integer not exceeding u, the result can be written more compactly as

$$f(t) = \sum_{n=0}^{[t/a]} f_n(t - na).$$

Thus equation (42) can be written

$$y(t) = \sum_{n=0}^{[t]} \left\{ 1 - \left(\frac{2}{3}\right)^{n+1} \right\} (t - n)^2.$$

In the solution of *homogeneous* equations, the terms to be inverted are of the form

$$\bar{f}(s) = \frac{1 - e^{-as}}{s(1 - re^{-as})}$$

where a is a positive constant and r is a non-zero constant. The above method is then modified as follows. For $s > a^{-1} \log r$, $\bar{f}(s)$ can be expanded as

$$\bar{f}(s) = \frac{1 - e^{-as}}{s} \sum_{n=0}^{\infty} (re^{-as})^n = \sum_{n=0}^{\infty} \frac{r^n}{s} (e^{-nas} - e^{-(n+1)as}),$$

and so, by the second shift property,

$$f(t) = \sum_{n=0}^{\infty} r^n \{ H(t - na) - H(t - na - a) \}.$$

That is,

$$f(t) = r^n \qquad \text{for } n \leqslant t/a < n + 1, \quad n = 0, 1, 2, \ldots$$

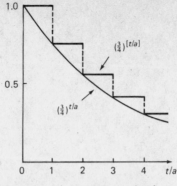

Fig. 3.8   Graph of $(\frac{3}{4})^{\lfloor t/a \rfloor}$

or, in terms of the entire function,

$$f(t) = \mathscr{L}^{-1}\left\{\frac{1 - e^{-as}}{s(1 - re^{-as})}\right\} = r^{\lfloor t/a \rfloor}, \tag{44}$$

which, for $r = \frac{3}{4}$, has the behaviour shown in Fig. 3.8. When $r = -1$, $f(t)$ is the square wave function shown in Fig. 3.5 with $a = 1$.

EXAMPLE 2
Express the following *recurrence relation* as a difference equation and find its solution:

$$6a_n = a_{n+1} + a_{n+2}, \quad a_0 = 1, \quad a_1 = 0.$$

A relation of this kind, connecting a sequence of constants $a_0, a_1, a_2, \ldots$, may be expressed as a difference equation by putting

$$f(t) = a_n, \quad \text{for } n \leqslant t < n + 1, \quad n = 0, 1, 2, \ldots,$$

with the result

$$f(t + 2) + f(t + 1) - 6f(t) = 0, \quad \text{for } t \geqslant 0, \tag{45}$$

$$f(t) = \begin{cases} 1, & 0 \leqslant t < 1, \\ 0, & 1 \leqslant t < 2. \end{cases}$$

The transforms of $f(t + 2)$ and $f(t + 1)$ are found in terms of $\bar{f}(s)$ by using the values of $f(t)$ in the initial interval $0 \leqslant t < 2$ as follows:

$$\mathscr{L}\{f(t + 1)\} = \int_0^\infty e^{-st} f(t + 1) \, dt = \int_1^\infty e^{-s(u-1)} f(u) \, du$$

$$= e^s\left[\bar{f}(s) - \int_0^1 e^{-su} f(u) \, du\right]$$

$$= e^s[\bar{f}(s) + s^{-1}(e^{-s} - 1)],$$

since $f(u) = 1$ for $0 \leqslant u < 1$, and

$$\mathscr{L}\{f(t+2)\} = \int_0^\infty e^{-st}f(t+2)dt = \int_2^\infty e^{-s(u-2)}f(u)du$$

$$= e^{2s}\left[\overline{f}(s) - \int_0^1 e^{-su}f(u)du - \int_1^2 e^{-su}f(u)du\right]$$

$$= e^{2s}[\overline{f}(s) + s^{-1}(e^{-s} - 1)].$$

Then the transform of equation (45) is

$$(e^{2s} + e^s - 6)\overline{f}(s) + s^{-1}(e^{2s} + e^s)(e^{-s} - 1) = 0,$$

and hence

$$\overline{f}(s) = \frac{(e^s + 1)(e^s - 1)}{s(e^{2s} + e^s - 6)}.$$

Then, by the method of partial fractions,

$$\overline{f}(s) = \frac{e^s - 1}{5s}\left\{\frac{3}{e^s - 2} + \frac{2}{e^s + 3}\right\} = \frac{1 - e^{-s}}{5s}\left\{\frac{3}{1 - 2e^{-s}} + \frac{2}{1 + 3e^{-s}}\right\}$$

and so, by equation (44),

$$f(t) = \tfrac{1}{5}\{3.2^{[t]} + 2(-3)^{[t]}\}$$

or

$$a_n = \tfrac{1}{5}\{3.2^n + 2(-3)^n\}.$$

It is easy to check that this is a solution of the problem.

Recurrence relations can be solved by means of the Z-transform, described by Jury [2], but all problems solved by the Z-transform respond equally well to the Laplace transform, as pointed out by Sneddon [3].

(b) *Integral Equations*

Equations of the form

$$af(t) = bg(t) + \int_0^t h(t-u)f(u)du, \quad t \geqslant 0, \tag{46}$$

where a may be zero and the functions $g(t)$ and $h(t)$ are known, are called *Volterra integral equations* and occur in the formulation of some kinds of physical problems. By using the convolution property, equation (33), we find that the Laplace transform of equation (46) is

$$a\overline{f}(s) = b\overline{g}(s) + \overline{h}(s)\,\overline{f}(s),$$

so that

$$\bar{f}(s) = \frac{b\bar{g}(s)}{a - \bar{h}(s)}$$

and

$$f(t) = \mathcal{L}^{-1}\left\{\frac{b\bar{g}(s)}{a - \bar{h}(s)}\right\}. \tag{47}$$

EXAMPLE 3
Solve the equation

$$y(t) = 6t + \int_0^t y(t-u)\sin u \, du, \qquad t \geqslant 0.$$

The transformed equation is

$$\bar{y} = \frac{6}{s^2} + \frac{\bar{y}}{s^2 + 1}$$

or

$$\bar{y} = \frac{6(s^2 + 1)}{s^4} = 6\left(\frac{1}{s^2} + \frac{1}{s^4}\right).$$

Hence

$$y = 6t + t^3.$$

This function satisfies the equation for $t < 0$ as well as for $t \geqslant 0$.

Exercises

1. Solve the following difference equations for $y(t)$ subject to the condition that $y(t) = 0$ for $t < 0$:

    (a) $3y(t) - 4y(t-1) + y(t-2) = t\,H(t),$
    (b) $2y(t) - y(t-1) - 6y(t-2) = 7\sin t\, H(t),$
    (c) $y(t) + 3y(t-1) - 4y(t-3) = H(t),$
    (d) $y(t) + 2y(t-1) + 2y(t-2) = H(t).$
    (Hint: Write $(1 \pm i)^n = 2^{n/2}\exp(\pm in\pi/4)$.)

2. Express each of the following recurrence relations as a difference equation and hence find the form of the general term:

    (a) $a_{n+2} + 2a_{n+1} - 3a_n = 0$ where $a_0 = 0,$ $a_1 = 1,$
    (b) $2a_{n+2} + 5a_{n+1} - 3a_n = 0$ where $a_0 = 3,$ $a_1 = -2.$

3. Find the function $f(t)$ such that

$$f(t+2) + f(t+1) - 2f(t) = \cosh t\, H(t)$$

and

$$f(t) = \begin{cases} 1, & 0 \leqslant t < 1, \\ 0, & 1 \leqslant t < 2. \end{cases}$$

4. Solve the differential-difference equation

$$y'(t) - 3y(t-1) = t\, H(t)$$

subject to the condition $y(t) = 0$ for $t \leqslant 0$.

5. Find the function $y(t)$ such that, for $t \geqslant 0$

$$y(t) + \int_0^t y(t-\tau)\,\tau \cos \tau \; d\tau = \sin t.$$

6. Solve the integro-differential equation

$$\frac{dy}{dt} = 3\int_0^t y(t-\tau)\,\cosh \tau \; d\tau$$

for $t \geqslant 0$, given that $y(0) = 1$.

7. Find the two solutions of the equation

$$\int_0^t f(t-u)\,f(u)du = t^3$$

and show that they hold for $t < 0$ as well as $t \geqslant 0$.

3.7 SOME PHYSICAL PROBLEMS

(a) *Forced Vibrations of a Sprung Mass with Damping*

This problem has already been considered in §1.8; treatment here by Laplace transforms will allow comparison of the methods. When the mass m shown in Fig. 1.3 is subjected to a downward force $F(t)$, its displacement satisfies equation (60) of §1.8, which, with α and ω^2 as defined by equation (64) of §1.8 and with $F(t) = mf(t)$, becomes

$$\frac{d^2y}{dt^2} + 2\alpha\frac{dy}{dt} + \omega^2 y = f(t). \tag{48}$$

This equation is of the same form as equation (34) and so, by reference to equation (36), we see that the solution for $\bar{y}(s)$ is

$$\bar{y}(s) = \frac{\bar{f}(s) + (s+2\alpha)y_0 + v_0}{(s+\alpha)^2 + \omega^2 - \alpha^2} \tag{49}$$

where $y_0 = y(0)$ and $v_0 = y'(0)$.

The displacement due to the imposed force $F(t)$ (as distinct from that due to non-zero initial conditions y_0 and v_0) is found by inverting equation (49) with $y_0 = v_0 = 0$. If $\bar{f}(s) = m^{-1}\bar{F}(s)$ and

$$\bar{g}(s) = \frac{1}{m\{(s+\alpha)^2 + \omega^2 - \alpha^2\}} \,,$$

then, by the convolution property, equation (33),

$$y(t) = \mathscr{L}^{-1}\{\bar{g}(s)\bar{F}(s)\} = \int_0^t g(\tau)F(t-\tau)\mathrm{d}\tau. \tag{50}$$

The form of $g(t)$ varies according as $\omega^2 - \alpha^2$ is positive, negative or zero. For example, if $\omega^2 - \alpha^2 = \beta^2 > 0$ we find that

$$y(t) = \int_0^t \frac{e^{-\alpha\tau}\sin\beta\tau}{m\beta} F(t-\tau)\mathrm{d}\tau.$$

The physical significance of $g(\tau)$ in equation (50) can be understood if we consider what happens when $F(t)$ is an impulsive force of unit impulse at $t = 0$, represented by $F(t) = \delta(t)$, so that $\bar{F}(s) = 1$. The resulting displacement is called the *impulse response* of the system and is simply $g(t)$. Similar results hold for all linear, time-dependent, non-ageing systems. In general, we may say that the response of such a system to any input is given by the convolution of that input and the impulse response of the system. Further examples and other aspects of such systems are discussed in §3.7 (c) and (d).

(b) *Bending of a Beam*

By the elementary theory of beam-bending, the transverse deflection $y(x)$ at a distance x along a uniform thin beam is governed by the equation

$$EI\frac{\mathrm{d}^4y}{\mathrm{d}x^4} = W(x), \tag{51}$$

where $W(x)$ is the transverse load per unit length, E is the Young's modulus and I is the second moment of area of the beam cross-section about an axis normal to the x and y directions. Let

$$\bar{y}(s) = \int_0^\infty e^{-sx}y(x)\mathrm{d}x, \quad \bar{W}(s) = \int_0^\infty e^{-sx}W(x)\mathrm{d}x$$

and write the conditions at $x = 0$ as

$$y(0) = y_0, \quad y'(0) = y_1, \quad y''(0) = y_2, \quad y'''(0) = y_3.$$

Then the Laplace transform of equation (51) is

$$EI(s^4\bar{y} - y_0s^3 - y_1s^2 - y_2s - y_3) = \bar{W}(s),$$

so that

$$\bar{y}(s) = \frac{\bar{W}(s)}{EIs^4} + \frac{y_0}{s} + \frac{y_1}{s^2} + \frac{y_2}{s^3} + \frac{y_3}{s^4}. \tag{52}$$

In practice, only two of the values y_0, y_1, y_2, y_3 will be known, together with two conditions at the other end, $x = l$, embodying such physical conditions as a *built-in end*, a *simply-supported* (or *hinged*) *end* or a *free end*. Those of the values y_0, y_1, y_2, y_3 which are unspecified have to be left as unknown constants until the final stage of solution, when they are determined by use of the conditions at $x = l$.

EXAMPLE 1

Find the deflection of a beam simply supported at the ends $x = 0, l$, bending under uniformly distributed self-weight M and a *concentrated load P* at $x = \frac{1}{2}l$.

The load function is

$$W(x) = (M/l)H(x) + P\delta(x - \tfrac{1}{2}l),$$

where the Dirac delta function is used to represent the 'point-force' P. The end conditions are $y_0 = y_2 = 0$ and $y(l) = y''(l) = 0$. The transform of $W(x)$ is

$$\bar{W}(s) = \frac{M}{ls} + Pe^{-ls/2}$$

and substitution in equation (52) gives

$$\bar{y}(s) = \frac{1}{EI}\left(\frac{M}{ls^5} + \frac{Pe^{-ls/2}}{s^4}\right) + \frac{y_1}{s^2} + \frac{y_3}{s^4}.$$

This function is inverted, with the aid of the second shift property, equation (26), to give

$$y(x) = \frac{M}{24EIl}x^4 + \frac{P}{6EI}(x - \tfrac{1}{2}l)^3 H(x - \tfrac{1}{2}l) + y_1 x + \frac{y_3}{6}x^3. \tag{53}$$

The second derivative of this is

$$y''(x) = \frac{M}{2EIl}x^2 + \frac{P}{EI}(x - \tfrac{1}{2}l)H(x - \tfrac{1}{2}l) + y_3 x, \tag{54}$$

and the use of the conditions $y(l) = y''(l) = 0$ with equations (53) and (54) yields the values of y_1 and y_3. The final result is, therefore,

$$y(x) = \frac{1}{48EI}\{2Mx^4/l + 8P(x - \tfrac{1}{2}l)^3 H(x - \tfrac{1}{2}l) - 4(M + P)x^3 + (2M + 3P)l^2 x\}.$$

(c) *Mutual Inductance*

Figure 3.9 represents a primary circuit equivalent to a resistance R_1 and an inductance L_1 in series with an impressed voltage $V(t)$, coupled through a mutual inductance M to

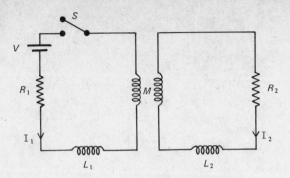

Fig. 3.9   Coupled L, C, R circuits

a secondary circuit equivalent to a resistance R_2 and an inductance L_2. Application of
Kirchhoff's second law to each loop gives the governing equations

$$L_1 \frac{dI_1}{dt} + R_1 I_1 + M \frac{dI_2}{dt} = V, \quad L_2 \frac{dI_2}{dt} + R_2 I_2 + M \frac{dI_1}{dt} = 0. \tag{55}$$

Suppose the switch S is open until $t = 0$, so that $I_1 = I_2 = V = 0$ for $t \leqslant 0$. Then the
Laplace transforms of equations (55) are

$$(L_1 s + R_1)\bar{I}_1 + Ms\bar{I}_2 = \bar{V}, \quad (L_2 s + R_2)\bar{I}_2 + Ms\bar{I}_1 = 0,$$

and $\bar{I}_1$ and $\bar{I}_2$ are easily obtained. In particular, the current induced in the secondary
circuit has the transform

$$\bar{I}_2(s) = \frac{Ms\bar{V}(s)}{M^2 s^2 - (L_1 s + R_1)(L_2 s + R_2)}. \tag{56}$$

If we put

$$\bar{G}(s) = \frac{-Ms}{(L_1 L_2 - M^2)(s + \alpha_1)(s + \alpha_2)}, \tag{57}$$

where

$$\alpha_1, \alpha_2 = \frac{L_1 R_2 + L_2 R_1 \pm \{(L_1 R_2 - L_2 R_1)^2 + 4R_1 R_2 M^2\}^{1/2}}{2(L_1 L_2 - M^2)}, \tag{58}$$

equation (56) may be written

$$\bar{I}_2(s) = \bar{G}(s)\bar{V}(s). \tag{59}$$

The inverse of equation (59) is the convolution

$$I_2(t) = G(t) * V(t) = \int_0^t G(\tau)V(t - \tau)d\tau, \tag{60}$$

in which $G(t)$ is the *impulse response* of the system and is the current in the secondary
circuit caused by a unit impulsive primary voltage $V(t) = \delta(t)$.

Inspection of equation (58) shows that α_1 and α_2 are real and unequal and so, in terms of partial fractions,

$$\bar{G}(s) = \frac{-M}{(L_1 L_2 - M^2)(\alpha_1 - \alpha_2)} \left(\frac{\alpha_1}{s + \alpha_1} - \frac{\alpha_2}{s + \alpha_2} \right),$$

which has the inverse

$$G(t) = - \frac{M}{L_1 L_2 - M^2} \frac{\alpha_1 \exp(-\alpha_1 t) - \alpha_2 \exp(-\alpha_2 t)}{\alpha_1 - \alpha_2}.$$

If $V(t)$ remains finite the behaviour of $I_2(t)$ as $t \to \infty$ will largely depend on the exponential character of $G(t)$, and so it is important to know whether α_1 and α_2 are positive or negative. If we make the realistic assumption that the mutual inductance M is comparatively small, so that $L_1 L_2 - M^2 > 0$, then equation (58) shows that α_1 and α_2 are both positive, and it follows that $I_2(t)$ will remain finite for finite $V(t)$.

It was observed in §3.7(a) that the relationship between input and response of any linear, time-dependent, non-ageing system is expressible by equations such as (50) and (60). In many applications, such as electrical theory, operations research and control theory, the characteristics of the system are often studied by way of the *transform* of the impulse response, here denoted by $\bar{G}(s)$, which is called the *transfer function* of the system.

In the present example the transfer function is given, by equation (59), as $\bar{G}(s) = \bar{I}_2(s)/\bar{V}(s)$. In general the transfer function is equal to $\mathscr{L}\{\text{Response}\}/\mathscr{L}\{\text{Input}\}$.

Of particular importance are the zeros of the denominator of the transfer function. The zeros $-\alpha_1$, $-\alpha_2$ in the denominator in equation (57) led to decaying exponentials in the response, while a complex conjugate pair $\alpha \pm i\beta$ would lead to terms involving $e^{\alpha t} \cos \beta t$ or $e^{\alpha t} \sin \beta t$ (or both). In general, we may say that the system is stable and non-oscillatory if the zeros of the denominator of its transfer function are all *negative*. The inclusion of some complex zeros having negative real parts leads to stable oscillations. If, however, any zeros are positive, or have positive real parts, the system is unstable.

(d) *Viscoelastic Extension of a Rod*

In a viscoelastic material, the strain at any given time t depends not only on the stress at the time, but also on the complete history of stress. The behaviour of a uniform, thin, linearly viscoelastic rod may be characterized by a *creep function* $\phi(t)$ such that the application of a constant longitudinal stress $\sigma = \sigma_0$ from time $t = t_0$ results in the longitudinal strain

$$\epsilon(t) = \sigma_0 \phi(t - t_0) H(t - t_0). \tag{61}$$

If the stress is zero for all $t \leqslant 0$, but varies with time for $t > 0$, the *principle of superposition* allows the deduction of the stress-strain relation

$$\epsilon(t) = \int_0^t \phi(t - \tau) \sigma'(\tau) d\tau. \tag{62}$$

Integration by parts provides the alternative form

$$\epsilon(t) = \phi(0)\sigma(t) + \int_0^t \phi'(t - \tau)\sigma(\tau)d\tau \tag{63}$$

which is valid even if $\sigma(0) \neq 0$ and $\sigma(t)$ has discontinuities in $t > 0$. Equation (62) is of the same form as equations (50) and (60) relating the input and response of a system, in this case $\sigma(t)$ and $\epsilon(t)$, respectively.

It is sometimes convenient to describe a linear time-dependent, non-ageing system by means of its *unit response*, which is defined as the response to unit input $H(t)$. In the viscoelastic rod the unit response is simply the creep function $\phi(t)$, as may be seen from equation (61) or by putting $\sigma(t) = H(t)$ in equation (63). The Laplace transform of either equation (62) or (63), obtained by means of the convolution property, equation (33), takes the simple form

$$\bar{\epsilon}(s) = s\bar{\phi}(s)\bar{\sigma}(s). \tag{64}$$

It follows that the transfer function, given by $\bar{\epsilon}(s)/\bar{\sigma}(s)$, is $s\bar{\phi}(s)$. This result can be written in the general form

Transfer function = $s\mathscr{L}\{\text{Unit response}\}$

and holds for *all* linear, time-dependent, non-ageing systems.

The following example shows how, for two simple creep functions, the Laplace transform facilitates the calculation of the strain response to a sinusoidal input. However, the really substantial advantages of the transform method appear in more complicated situations, for example wave propagation problems.

EXAMPLE 2
Find the strain $\epsilon(t)$ due to a stress $\sigma(t) = Q \sin \omega t$ applied for $t \geqslant 0$ to a rod with stress-strain relation (62) in which (1) $\phi(t) = \phi_0 (1 + \alpha t)$ and (2) $\phi(t) = \phi_\infty (1 - e^{-\gamma t})$.

Substitute $\bar{\sigma}(s) = Q\omega(s^2 + \omega^2)^{-1}$ in equation (64) to obtain

$$\bar{\epsilon}(s) = \frac{Q\omega s\bar{\phi}(s)}{s^2 + \omega^2}. \tag{65}$$

(1) $\phi(t) = \phi_0(1 + \alpha t)$. A material with this creep function is called a *Maxwell solid*. Substitute $\bar{\phi}(s) = \phi_0(s^{-1} + \alpha s^{-2})$ in equation (65):

$$\bar{\epsilon}(s) = \frac{Q\omega\phi_0(1 + \alpha s^{-1})}{s^2 + \omega^2}.$$

The inverse is found, with the aid of equation (29) or by partial fractions, as

$$\epsilon(t) = Q\phi_0 \left\{ \sin \omega t + \frac{\alpha}{\omega}(1 - \cos \omega t) \right\}.$$

(2) $\phi(t) = \phi_\infty (1 - e^{-\gamma t})$. This creep function characterizes the *Voigt solid*.

Substitute in equation (65) the transform

$$\bar{\phi}(s) = \phi_\infty \left(\frac{1}{s} - \frac{1}{s+\gamma} \right) = \frac{\phi_\infty \gamma}{s(s+\gamma)}$$

to obtain

$$\bar{\epsilon}(s) = \frac{Q\phi_\infty \gamma \omega}{(s+\gamma)(s^2 + \omega^2)} = \frac{Q\phi_\infty \gamma \omega}{\gamma^2 + \omega^2} \left(\frac{\gamma - s}{s^2 + \omega^2} + \frac{1}{s+\gamma} \right).$$

Hence

$$\epsilon(t) = \frac{Q\phi_\infty \gamma \omega}{\gamma^2 + \omega^2} \left(\frac{\gamma}{\omega} \sin \omega t - \cos \omega t + e^{-\gamma t} \right).$$

(e) Poissonian Distribution

An alternative approach to that given in § 12.6 for the derivation of the Poissonian distribution shows that, for such a variate, the probability $p_n(t)$ of n events in the interval $(0, t)$ satisfies the set of simultaneous differential equations

$$\frac{dp_n(t)}{dt} = -\lambda\{p_n(t) - p_{n-1}(t)\}, \quad \text{for } n \geqslant 1,$$

$$\frac{dp_0(t)}{dt} = -\lambda p_0(t),$$

(66)

with the initial conditions $p_0(0) = 1, p_n(0) = 0$ for $n \geqslant 1$.

Application of the Laplace transform to equations (66) gives

$$s\bar{p}_n(s) = -\lambda\{\bar{p}_n(s) - \bar{p}_{n-1}(s)\}, \quad n \geqslant 1,$$

$$s\bar{p}_0(s) - 1 = -\lambda \bar{p}_0(s),$$

and hence

$$\bar{p}_n = \frac{\lambda}{s+\lambda} \bar{p}_{n-1}, \quad n \geqslant 1, \qquad \bar{p}_0 = \frac{1}{s+\lambda}.$$

It follows that

$$\bar{p}_n = \frac{\lambda^n}{(s+\lambda)^{n+1}}, \quad n \geqslant 0,$$

and, by the first shift property, equation (25),

$$p_n(t) = \frac{(\lambda t)^n e^{-\lambda t}}{n!}, \quad n > 0,$$

which therefore corresponds to the Poissonian distribution $Po(\lambda t)$ (see p. 475).

Exercises

1. Find the impulse response of the system represented by equation (48) when
(a) $2\alpha = 10$, $\omega^2 = 9$, and (b) $\alpha^2 = \omega^2 = 4$. For the second case calculate the response to
the input functions (1) $F(t) = H(t)$ and (2) $F(t) = \sin 2t\ H(t)$.

2. Solve the rotating shaft problem (exercise 3 of §1.7) by Laplace transform methods
when the ends $x = \pm l$ are (a) simply supported and (b) built-in.

3. A uniform thin beam of unit length is built-in at $x = 0$ and free at $x = 1$. Calculate
its deflection $y(x)$ under its own weight M and a concentrated load P at $x = \frac{2}{3}$.
(Mathematically, the end conditions are $y = dy/dx = 0$ at $x = 0$ and $d^2y/dx^2 = 0$,
$d^3y/dx^3 = 0$ at $x = 1$.)

4. Given that the system indicated by Fig. 3.9 has the impulse response

$$G(t) = -\frac{\gamma}{\alpha_1 - \alpha_2}\{\alpha_1 \exp(-\alpha_1 t) - \alpha_2 \exp(-\alpha_2 t)\},$$

where $\alpha_1, \alpha_2, \gamma$ are all positive, use equation (60) to find the response to the input
$V(t) = \cos \lambda t\ H(t)$.

5. Calculate the strain $\epsilon(t)$ in a thin rod of (1) Maxwell solid, (2) Voigt solid when it is
subjected to the loading cycle

$$\sigma(t) = \begin{cases} 0, & t < 0, \\ \sigma_0 t, & 0 \leqslant t \leqslant T, \\ \sigma_0(2T - t), & T \leqslant t \leqslant 2T, \\ 0, & t > 2T. \end{cases}$$

PROBLEMS

1. By considering

$$\lim_{s \to \infty} \int_0^\infty e^{-st} f'(t)\,dt,$$

where $f'(t)$ is piecewise continuous and of exponential order, show that

$$\lim_{s \to \infty} s\bar{f}(s) = \lim_{t \to 0} f(t).$$

2. Deduce from the properties (c) and (e) of §3.4 that a Laplace transform
$\mathscr{L}\{f(t)\} = \bar{f}(s)$ has the property

$$\mathscr{L}\left\{\int_0^t u^{-1} f(u)\,du\right\} = s^{-1} \int_s^\infty \bar{f}(\sigma)\,d\sigma.$$

3. Show that $\displaystyle\int_0^\infty \bar{f}(s)\,ds = \int_0^\infty t^{-1}f(t)\,dt$ and use this result with that of problem 2 to show that

$$\mathscr{L}\left\{\int_t^\infty u^{-1}f(u)\,du\right\} = s^{-1}\int_0^s \bar{f}(\sigma)\,d\sigma.$$

4. Prove the following extension of property (c) of §3.4:

$$\mathscr{L}\left\{\int_0^t \int_0^t \cdots \int_0^t f(t)(dt)^n\right\} = s^{-n}\bar{f}(s).$$

Use the result to find

(a) $\displaystyle\mathscr{L}^{-1}\left\{\frac{k}{s^2(s^2+k^2)}\right\}$,   (b) $\displaystyle\mathscr{L}^{-1}\left\{\frac{k}{s^3(s^2+k^2)}\right\}$.

5. Find the solution of the equation

$$\frac{d^3x}{dt^3} - 2\frac{d^2x}{dt^2} + \frac{dx}{dt} - 2x = e^{-t}$$

which is bounded as $t \to \infty$ and such that $x = 0$ and $dx/dt = 1$ at $t = 0$.

6. Obtain the result of example 6 of §3.4 by expressing the square wave function in the form

$$f(t) = -1 + 2\sum_{n=0}^\infty \{H(t-2n) - H(t-2n-1)\}$$

and using the second shift property.

7. Use the convolution property to solve the equation

$$\frac{d^2y}{dt^2} + 4y = \sum_{n=0}^\infty H(t-n)$$

with the conditions $y = dy/dt = 0$ at $t = 0$.

8. Solve the differential-difference equation

$$y'(t) - y(t-1) = \sin t\, H(t)$$

when $y(t) = 0$ for $t < 0$ and $y(0) = -1$.

9. Find the function $y(t)$ such that, for $t \geqslant 0$,

$$y(t) + \int_0^t e^{-u}y(t-u)\,du = 1.$$

10. A uniform thin beam $-1 \leqslant x \leqslant 1$, of mass 2, is simply supported at $x = \pm\tfrac{1}{2}$ and deforms under its own weight and a point load of 8 at $x = 0$. Find an

expression for the deflection $y(x)$ of the beam in $0 \leqslant x \leqslant 1$ by using the conditions $dy/dx = 0$ at $x = 0$, $d^2y/dx^2 = d^3y/dx^3 = 0$ at $x = 1$ with equation (51) with $W(x) = 1 - 4\delta(x - \frac{1}{2})$. How much is the point $x = 0$ deflected below the points of support?

11. Use property (e) of §3.4 to show that the transform of the equation

$$ty''(t) + 2y'(t) + 4ty(t) = 0$$

such that $y(0) = 1$ is

$$-(s^2 + 4)\bar{y}'(s) - 1 = 0.$$

Integrate this equation, deducing the constant of integration from the fact that $\bar{y}(s) \to 0$ as $s \to \infty$, and so find $y(t)$.

BIBLIOGRAPHY

[1]   Erdélyi, A., W. Magnus, F. Oberhettinger and F. G. Tricomi, *Tables of Integral Transforms, Vol. 1*, McGraw-Hill, New York (1954).

[2]   Jury, E. I., *Theory and Application of the Z-transform*, Wiley, New York (1964).

[3]   Sneddon, I. N., *The Use of Integral Transforms*, McGraw-Hill, New York (1972).

CHAPTER 4

Partial Differentiation, with Applications

4.1 BASIC RESULTS

Introduction

In some engineering problems the quantity of most interest has a value depending on the values of many other quantities. In such situations the first quantity may be expressed mathematically as a *function of many variables*. A familiar example of a function of three variables is the formula $V = xyz$ for the volume V of a rectangular box of length x, breadth y and height z. By considering the *partial derivatives* of the function $f(x, y, z) \equiv xyz$ typical questions which may be answered are:

What is the error in V caused by small measurement errors in x, y and z?

What is the maximum volume V possible when some *constraint* is imposed, such as specification of the value $2(yz + zx + xy)$ of the surface area?

Other uses of partial derivatives occur in the analysis of spatial variations and time rates of changes of familiar physical quantities such as pressure, temperature, magnetic field, etc. These considerations are the key to the vector analysis of Chapter 6, and lead naturally to the partial differential equations of Chapter 7.

Partial Derivatives

If $g(x)$ is a sufficiently smooth function of a single real variable x, its derivative is denoted by dg/dx or $g'(x)$ and is formally defined as

$$\frac{dg}{dx} = g'(x) = \lim_{\delta x \to 0} \frac{g(x + \delta x) - g(x)}{\delta x}.$$

It expresses the rate at which the value of g varies with x. However, a function $f(x, y)$ of two real variables x and y has a value which varies when either x varies alone, or y varies alone, or both x and y vary simultaneously. This is easily seen if x and y are taken as cartesian coordinates in a plane and a surface is envisaged with elevation $z = f(x, y)$ above this, as in Fig. 4.1. Then, if P is the point of this surface having coordinates (x, y, z), the rate of change of f with x when y is held constant measures the slope at P of the curve C_1 in which the plane $y = $ constant meets the surface $z = f(x, y)$. This is the derivative of $f(x, y)$ with respect to x when y is treated as a constant, and is called the *partial derivative of f with respect to x*.

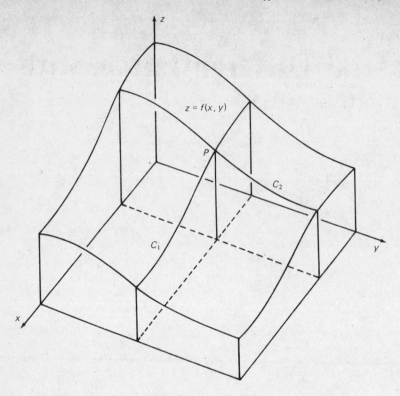

Fig. 4.1   The curves C_1 and C_2 of constant y and x respectively on the surface $z = f(x, y)$

DEFINITION   If the limit

$$\lim_{\delta x \to 0} \frac{f(x + \delta x, y) - f(x, y)}{\delta x}$$

exists, it is called the *partial derivative* of the function f with respect to x. It may be denoted by any of the alternatives

$$\frac{\partial f}{\partial x}, \quad f_x(x, y), \quad f_x \quad \text{or} \quad f_{,x}.$$

Similarly, the partial derivative of f with respect to y may be written as

$$\frac{\partial f}{\partial y} = f_y(x, y) = f_y = f_{,y} \equiv \lim_{\delta y \to 0} \frac{f(x, y + \delta y) - f(x, y)}{\delta y},$$

at values of (x, y) for which the limit exists.

The partial derivative $f_y(x, y)$ measures the slope at the point P of the curve C_2 in which the plane $x = \text{constant}$ meets the surface $z = f(x, y)$. Like all derivatives it is a limit, not a ratio, and so it should be remembered that neither ∂f, nor ∂x nor ∂y has any meaning in isolation.

The notations $f_x(x, y)$ and $f_y(x, y)$ emphasize that the value of each partial derivative may vary with x and y. Just as the ordinary derivative $g'(x)$ of $g(x)$ is a function of x, the partial derivatives f_x and f_y are functions of both x and y. To determine these functions it is not normally necessary to undertake any formal limiting process. Indeed, $f_x(x, y)$ may be obtained as the derivative of $f(x, y)$ with respect to x, when y is regarded as a constant parameter. Moreover the rules

$$\frac{\partial}{\partial x}(u + v) = \frac{\partial u}{\partial x} + \frac{\partial v}{\partial x}, \qquad \frac{\partial}{\partial x}(uv) = u\frac{\partial v}{\partial x} + v\frac{\partial u}{\partial x}$$

for partial differentiation of sums and products follow from the definition, and are direct generalizations of the corresponding rules for ordinary derivatives.

EXAMPLE 1
Find $f_x(x, y)$ and $f_y(x, y)$, when $f(x, y) = x^2y + y^3 \sin x$.

Treating y as a constant, and differentiating $f(x, y)$ with respect to x gives $\frac{\partial f}{\partial x} \equiv f_x(x, y) = 2xy + y^3 \cos x$. Likewise $\frac{\partial f}{\partial y} \equiv f_y(x, y) = x^2 + 3y^2 \sin x$. These quantities exist for all x and y, so that $f(x, y)$ possesses partial derivatives f_x and f_y everywhere.

In a more complicated example it may be convenient to express $f(x, y)$ as some function $\phi(u)$ of an intermediate function $u(x, y)$, so that $f(x, y) = \phi(u)$ where $u = u(x, y)$. Then it may be seen that

$$\frac{\partial f}{\partial x} = \frac{\partial}{\partial x}[\phi(u)] = \frac{d\phi}{du}\frac{\partial u}{\partial x} \quad \text{and} \quad \frac{\partial f}{\partial y} = \frac{\partial}{\partial y}[\phi(u)] = \frac{d\phi}{du}\frac{\partial u}{\partial y}$$

are generalizations of the formula for the ordinary derivative of a function of a function.

EXAMPLE 2
Find $f_x(x, y)$ and $f_y(x, y)$, for $f(x, y) = \log(x^2 + y^2)^{1/2}$.

Let $u(x, y) = x^2 + y^2$, so that $f(x, y) = \log u^{1/2} = \frac{1}{2}\log u \equiv \phi(u)$. Then, since $u_x = 2x, u_y = 2y$ and $\frac{d\phi}{du} = \frac{1}{2u} = \frac{1}{2}(x^2 + y^2)^{-1}$, it is found that

$$\frac{\partial f}{\partial x} = \frac{\frac{1}{2}}{x^2 + y^2}2x = \frac{x}{x^2 + y^2} \quad \text{and} \quad \frac{\partial f}{\partial y} = \frac{\frac{1}{2}}{x^2 + y^2}2y = \frac{y}{x^2 + y^2}.$$

In this example, f_x and f_y exist everywhere except at $x = 0, y = 0$. Thus $f(x, y)$ is said to possess partial derivatives f_x and f_y everywhere except at the origin of the x, y plane.

Partial Derivatives of Higher Order

It is often possible to differentiate the partial derivatives f_x and f_y of a function $f(x,y)$ to form *second-order partial derivatives*. This is an example of the process of *repeated partial differentiation*.

DEFINITION   If the two *first-order partial derivatives* f_x and f_y of a function $f(x, y)$ themselves possess partial derivatives with respect to x and y, then $f(x, y)$ is said to have the *second-order partial derivatives*

$$f_{xx} = \frac{\partial^2 f}{\partial x^2} = \frac{\partial}{\partial x}(f_x), \qquad f_{xy} = \frac{\partial^2 f}{\partial y \partial x} = \frac{\partial}{\partial y}(f_x),$$

$$f_{yx} = \frac{\partial^2 f}{\partial x \partial y} = \frac{\partial}{\partial x}(f_y), \qquad f_{yy} = \frac{\partial^2 f}{\partial y^2} = \frac{\partial}{\partial y}(f_y).$$

EXAMPLE 3

Find the four second-order partial derivatives of $f(x, y) = \log(x^2 + y^2)^{1/2}$, wherever they exist.

Differentiation of the expressions for f_x and f_y in example 2 leads to

$$f_{xx} = \frac{\partial}{\partial x}\left(\frac{x}{x^2 + y^2}\right) = \frac{1}{x^2 + y^2} - \frac{2x^2}{(x^2 + y^2)^2} = \frac{y^2 - x^2}{(x^2 + y^2)^2},$$

$$f_{xy} = \frac{\partial}{\partial y}\left(\frac{x}{x^2 + y^2}\right) = -\frac{2xy}{(x^2 + y^2)^2},$$

and similarly $\quad f_{yx} = \dfrac{-2yx}{(x^2 + y^2)^2} \quad$ and $\quad f_{yy} = \dfrac{x^2 - y^2}{(x^2 + y^2)^2}.$

Again each partial derivative exists everywhere except at $x = 0, y = 0$.

It may be noted that in example 3 the two *mixed partial derivatives* f_{xy} and f_{yx} are equal. This suggests that it may be possible to equate f_{xy} and f_{yx} whenever they both exist. Although for most functions this is true, the following example shows the existence of functions for which $f_{xy} \neq f_{yx}$.

EXAMPLE 4

Consider the function $f(x, y)$ defined by

$$f(x, y) = xy\,\frac{x^2 - y^2}{x^2 + y^2} \quad \text{for } (x, y) \neq (0, 0), \text{ with } f(0, 0) = 0.$$

This has partial derivatives $f_x(0, y) = -y$ and $f_y(x, 0) = x$ defined at all points of the y and x axes respectively. Consequently, at the origin $(0, 0)$ the mixed partial derivatives have the distinct values $f_{xy}(0, 0) = -1$ and $f_{yx}(0, 0) = 1$.

This difference arises because the functions $f_{xy}(x, y)$ and $f_{yx}(x, y)$ are not continuous at the origin, and the quantities $f_{xy}(0, 0)$ and $f_{yx}(0, 0)$ involve limits obtained by approaching the origin from different directions. Such a phenomenon cannot arise at a point (x, y) at which f_{xy} and f_{yx} are both *continuous*.

DEFINITION   A function $f(x, y)$ is said to possess the *limit* f_0 at the point (x_0, y_0) if for any choice of positive number ϵ it is possible to make

$|f(x,y) - f_0| < \epsilon$ purely by restricting (x,y) to some disc

$$[(x - x_0)^2 + (y - y_0)^2]^{1/2} < \delta = \delta(\epsilon),$$

centred at (x_0, y_0) and having suitably small radius δ.

The limit is written as

$$\lim_{\substack{x \to x_0 \\ y \to y_0}} f(x,y) = f_0.$$

It exists only if $f(x,y)$ tends to f_0 independently of the manner in which (x,y) approaches (x_0, y_0).

This is a natural extension of the definition of a limit as applied to functions of a single variable. Likewise, the concept of continuity (see §2.2) may be generalized as:

DEFINITION A function $f(x,y)$ is said to be *continuous* at the point (x_0, y_0) if and only if it possesses a limit at (x_0, y_0) and

$$\lim_{\substack{x \to x_0 \\ y \to y_0}} f(x,y) = f(x_0, y_0).$$

In other words, $f(x,y)$ is continuous at (x_0, y_0) only if $|f(x,y) - f(x_0, y_0)|$ may be made arbitrarily small purely by insisting that $(x - x_0)^2 + (y - y_0)^2$ is suitably small.

In terms of Fig. 4.1 this definition ensures that by restricting (x,y) to a sufficiently small disc of the x,y plane centred at (x_0, y_0), we may restrict the difference $f(x,y) - f(x_0, y_0)$ in the elevations as much as we like. Behaviours like those of the functions

$$\frac{y}{x}, \quad \frac{y}{x+y} \quad \text{and the polar angle } \theta = \tan^{-1} \frac{y}{x}$$

violate these conditions near $(x,y) = (0,0)$, since in each case the function has a different constant value on each radial line of the x,y plane.

Using this definition of continuity, it can be shown that:

If everywhere near $(x,y) = (x_0, y_0)$ the function $f(x,y)$ is defined, and $f_x(x,y)$, $f_y(x,y)$, $f_{xy}(x,y)$ and $f_{yx}(x,y)$ all exist, and moreover $f_{yx}(x,y)$ is continuous at (x_0, y_0), then

$$f_{xy}(x_0, y_0) = f_{yx}(x_0, y_0).$$

Most functions encountered in engineering satisfy the above conditions, and the order of differentiation is usually immaterial.

Frequently partial derivatives of higher orders may be found. Thus, $f(x,y)$ has eight *third-order partial derivatives*

$$f_{xxx}, f_{xxy}, f_{xyx}, f_{xyy}, f_{yxx}, f_{yxy}, f_{yyx} \text{ and } f_{yyy},$$

where, for example,

$$f_{xxx} = \frac{\partial}{\partial x}(f_{xx}) = \frac{\partial^3 f}{\partial x^3}, \quad f_{xxy} = \frac{\partial}{\partial y}(f_{xx}) = \frac{\partial^3 f}{\partial y \partial x^2},$$

and

$$f_{xyx} = \frac{\partial}{\partial x}(f_{xy}) = \frac{\partial^3 f}{\partial x \partial y \partial x}.$$

Provided all mixed partial derivatives are continuous, order of differentiation is immaterial, so that

$$f_{xxy} = f_{xyx} = f_{yxx}, \quad f_{xyy} = f_{yxy} = f_{yyx}.$$

As illustration, it may be checked that for example 3

$$f_{xxy} = f_{xyx} = f_{yxx} = \frac{2y(3x^2 - y^2)}{(x^2 + y^2)^3},$$

$$f_{xyy} = f_{yxy} = f_{yyx} = \frac{2x(3y^2 - x^2)}{(x^2 + y^2)^3}, \quad \text{for all } (x, y) \neq (0, 0).$$

Functions of Several Variables

All the rules and operations developed here for functions of two variables may be extended to functions of several independent variables. Thus a function $f(x, y, z)$ may possess three first-order partial derivatives f_x, f_y and f_z, where

$$f_x(x, y, z) = \lim_{\delta x \to 0} \frac{f(x + \delta x, y, z) - f(x, y, z)}{\delta x}, \text{ etc.}$$

Similarly, for a function $f(x_1, x_2, \ldots, x_n)$ of n variables $x_1, x_2, \ldots, x_n$ it is possible to define a first-order partial derivative with respect to each variable $x_i (i = 1, 2, \ldots, n)$ as

$$\frac{\partial f}{\partial x_i} \equiv \lim_{\delta x_i \to 0} \frac{f(x_1, \ldots, x_i + \delta x_i, \ldots, x_n) - f(x_1, \ldots, x_i, \ldots, x_n)}{\delta x_i}$$

wherever this limit exists. Again, when mixed partial derivatives are continuous, the order of differentiation is immaterial, so that

$$\frac{\partial^2 f}{\partial x_i \partial x_j} = \frac{\partial^2 f}{\partial x_j \partial x_i} \quad \text{for each } i, j = 1, 2, \ldots, n.$$

Similar remarks apply to partial derivatives of higher orders.

Note that, for $n = 3$ the variables are often denoted by x, y and z, but that for $n > 3$ the subscript notation is more convenient.

EXAMPLE 5

The pressure p in a plane sound wave propagating in the direction of the unit vector with direction cosines l, m, n is

$$p(x, y, z, t) = A \sin \frac{\omega}{c} (lx + my + nz - ct).$$

Here A is the amplitude, ω is the angular frequency, and c is the speed of sound.

Parallel to the x, y and z axes respectively, the spatial derivatives of pressure are

$$\frac{\partial p}{\partial x} = \frac{A\omega l}{c} \cos \frac{\omega}{c} (lx + my + nz - ct), \quad \frac{\partial p}{\partial y} = \frac{A\omega m}{c} \cos \frac{\omega}{c} (lx + my + nz - ct),$$

$$\frac{\partial p}{\partial z} = \frac{A\omega m}{c} \cos \frac{\omega}{c} (lx + my + nz - ct).$$

All these are evaluated at constant time, whilst $\frac{\partial p}{\partial t} = -A\omega \cos \frac{\omega}{c} (lx + my + nz - ct)$ is the partial derivative with respect to time at a fixed position (x, y, z).

A Warning

One rule of ordinary differentiation does not carry over simply to partial derivatives. This concerns derivatives of a function and its inverse function.

If the relation $w = g(x)$ may be inverted as $x = h(w)$ the derivatives of the two functions g and h are reciprocal and are related by

$$g'(x) \equiv \frac{dw}{dx} = \left(\frac{dx}{dw} \right)^{-1} = \left[h'(w) \right]^{-1}.$$

Suppose, however, that the relations $u = u(x, y)$, $v = v(x, y)$ define both x and y uniquely as functions of u and v. Then it is possible to write $x = x(u, v)$, $y = y(u, v)$. It is not true that the corresponding derivatives are reciprocal, tnat is

$$x_u \neq (u_x)^{-1}, \quad y_u \neq (u_y)^{-1}, \quad x_v \neq (v_x)^{-1}, \quad y_v \neq (v_y)^{-1}.$$

The correct relations between the partial derivatives will later be deduced using ideas from §4.2.

EXAMPLE 6
Consider the relationships $x = r \cos \theta \equiv x(r, \theta)$, and $y = r \sin \theta \equiv y(r, \theta)$ between cartesian coordinates (x, y) and plane polar coordinates (r, θ). It is possible to invert these to find r as

$$r = (x^2 + y^2)^{1/2} \equiv r(x, y).$$

If the point (x, y) is on neither axis, then

$$x_r = \frac{\partial x}{\partial r} = \cos \theta = \frac{x}{r} = \frac{x}{(x^2 + y^2)^{1/2}}, \quad \text{whilst } r_x = \frac{\partial r}{\partial x} = \frac{x}{(x^2 + y^2)^{1/2}}$$

so that here x_r and r_x are equal, and are not reciprocal. The explanation may be seen

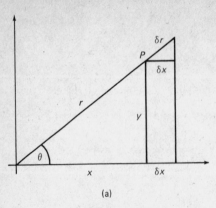
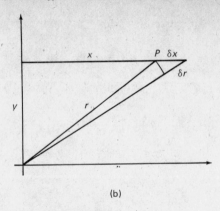

(a)   (b)

Fig. 4.2   The increment δr corresponding to δx (a) at constant θ, and (b) at constant y

by comparing Fig. 4.2(a) with Fig. 4.2(b). At a typical point P of the x, y plane, x_r measures the rate of change of x with respect to r along the radial line as in Fig. 4.2(a), whilst r_x measures the rate of change of r with respect to x when y is held fixed as in Fig. 4.2(b). Consequently, even though $(r_x)^{-1}$ measures a rate of change of x with respect to r, it generally differs from x_r.

Exercises

1. Find $f_x(x, y)$ and $f_y(x, y)$ for

   (a) $f(x, y) = x^2 + 5xy + 2y^2 + y$,   (b) $f(x, y) = e^{xy}$,

   (c) $f(x, y) = \dfrac{\tan^{-1} x}{1 + y^2}$.

2. In the region $y \geqslant 0$ of the x, y plane, it is possible to specify position by using x and $r \equiv (x^2 + y^2)^{1/2}$ as coordinates. Find $y = y(x, r)$ and its first partial derivatives. Find r_y and explain why $y_r = [r_y]^{-1}$ in this case.

3. Position in the x, y plane may be specified by use of parabolic coordinates (u, v) for which $x = u^2 - v^2$, $y = 2uv$. Find x_u, y_u, x_v and y_v. Show that $u(x, y)$ is defined by $x = u^2 - \dfrac{y^2}{4u^2}$. By differentiating this directly, deduce that

$$u_x = \frac{u}{2(u^2 + v^2)}, \quad u_y = \frac{v}{2(u^2 + v^2)} \, .$$

4. Show that $u_{xx} + u_{yy} = 0$ for

   (a) $u = \log r$,   (b) $u = x/r^2$,
   (c) $u = \sin(x^2 - y^2)\cosh 2xy$,   (d) $u = \tan^{-1} y/x$,
   where $r = (x^2 + y^2)^{1/2}$.

   [$u_{xx} + u_{yy} = 0$ is Laplace's equation, see Chapter 7].

5. Show that, if k is *any* constant, $u(x, t) = \sin kx \cos kct$ satisfies the *wave equation*

$$u_{xx} = c^{-2} u_{tt}. \quad \text{[see Chapter 7]}$$

4.2 THE CHAIN RULE AND TAYLOR'S THEOREM

The Chain Rule

If x and y are easterly and northerly map coordinates, the surface $z = f(x, y)$ of Fig. 4.1 represents the ground elevation. Then the partial derivatives $f_x(x, y)$ and $f_y(x, y)$ measure the slopes which would be encountered if a walker were to pass the point P having coordinates (x, y) along easterly or northerly paths respectively. Suppose that the walker travelled along a general path through P, and that the path were specified parametrically as $x = x(t), y = y(t)$. (To fix ideas, regard t as time.) The rate at which the corresponding elevation $z = f[x(t), y(t)]$ would change with t is related to $f_x, f_y, \mathrm{d}x/\mathrm{d}t$ and $\mathrm{d}y/\mathrm{d}t$ at the point P through a formula known as the *chain rule*.

At each point of the path the value of z depends on the corresponding value of the parameter t, and may be written as

$$z = f[x(t), y(t)] \equiv g(t).$$

The ordinary derivative $\mathrm{d}g/\mathrm{d}t$ may be calculated either directly, or as

$$g'(t) = \frac{\mathrm{d}g}{\mathrm{d}t} \equiv \lim_{\delta t \to 0} \frac{g(t + \delta t) - g(t)}{\delta t} = \lim_{\delta t \to 0} \frac{f[x(t + \delta t), y(t + \delta t)] - f[x(t), y(t)]}{\delta t}. \quad (1)$$

Over the increment $\delta t, x$ and y change by amounts δx and δy respectively, where

$$\delta x \equiv x(t + \delta t) - x(t) \text{ and } \delta y \equiv y(t + \delta t) - y(t).$$

The total increment δf in f may be expressed as the sum of the change in f due to the increment δx in x followed by the change due to the increment δy in y. Thus, as in Fig. 4.3,

$$f[x(t + \delta t), y(t + \delta t)] - f[x(t), y(t)]$$
$$= f(x + \delta x, y + \delta y) - f(x, y)$$
$$= QC = QR + RC = PB + RC$$
$$= [f(x + \delta x, y) - f(x, y)] + [f(x + \delta x, y + \delta y) - f(x + \delta x, y)]. \quad (2)$$

Now, since $\delta x \to 0$ as $\delta t \to 0$,

$$\lim_{\delta t \to 0} \frac{f(x + \delta x, y) - f(x, y)}{\delta t} = \lim_{\delta t \to 0} \left[\frac{f(x + \delta x, y) - f(x, y)}{\delta x} \frac{\delta x}{\delta t} \right]$$

$$= \lim_{\delta x \to 0} \frac{f(x + \delta x, y) - f(x, y)}{\delta x} \lim_{\delta t \to 0} \frac{\delta x}{\delta t}$$

$$= f_x(x, y) x'(t) = \frac{\partial f}{\partial x} \frac{\mathrm{d}x}{\mathrm{d}t}, \quad (3)$$

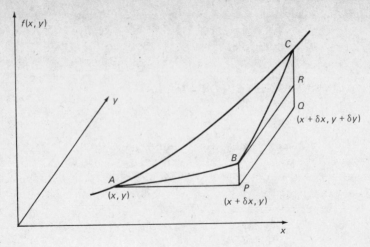

Fig. 4.3

where both derivatives are evaluated at A. Similarly the second bracket in equation (2) contributes to $g'(t)$ an expression

$$\lim_{\substack{\delta y \to 0 \\ \delta x \to 0}} \frac{f(x + \delta x, y + \delta y) - f(x + \delta x, y)}{\delta y} \lim_{\delta t \to 0} \frac{\delta y}{\delta t} = \lim_{\delta x \to 0} f_y(x + \delta x, y)\, y'(t)$$

$$= f_y(x, y)\, y'(t) = \frac{\partial f}{\partial y} \frac{dy}{dt}. \qquad (4)$$

Substitution of equations (3) and (4) into equation (1) gives

$$\frac{d}{dt} f[x(t), y(t)] = \frac{\partial f}{\partial x} \frac{dx}{dt} + \frac{\partial f}{\partial y} \frac{dy}{dt} = f_x(x, y)\, x'(t) + f_y(x, y)\, y'(t). \qquad (5)$$

This is known as the *chain rule for ordinary derivatives*, and is valid at all points (x, y) at which both f_x and f_y are continuous.

EXAMPLE 1
If $f(x, y) = y^2 \sin 2x$, find df/dt along the curve $x = t^2$, $y = 2t$ by the chain rule. Confirm the answer by direct differentiation.

Since $f_x = 2y^2 \cos 2x$ and $f_y = 2y \sin 2x$, and $\dfrac{dx}{dt} = 2t$, $\dfrac{dy}{dt} = 2$, the chain rule gives

$$\frac{df}{dt} = (2y^2 \cos 2x)2t + (2y \sin 2x)2 = 8t(2t^2 \cos 2t^2 + \sin 2t^2).$$

Substitution of $x = t^2$ and $y = 2t$ into $f(x, y)$ gives $f = 4t^2 \sin 2t^2$, then

$$\frac{df}{dt} = 8t \sin 2t^2 + 4t^2 (4t \cos 2t^2) = 8t(\sin 2t^2 + 2t^2 \cos 2t^2).$$

First Mean Value Theorems

The above proof of the chain rule involves a double limit $\delta x \to 0$, $\delta y \to 0$. On occasions such limits can give trouble. A more rigorous proof follows from a theorem concerning functions of a single variable.

FIRST MEAN VALUE THEOREM   If $v(t)$ has a continuous first derivative for all t lying between t_0 and $t_0 + T$, and $v(t)$ is continuous at both t_0 and $t_0 + T$, then

$$v(t_0 + T) - v(t_0) = Tv'(t_0 + \theta T) \quad \text{for at least one } \theta \text{ in } 0 < \theta < 1.$$

Note that T may be positive or negative, and in either case the value $t = t_0 + \theta T$ lies between t_0 and $t_0 + T$. The theorem is illustrated by Fig. 4.4, which shows that, on the graph of $v(t)$, there is a point $t = t_0 + \theta T$ at which the tangent is parallel to the chord joining the points $t = t_0$ and $t = t_0 + T$.

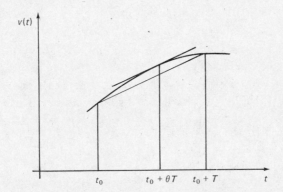

Fig. 4.4   Illustration of the first mean value theorem for a function $v(t)$

The theorem may be applied to each of the contributions PB and RC in equation (2) to give

$$f[x(t + \delta t), y(t + \delta t)] - f[x(t), y(t)] = f_x(x + \theta \delta x, y)\delta x + f_y(x + \delta x, y + \theta' \delta y)\delta y$$

for some choices of θ and θ' satisfying $0 < \theta < 1$, $0 < \theta' < 1$. It may be seen that the partial derivatives are evaluated at points of AB and BC of Fig. 4.3 respectively. Then, under the assumption that both f_x and f_y are continuous at (x, y), we may divide by δt and consider the limit $\delta t \to 0$ in which $f_x(x + \theta \delta x, y) \to f_x(x, y)$ and $f_y(x + \delta x, y + \theta' \delta y) \to f_y(x, y)$. The chain rule (5) is then obtained.

By applying the mean value theorem to the function $F(t) \equiv f(a + th, b + tk)$ over the interval $0 \leqslant t \leqslant 1$, noting that $F(1) = f(a + h, b + k)$ and $F(0) = f(a, b)$, and by using the chain rule (5) the generalization of the first mean value theorem to functions of two variables may be obtained.

THEOREM   If $f(x, y)$ possesses continuous first-order partial derivatives within the rectangle $a < x < a + h$, $b < y < b + k$, and $f(x, y)$ is itself continuous both inside and on the boundary of that rectangle, then

$$f(a + h, b + k) - f(a, b) = hf_x(a + \theta h, b + \theta k) + kf_y(a + \theta h, b + \theta k), \qquad (6)$$

for at least one choice of θ in $0 < \theta < 1$.

The theorem involves partial derivatives of $f(x, y)$ evaluated at the point which divides the straight segment joining $(x, y) = (a, b)$ to $(x, y) = (a + h, b + k)$ in the ratio $\theta : 1 - \theta$.

The extension of the chain rule (5) to functions $f(x_1, x_2, \ldots, x_n)$ of n variables is the *generalized chain rule*

$$\frac{d}{dt} f[x_1(t), x_2(t), \ldots, x_n(t)] = \frac{\partial f}{\partial x_1} \frac{dx_1}{dt} + \frac{\partial f}{\partial x_2} \frac{dx_2}{dt} + \ldots + \frac{\partial f}{\partial x_n} \frac{dx_n}{dt}, \qquad (7)$$

which applies at any point where all the first-order partial derivatives of f are continuous. Similarly, the first mean value theorem may be extended.

Taylor's Theorem

If $v(t)$ is a function of a single variable it is often convenient to express $v(t_0 + T)$ in terms of the behaviour of the function v at $t = t_0$ by

$$v(t_0 + T) = v(t_0) + T v'(t_0) + \frac{T^2}{2!} v''(t_0) + \ldots + \frac{T^{n-1}}{(n-1)!} v^{(n-1)}(t_0) + R_n, \qquad (8)$$

where R_n denotes the remainder after n terms of the power series in T.

TAYLOR'S THEOREM   (see Lennox and Chadwick [1]) states that, if v and all its derivatives up to nth order are continuous everywhere between t_0 and $t_0 + T$ the remainder has value

$$R_n = \frac{T^n}{n!} v^{(n)}(t_1), \qquad (9)$$

for some t_1 between t_0 and $t_0 + T$.

The case $n = 1$ is the first mean value theorem, and for this reason Taylor's theorem is often called the nth *mean value theorem*.

As will now be shown, this theorem may be extended to apply to functions of many variables. In particular, for a function $f(x, y)$ of two variables, it relates the value of $z = f(x, y)$ at points $(x, y) = (a + h, b + k)$, in the vicinity of some point (a, b), to f and its partial derivatives evaluated at (a, b). (Some authors use the symbols Δx and Δy for h and k.)

Again consider the function $F(t) \equiv f(a + th, b + tk)$ which, for $0 \le t \le 1$, gives the values of f at points (x, y) of the straight line joining (a, b) to $(a + h, b + k)$. Applying equations (8) and (9) to $F(t)$, recalling that $F(0) = f(a, b)$ and $F(1) = f(a + h, b + k)$, we obtain

$$F(t) = F(0) + tF'(0) + \frac{t^2}{2!}F''(0) + \ldots + \frac{t^{n-1}}{(n-1)!}F^{(n-1)}(0) + R_n, \tag{10}$$

with

$$R_n = \frac{t^n}{n!}F^{(n)}(\theta_n t), \quad \text{for some } \theta_n \text{ in } 0 < \theta_n < 1.$$

The derivatives in equation (10), calculated by the chain rule (5), are

$$F'(t) = \frac{dF}{dt} = \frac{\partial f}{\partial x}\frac{dx}{dt} + \frac{\partial f}{\partial y}\frac{dy}{dt} = h\frac{\partial f}{\partial x} + k\frac{\partial f}{\partial y},$$

$$F''(t) = \frac{d^2 F}{dt^2} = h\frac{\partial}{\partial x}F'(t) + k\frac{\partial}{\partial y}F'(t)$$

$$= h^2\frac{\partial^2 f}{\partial x^2} + 2hk\frac{\partial^2 f}{\partial x \partial y} + k^2\frac{\partial^2 f}{\partial y^2},$$

etc., where each successive differentiation requires the combination of operations

$$h\frac{\partial}{\partial x} + k\frac{\partial}{\partial y}.$$

Thus the rth derivative may be written as

$$F^{(r)}(t) = h^r\frac{\partial^r f}{\partial x^r} + {}^r C_1 h^{r-1}k\frac{\partial^r f}{\partial x^{r-1}\partial y} + \ldots + k^r\frac{\partial^r f}{\partial y^r},$$

where the binomial coefficients ${}^r C_p$ are defined by

$${}^r C_p \equiv \frac{r!}{p!(r-p)!} = {}^r C_{r-p}.$$

Alternatively $F^{(r)}(t)$ may be written in *operator notation* as

$$F^{(r)}(t) = \left(h\frac{\partial}{\partial x} + k\frac{\partial}{\partial y}\right)^r f.$$

Setting $t = 1$ in equation (10) then gives four equivalent forms (11) of

TAYLOR'S THEOREM FOR FUNCTIONS OF TWO VARIABLES   If all $(n-1)$th-order partial derivatives of $f(x, y)$ are continuous inside and on the boundary of the rectangle having vertices at (a, b), $(a + h, b)$, $(a, b + k)$ and $(a + h, b + k)$, and all nth-order partial derivatives are continuous within the rectangle, then

$$f(a + h, b + k) = f(a, b) + hf_x(a, b) + kf_y(a, b)$$

$$+ \frac{1}{2!}[h^2 f_{xx}(a,b) + 2hkf_{xy}(a,b) + k^2 f_{yy}(a,b)] + \ldots + R_n, \tag{11a}$$

$$\equiv \sum_{r=0}^{n-1} \sum_{p=0}^{r} \frac{h^p k^{r-p}}{p!(r-p)!} \frac{\partial^r f(a,b)}{\partial x^p \partial y^{r-p}} + R_n, \tag{11b}$$

$$\equiv \sum_{p,q}^{p+q \leqslant n-1} \frac{h^p k^q}{p! q!} \frac{\partial^{p+q} f(a,b)}{\partial x^p \partial y^q} + R_n, \tag{11c}$$

$$\equiv \sum_{r=0}^{n-1} \left(h \frac{\partial}{\partial x} + k \frac{\partial}{\partial y} \right)^r f(a,b) + R_n. \tag{11d}$$

In each formula the remainder R_n is the value of

$$\sum_{p=0}^{n} \frac{h^p k^{n-p}}{p!(n-p)!} \frac{\partial^n f}{\partial x^p \partial y^{n-p}} \tag{12}$$

at some point $(x,y) = (a + \theta_n h, b + \theta_n k)$ of the straight line segment joining (a,b) to $(a+h, b+k)$, where $0 < \theta_n < 1$.

Notice that the case $n = 1$ of equations (10) and (11) gives the first mean value theorem (6).

Taylor Series

For many functions $v(t)$ the remainder R_n in equations (8) and (9) tends to zero as $n \to \infty$, provided that $|T|$ is suitably restricted. Equation (8) shows that, when $|T|$ lies within this range such a function may be expanded in the convergent power series

$$v(t_0 + T) = v(t_0) + T v'(t_0) + \frac{T^2}{2!} v''(t_0) + \ldots + \frac{T^n}{n!} v^{(n)}(t_0) + \ldots, \tag{13}$$

known as its *Taylor series about t_0*. Conversely, if $v(t)$ possesses a Taylor series (13), the error produced by truncating the series to one of just n terms is given by R_n. This error may be made arbitrarily close to zero by taking n sufficiently large.

Similarly, if in expressions (11) and (12) $R_n \to 0$ as $n \to \infty$, the function f may be represented by the convergent double power series

$$f(a+h, b+k) = \sum_{p=0}^{\infty} \sum_{q=0}^{\infty} \frac{h^p k^q}{p! q!} \frac{\partial^{p+q}}{\partial x^p \partial y^q} f(a,b), \tag{14}$$

known as its *Taylor series expansion about the point (a,b)*. In the alternative notation in which $a + h = x$ and $b + k = y$ the series (14) becomes

$$f(x,y) = \sum_{p=0}^{\infty} \sum_{q=0}^{\infty} \frac{(x-a)^p (y-b)^q}{p! q!} \frac{\partial^{p+q}}{\partial x^p \partial y^q} f(a,b). \tag{14a}$$

The roles of the terms of each successive order r in equations (11) and (14) may be clarified by consideration of the surface $z = f(x,y)$ of Fig. 4.1, near the point with $x = a, y = b$. When only the first-order terms are retained the surface is approximated by a plane, which in the notation of equation (14a) is given by

$$z = f(a, b) + (x - a)f_x(a, b) + (y - b)f_y(a, b).$$ (15)

This plane contains the tangents at $(x, y) = (a, b)$ to the two curves C_1 and C_2. Moreover, it contains the tangent at $(x, y) = (a, b)$ to each smooth curve passing through $(x, y) = (a, b)$ and lying in the surface. To prove this, let the curve be $x = x(t)$, $y = y(t)$, $z = z(t) \equiv f[x(t), y(t)]$ with $x(0) = a$, $y(0) = b$. Then at $t = 0$ the chain rule (5) gives

$$\frac{dz}{dt} = z'(0) = f_x(a, b)\frac{dx}{dt} + f_y(a, b)\frac{dy}{dt}, \quad \text{where} \quad \frac{dx}{dt} = x'(0), \quad \frac{dy}{dt} = y'(0),$$

so that the tangent may be expressed in terms of a parameter λ as

$$x - a = \lambda x'(0), \quad y - b = \lambda y'(0),$$

$$z - f(a, b) = \lambda z'(0) = \lambda[f_x(a, b)x'(0) + f_y(a, b)y'(0)],$$

and lies in the plane (15). For this reason the plane (15) is known as the *tangent plane* to $z = f(x, y)$ at $(x, y) = (a, b)$. It is the plane which provides the 'best fit' to $z = f(x, y)$ near the point (a, b).

Just as successive terms of the series (13) improve the approximation for $v(t)$ near $t = t_0$ by approximating its graph successively by a straight line, a parabola, a cubic curve, etc., the terms of successive orders $r = p + q$ in the series (14) improve the tangent plane approximation by quadratic surfaces, cubic surfaces, and so on. The following example illustrates this.

EXAMPLE 2
Find the cubic approximation to the Taylor series at $(1, 0)$ for $f(x, y) = (x^2 + y^2)^{1/2}$. Use this to obtain linear, quadratic and cubic approximations for $f(0.9, 0.1)$.

The function $f(x, y)$ has the partial derivatives

$$f_x = \frac{x}{(x^2 + y^2)^{1/2}}, \qquad f_y = \frac{y}{(x^2 + y^2)^{1/2}},$$

$$f_{xx} = \frac{y^2}{(x^2 + y^2)^{3/2}}, \qquad f_{xy} = \frac{-xy}{(x^2 + y^2)^{3/2}}, \qquad f_{yy} = \frac{x^2}{(x^2 + y^2)^{3/2}},$$

and

$$f_{xxx} = \frac{-3xy^2}{(x^2 + y^2)^{5/2}}, \qquad f_{xxy} = \frac{y(2x^2 - y^2)}{(x^2 + y^2)^{5/2}}, \qquad f_{xyy} = \frac{x(2y^2 - x^2)}{(x^2 + y^2)^{5/2}},$$

$$f_{yyy} = \frac{-3x^2 y}{(x^2 + y^2)^{5/2}},$$

which exist everywhere except at the origin $(x, y) = (0, 0)$. Evaluating these at $x = 1$, $y = 0$ gives the cubic approximation to the Taylor series about $(x, y) = (1, 0)$ as

$$f(1 + h, k) \simeq 1 + h + \frac{1}{2}k^2 - \frac{3}{3!}hk^2 = x + \frac{1}{2}y^2 - \frac{1}{2}(x - 1)y^2.$$

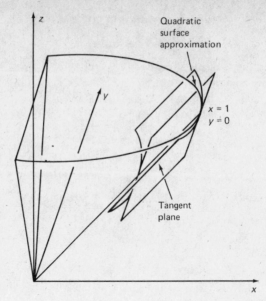

Fig. 4.5   Linear and quadratic approximations to the cone $z = (x^2 + y^2)^{1/2}$ near $(x, y) = (1, 0)$

Setting $h = -0.1, k = 0.1$ gives the linear, quadratic and cubic approximations to $f(0.9, 0.1)$ as 0.9, 0.905 and 0.9055 respectively, whilst the exact value is $(0.82)^{1/2} = 0.90554$ to 5 decimal places. The tangent plane and quadratic surface approximations to $z = (x^2 + y^2)^{1/2}$ at $(x, y) = (1, 0)$ are shown in Fig. 4.5.

Although, in example 2, $f(0.9, 0.1)$ is readily evaluated explicitly, in many problems it is useful to approximate a function $f(x, y)$ near a point (a, b) by a low order polynomial in $(x - a)$ and $(y - b)$. In this case, the order of error involved may be estimated by summing suitable overestimates of the moduli of the contributions to R_n in expression (12).

Finally, it may be mentioned that *Taylor's Theorem* extends naturally to functions $f(x_1, x_2, \ldots, x_m)$ of many variables $x_1, x_2, \ldots, x_m$. The expansion about the point $(a_1, a_2, \ldots, a_m)$ is

$$f(a_1 + h_1, a_2 + h_2, \ldots, a_m + h_m) = f(a_1, a_2, \ldots, a_m)$$

$$+ \left(h_1 \frac{\partial}{\partial x_1} + h_2 \frac{\partial}{\partial x_2} + \ldots + h_m \frac{\partial}{\partial x_m} \right) f(a_1, a_2, \ldots, a_m)$$

$$+ \ldots + \frac{1}{(n-1)!} \left(h_1 \frac{\partial}{\partial x_1} + h_2 \frac{\partial}{\partial x_2} + \ldots + h_m \frac{\partial}{\partial x_m} \right)^{n-1} f(a_1, a_2, \ldots, a_m) + R_n,$$

$$(16)$$

where again R_n is a remainder term similar to expression (12). Under suitable restrictions, this may be used to express f in its Taylor series, which is an m-fold power series.

The Chain Rule for Partial Derivatives

Equation (5) gives the derivative of $f(x, y)$ with respect to a parameter t when x and y each depend only on t. A similar rule may be obtained for partial derivatives, when x and y each depend on more than one variable.

Suppose a problem involving a function $f(x, y)$ is more suitably analysed in terms of alternative coordinates u and v. If the coordinates (x, y) are uniquely related to the pair of values (u, v) through the functions $x = x(u, v)$ and $y = y(u, v)$ then the value of f is related uniquely to (u, v) by a function F defined by

$$f[x(u, v), y(u, v)] \equiv F(u, v).$$

The new partial derivatives F_u, F_v are expressible in terms of f_x, f_y and the set of partial derivatives x_u, x_v, y_u, y_v as follows. The locus of points $v = $ constant is a curve in the x, y plane. Along this, the value of f, like x and y, depends only on the single parameter u, so that F_u measures the derivative of f with respect to u along this curve.

The chain rule (5) thus gives

$$\frac{\partial f}{\partial u} = \frac{\partial F}{\partial u} = F_u(u, v) = f_x x_u + f_y y_u = \frac{\partial f}{\partial x} \frac{\partial x}{\partial u} + \frac{\partial f}{\partial y} \frac{\partial y}{\partial u}. \tag{17a}$$

Similarly,

$$\frac{\partial f}{\partial v} = \frac{\partial F}{\partial v} = F_v(u, v) = f_x x_v + f_y y_v = \frac{\partial f}{\partial x} \frac{\partial x}{\partial v} + \frac{\partial f}{\partial y} \frac{\partial y}{\partial v}. \tag{17b}$$

These rules may be extended to apply to a function $f(x_1, x_2, \ldots, x_n)$ of a set of n variables $x_1, x_2, \ldots, x_n$. When each of these itself is a function of another set of quantities $u_1, u_2, \ldots, u_p$, it is possible to write

$$f(x_1, x_2, \ldots, x_n) \equiv F(u_1, u_2, \ldots, u_p).$$

The *chain rule for partial derivatives* is

$$\frac{\partial f}{\partial u_1} = \frac{\partial F}{\partial u_1} = \frac{\partial f}{\partial x_1} \frac{\partial x_1}{\partial u_1} + \frac{\partial f}{\partial x_2} \frac{\partial x_2}{\partial u_1} + \ldots + \frac{\partial f}{\partial x_n} \frac{\partial x_n}{\partial u_1},$$

$$\frac{\partial f}{\partial u_2} = \frac{\partial F}{\partial u_2} = \frac{\partial f}{\partial x_1} \frac{\partial x_1}{\partial u_2} + \frac{\partial f}{\partial x_2} \frac{\partial x_2}{\partial u_2} + \ldots + \frac{\partial f}{\partial x_n} \frac{\partial x_n}{\partial u_2},$$

$$\vdots$$

$$\frac{\partial f}{\partial u_p} = \frac{\partial F}{\partial u_p} = \frac{\partial f}{\partial x_1} \frac{\partial x_1}{\partial u_p} + \frac{\partial f}{\partial x_2} \frac{\partial x_2}{\partial u_p} + \ldots + \frac{\partial f}{\partial x_n} \frac{\partial x_n}{\partial u_p}. \tag{18}$$

More compactly, equations (18) may be written as

$$\frac{\partial F}{\partial u_i} = \frac{\partial f}{\partial x_1} \frac{\partial x_1}{\partial u_i} + \frac{\partial f}{\partial x_2} \frac{\partial x_2}{\partial u_i} + \ldots + \frac{\partial f}{\partial x_n} \frac{\partial x_n}{\partial u_i}$$

$$= \sum_{r=1}^{n} \frac{\partial f}{\partial x_r} \frac{\partial x_r}{\partial u_i}, \quad \text{for each } i = 1, 2, \ldots, p. \tag{19}$$

EXAMPLE 3

Suppose that $f(x,y,z) = z(x^2 + y^2)^{-1}$. In situations for which x, y and z can be specified in terms of two quantities u and v as $x = u + v$, $y = u$ and $z = uv$, find the rates of change of f with u and v respectively.

Since $f_x = \dfrac{-2xz}{(x^2 + y^2)^2}$, $f_y = \dfrac{-2yz}{(x^2 + y^2)^2}$, $f_z = \dfrac{1}{x^2 + y^2}$, and

$$x_u = 1, \quad x_v = 1, \quad y_u = 1, \quad y_v = 0, \quad z_u = v, \quad z_v = u,$$

the chain rule (18) gives

$$\frac{\partial f}{\partial u} = \frac{-2xz}{(x^2 + y^2)^2} - \frac{2yz}{(x^2 + y^2)^2} + \frac{1}{x^2 + y^2} \times v = \frac{v(v^2 - 2u^2)}{(2u^2 + 2uv + v^2)^2},$$

$$\frac{\partial f}{\partial v} = \frac{-2xz}{(x^2 + y^2)^2} - \frac{2yz}{(x^2 + y^2)^2} \times 0 + \frac{1}{x^2 + y^2} \times u = \frac{u(2u^2 - v^2)}{(2u^2 + 2uv + v^2)^2}.$$

These results may be checked by direct differentiation, since for all values of u and v the value of f is given by

$$f(x, y, z) = \frac{uv}{2u^2 + 2uv + v^2} \equiv F(u, v), \quad \text{say.}$$

In example 3, notice that even though $y = u$,

$$\frac{\partial f}{\partial u} \neq \frac{\partial f}{\partial y} = f_y = \frac{-2u^2 v}{(2u^2 + 2uv + v^2)^2}.$$

The reason for this is that both x and z are held fixed during calculation of f_y, whilst they vary when v is held fixed during calculation of $\partial f/\partial u$. This calls for careful use of notation. One procedure is to use the distinct symbol F to denote the dependence of the value of f on u and v. Then, since $u = y$, we have

$$\frac{\partial F}{\partial u} = F_u(u, v) = \frac{v(v^2 - 2u^2)}{(2u^2 + 2uv + v^2)^2} = \frac{v(v^2 - 2y^2)}{(2y^2 + 2yv + v^2)^2} = F_y(y, v).$$

This expression is clearly distinguishable from $f_y = f_y(x, y, z)$.

Alternatively the set of quantities being held fixed may be listed after brackets or a vertical bar, as for example

$$\left(\frac{\partial f}{\partial y} \right)_{x,z} = \frac{\partial f}{\partial y} \bigg|_{x,z} = \frac{-2yz}{(x^2 + y^2)^2}$$

whilst

$$\left(\frac{\partial f}{\partial u} \right)_v = \frac{\partial f}{\partial u} \bigg|_v = \frac{v(v^2 - 2u^2)}{(2u^2 + 2uv + v^2)^2}.$$

This practice is particularly convenient when a single symbol for a physical quantity is conventional. An example follows.

EXAMPLE 4

The volume of a right circular cone of height h, radius r and semi-vertex angle α may be written as

$$V = \frac{1}{3}\pi r^2 h = \frac{1}{3}\pi h^3 \tan^2 \alpha = \frac{1}{3}\pi r^3 \cot \alpha.$$

Then $\quad \dfrac{\partial V}{\partial r}\bigg|_h = \dfrac{2}{3}\pi r h \quad$ whilst $\quad \dfrac{\partial V}{\partial r}\bigg|_\alpha = \pi r^2 \cot \alpha = \pi r h,$

$\dfrac{\partial V}{\partial h}\bigg|_r = \dfrac{1}{3}\pi r^2 \quad$ whilst $\quad \dfrac{\partial V}{\partial h}\bigg|_\alpha = \pi h^2 \tan^2 \alpha = \pi r^2,$

and $\quad \dfrac{\partial V}{\partial \alpha}\bigg|_r = -\dfrac{1}{3}\pi r^3 \cosec^2 \alpha = -\dfrac{1}{3}\pi r(r^2 + h^2)$

whilst $\quad \dfrac{\partial V}{\partial \alpha}\bigg|_h = \dfrac{2}{3}\pi h^3 \tan \alpha \sec^2 \alpha = \dfrac{2}{3}\pi r(r^2 + h^2).$

Consideration of the physical significance of the various partial derivatives readily explains the distinction within each pair.

Exercises

1. Calculate the partial derivatives f_x and f_y, when $f(x, y) = y(x^2 + y^2)^{1/2}$. Use the chain rule to calculate the derivative $df/d\theta$ along the circle given parametrically by $x = 1 - \cos\theta, y = \sin\theta$, and verify the answer by direct differentiation.

2. If $x = e^u + v, y = e^{-u} + v$ and $f(x, y) = xy$, use the chain rule for partial derivatives to show that

$$\frac{\partial f}{\partial u}\bigg|_v = 2v \sinh u, \quad \text{and} \quad \frac{\partial f}{\partial v}\bigg|_u = 2\cosh u + 2v.$$

Express f in terms of u and v and so verify these formulae directly.

3. A function $g(x, y)$ is expressed in terms of x and u as $g(x, y) = G(x, u)$, where, as in example 2, $x = e^u + v, y = e^{-u} + v$. Differentiate partially with respect to both x and y and so deduce that

$$g_y = -\tfrac{1}{2}G_u \sech u, \quad g_x = G_x + \tfrac{1}{2}G_u \sech u.$$

Use these, when $g(x, y) = xy$, to find G_x and G_u. Check the answer by direct differentiation of the function $G(x, u)$ corresponding to $g(x, y) = xy$.

4. Find all the first, second and third-order partial derivatives of $f(x, y) = x \log(x + y)$. Use these to write down the Taylor series at $x = 1, y = 0$ correct to terms cubic in the increments h and k. From this series, estimate $f(1.1, 0.1)$. Compare this estimate with the answer 0.200554 correct to 6 decimal places.

4.3 TOTAL DERIVATIVES

The Directional Derivative

A curve C in the x, y plane may be specified parametrically in the form $x = x(t)$, $y = y(t)$ for many distinct choices of parameter t. For each, the rate of change of $f(x, y)$ with respect to t was found in §4.2 to be given by the chain rule

$$\frac{d}{dt} f[x(t), y(t)] = f_x(x, y) \frac{dx}{dt} + f_y(x, y) \frac{dy}{dt}. \tag{5}$$

Certain special choices of parameter are particularly important.

At all points of C where $dy/dx = y'(x)$ is finite it is possible to set $t = x$ and so obtain

$$\frac{d}{dx} f[x, y(x)] = f_x(x, y) + f_y(x, y) \frac{dy}{dx}. \tag{20}$$

This is known as the *total derivative of f with respect to x* along C. Notice that, at any point (x, y) the total derivative has the same value for all curves having the same gradient dy/dx as C. Similarly, along any curve which may be written as $x = x(y)$ the total derivative of f with respect to y is given by

$$\frac{d}{dy} f[x(y), y] = f_x(x, y) \frac{dx}{dy} + f_y(x, y). \tag{20a}$$

Frequently it is convenient to choose as parameter t the distance s measured along the curve from some reference point. The rate of change of f with distance along the curve is then given by

$$\frac{df}{ds} = f_x(x, y) \frac{dx}{ds} + f_y(x, y) \frac{dy}{ds}.$$

This may be written in terms of the inclination ψ of the curve to the positive x axis (see Fig. 4.6) as

$$\frac{df}{ds} = f_x(x, y) \cos \psi + f_y(x, y) \sin \psi, \tag{21}$$

since $dx/ds = \cos \psi$ and $dy/ds = \sin \psi$. The expression in equation (21) is known as the *directional derivative* of f in the direction having inclination ψ to the x axis. At any point (x, y) the formula (21) may be used to calculate the rate of change of f with distance along an arbitrary curve by choosing ψ appropriately.

EXAMPLE 1

For $f(x, y) = x^2 + 2yx$, the total derivative of $f(x, y)$ with respect to x is

$$\frac{df}{dx} = \frac{\partial f}{\partial x} + \frac{\partial f}{\partial y} \frac{dy}{dx} = 2(x + y) + 2x \frac{dy}{dx}.$$

The directional derivative at inclination ψ to the x axis is

$$2(x+y)\cos\psi + 2x\sin\psi.$$

Implicit Functions

Some relations between x and y cannot be written in the *explicit* form $y = g(x)$ by use of standard functions. They must be expressed in the form

$$f(x,y) = \text{constant}, \tag{22}$$

which is said to be an *implicit relation* between y and x. Then, as x varies, y must vary at such a rate that the total derivative of f vanishes. Equation (20) then gives

$$f_x(x,y) + f_y(x,y)\frac{\mathrm{d}y}{\mathrm{d}x} = 0.$$

This determines the gradient of the curve in the x, y plane as

$$\frac{\mathrm{d}y}{\mathrm{d}x} = -\frac{f_x}{f_y} \quad \text{whenever} \quad f_y \neq 0. \tag{23}$$

Similarly, at points where $f_x \neq 0$, the rate of change of x with y subject to equation (22) is $\mathrm{d}x/\mathrm{d}y = -f_y/f_x$. Equation (23) is useful for evaluating $\mathrm{d}y/\mathrm{d}x$ for any implicit relation between y and x. Similarly, if x, y and z are implicitly related by an equation $F(x,y,z) = 0$, then

$$\left.\frac{\partial y}{\partial x}\right|_z = -\frac{F_x}{F_y}, \quad \text{etc.}$$

Level Curves and Contours

On a survey map the ground surface $z = f(x,y)$ is portrayed by certain representative curves of constant elevation z. Similarly the locus of points in the x, y plane for which $f(x,y) = \text{constant}$ is called a *level curve* (or *contour*) of the function f. Its direction at any point (x, y) is given by $\mathrm{d}y/\mathrm{d}x$ as in equation (23). If a walker proceeds from the point (x, y) in the direction for which $\mathrm{d}y/\mathrm{d}x = -f_x/f_y \equiv \tan\chi(x,y)$, he neither climbs nor descends. In other directions $\mathrm{d}y/\mathrm{d}x = \tan\psi$, he encounters a slope given by the directional derivative (21). Using the substitution

$$f_x = -(f_x^2 + f_y^2)^{1/2}\sin\chi, \quad f_y = (f_x^2 + f_y^2)^{1/2}\cos\chi,$$

gives expression (21) as

$$\frac{\mathrm{d}f}{\mathrm{d}s} = (f_x^2 + f_y^2)^{1/2}(-\sin\chi\cos\psi + \cos\chi\sin\psi) = (f_x^2 + f_y^2)^{1/2}\sin(\psi - \chi).$$

The maximum value $(f_x^2 + f_y^2)^{1/2}$ of $\mathrm{d}f/\mathrm{d}s$ at (x, y) is called the slope of the surface. It is the slope encountered during travel perpendicular to the contours, at inclination $(\chi + \pi/2)$ to the x axis. The *curves of steepest ascent* (or *descent*) are the curves tangential to such directions, and are the orthogonal trajectories to the contours.

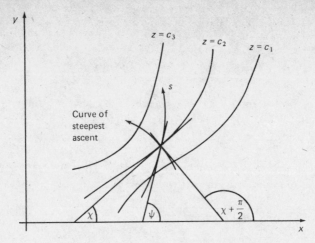

Fig. 4.6   Contours and a curve of steepest ascent. Since $f_x < 0$ and $f_y > 0$ the angle χ lies in the quadrant $0 < \chi < \pi/2$

Customarily the contours are drawn at equal intervals of z, so that the perpendicular spacing between contours is a representative value of the reciprocal of the slope $(f_x^2 + f_y^2)^{1/2}$. Indeed, a walker knows that, in regions where the spacing between contours is small, the hillside is steep.

EXAMPLE 2

Find the direction of steepest ascent for $z = y^2 e^x$.

Since $z_x = y^2 e^x$ and $z_y = 2ye^x$, the angle $\chi(x, y)$ is given by

$$\sin \chi : \cos \chi : 1 = -y^2 e^x : 2ye^x : y(y^2 + 4)^{1/2} e^x.$$

Since $\sin \chi \leqslant 0$ for all x and y, the angle χ lies in $-\pi \leqslant \chi \leqslant 0$. Hence the direction $\psi = \chi + \pi/2$ of steepest ascent lies in $-\pi/2 \leqslant \psi \leqslant \pi/2$, and is given by $\psi = \tan^{-1} 2/y$. (The curves of steepest ascent are the solutions $y^2 - 4x = $ constant of the differential equation $dy/dx = \tan(\chi + \pi/2) = 2/y$.)

Total Derivatives along Implicitly Defined Curves

Suppose a total derivative of $z = f(x, y)$ is required along a curve given implicitly by some equation $g(x, y) = $ constant. Then, since equation (23) gives

$$\frac{dy}{dx} = \frac{-g_x(x, y)}{g_y(x, y)},$$

expression (20) becomes

$$\frac{dz}{dx} = f_x(x, y) - \frac{f_y(x, y)g_x(x, y)}{g_y(x, y)} = \frac{f_x g_y - f_y g_x}{g_y}. \tag{24}$$

The numerator of the right-hand side of equation (24) is an important combination of partial derivatives since it vanishes if and only if the curve g = constant is tangential to a contour of f. It is known as the *Jacobian* of f and g with respect to x and y, and is normally denoted by $\dfrac{\partial(f, g)}{\partial(x, y)}$. It may be evaluated as a determinant

$$\frac{\partial(f, g)}{\partial(x, y)} \equiv f_x g_y - f_y g_x = \begin{vmatrix} f_x & f_y \\ g_x & g_y \end{vmatrix}.$$

Amongst other important applications, it arises during change of variables in multiple integrals (see §5.2).

Another useful formula involving implicit functions is the *triple product rule*

$$\left.\frac{\partial x}{\partial y}\right|_z \left.\frac{\partial y}{\partial z}\right|_x \left.\frac{\partial z}{\partial x}\right|_y = -1 \quad \text{and} \quad \left.\frac{\partial z}{\partial y}\right|_x \left.\frac{\partial y}{\partial x}\right|_z \left.\frac{\partial x}{\partial z}\right|_y = -1, \tag{25}$$

which connects the partial derivatives of three quantities related implicitly by some equation of the form $F(x, y, z) = 0$. This result is obtained by differentiating the identity $F(x, y, z) = 0$ with x, y and then z successively held constant, and is left as an exercise for the reader. Notice also the identity

$$\left.\frac{\partial x}{\partial z}\right|_y = \left(\left.\frac{\partial z}{\partial x}\right|_y\right)^{-1},$$

and the two similar results obtained by cyclic interchange of x, y and z.

Exercises

1. Find the directional derivative at $(1, 2)$ of $f(x, y) = y^2 \tan^{-1} x + xy$ in the direction having inclination ψ to the x axis.

2. If $z(x, y)$ is determined from $F(x, y, z) = 0$ determine z_{xx} and z_{xy} in terms of partial derivatives of F. Check your results for the case $F \equiv z^2 + 2yz + y^2 - \sin x - 1$.

3. The traffic speed $u(x, t)$ at position x and time t on a busy road is given by $u = k - k \tanh\{kx - u(u - k)t\}$. Find u_x and u_t, and verify that $ku_t + u(u - k)u_x = 0$.

   Show that 'shocks' arise (u_t becomes infinite) at instants and locations given parametrically by

$$t = k\{u(2k - u)(2u - k)\}^{-1}, \quad kx = \tanh^{-1}\left(\frac{k - u}{k}\right) + u(u - k)t.$$

4. The pressure p, temperature T and specific volume V of a van der Waal gas are related by

$$p = \frac{RT}{V - \beta} - \frac{\alpha}{V^2}.$$

Find

$$\left(\frac{\partial T}{\partial p}\right)_V, \quad \left(\frac{\partial p}{\partial V}\right)_T, \quad \text{and} \quad \left(\frac{\partial V}{\partial T}\right)_p,$$

and verify that their product equals -1.

5. The specific entropy s and specific volume V of a perfect gas may be expressed in terms of the pressure p and the temperature T as $s = s(p, T)$ and $V = V(p, T)$, where

$$\left.\frac{\partial s}{\partial p}\right|_T = -\left.\frac{\partial V}{\partial T}\right|_p.$$

Deduce that the following identities also hold:

(a) $\left.\dfrac{\partial T}{\partial p}\right|_s = \left.\dfrac{\partial V}{\partial s}\right|_p,$ (b) $\left.\dfrac{\partial T}{\partial V}\right|_s = -\left.\dfrac{\partial p}{\partial s}\right|_V,$ (c) $\left.\dfrac{\partial s}{\partial V}\right|_T = \left.\dfrac{\partial p}{\partial T}\right|_V.$

Hint: In case (a), substitute $T = T(p, s)$ into V.

4.4 STATIONARY POINTS

Maxima, Minima and Saddle Points

In many problems it is important to determine the maximum and minimum values taken by a function and to find the *maxima* and *minima* which are the points where these extreme values occur. Just as the local maxima and minima of a function $g(x)$ of a single variable may be found as solutions of $g'(x) = 0$, the *relative* (or *local*) *maxima* and *minima* of a function of several variables are identified by inspection of certain of its partial derivatives. If the function has more than one relative maximum, the *absolute* (or *global*) *maximum* is found as the relative maximum with greatest value.

The *relative extrema* of a continuously differentiable function $f(x, y)$ must be points where the tangent plane (15) to the surface $z = f(x, y)$ is level. Thus each *relative maximum* and *relative minimum* of $f(x, y)$ is located by solving the pair of equations

$$f_x = 0 \quad \text{and} \quad f_y = 0. \tag{26}$$

Each solution $(x, y) = (a, b)$ of equations (26) is known as a *stationary point*. As will shortly become clear, not all stationary points are relative extrema.

A stationary point (a, b) of $f(x, y)$ is a *relative maximum* if and only if $f(a + h, b + k) < f(a, b)$ whenever $|h|$ and $|k|$ are suitably small but not simultaneously zero. Similarly,

         if there exists some number ϵ for which $f(a + h, b + k) > f(a, b)$ whenever (h, k) satisfies

$$0 < h^2 + k^2 < \epsilon^2$$

then the point (a, b) is a relative minimum.

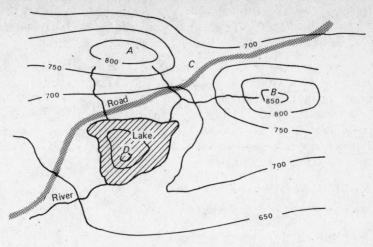

Fig. 4.7

(This is a mathematical statement ensuring that the region in which $f(x, y)$ is not less than $f(a, b)$ includes a disc of radius $|\epsilon|$ centred at (a, b), and so completely surrounds the point (a, b)). Figure 4.7 represents a portion of a survey map, on which the summits of the hills A and B are local maxima of elevation, whilst the deepest point D of the lake is a local minimum. The point C also is a stationary point of elevation, but although it is the summit of the road, it is the lowest point of the ridge joining A to B, and so is neither a local maximum nor a local minimum. Points of this nature are called *saddles* or *cols*, and constitute an important type of stationary point for functions $f(x, y)$. This type has no analogue for functions of a single variable.

EXAMPLE 1
Locate, and classify, all the stationary points of

(a) $f(x, y) = x^2 + 2y^2$,   (b) $f(x, y) = 2x - x^2 - 2y^2$,
(c) $f(x, y) = x^2 - 2y^2$.

In each of these examples, the stationary points are located by solving the simultaneous equations $f_x = 0, f_y = 0$.

(a) The equations

$$f_x = 2x = 0, \quad f_y = 4y = 0$$

show that the origin $(x, y) = (0, 0)$ is the only stationary point. Moreover, since $f(0, 0) = 0$ and $f(x, y) > 0$ for $(x, y) \neq (0, 0)$, the origin is an absolute minimum for $f(x, y)$, with value zero. The contours are ellipses enclosing the extremum, as may be seen in Fig. 4.8(a).

(b) Setting

$$f_x = 2 - 2x = 0, \quad f_y = -4y = 0$$

we find that $(x, y) = (1, 0)$ is the only stationary point of $f(x, y)$. To classify it, consider $f(x, y) - f(1, 0)$. Then, since $f(x, y) - f(1, 0) = 2x - x^2 - 2y^2 - 2 + 1 = -(x - 1)^2 - 2y^2 < 0$ for $(x, y) \neq (1, 0)$, the stationary point $(1, 0)$ is an absolute maximum, with value 1. Again the contours are ellipses, as in Fig. 4.8(b).

(c)   Solving $f_x = 2x = 0$ and $f_y = -4y = 0$, gives the origin $(x, y) = (0, 0)$ as the only stationary point, with $f(0, 0) = 0$. However, $f(x, y)$ may be positive or negative depending upon the relative magnitude of $|x|$ and $|y|$. Along $y = 0$, the function $f(x, 0) = x^2$ is never negative, whilst, along $x = 0$, the function $f(0, y) = -2y^2$ is never positive. Both functions reach the value zero at the stationary point. This stationary point is therefore a saddle point of $f(x, y)$. Near it, the contours are the hyperbolae $x^2 - 2y^2 = $ constant, showing that

$$f(x, y) > f(0, 0) = 0 \quad \text{in the regions } |x| > \sqrt{2}\,|y|$$

$$f(x, y) < f(0, 0) = 0 \quad \text{in the regions } |x| < \sqrt{2}\,|y|,$$

as in Fig. 4.8(c).

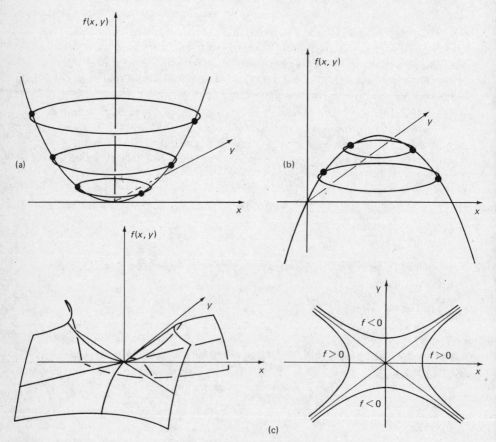

Fig. 4.8   The surfaces (a) $f(x, y) = x^2 + 2y^2$ near its minimum, (b) $f(x, y) = 2x - x^2 - 2y^2$ near its maximum, and (c) $f(x, y) = x^2 - 2y^2$ near its saddle point

The stationary points (a, b) of each function $f(x, y)$ in example 1 have been classified as either a *relative maximum*, a *relative minimum* or a *saddle point* by inspection of $f(a + h, b + k) - f(a, b)$ for all small values of $h^2 + k^2$. An alternative procedure is to use a criterion deducible from Taylor's theorem (11). This criterion is a generalization of the rule concerning the sign of $g''(x)$ at stationary points of a function $g(x)$ of a single variable.

At a stationary point (a, b) of $f(x, y)$ equation (11) may be written as

$$f(a + h, b + k) = f(a, b) + \frac{1}{2} [h^2 f_{xx}(a, b) + 2hk f_{xy}(a, b) + k^2 f_{yy}(a, b)] + R_3$$

$$= f(a, b) + \frac{1}{2} \Delta + R_3,$$

where

$$\Delta \equiv h^2 f_{xx}(a, b) + 2hk f_{xy}(a, b) + k^2 f_{yy}(a, b). \tag{27}$$

In most functions arising in engineering R_3 is negligible in comparison with Δ when $h^2 + k^2$ is sufficiently small, so that the sign of Δ determines the sign of $f(a + h, b + k) - f(a, b)$ in a disc completely surrounding the point (a, b). For displacements with $k = 0$, Δ reduces to $h^2 f_{xx}(a, b)$ and therefore has the same sign as $f_{xx}(a, b)$, whilst for displacements with $h = 0$, Δ has the same sign as $f_{yy}(a, b)$. Thus, if $f_{xx}(a, b)$ and $f_{yy}(a, b)$ have different signs the stationary point must be a saddle point. However, even when $f_{xx}(a, b)$ and $f_{yy}(a, b)$ have the same sign the point (a, b) will be a saddle point if Δ may take either sign. For, consider any line $k = \lambda h$, where λ is constant. The expression

$$\Delta = h^2 [f_{xx} + 2\lambda f_{xy} + \lambda^2 f_{yy}],$$

in which all partial derivatives are evaluated at $(x, y) = (a, b)$, shows that on this line Δ has the same sign as the bracketed term, which is quadratic in λ. Thus Δ may take either sign only if the quadratic term vanishes for two distinct real values of λ, in which case $f_{xx} f_{yy} - f_{xy}^2 < 0$. Consequently Δ is always positive for $f_{xx} f_{yy} - f_{xy}^2 > 0$ with $f_{xx} > 0$, is always negative for $f_{xx} f_{yy} - f_{xy}^2 > 0$ with $f_{xx} < 0$, but has sign depending on λ for $f_{xx} f_{yy} - f_{xy}^2 < 0$.

The Location and Classification of Stationary Points

The preceding considerations lead to the following rules:

Stationary points of a function $f(x, y)$ are found by simultaneously solving $f_x(x, y) = 0$ and $f_y(x, y) = 0$. Let $x = a, y = b$ be one such stationary point. Then,

whenever $f_{xx}(a, b) f_{yy}(a, b) - f_{xy}^2(a, b) < 0$ the point is a *saddle point*,
whilst if $f_{xx}(a, b) f_{yy}(a, b) - f_{xy}^2(a, b) > 0$ it is a *relative extremum*.
If $f_{xx}(a, b) f_{yy}(a, b) - f_{xy}^2(a, b) = 0$ the test is inconclusive.

A relative extremum is

a *relative maximum* whenever $f_{xx}(a, b) < 0$, but
a *relative minimum* whenever $f_{xx}(a, b) > 0$.

Notice that at each relative extremum f_{xx} and f_{yy} have the same sign, so that the conditions on f_{xx} may be replaced by conditions on f_{yy}.

In the case $f_{xx}f_{yy} - f_{xy}^2 = 0$, more terms of the Taylor series (14) may be studied, but it is usually found more convenient to investigate $f(a + h, b + k) - f(a, b)$ directly.

Exercise

Show that $f(x, y) = 2x^2 - 5xy + 2y^2$ has only one stationary point (a, b), and that at this point both $f_{xx} > 0$ and $f_{yy} > 0$. By sketching the region of the x, y plane in which $f(x, y) < 0$, verify that this pair of conditions does not ensure that the point (a, b) is a relative minimum.

EXAMPLE 2
Find and classify the stationary points of $x^2 + a^2 y^2 - \tfrac{1}{2}y^4$, for $a \neq 0$. Examine also the case $a = 0$.

Setting $f(x, y) \equiv x^2 + a^2 y^2 - \tfrac{1}{2}y^4$ gives $f_x = 2x$ and $f_y = 2y(a^2 - y^2)$, so that the only stationary points are at $(0, 0)$ and $(0, \pm a)$. Also $f_{xx} = 2 > 0, f_{xy} = 0$ and $f_{xy} = 2(a^2 - 3y^2)$, so that $f_{xx}f_{yy} - f_{xy}^2 = 4a^2, -8a^2, -8a^2$ at $(0, 0), (0, a), (0, -a)$ respectively. For $a \neq 0$ the stationary points are distinct. The points $(0, a)$ and $(0, -a)$ both are saddle points, whilst at $(0, 0)$ the quantities $f_{xx}f_{yy} - f_{xy}^2$ and f_{xx} are both positive, so that the origin is a relative minimum. For $a = 0$ the origin is the only stationary point, and here $f_{xx}f_{yy} - f_{xy}^2 = 0$ so that the test fails. However, for $(x, y) \neq (0, 0), f(x, y) = x^2 - \tfrac{1}{2}y^4$ is positive on the x axis and negative on the y axis, so that the origin must be a saddle point.

Many Independent Variables

Conditions (26) may be immediately generalized to state that a continuously differentiable function $f(x_1, x_2, \ldots, x_n)$ of n independent variables is stationary only at any 'point' $(a_1, a_2, \ldots, a_n)$ which satisfies the n simultaneous conditions

$$\frac{\partial f}{\partial x_1} = 0, \quad \frac{\partial f}{\partial x_2} = 0, \ldots, \frac{\partial f}{\partial x_n} = 0. \tag{28}$$

These are necessary and sufficient conditions that the rate of change of f along all curves through $(a_1, a_2, \ldots, a_n)$ should be zero. Then the sign of $f(a_1 + h_1, a_2 + h_2, \ldots, a_n + h_n) - f(a_1, a_2, \ldots, a_n)$ at points close to the stationary point is essentially determined by the quadratic terms

$$h_1^2 \frac{\partial^2 f}{\partial x_1^2} + \ldots + h_n^2 \frac{\partial^2 f}{\partial x_n^2} + 2 \left(h_1 h_2 \frac{\partial^2 f}{\partial x_1 \partial x_2} + h_1 h_3 \frac{\partial^2 f}{\partial x_1 \partial x_3} + \ldots \right.$$

$$\left. \ldots + h_{n-1} h_n \frac{\partial^2 f}{\partial x_{n-1} \partial x_n} \right)$$

of the Taylor series (16). When the matrix **A**, having elements $a_{ij} = \partial^2 f / \partial x_i \partial x_j$, is positive definite (see §8.9) this 'quadratic form' is never negative and the point

$(a_1, a_2, \ldots, a_n)$ is a relative minimum. Similarly if **A** is negative definite the stationary point is a relative maximum.

Extrema on the Boundary of a Region

Conditions (26) and (28) determine all stationary points of a function, but not necessarily all the extrema, since these may occur at points where the function f is not differentiable. Moreover, when a function is defined only at points of some restricted region the extrema may occur on the boundary of that region. For example, the function f defined for $|x| \leqslant 1, |y| \leqslant 1$ as $f(x, y) = (x^2 + y^2)^{1/2}$ has no stationary points, but has a minimum at $(x, y) = (0, 0)$ and four maxima at $(x, y) = (\pm 1, \pm 1)$, as may be seen by inspection of Fig. 4.5.

Extrema Subject to Constraints

An important class of problems involves determination of extrema of some function $f(x_1, x_2, \ldots, x_n)$ when the variables $x_1, x_2, \ldots, x_n$ are subject to one or more constraints. Two approaches are generally possible, and are illustrated for the case of functions of three variables x, y, and z. In the following it is assumed that all the required partial derivatives exist.

METHOD 1
Extrema of $f(x, y, z)$ are sought amongst all the points for which $z = G(x, y)$. In this case, substitution for z enables the problem to be replaced by one for the function

$$F(x, y) \equiv f[x, y, G(x, y)] .$$

Hence, the equations $\dfrac{\partial F}{\partial x} = 0 = \dfrac{\partial F}{\partial y}$ for the determination of the stationary points take the form

$$\frac{\partial f}{\partial x} + \frac{\partial f}{\partial z} \frac{\partial G}{\partial x} = 0, \quad \frac{\partial f}{\partial y} + \frac{\partial f}{\partial z} \frac{\partial G}{\partial y} = 0, \quad \text{with } z = G(x, y). \tag{29}$$

EXAMPLE 3
Find the warmest place on the surface of the sphere $x^2 + y^2 + z^2 = a^2$, when the temperature T is given by $T = x^2 + bz$ $(b > 0)$.

On the upper and lower halves of the sphere we may write $z = (a^2 - x^2 - y^2)^{1/2}$ and $z = -(a^2 - x^2 - y^2)^{1/2}$ respectively. Then the stationary points of $T = F(x, y) = x^2 \pm b(a^2 - x^2 - y^2)^{1/2}$ are given by

$$0 = \frac{\partial F}{\partial x} = 2x \pm \frac{(-bx)}{(a^2 - x^2 - y^2)^{1/2}} \quad \text{and} \quad 0 = \frac{\partial F}{\partial y} = \frac{\pm(-by)}{(a^2 - x^2 - y^2)^{1/2}} \,,$$

and so all lie on $y = 0$.

For $b > 2a$, the only stationary points are at $(0, 0, \pm a)$, and it may be checked that $(0, 0, a)$ has maximum temperature, and $(0, 0, -a)$ has minimum temperature.

For $b < 2a$, there are stationary points at $[(a^2 - \tfrac{1}{4}b^2)^{1/2}, 0, \tfrac{1}{2}b]$ and

$[-(a^2 - \tfrac{1}{4}b^2)^{1/2}, 0, \tfrac{1}{2}b]$ in addition to the pair at $(0, 0, \pm a)$. The points $[\pm(a^2 - \tfrac{1}{4}b^2)^{1/2}, 0, \tfrac{1}{2}b]$ are both temperature maxima, the point $(0, 0, a)$ is a saddle point, whilst $(0, 0, -a)$ remains the minimum.

METHOD 2

Often it is awkward, or even impossible, to use the equation of the constraint to eliminate any of the variables, and consequently all three variables must be retained. The problem is to find extrema of $f(x, y, z)$ amongst all values of (x, y, z) satisfying the constraint

$$g(x, y, z) = 0. \tag{30}$$

Such points are called *conditional extrema*.

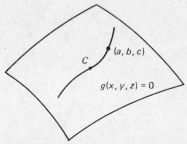

Fig. 4.9   An arbitrary curve C lying in the constraint surface $g(x, y, z) = 0$ and passing through the point (a, b, c)

Let $(x, y, z) = (a, b, c)$ be a conditional extremum. Then $df/ds = 0$ along any curve C passing through (a, b, c), and lying entirely within the constraint surface defined by equation (30). Also $dg/ds = 0$, since $g(x, y, z) = 0$ everywhere on C. Thus the equation

$$\frac{df}{ds} = f_x(a, b, c)\frac{dx}{ds} + f_y(a, b, c)\frac{dy}{ds} + f_z(a, b, c)\frac{dz}{ds} = 0 \tag{31}$$

must be satisfied whenever the direction cosines dx/ds, dy/ds and dz/ds also satisfy

$$g_x(a, b, c)\frac{dx}{ds} + g_y(a, b, c)\frac{dy}{ds} + g_z(a, b, c)\frac{dz}{ds} = 0. \tag{32}$$

Since equations (31) and (32) are linear equations for dx/ds, dy/ds and dz/ds, their solutions can be identical only when their coefficients are in a constant ratio. Hence,

$$\frac{f_x(a, b, c)}{g_x(a, b, c)} = \frac{f_y(a, b, c)}{g_y(a, b, c)} = \frac{f_z(a, b, c)}{g_z(a, b, c)} = -\lambda, \quad \text{say.}$$

Thus, the equations

$$f_x + \lambda g_x = 0, \quad f_y + \lambda g_y = 0, \quad f_z + \lambda g_z = 0 \quad \text{and} \quad g(x, y, z) = 0, \tag{33}$$

are the equations determining all conditional stationary points. Their geometrical interpretation is that the conditional extrema (a, b, c) are points at which the surface $f = \text{constant}$ is tangential to the constraint surface $g(x, y, z) = 0$.

The extra parameter λ in equations (33) is called a *Lagrange multiplier*. The equations (33) can alternatively be obtained by the *method of Lagrange multipliers*, which determines the stationary points of $f(x, y, z)$ subject to the constraint $g(x, y, z) = 0$ as stationary points of the auxiliary function

$$F(x, y, z, \lambda) = f(x, y, z) + \lambda g(x, y, z)$$

of the four variables x, y, z and λ. Indeed the resulting equations

$$F_x = f_x + \lambda g_x = 0, \quad F_y = f_y + \lambda g_y = 0, \quad F_z = f_z + \lambda g_z = 0, \quad F_\lambda = g = 0,$$

are equivalent to equations (33).

More generally, the method of Lagrange multipliers determines the stationary points of $f(x_1, x_2, \ldots, x_n)$ subject to p ($<n$) constraint equations $g_j(x_1, x_2, \ldots, x_n) = 0$, for $j = 1, 2, \ldots, p$, as stationary points of the auxiliary function $F \equiv f + \lambda_1 g_1 + \lambda_2 g_2 + \ldots + \lambda_p g_p$. The resulting $n + p$ equations

$$0 = \frac{\partial F}{\partial x_i} = \frac{\partial f}{\partial x_i} + \sum_{j=1}^{p} \lambda_j \frac{\partial g_j}{\partial x_i} \quad \text{for } i = 1, 2, \ldots, n,$$

$$0 = \frac{\partial F}{\partial \lambda_j} = g_j \quad \text{for } j = 1, 2, \ldots, p$$

are to be solved for $x_1, x_2, \ldots, x_n$ and the p Lagrange multipliers $\lambda_1, \lambda_2, \ldots, \lambda_p$.

Criteria for the classification of conditional stationary points into maxima, minima or saddle points are very awkward. In most practical problems, physical reasoning identifies the relevant points.

EXAMPLE 4

If a rectangular block is to fit inside a given sphere, show that its volume is maximum when its shape is a cube.

Let the block have edges of lengths $2x$, $2y$ and $2z$. Take axes Ox, Oy, Oz parallel to the edges of the block, so that all eight corners $(\pm x, \pm y, \pm z)$ lie on the sphere $x^2 + y^2 + z^2 = a^2$. The problem is then to maximize the volume $V = 8xyz$ subject to the single constraint $x^2 + y^2 + z^2 = a^2$.

Look for the stationary points of the auxiliary function

$$F(x, y, z, \lambda) \equiv 8xyz + \lambda(x^2 + y^2 + z^2 - a^2),$$

where λ is the Lagrange multiplier. The governing equations then become

$$F_x = 8yz + 2\lambda x = 0, \quad F_y = 8xz + 2\lambda y = 0, \quad F_z = 8xy + 2\lambda z = 0,$$

with $x^2 + y^2 + z^2 - a^2 = 0$.

These may be combined as

$$8xyz = -2\lambda x^2 = -2\lambda y^2 = -2\lambda z^2.$$

Consequently, either $x^2 = y^2 = z^2$ or $\lambda = 0$. The choice $\lambda = 0$ gives $V = 8xyz = 0$, which obviously is the minimum volume. Thus, since x, y and z are non-negative, we have $x = y = z$. Substitution into the equation of constraint gives $3x^2 = a^2$. Hence the box of maximum shape is the cube with $x = y = z = a/\sqrt{3}$, and has volume $V = 8a^3/3\sqrt{3}$. In this solution $\lambda = -4a/\sqrt{3}$.

In this example the original problem strictly is one with an inequality constraint $x^2 + y^2 + z^2 \leq a^2$, which prevents the point (x, y, z) from lying outside a sphere of radius a. However the only extremum of $V = 8xyz$ occurring when no constraint is imposed on (x, y, z) is the minimum at $(x, y, z) = (0, 0, 0)$. Consequently the maximum of V must be a conditional maximum for which the point (x, y, z) lies on the surface of the sphere. More generally, if extrema of $f(x, y, z)$ are sought subject to some inequality constraint $g(x, y, z) \leq 0$ they are either extrema of f for which the point (x, y, z) satisfies the strict inequality $g < 0$, or they are conditional extrema of $f(x, y, z)$ for which (x, y, z) lies on the boundary $g(x, y, z) = 0$ of the feasible region. These extrema are often found directly by search methods, as in Chapter 2 of Volume 2, in problems where the equations (33) are difficult to solve.

Exercises

1. Show that $f(x, y) = x^3 + y^3 - 2(x^2 + y^2) + 3xy$ has stationary points at $(0, 0)$ and $(\frac{1}{3}, \frac{1}{3})$. Investigate their nature.

2. The Post Office will accept packages for 'parcel post' only if (a) the *length* z does not exceed 1.07 m, and (b) the sum of the length and the girth around a perpendicular cross-section does not exceed 2 m. If a parcel is rectangular with dimensions x, y and z and satisfies restriction (b) substitute for z and so find its maximum volume. Check that the corresponding dimensions satisfy restriction (a) also, and so deduce the dimensions of the rectangular parcel of greatest volume acceptable to the Post Office.

3. Rework exercise 2 using the method of Lagrange multipliers.

4. Minimize $(x^2 + y^2 + z^2)^{1/2}$ amongst all (x, y, z) satisfying $2x + y - 2z + 3 \leq 0$. Interpret this problem, and your result, geometrically.

5. Find and classify the stationary points of $f(x, y) = \cos y - x^2$. Check your answers by interpreting $f(x, y)$ as the height at (x, y) of a corrugated parabolic arch roof.

6. Set $g(x, y, z) = G(x, y) - z$ in equation (30) and so show that equations (29) are a special case of equations (33).

7. The angles of a triangle are measured as a, b, c respectively. Find the estimates A, B, C of the angles which satisfy $A + B + C = 180°$, and which minimize the weighted sum S of the squares of the errors in the measurements, where

$$S = W_a(A - a)^2 + W_b(B - b)^2 + W_c(C - c)^2,$$

and W_a, W_b and W_c are given.
   If $a = 81°$, $b = 46°$ and $c = 55°$, find A, B and C when $W_a = 1$, $W_b = W_c = 2$.

4.5 FURTHER APPLICATIONS

Certain important applications of partial derivatives are outlined in this section. Other examples occur throughout the book.

Estimation of Small Errors

In practical situations, measurements necessarily include some experimental error, and it is important to be able to estimate the consequent error in any quantity calculated from the measurements.

Suppose the required quantity w is related through some function f to n other quantities which have values measured experimentally as $x_1, x_2, \ldots, x_n$. The predicted value of w is then obtained as $w = f(x_1, x_2, \ldots, x_n)$, whilst the actual value is $f(x_1 + \Delta x_1, x_2 + \Delta x_2, \ldots, x_n + \Delta x_n)$, where $\Delta x_1, \Delta x_2, \ldots, \Delta x_n$ are the errors in the experimental measurements. The Taylor series (16) relates these values by

$$f(x_1 + \Delta x_1, x_2 + \Delta x_2, \ldots, x_n + \Delta x_n) - f(x_1, x_2, \ldots, x_n) \simeq \sum_{p=1}^{n} \Delta x_p \frac{\partial f}{\partial x_p},$$

so that neglect of terms having second and higher order in $\Delta x_1, \Delta x_2, \ldots, \Delta x_n$ gives an estimate of the error in w as

$$\Delta w \equiv \Delta x_1 \frac{\partial f}{\partial x_1} + \Delta x_2 \frac{\partial f}{\partial x_2} + \ldots + \Delta x_n \frac{\partial f}{\partial x_n} = \sum_{p=1}^{n} \Delta x_p \frac{\partial f}{\partial x_p}(x_1, x_2, \ldots, x_n). \quad (34)$$

If it is known that $B_1, B_2, \ldots, B_n$ are upper bounds to the experimental errors, so that

$$|\Delta x_1| \leqslant B_1, \, |\Delta x_2| \leqslant B_2, \ldots, |\Delta x_n| \leqslant B_n,$$

a consequent upper bound for the error in w is given by

$$|\Delta w| \leqslant B_1 \, |\partial f/\partial x_1| + B_2 \, |\partial f/\partial x_2| + \ldots + B_n \, |\partial f/\partial x_n|. \quad (35)$$

EXAMPLE 1
A rectangular box having sides of lengths x, y and z has volume $V = xyz$. It is designed to have sides of lengths 2 m, 1.5 m and 0.4 m, but the actual measurements are 1.98 m, 1.51 m and 0.41 m. Show that its volume exceeds the design volume by approximately 0.026 m^3.

Since, neglecting second-order effects,

$$\Delta V \simeq yz\Delta x + xz\Delta y + xy\Delta z,$$

and $x = 2, y = 1.5, z = 0.4, \Delta x = -0.02, \Delta y = 0.01$ and $\Delta z = 0.01,$

$$\Delta V \simeq 0.026 \text{ m}^3.$$

(The exact error is $1.98 \times 1.51 \times 0.41 - 2 \times 1.5 \times 0.4 = 0.025818$.)

Logarithmic Differentiation

Calculations of the previous type may often be simplified when f is the product of many relatively simple functions, so that $\log f$ is a sum of functions. The basic formula

$$\frac{\Delta w}{w} = \frac{\Delta x_1}{f}\frac{\partial f}{\partial x_1} + \frac{\Delta x_2}{f}\frac{\partial f}{\partial x_2} + \ldots + \frac{\Delta x_n}{f}\frac{\partial f}{\partial x_n} = \sum_{p=1}^{n} \Delta x_p \frac{\partial(\log f)}{\partial x_p} \tag{36}$$

gives the *relative error* in w (see §9.1) and may usually be evaluated more simply than can relation (34). Thus, in example 1, where $\log V = \log x + \log y + \log z$, the calculation gives

$$\frac{\Delta V}{V} = \frac{\Delta x}{x} + \frac{\Delta y}{y} + \frac{\Delta z}{z} = -\frac{0.02}{2} + \frac{0.01}{1.5} + \frac{0.01}{0.4} = \frac{0.065}{3}.$$

Then, since $V = xyz = 1.2 \text{ m}^3$, $\Delta V = 0.026 \text{ m}^3$ as before.

The Method of Least Squares

In many experiments, pairs of values (x_i, y_i) (for $i = 1, 2, \ldots, n$) of two quantities are observed. The aim is to 'fit' these experimental data to some function $y = f(x, a_1, \ldots, a_r)$ by a suitable choice of the parameters $a_1, a_2, \ldots, a_r$. The *method of least squares*, which is discussed in §3.7 of Volume 2, chooses these parameters to minimize the sum of the squares of the deviations of the experimental data points from the function $y = f(x, a_1, \ldots, a_r)$.

Partial Differential Equations

Many functions describing phenomena in physics and engineering are governed by equations involving their partial derivatives. Such equations are called *partial differential equations*. Their study is a vast topic, not yet fully explored. Since some of the most important examples of partial differential equations are the subject of Chapter 7, only a few simple types are discussed here.

(a)   Every function $u(x, y)$ for which the value $u(x, y) = F(y)$ is independent of x has the property $\partial u/\partial x = 0$. It is said to satisfy the partial differential equation

$$\frac{\partial u}{\partial x} = 0.$$

(b)   Similarly, when $u(x, y)$ has a value depending only on x, it is a solution of

$$\frac{\partial u}{\partial y} = 0.$$

(c)   A disturbance $u(x, t) = f(x - ct)$ represents a waveform travelling with constant speed c in the direction of increasing x, when t measures time. Although the shape $u(x, 0) = f(x)$ of the profile at time $t = 0$ may be arbitrary, $u(x, t)$ satisfies the partial differential equation

$$\frac{\partial u}{\partial t} + c\frac{\partial u}{\partial x} = 0, \quad \text{whenever } f(x) \text{ is differentiable.}$$

Often, the physically important problem is to determine certain solutions of a given equation. Some techniques are discussed in Chapter 7. However, for examples (a)–(c) it can be shown that every solution is of the form stated. Thus $u_x = 0$ implies that $u(x, y)$ remains constant whenever y is held constant. Hence, associated with each constant value of y there is a constant value of u, which may be expressed as $u = F(y)$. Similarly every solution of $u_y = 0$ can have an arbitrary constant value for each value of x, and so is of the form $u = G(x)$. Note that $F(y)$ and $G(x)$ are arbitrary *functions* and are therefore more general than the arbitrary constants associated with ordinary differential equations.

One procedure for showing that $u = f(x - ct)$ is the general solution of $u_t + cu_x = 0$ is indicated in problem 13.

The Envelope of a Family of Curves

For each value of α the relation $F(x, y, \alpha) = 0$ defines a curve in the x, y plane. The total collection of such curves forms a *family of curves*. Some families of curves possess an *envelope* — a curve which touches each member of the family. Figure 4.10 illustrates a typical situation.

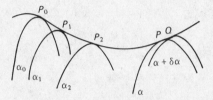

Fig. 4.10   The envelope of a family of curves

Let P be the point at which the curve $F(x, y, \alpha) = 0$ touches the envelope. Then, in principle, the points corresponding to different values α may be written parametrically as $x = x(\alpha), y = y(\alpha)$, where the functions satisfy

$$F[x(\alpha), y(\alpha), \alpha] \equiv 0$$

identically for a range of values of α. Total differentiation then gives

$$F_x[x(\alpha), y(\alpha), \alpha] x'(\alpha) + F_y[x(\alpha), y(\alpha), \alpha] y'(\alpha) + F_\alpha[x(\alpha), y(\alpha), \alpha] = 0. \qquad (37)$$

Also, at each point P, the tangents to the envelope and to the curve $\alpha = $ constant must coincide. However, the curve of constant α has gradient dy/dx given by

$$0 = \frac{d}{dx} F(x, y, \alpha) = F_x + F_y \frac{dy}{dx},$$

whilst the envelope has gradient

$$\frac{dy}{dx} = \frac{y'(\alpha)}{x'(\alpha)}.$$

Thus we find that

$$F_x[x(\alpha), y(\alpha), \alpha]\, x'(\alpha) + F_y[x(\alpha),\, y(\alpha), \alpha]\, y'(\alpha) = 0.$$

This may be subtracted from equation (37) to give

$$F_\alpha[x(\alpha), y(\alpha), \alpha] = 0.$$

Consequently the points P of the envelope may be determined as the solutions to the simultaneous equations

$$F(x, y, \alpha) = 0, \quad F_\alpha(x, y, \alpha) = 0. \tag{38}$$

EXAMPLE 2

After t seconds a point source of sound propagates waves to radial distance ct. In a uniform air stream of speed U this circular *wavefront* will have been swept downstream a distance Ut. Thus a source fixed at the origin can propagate disturbances only out as far as the envelope of the circular wavefronts $(x - Ut)^2 + y^2 = c^2 t^2$. Find this envelope, if it exists.

The family of curves may be written as

$$F(x, y, t) \equiv (x - Ut)^2 + y^2 - c^2 t^2 = 0,$$

where t plays the role of the parameter α. The points $x(t), y(t)$ of the envelope must also satisfy

$$0 = F_t(x, y, t) = -2U(x - Ut) - 2c^2 t = 0.$$

Hence the envelope is given parametrically as

$$x = (U - c^2/U)t, \quad y^2 = c^2 t^2 - c^4 t^2/U^2 = c^2(1 - c^2/U^2)t^2,$$

and is therefore real only for $U > c$, in which case the flow is said to be *supersonic*.

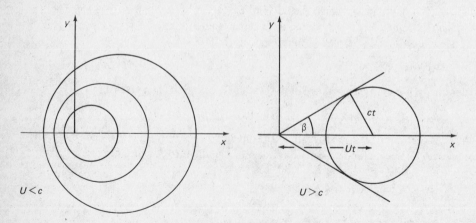

Fig. 4.11   Wavefronts at successive times in subsonic flow ($U < c$) and the envelope of wavefronts for supersonic flow ($U > c$)

On elimination of t, the envelope is found to be the pair of straight lines
$y = \pm c(U^2 - c^2)^{-1/2}x$.

Figure 4.11 shows how for *subsonic* flow ($U < c$) disturbances travel to all points, and the wavefronts have no envelope. However, when the *Mach number* $M = U/c$ exceeds unity the disturbance is bounded by two *Mach lines*, inclined at $\pm\beta$ to the downstream flow, where $\beta = \sin^{-1} c/U$ is the *Mach angle*.

Exercises

1. The focal length f of a lens is given by $f^{-1} = x^{-1} + y^{-1}$, where x and y are the distance from the lens to an object and to its image. If $x = 0.90 \pm 0.005$, $y = 0.30 \pm 0.005$, find f together with an error estimate. All lengths are measured in metres.

2. If $w = f(y - z, z - x, x - y)$, prove that $\dfrac{\partial w}{\partial x} + \dfrac{\partial w}{\partial y} + \dfrac{\partial w}{\partial z} = 0$.

3. If $u = xy\sqrt{(x + 2y)}$, verify that $x\dfrac{\partial u}{\partial x} + y\dfrac{\partial u}{\partial y} = \dfrac{5u}{2}$.

4. Show that $u = \sin(x + y)$ satisfies the equation $\dfrac{\partial u}{\partial x} = \dfrac{\partial u}{\partial y}$.

5. A function $f(x, y)$ is rewritten in terms of new variables $u = e^x \cos y$, and $v = e^x \sin y$. Show that $\dfrac{\partial f}{\partial x} = u\dfrac{\partial f}{\partial u} + v\dfrac{\partial f}{\partial v}$, and $\dfrac{\partial f}{\partial y} = -v\dfrac{\partial f}{\partial u} + u\dfrac{\partial f}{\partial v}$, and so deduce that

$$\frac{\partial^2 f}{\partial x^2} + \frac{\partial^2 f}{\partial y^2} = (u^2 + v^2)\left(\frac{\partial^2 f}{\partial u^2} + \frac{\partial^2 f}{\partial v^2}\right).$$

6. A straight rod of unit length slides in the x, y plane with its ends on the x and y axes respectively. Find its envelope.

PROBLEMS

1 Calculate all the second-order partial derivatives of $f(r, \theta) = r^n \cos n\theta$, and so verify that $f(r, \theta)$ is a solution of the partial differential equation

$$\frac{\partial^2 f}{\partial r^2} + \frac{1}{r}\frac{\partial f}{\partial r} + \frac{1}{r^2}\frac{\partial^2 f}{\partial \theta^2} = 0.$$

2. If (x, y) are plane cartesian coordinates and (r, θ) are polar coordinates defined by $x = r\cos\theta$, $y = r\sin\theta$, calculate the Jacobians $\dfrac{\partial(x, y)}{\partial(r, \theta)}$ and $\dfrac{\partial(r, \theta)}{\partial(x, y)}$ (see p. 149). Verify

that these Jacobians satisfy

$$\frac{\partial(x,y)}{\partial(r,\theta)} = \left[\frac{\partial(r,\theta)}{\partial(x,y)}\right]^{-1}.$$

3. If the equations $u = u(x, y)$ and $v = v(x, y)$ define a change of coordinates and the equations $x = x(u, v)$ and $y = y(u, v)$ define the inverse transformation, differentiate the identities $x = x[u(x, y), v(x, y)]$ and $y = y[u(x, y), v(x, y)]$ partially with respect to x and y by use of the chain rule. Hence deduce the equation

$$\frac{\partial(x,y)}{\partial(u,v)}\frac{\partial(u,v)}{\partial(x,y)} = 1$$

relating the Jacobians of a transformation and its inverse.

4. Use the Taylor series to find a quadratic approximation to each of the following functions at the specified points:

(a) $2x^2 - 3xy + x$ at $(1, 1)$,   (b) $x^{1/2} + (y + 1)$ at $(1, 1)$,

(c) e^{x+y-z} at $(0, 0, 0)$,   (d) $\cos xy$ at $(1, \pi)$.

5. The dimensions of a rectangular room are measured as 12 m, 4 m, and 3 m. If the measurements may be in error by ± 0.03 m, ± 0.01 m, and ± 0.01 m respectively, calculate the length of the diagonal and estimate the largest possible error in this length.

6. Prove that the function $f(x, y) = x^3 + 3kxy^2 - 3x^2 - 3y^2 + 4$, where k is a real constant, always has one and only one maximum. Prove also that $f(x, y)$ has a minimum if $k > \frac{1}{2}$ but not if $k < \frac{1}{2}$. Find the values of x, y and $f(x, y)$ which correspond to these maxima and minima.

7. What are the values of $x_1, x_2, \ldots, x_n$ which minimize

$$\sum_{i=1}^{n} a_i^2 x_i^2 \quad \text{subject to the constraint} \quad \sum_{i=1}^{n} x_i = 1?$$

8. A cylindrical trough of length l has a cross-section which is an arc (of angle 2α) of a circle of radius r, and has surface area

$$S = \frac{2V}{l} + 2lr\alpha$$

where V is the capacity $V = lr^2 (\alpha - \sin\alpha\cos\alpha)$. Show that when the design capacity is specified, the surface area will be a minimum when the cross-section is a semicircle ($\alpha = \frac{1}{2}\pi$), and when $l = 2r$.

9. The problem of finding stationary points for $f(x, y, z)$ subject to $g(x, y, z) = $ const. and of finding stationary points for $g(x, y, z)$ subject to $f(x, y, z) = $ constant are said to be *dual*. Show that both problems lead to the equations

$$f_x + \lambda g_x = 0, \quad f_y + \lambda g_y = 0, \quad f_z + \lambda g_z = 0.$$

(These imply that the surfaces f = constant and g = constant share a common tangent plane at conditional stationary points.)

10. Show that when $f(x)$ is specified in $0 \leqslant x \leqslant \pi$, the integral

$$I \equiv \int_0^\pi \left[f(x) - \sum_{n=1}^N a_n \sin nx \right]^2 dx$$

may be regarded as a function $I(a_1, a_2, \ldots, a_N)$ and is minimized by the choices $a_n = \dfrac{2}{\pi} \int_0^\pi f(x) \sin nx \, dx$. (Compare this with the *half-range Fourier sine series* of Chapter 2. Note that the values of the coefficients do not depend on N.)

11. A function $f(x, y)$ of the form $f(x, y) = x^m F(y/x)$ is said to be *homogeneous in x and y of degree m* (cf. §1.3). Express f_x and f_y in terms of F and its first derivative. Hence verify *Euler's identity*

$$x \frac{\partial f}{\partial x} + y \frac{\partial f}{\partial y} = mf.$$

12. Prove that if $V(x, y) = (1 - 2xy + y^2)^{-1/2}$ then V satisfies the partial differential equation

$$\frac{\partial}{\partial x} \left[(1 - x^2) \frac{\partial V}{\partial x} \right] + \frac{\partial}{\partial y} \left[y^2 \frac{\partial V}{\partial y} \right] = 0.$$

13. If $\xi = x - ct$ and $\eta = x + ct$, derive expressions for the partial derivatives Φ_x, Φ_t, Φ_{xx}, Φ_{xt} and Φ_{tt} of $\Phi(x, t)$ in terms of partial derivatives of Φ with respect to ξ and η. Deduce that (a) when Φ satisfies the equation $c\Phi_x + \Phi_t = 0$, then $\partial\Phi/\partial\eta = 0$, so that Φ may be expressed as $\Phi = F(\xi) = F(x - ct)$, and that (b) when Φ satisfies the wave equation $c^2\Phi_{xx} = \Phi_{tt}$, then $\partial^2\Phi/\partial\xi\,\partial\eta = 0$. (This analysis leads to *D'Alembert's solution* of the wave equation, see §7.2.)

BIBLIOGRAPHY

[1] Lennox, S. C. and M. Chadwick. *Mathematics for Engineers and Applied Scientists*, p. 85, Heinemann, London (1970).

CHAPTER 5

Multiple Integrals

5.1 MULTIPLE INTEGRALS AND ORDINARY INTEGRALS

The theory of multiple integration is an extension, for functions of several variables, of the theory of 'ordinary' integration of a function of one variable. Multiple integrals occur in all branches of engineering and pure science, their most frequent applications being in theories involving the 'total' effect of a property over a portion of surface or throughout a region of space.

The reader is assumed to be familiar with the elementary theory of integration, and with the various analytical techniques employed when analytical expressions are sought for given integrals (numerical methods for evaluating integrals are treated in Chapter 11). However, since the basic ideas of that theory can be generalized to give the theory of multiple integration, and since the actual evaluation of multiple integrals reduces to evaluation of a succession of single integrals, we briefly recall some of the principal features of the theory.

If $g(t)$ is a function of a single variable t, the *definite integral* of $g(t)$ with respect to t over the *range of integration* $a \leqslant t \leqslant b$ is written as

$$\int_a^b g(t)\, dt.$$

This is defined by the following limiting process. The range $[a, b]$ is divided into n arbitrary subdivisions $[a, t_1], [t_1, t_2], \ldots, [t_{n-1}, b]$. Then, if $\delta t_i = t_i - t_{i-1}$ and ξ_i is a value of t in the interval $[t_{i-1}, t_i]$, we write

$$\int_a^b g(t)\, dt = \lim_{n \to \infty} \sum_{i=1}^n g(\xi_i)(t_i - t_{i-1}) = \lim_{\delta t_i \to 0} \sum_{[a,b]} g(t_i)\delta t_i \tag{1}$$

provided the limit exists and is independent of the choice of ξ_i in each interval. Here $t_0 = a$, $t_n = b$ and the notation $\sum_{[a,b]}$ implies summation over all the elementary subdivisions $\delta t_1, \delta t_2, \ldots$ of the range $[a, b]$. The values a and b are called the *limits of integration* and $g(t)$ is the *integrand*.

The value of the integral is given by the *fundamental theorem of integral calculus*. This states that if $G(t)$ is a differentiable function such that

$$dG(t)/dt = g(t) \tag{2}$$

then

$$\int_a^b g(t)dt = G(b) - G(a). \tag{3}$$

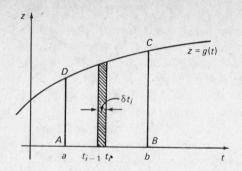

Fig. 5.1 Graphical representation of ordinary integration

$G(t)$ is termed the *indefinite integral* of $g(t)$, and is usually written in the form

$$G(t) = \int g(t)\,dt. \tag{4}$$

By associating the ith term in equation (1) with the area of the strip *PQRS* built on the typical elementary interval *PQ* of length δt_i (see Fig. 5.1), it can be seen that graphically the definite integral $\int_a^b g(t)\,dt$ represents the plane area *ABCD* between the curve $z = g(t)$ and the range of integration $[a, b]$ on the t axis.

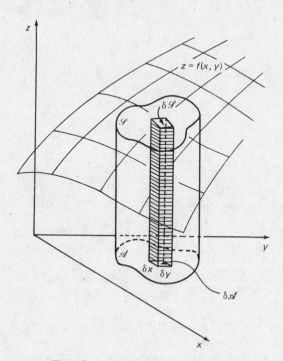

Fig. 5.2 Volume below a curved surface

The double integral of a function $z = f(x, y)$ of two variables x and y may be derived and evaluated by considering the analogous situation in three dimensions. The relation $z = f(x, y)$ defines a *surface* in space. We now determine the *volume* enclosed by the right cylinder erected on the *plane region* $\mathscr{A}$ in the x, y plane (see Fig. 5.2) and below the surface $z = f(x, y)$. The region $\mathscr{A}$ may be subdivided into a large number of elementary areas with typical area δA (where, for example, $\delta A = \delta x \delta y$ if $\delta \mathscr{A}$ is a rectangle with sides δx and δy). The volume of an elementary cylinder based on such an area about a typical point (x, y) is approximately $f(x, y) \, \delta A$. The total volume V required is then given by summing all such elementary volumes and taking the limit as the number of elementary areas becomes infinite and each $\delta A \to 0$. Thus

$$V = \lim_{\delta A \to 0} \left\{ \sum_{\mathscr{A}} f(x, y) \, \delta A \right\} \quad \text{or} \quad V = \iint_{\mathscr{A}} f(x, y) \, \mathrm{d}A. \tag{5}$$

This is the *double integral* of $f(x, y)$ over the *region of integration* $\mathscr{A}$.

For ranges of t for which $g(t)$ is negative, it is conventional to interpret the single integral of $g(t)$ over that range as defining a *negative* area. A similar convention applies to double integrals; if $z = f(x, y)$ is negative in the region $\mathscr{A}$, then $\iint_{\mathscr{A}} f \mathrm{d}A$ represents a negative volume.

EXAMPLE 1
Write down the double integral representing the volume described by $x \geqslant 0$, $y \geqslant 0$, $z \geqslant 0$ and $x^2 + y^2 + z \leqslant a^2$.

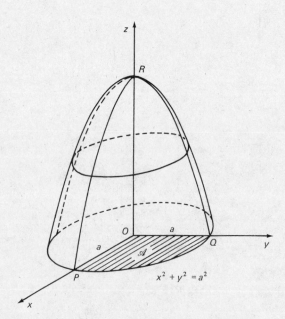

Fig. 5.3   Paraboloid of revolution $z = a^2 - x^2 - y^2$

The volume is depicted in Fig. 5.3; the curved surface is a paraboloid of revolution about the z axis, intersecting the x, y plane in the circle $x^2 + y^2 = a^2$. Hence the region of integration $\mathscr{A}$ is the quadrant OPQ bounded by $x^2 + y^2 = a^2$, $x = 0$, $y = 0$, and the required volume is

$$V = \iint_{\mathscr{A}} (a^2 - x^2 - y^2) \, dA = \iint_{\mathscr{A}} (a^2 - x^2 - y^2) \, dx \, dy. \qquad (6)$$

It should be noted that other double integrals can represent the required volume. From Fig. 5.3 it is evident that in this case two alternatives are

$$V = \iint_{OPR} (a^2 - x^2 - z)^{1/2} \, dx \, dz \quad \text{and} \quad V = \iint_{OQR} (a^2 - y^2 - z)^{1/2} \, dy \, dz.$$

Double integrals arise also when quantities other than volumes are evaluated. An example is that of the mass M of a lamina or thin plate with surface $\mathscr{A}$ and mass per unit area $\rho(x, y)$, where (x, y) are the cartesian coordinates of a point in $\mathscr{A}$; the mass of an elementary portion δA is $\rho \, \delta A$, so that the total mass is

$$M = \iint_{\mathscr{A}} \rho(x, y) \, dA. \qquad (7)$$

A similar relation holds when ρ represents any surface density function; for example, if ρ represents the electric charge per unit area, then M would be the total electric charge on the lamina. The double integral in equation (7) also represents the second moment of area of the lamina about the origin when $\rho(x, y)$ is replaced by $x^2 + y^2$.

EXAMPLE 2
Show that the double integral $\iint_{\mathscr{A}} dx \, dy$ represents the area of $\mathscr{A}$.

Choose the surface $z = f(x, y)$ to be the *plane* $z = 1$. Then the double integral

$$\iint_{\mathscr{A}} f(x, y) \, dx \, dy = \iint_{\mathscr{A}} dx \, dy$$

is the volume of a cylinder of unit height standing on $\mathscr{A}$; hence

$$\iint_{\mathscr{A}} dx \, dy = A.$$

Exercises

1. Write down the double integral representing the volume of a hemisphere of radius R.

2. Express, as a double integral, the volume cut from the sphere $x^2 + y^2 + z^2 \leqslant 4a^2$ by the cylinder $x^2 + y^2 \leqslant a^2$.

5.2 EVALUATION OF DOUBLE INTEGRALS

Double integrals have been defined and interpreted in the previous section. However, no practical method of evaluating such an integral has yet been given, except possibly

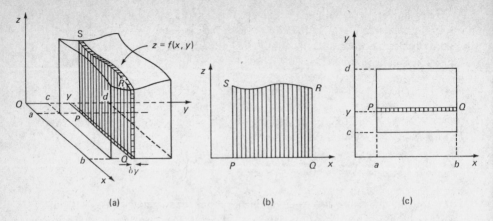

Fig. 5.4   Double integration over a rectangular region of integration

that of weighing a body constructed with the appropriate shape! In fact, double
integration can be performed in two operations, each being an ordinary integration.

Rectangular Regions of Integration

The general method of evaluation is most easily understood in the context of double
integrals over rectangular regions of integration.

Consider the volume represented by $\iint_{\mathcal{A}} f(x, y)\, \mathrm{d}A$ where $\mathcal{A}$ is the rectangular
region

$$a \leqslant x \leqslant b, \quad c \leqslant y \leqslant d,$$

as shown in Fig. 5.4. If PQ is an elementary strip of width δy and parallel to the x axis,
then the elementary slice of V standing on this strip has volume δV which is δy
multiplied by the area of $PQRS$. The theory of single integrals gives

$$\text{area } PQRS = \int_a^b f(x,\ y)\,\mathrm{d}x$$

where the integration is carried out with respect to x. In this integration the value of y
is *treated like a constant*, since y does not change as x varies along PQ. Hence we
obtain

$$\delta V = \left\{ \int_a^b f(x, y)\,\mathrm{d}x \right\} \delta y.$$

The integral in the curly brackets gives a function involving y but not x, because the
x dependence is eliminated when the limits of integration are inserted. Then summing
the volumes of all the elementary slices as y varies between c and d, and taking the
limit as the number of slices becomes infinite, gives another ordinary integration, this

time with respect to y. Hence the total volume is

$$V = \int_c^d \left\{ \int_a^b f(x, y) \, dx \right\} dy. \tag{8}$$

The curly brackets in this expression are unnecessary if we adopt the standard convention that the *inner integral* (in this case $\int_a^b f(x, y) \, dx$) *is always evaluated first.*

EXAMPLE 1
Evaluate the double integral

$$I = \int_0^{\pi/2} \int_a^b \sin(2x - y) \, dx \, dy.$$

$$I = \int_0^{\pi/2} \left\{ \int_a^b \sin(2x - y) \, dx \right\} dy = \int_0^{\pi/2} \left[-\tfrac{1}{2} \cos(2x - y) \right]_{x=a}^{x=b} dy$$

$$= -\frac{1}{2} \int_0^{\pi/2} \left\{ \cos(2b - y) - \cos(2a - y) \right\} dy$$

$$= -\frac{1}{2} \left[-\sin(2b - y) + \sin(2a - y) \right]_0^{\pi/2}$$

$$= \tfrac{1}{2}(\sin 2a + \cos 2a - \sin 2b - \cos 2b).$$

An alternative method of evaluating the double integral (8) is obtained by observing that the rectangular region $\mathscr{A}$ could just as well have been divided into elementary strips of width δx parallel to the y axis. In this case, the volume would be given by

$$V = \int_a^b \int_c^d f(x, y) \, dy \, dx \tag{9}$$

where the convention concerning the order of integration has been adopted. Thus, the double integral in equation (9) is computed by first integrating $f(x, y)$ with respect to y between the limits $y = c$ and $y = d$, treating x as a constant, and then integrating the resulting function of x between the limits $x = a$ and $x = b$.

If the limits are constants, i.e. the region of integration is rectangular, equations (8) and (9) show that changing the order of integration merely requires a change in the order of the limits; that is,

$$\int_c^d \int_a^b f(x, y) \, dx \, dy = \int_a^b \int_c^d f(x, y) \, dy \, dx. \tag{10}$$

EXAMPLE 2
Evaluate the double integral $I = \int_a^b \int_0^{\pi/2} \sin(2x - y) \, dy \, dx$

and show that the answer is the same as that of example 1.

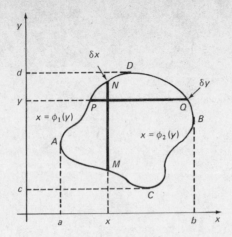

Fig. 5.5   Non-rectangular region of integration

$$I = \int_a^b \left\{ \int_0^{\pi/2} \sin(2x - y) \, dy \right\} dx = \int_a^b \left[\cos(2x - y) \right]_{y=0}^{y=\pi/2} dx$$

$$= \int_a^b (\sin 2x - \cos 2x) \, dx = \tfrac{1}{2}(-\cos 2b + \cos 2a - \sin 2b + \sin 2a).$$

Non-rectangular Regions of Integration

We now consider the more general case in which the region of integration is described by

$$\phi_1(y) \leqslant x \leqslant \phi_2(y), \quad c \leqslant y \leqslant d; \tag{11}$$

an example is the region $ACBD$ shown in Fig. 5.5. The functions $\phi_1(y)$ and $\phi_2(y)$ are known, continuous functions; $x = \phi_1(y)$ is the equation of the curve CAD for y varying between c and d, and $x = \phi_2(y)$ is the equation of the remaining part CBD of the boundary. Alternatively, the region could be described by

$$\psi_1(x) \leqslant y \leqslant \psi_2(x), \quad a \leqslant x \leqslant b, \tag{12}$$

where $y = \psi_1(x)$ is the equation of ACB and $y = \psi_2(x)$ gives the curve ADB. The two descriptions (11) and (12) are completely equivalent, although the forms of the functions $\phi_1(x)$, $\phi_2(x)$, $\psi_1(y)$ and $\psi_2(y)$ are usually quite different.

Just as in the analysis for rectangular regions, we integrate $f(x, y)$ over the region $\mathcal{A}$ by dividing $\mathcal{A}$ into elementary strips PQ parallel to the x axis and then take the limit as the typical strip width δy becomes infinitesimally small. The volume of the elementary slice above PQ and below the surface $z = f(x, y)$ is given by

$$\delta V = \left\{ \int_{x=\phi_1(y)}^{x=\phi_2(y)} f(x, y) \, dx \right\} \delta y,$$

in which $f(x, y)$ is again integrated with respect to x, treating y as a constant. In general, the limits of integration are *not* now constant, but vary with y. Inserting these limits still results in a function which depends on y only. Summing the elementary slices and taking the limit as their thicknesses tend to zero gives

$$V = \int_c^d \int_{\phi_1(y)}^{\phi_2(y)} f(x, y) \, \mathrm{d}x \, \mathrm{d}y.$$

Again we could just as well have started with the y integration by dividing the region of integration into elementary strips such as MN parallel to the y axis. This now results in

$$V = \int_a^b \int_{\psi_1(x)}^{\psi_2(x)} f(x, y) \, \mathrm{d}y \, \mathrm{d}x.$$

Hence

$$\int_c^d \int_{\phi_1(y)}^{\phi_2(y)} f(x, y) \, \mathrm{d}x \, \mathrm{d}y = \iint_{\mathscr{A}} f(x, y) \, \mathrm{d}A = \int_a^b \int_{\psi_1(x)}^{\psi_2(x)} f(x, y) \, \mathrm{d}y \, \mathrm{d}x. \tag{13}$$

Obviously, the change of order of integration now requires changing the actual values of the limits of integration.

EXAMPLE 3

Evaluate the double integral $\iint_{\mathscr{A}} y \, \mathrm{d}A$ where $\mathscr{A}$ is the region enclosed by the semi-parabola $y = \sqrt{x}$ and the lines $y = 0, x = 2$.

The first step is to determine the appropriate limits of integration. To do this it is advisable *always* to sketch the region of integration. The region appropriate to this example is shown in Fig. 5.6. If the integration is to be carried out first with respect to x, we draw a line PQ at a typical y and ask, 'Between which limits does x vary for this typical y?' In this example, the answer is evidently that x varies between $x = y^2$, its value at P, and $x = 2$, its value at Q, i.e. $\phi_1(y) = y^2$ and $\phi_2(y) = 2$. Then we ask 'Which values can this typical y take?' Here the answer is that y takes all values such that $0 \leqslant y \leqslant \sqrt{2}$, so that $c = 0$ and $d = \sqrt{2}$. Hence the integral may be evaluated as

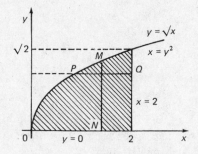

Fig. 5.6   Region of integration for example 3

$$\int_0^{\sqrt{2}} \int_{y^2}^2 y \, dx \, dy = \int_0^{\sqrt{2}} \left\{ \int_{y^2}^2 y \, dx \right\} dy = \int_0^{\sqrt{2}} \left[yx \right]_{x=y^2}^{x=2} dy$$

$$= \int_0^{\sqrt{2}} y(2 - y^2) dy = \left[y^2 - \frac{1}{4} y^4 \right]_0^{\sqrt{2}} = 1.$$

If the y integration is carried out first, a line MN should be drawn at a typical x value. This shows that y varies between 0 and x^2 for any choice of x. The entire range of x is seen to be $0 \leqslant x \leqslant 2$, and the integral can now be evaluated as

$$\int_0^2 \int_0^{\sqrt{x}} y \, dy \, dx = \int_0^2 \left[\tfrac{1}{2} y^2 \right]_0^{\sqrt{x}} dx = \int_0^2 \tfrac{1}{2} x \, dx = 1.$$

If just the region of integration is explicitly given, and not the actual limits, then a choice must be made between the two alternative orders of integration. In example 3 above, there is very little advantage gained one way or the other. In many cases, however, the order of integration matters, and the more convenient order of integration can usually be determined by drawing lines at typical x and y values on the sketch of the region of integration, as illustrated in the following example.

EXAMPLE 4
Evaluate $I = \int \int_{\mathscr{A}} x^2 \, dA$ where $\mathscr{A}$ is the region enclosed by the parabola $x^2 + y = 8$ and the line $y = 2x$.

The sketch of $\mathscr{A}$ is shown in Fig. 5.7. $P_1 Q_1$ and $P_2 Q_2$ represent lines at typical y values. Although in each case the lower limit for x has the form $x = -(8 - y)^{1/2}$, the upper limits at Q_1 and Q_2 are different, being $x = \tfrac{1}{2} y$ for $y \leqslant 4$ and $x = (8 - y)^{1/2}$ for $y \geqslant 4$. Thus, for this order of integration, the integral must be computed in two parts:

$$I = \int_{-8}^4 \int_{-(8-y)^{1/2}}^{y/2} x^2 \, dx \, dy + \int_4^8 \int_{-(8-y)^{1/2}}^{(8-y)^{1/2}} x^2 \, dx \, dy.$$

Alternatively, drawing a line MN at a typical x value shows that the lower limit for y is $2x$ and the upper limit is $8 - x^2$ for all possible x values. Hence the preferred calculation is

$$I = \int_{-4}^2 \int_{2x}^{8-x^2} x^2 \, dy \, dx = 100^4/s .$$

Change of Order of Integration

When the limits of integration are given *a priori*, we can still deduce the relevant region of integration and hence reverse the order of integration. This deliberate change of the order is often a useful device when evaluating a double integral whose inner integral cannot be expressed in terms of standard functions or whose outer integration cannot be analytically performed even if the inner one can.

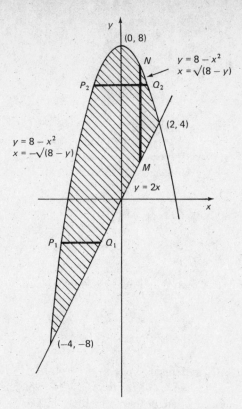

Fig. 5.7 Region of integration for example 4

EXAMPLE 5

Evaluate $I = \int_0^1 \int_{y/2}^{1/2} \exp(x^2)\,dx\,dy$.

The integral with respect to x cannot be expressed in terms of standard functions. Hence it is worth reversing the order of integration and trying to evaluate the integral by performing the y integration first.

The relevant region of integration is the shaded triangle shown in Fig. 5.8. It is obtained by interpreting the inner limits as the statement that, for any typical y line PQ, the lower limit of the range of x lies on the line $x = \frac{1}{2}y$ and the upper limit is $x = \frac{1}{2}$. The outer integral then implies that the appropriate range for y is $0 \leqslant y \leqslant 1$.

We now consider a typical x-line MN, on which the range of y is from $y = 0$ to $y = 2x$; all the typical x values must lie between $x = 0$ and $x = \frac{1}{2}$. Hence

$$I = \int_0^{1/2} \int_0^{2x} \exp(x^2)\,dy\,dx = \int_0^{1/2} \exp(x^2)\,[y]_0^{2x}\,dx = \int_0^{1/2} \exp(x^2)2x\,dx$$

$$= [\exp(x^2)]_0^{1/2} = e^{1/4} - 1.$$

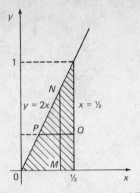

Fig. 5.8   Region of integration for $\displaystyle\int_0^1 \int_{y/2}^{1/2} \exp(x^2) \mathrm{d}x \, \mathrm{d}y$

Change of Variables of Integration

'Difficult' single integrals are often simplified by making a suitable change of variable. Thus, if $t = T(u)$,

$$\int_{t_1}^{t_2} g(t)\mathrm{d}t = \int_{u_1}^{u_2} g\{T(u)\} \frac{\mathrm{d}T(u)}{\mathrm{d}u} \, \mathrm{d}u$$

where the new limits u_1, u_2 are defined implicitly through $t_1 = T(u_1)$, $t_2 = T(u_2)$.

This technique can be extended to the theory of double integrals. Let the relationship between the original independent variables x, y and the new variables u, v be described by

$$x = X(u, v), \quad y = Y(u, v), \tag{14}$$

where X and Y denote continuously differentiable functions of u and v. This pair of equations defines the *transformation* or *mapping* of the u, v plane, and gives the coordinates of a point in the x, y plane corresponding to a point in the u, v plane. If the equations (14) are solved for u and v in terms of x and y to give

$$u = U(x, y), \quad v = V(x, y), \tag{15}$$

we obtain the transformation of the x, y plane into the u, v plane. This is termed the *inverse* transformation or mapping of equations (14).

To express the double integral $\iint_{\mathscr{A}} f(x, y)\mathrm{d}A$ in terms of u and v instead of x and y, we use equations (14) to transform $f(x, y)$ into a new function of u and v and equations (15) to determine the new region of integration $\mathscr{A}'$ in the u, v plane corresponding to $\mathscr{A}$ in the x, y plane (see Fig. 5.9). It is not so straightforward to express $\mathrm{d}A \ (= \mathrm{d}x \, \mathrm{d}y)$ in terms of $u, v, \mathrm{d}u$ and $\mathrm{d}v$. In order to do this, it is convenient to consider a typical elementary rectangle in $\mathscr{A}'$, with vertices at (u, v), $(u + \delta u, v)$, $(u, v + \delta v)$ and $(u + \delta u, v + \delta v)$. This has area

$$\delta A' = \delta u \, \delta v.$$

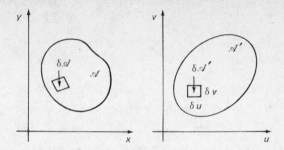

Fig. 5.9 Equivalent regions of integration under a transformation of coordinates

For small δu and δv, the corresponding region $\delta \mathscr{A}$ in the x, y plane is approximately a parallelogram with vertices at (X, Y), $\left(X + \dfrac{\partial X}{\partial u} \delta u, \ Y + \dfrac{\partial Y}{\partial u} \delta u \right)$,

$\left(X + \dfrac{\partial X}{\partial v} \delta v, \ Y + \dfrac{\partial Y}{\partial v} \delta v \right)$ and $\left(X + \dfrac{\partial X}{\partial u} \delta u + \dfrac{\partial X}{\partial v} \delta v, \ Y + \dfrac{\partial Y}{\partial u} \delta u + \dfrac{\partial Y}{\partial v} \delta v \right)$

respectively. These coordinates are obtained by expanding the relevant functions X and Y as Taylor series (see §4.2) about the point (u, v) and neglecting all the terms involving $(\delta u)^2$, $\delta u \, \delta v$, $(\delta v)^2$ and higher powers of δu and δv. The area of the parallelogram is therefore

$$\delta A \simeq \frac{\partial (x, y)}{\partial (u, v)} \, \delta u \, \delta v \tag{16}$$

where

$$\frac{\partial (x, y)}{\partial (u, v)} = \begin{vmatrix} \dfrac{\partial X}{\partial u} & \dfrac{\partial Y}{\partial u} \\[2ex] \dfrac{\partial X}{\partial v} & \dfrac{\partial Y}{\partial v} \end{vmatrix} = \begin{vmatrix} \dfrac{\partial X}{\partial u} & \dfrac{\partial X}{\partial v} \\[2ex] \dfrac{\partial Y}{\partial u} & \dfrac{\partial Y}{\partial v} \end{vmatrix} \tag{17}$$

is termed the *Jacobian* of the transformation of the x, y plane into the u, v plane. Hence the double integral can be rewritten according to

$$\iint\limits_{\mathscr{A}} f(x, y) \, \mathrm{d}A = \iint\limits_{\mathscr{A}'} f\{X(u, v), Y(u, v)\} \frac{\partial (x, y)}{\partial (u, v)} \, \mathrm{d}A' \tag{18}$$

where $\mathrm{d}A' = \mathrm{d}u \, \mathrm{d}v$.

It is clear from the relations (16) and (18) that it is essential to choose transformations with *non-zero* Jacobians. A Jacobian which is identically zero implies a non-unique correspondence between points in the x, y and u, v planes; it also implies that the functions $X(u, v)$ and $Y(u, v)$ cannot be independent. However, if the value of a Jacobian is zero only at isolated points, called *singular points*, in the region of integration, the transformation is still acceptable.

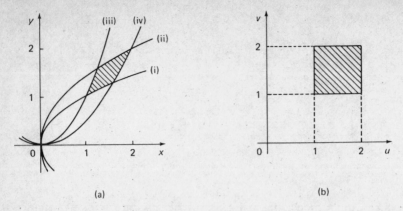

Fig. 5.10   Equivalent regions of integration for example 6

EXAMPLE 6

Evaluate $\iint_{\mathscr{A}} xy \, \mathrm{d}A$, where $\mathscr{A}$ is the region enclosed by the four parabolae (i) $y^2 = x$, (ii) $y^2 = 2x$, (iii) $x^2 = y$ and (iv) $x^2 = 2y$.

The region of integration is shown in Fig. 5.10(a). It is evident that when expressed in terms of x and y, the integral must be split up into three distinct double integrals regardless of the order of integration. Hence we try to find a change of variables which simplifies the region of integration whilst at the same time preserving the simplicity of the integrand. In this example an obvious choice of new variables is

$$u = \frac{x^2}{y}, \qquad v = \frac{y^2}{x}.$$

Then the parabolae transform to (i) $v = 1$, (ii) $v = 2$, (iii) $u = 1$ and (iv) $u = 2$ respectively giving the square region of integration shown in Fig. 5.10(b). The inverse transformation is

$$x = u^{2/3} v^{1/3}, \qquad y = u^{1/3} v^{2/3}$$

so that the Jacobian of the transformation from x, y to u, v is

$$\frac{\partial(x,y)}{\partial(u,v)} = \begin{vmatrix} \tfrac{2}{3}u^{-1/3}v^{1/3} & \tfrac{1}{3}u^{2/3}v^{-2/3} \\ \tfrac{1}{3}u^{-2/3}v^{2/3} & \tfrac{2}{3}u^{1/3}v^{-1/3} \end{vmatrix} = \tfrac{1}{3}.$$

Hence

$$\iint_{\mathscr{A}} xy \, \mathrm{d}A = \int_1^2 \int_1^2 (uv)\tfrac{1}{3} \mathrm{d}u \, \mathrm{d}v = \tfrac{3}{4}.$$

Properties of Jacobians

Jacobians satisfy a chain rule. If x and y are functions of u and v while u and v are functions of r and s, then

$$\frac{\partial(x,y)}{\partial(u,v)}\frac{\partial(u,v)}{\partial(r,s)} = \frac{\partial(x,y)}{\partial(r,s)}. \tag{19}$$

By choosing $r = x$ and $s = y$, we immediately deduce the important result that

$$\frac{\partial(x,y)}{\partial(u,v)} = \frac{1}{\dfrac{\partial(u,v)}{\partial(x,y)}}. \tag{20}$$

The reader should note that this result does *not* contradict the general rule that $\partial x/\partial u \neq 1/(\partial u/\partial x)$, as discussed in §4.1 (see also problems 2 and 3 of Chapter 4).

Jacobians are not restricted to two variables. The definition is easily extended. Thus the Jacobian of the transformation from variables x, y, z to u, v, w with

$$x = X(u, v, w), \quad y = Y(u, v, w), \quad z = Z(u, v, w),$$

is

$$\frac{\partial(x,y,z)}{\partial(u,v,w)} = \begin{vmatrix} \dfrac{\partial X}{\partial u} & \dfrac{\partial Y}{\partial u} & \dfrac{\partial Z}{\partial u} \\[2mm] \dfrac{\partial X}{\partial v} & \dfrac{\partial Y}{\partial v} & \dfrac{\partial Z}{\partial v} \\[2mm] \dfrac{\partial X}{\partial w} & \dfrac{\partial Y}{\partial w} & \dfrac{\partial Z}{\partial w} \end{vmatrix} = \frac{1}{\dfrac{\partial(u,v,w)}{\partial(x,y,z)}}. \tag{21}$$

Plane Polar Coordinates

When the region of integration is bounded by circular arcs, or when the integrand is simplified by using plane polar coordinates r, θ where $x = r \cos \theta, y = r \sin \theta$, it is usually advisable to express the double integral in terms of r and θ. The relevant relation is

$$\iint_{\mathscr{A}} f(x, y)\,dA = \iint_{\mathscr{A}'} f(r \cos \theta, r \sin \theta) r\, dr\, d\theta, \tag{22}$$

where $\mathscr{A}'$ is the region of integration in the r, θ plane. Equation (22) provides a simple example of a change of variables, the Jacobian of the transformation from cartesian to plane polar coordinates being

$$\frac{\partial(x,y)}{\partial(r,\theta)} = \begin{vmatrix} \dfrac{\partial x}{\partial r} & \dfrac{\partial y}{\partial r} \\[2mm] \dfrac{\partial x}{\partial \theta} & \dfrac{\partial y}{\partial \theta} \end{vmatrix} = \begin{vmatrix} \cos \theta & \sin \theta \\[1mm] -r \sin \theta & r \cos \theta \end{vmatrix} = r.$$

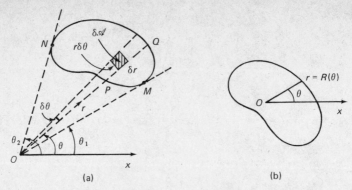

Fig. 5.11   Regions of integration using plane polar coordinates

Alternatively we can deduce from first principles that the elementary rectangle with area δA at a typical point (see Fig. 5.11) has sides of length δr in the radial direction and of length $r\delta\theta$ in the transverse direction, immediately giving $\delta A = r\,\delta r\,\delta\theta$.

It is usually preferable to perform the r integration first. In that case, the lower and upper limits of the r integration are $r_1(\theta)$ and $r_2(\theta)$ respectively, where $r = r_1(\theta)$ is the equation of MPN and $r = r_2(\theta)$ defines MQN. Then if θ_1 and θ_2 are the polar angles at M and N, the double integral becomes

$$\int_{\theta_1}^{\theta_2}\int_{r_1(\theta)}^{r_2(\theta)} f(r\cos\theta, r\sin\theta)r\,dr\,d\theta.$$

If the origin lies inside the region of integration, the limits are simplified and the integral becomes

$$\int_{0}^{2\pi}\int_{0}^{R(\theta)} f(r\cos\theta, r\sin\theta)r\,dr\,d\theta$$

where $r = R(\theta)$ is the equation of the boundary.

EXAMPLE 7
Determine the mass M and the moment of inertia I_0 about the origin of a uniform lamina in the shape of a cardioid $r = a(1 - \cos\theta)$.

The region of integration is shown in Fig. 5.12. Construction of the typical radial line OP shows that the region of integration is

$$0 \leqslant r \leqslant a(1 - \cos\theta), \quad 0 \leqslant \theta \leqslant 2\pi.$$

Hence if σ represents the constant mass per unit area,

$$M = \sigma \int_{0}^{2\pi}\int_{0}^{a(1-\cos\theta)} r\,dr\,d\theta = \sigma \int_{0}^{2\pi} \tfrac{1}{2}\{a(1-\cos\theta)\}^2\,d\theta$$

$$= \tfrac{3}{2}\pi a^2 \sigma;$$

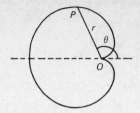

Fig. 5.12 Graph of the cardioid $r = a(1 - \cos\theta)$ for example 7

$$I_0 = \sigma \int_0^{2\pi} \int_0^{a(1-\cos\theta)} r^2\, r\, dr\, d\theta = \sigma \int_0^{2\pi} \tfrac{1}{4}\{a(1-\cos\theta)\}^4\, d\theta$$

$$= \tfrac{35}{16}\pi a^4 \sigma = \tfrac{35}{24}Ma^2.$$

EXAMPLE 8

Integrate $f(x, y) = \exp(-x^2 - y^2)$ over the three regions $\mathscr{A}_1$, $\mathscr{A}_2$ and $\mathscr{A}_3$ where $\mathscr{A}_1$ is the quadrant with maximum radius a, $\mathscr{A}_2$ is the quadrant with maximum radius $\sqrt{2}a$ and $\mathscr{A}_3$ is the square of side a. By comparing the three results, deduce that

$$\int_0^\infty \exp(-x^2)dx = \tfrac{1}{2}\sqrt{\pi}.$$

The three regions are shown in Fig. 5.13.

$$I_1 = \iint_{\mathscr{A}_1} \exp(-x^2 - y^2)dA = \int_0^{\pi/2} \int_0^a \exp(-r^2)r\, dr\, d\theta$$

$$= \int_0^{\pi/2} [-\tfrac{1}{2}\exp(-r^2)]_0^a\, d\theta = \tfrac{1}{4}\pi\{1 - \exp(-a^2)\}.$$

$$I_2 = \iint_{\mathscr{A}_2} \exp(-x^2 - y^2)dA = \int_0^{\pi/2} \int_0^{2a} \exp(-r^2)r\, dr\, d\theta$$

$$= \tfrac{1}{4}\pi\{1 - \exp(-4a^2)\}.$$

$$I_3 = \iint_{\mathscr{A}_3} \exp(-x^2 - y^2)dA = \int_0^a \int_0^a \exp(-y^2)\exp(-y^2)dx\, dy$$

$$= \left(\int_0^a \exp(-x^2)dx\right)\left(\int_0^a \exp(-y^2)dy\right)$$

$$= \{I(a)\}^2 \quad \text{where} \quad I(a) = \int_0^a \exp(-x^2)dx.$$

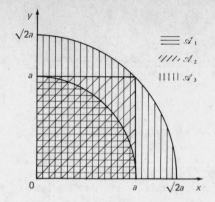

Fig. 5.13   The three regions of integration for example 8

Since $\exp(-x^2 - y^2)$ is never negative in any of the three regions, it is clear from Fig. 5.13 that $I_1 < I_3 < I_2$ so that

$$\sqrt{I_1} < I(a) < \sqrt{I_2}.$$

Letting $a \to \infty$ and noting that $I_1 \to \pi/4, I_2 \to \pi/4$, then gives the required result.

EXAMPLE 9
Prove the convolution property of Laplace transforms, namely

$$\mathscr{L}\left\{\int_0^t f(u)g(t - u)\,\mathrm{d}u\right\} = \mathscr{L}\{f(t)\}\,\mathscr{L}\{g(t)\}.$$

From §3.1, the definition of the Laplace transform with respect to t gives

$$\mathscr{L}\left\{\int_0^t f(u)g(t - u)\,\mathrm{d}u\right\} = \int_0^\infty \mathrm{e}^{-st}\int_0^t f(u)g(t - u)\,\mathrm{d}u\,\mathrm{d}t$$

$$= \int\!\!\int_{\mathscr{A}} \mathrm{e}^{-st}f(u)g(t - u)\,\mathrm{d}u\,\mathrm{d}t,$$

where $\mathscr{A}$ is the infinite wedge region enclosed by the straight lines $u = 0$ and $u = t$ for $t \geqslant 0$ in the u, t plane (see Fig. 5.14(a)). The integrand is simplified if the independent variables are changed from u, t to u, v where

$$u = u, \quad v = t - u; \quad \text{so that} \quad u = u, \quad t = u + v.$$

The region of integration $\mathscr{A}$ then transforms into the first quadrant $\mathscr{A}'$ in the u, v plane as shown in Fig. 5.14(b), with $0 \leqslant u < \infty, 0 \leqslant v < \infty$. The Jacobian of the transformation is $\partial(u, t)/\partial(u, v) = 1$. Hence

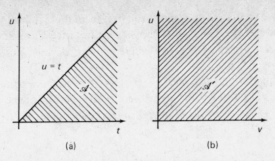

Fig. 5.14 Equivalent regions of integration for example 9

$$\mathscr{L}\left\{\int_0^t f(u)g(t-u)\,du\right\} = \int_0^\infty \int_0^\infty e^{-s(u+v)}f(u)g(v)\,du\,dv$$

$$= \left\{\int_0^\infty e^{-su}f(u)\,du\right\}\left\{\int_0^\infty e^{-sv}g(v)\,dv\right\},$$

proving the required result.

Exercises

1. Evaluate the double integral $\displaystyle\int_1^2 \int_0^1 (x+y)\exp(xy)\,dx\,dy.$

2. Evaluate $\displaystyle\int_1^2 \int_{\pi/6}^{\pi/2} x\sin(xy)\,dx\,dy$ both directly and by reversing the order of integration.

3. If $\mathscr{A}$ is the disc $x^2+y^2\leqslant a^2$, evaluate $\displaystyle\iint_{\mathscr{A}} \exp\{-(x^2+y^2)^{1/2}\}\,dA.$

4. Sketch the region of integration for the integral

$$\int_0^a \int_0^y \frac{dx\,dy}{\sqrt{\{(a^2-x^2)(y-x)\}}}.$$

Change the order of integration and show that the value of the integral is $4(\sqrt{2}-1)\sqrt{a}.$

5. Evaluate $\displaystyle\int_0^{\pi/2} \int_{a\cos\theta}^a r^4\,dr\,d\theta.$

6. Evaluate the double integrals derived in exercises 1 and 2 of §5.2.

7. Determine the Jacobian of the transformation from the x, y plane to the u, v plane, where $u = y/x$ and $v = xy$. Hence, or otherwise, deduce the area enclosed by the curves $y = m_1 x$, $y = m_2 x$, $xy = c_1^2$ and $xy = c_2^2$ where m_1, m_2, c_1 and c_2 are constants.

8. Express the equation of the circle $(x - a)^2 + y^2 = a^2$ in terms of the plane polar coordinates r and θ. Find the volume enclosed by that part of the cone $z = \{2a - \sqrt{(x^2 + y^2)}\} \cot \alpha$ which lies within the cylinder $(x - a)^2 + y^2 = a^2$ and above the plane $z = 0$.

5.3 TRIPLE INTEGRALS

The ideas involved in the integration of a function of two variables x and y over a region $\mathscr{A}$ of the x, y plane extend readily to the integration of a function $f(x, y, z)$ of three variables over a volume $\mathscr{V}$ of x, y, z space. Multiple integration of functions of even more variables can be interpreted as integration over a region of higher-dimensional space.

Thus, if $\mathscr{V}$ is the volume described by

$$x_1(y, z) \leqslant x \leqslant x_2(y, z), \quad y_1(z) \leqslant y \leqslant y_2(z), \quad z_1 \leqslant z \leqslant z_2,$$

then

$$\iiint_{\mathscr{V}} f(x, y, z) \mathrm{d}V = \int_{z_1}^{z_2} \int_{y_1}^{y_2} \int_{x_1}^{x_2} f(x, y, z) \mathrm{d}x \, \mathrm{d}y \, \mathrm{d}z.$$

Here the integration is performed by first integrating $f(x, y, z)$ with respect to x, treating y and z as constants during the integration and inserting the limits for x. The result is a function of y and z. The triple integral has then been reduced to a double integral expressed in terms of y and z, for which the region of integration is the region in the y, z plane described by $y_1(z) \leqslant y \leqslant y_2(z)$, $z_1 \leqslant z \leqslant z_2$. This can be evaluated by using the procedures described in §5.2.

When the limits of integration are not explicitly given in a problem, great care must be taken to ensure that the correct limits are inserted. If the x integration is the first to be carried out, then the innermost limits are determined by answering the question, 'For a typical choice of line at constant y *and* z, between which values does x vary in $\mathscr{V}$?' The remaining limits are then determined from the maximum possible range of choices of (y, z). This range describes a region of integration in the y, z plane, and is obviously the projection of $\mathscr{V}$ onto the y, z plane.

EXAMPLE 1

Evaluate $\iiint_{\mathscr{V}} \dfrac{\mathrm{d}V}{(x + y + 2z + 1)^3}$, where $\mathscr{V}$ is the region enclosed by the planes $x = 0$, $y = 0, z = 0$ and $x + y + z = 1$.

The region of integration is shown in Fig. 5.15. PQ represents a typical line drawn at constant (y, z), with P lying on the boundary plane $x = 0$ and Q on the oblique

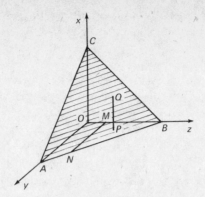

Fig. 5.15   Volume of integration for example 1

plane $x + y + z = 1$. Hence x must vary between its values $x = 0$ at P and $x = 1 - y - z$ at Q. All the possible choices of (y, z) are now described by the plane region OAB, which is the projection of $\mathscr{V}$ onto the y, z plane and has boundaries $y = 0$, $z = 0$ and $y + z = 1$. Drawing a typical line MN at constant z then shows that y varies between $y = 0$ at M and $y = 1 - z$ at N. Finally we note that the range of z is $0 \leqslant z \leqslant 1$, so that the triple integral becomes

$$\int_0^1 \int_0^{1-z} \int_0^{1-y-z} \frac{1}{(x + y + 2z + 1)^3} \, dx \, dy \, dz$$

$$= \int_0^1 \int_0^{1-z} \left[\frac{-1}{2(x + y + 2z + 1)^2} \right]_{x=0}^{x=1-y-z} dy \, dz$$

$$= \int_0^1 \int_0^{1-z} \frac{1}{2} \left\{ \frac{1}{(y + 2z + 1)^2} - \frac{1}{(z + 2)^2} \right\} dy \, dz$$

$$= \int_0^1 \frac{1}{2} \left[-\frac{1}{y + 2z + 1} - \frac{y}{(z + 2)^2} \right]_{y=0}^{y=1-z} dz$$

$$= \int_0^1 \frac{1}{2} \left\{ \frac{-3}{(z + 2)^2} + \frac{1}{2z + 1} \right\} dz = \tfrac{1}{4}(\log 3 - 1).$$

Change of Variables of Integration

If the variables of integration are changed from (x, y, z) to (u, v, w) then it may be shown (by an extension of the two-dimensional treatment given in §5.2) that the elementary volume elements $\delta V = \delta x \, \delta y \, \delta z$ and $\delta V' = \delta u \, \delta v \, \delta w$ in the respective regions of integration are related by

$$\delta x \, \delta y \, \delta z \simeq \frac{\partial(x, y, z)}{\partial(u, v, w)} \, \delta u \, \delta v \, \delta w.$$

If, under the transformation, $f(x, y, z)$ transforms to $F(u, v, w)$ then

$$\iiint_{\mathcal{V}} f(x, y, z) \mathrm{d}x \, \mathrm{d}y \, \mathrm{d}z = \iiint_{\mathcal{V}'} F(u, v, w) \frac{\partial(x, y, z)}{\partial(u, v, w)} \, \mathrm{d}u \, \mathrm{d}v \, \mathrm{d}w,$$

where $\mathcal{V}'$ is the region in u, v, w space corresponding to the region $\mathcal{V}$ of x, y, z space.

Cylindrical Polar Coordinates (ρ, ϕ, z)

To express the triple integral in terms of cylindrical polar coordinates (ρ, ϕ, z), we note that

$$x = \rho \cos \phi, \quad y = \rho \sin \phi, \quad z = z,$$

$$\frac{\partial(x, y, z)}{\partial(\rho, \phi, z)} = \begin{vmatrix} \cos \phi & \sin \phi & 0 \\ -\rho \sin \phi & \rho \cos \phi & 0 \\ 0 & 0 & 1 \end{vmatrix} = \rho,$$

so that

$$\iiint_{\mathcal{V}} f(x, y, z) \mathrm{d}x \, \mathrm{d}y \, \mathrm{d}z = \iiint_{\mathcal{V}'} F(\rho, \phi, z) \rho \, \mathrm{d}\rho \, \mathrm{d}\phi \, \mathrm{d}z.$$

Spherical Polar Coordinates (r, θ, ϕ)

The relations between cartesian and spherical polar coordinates are

$$x = r \sin \theta \cos \phi, \quad y = r \sin \theta \sin \phi, \quad z = r \cos \theta,$$

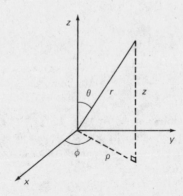

Fig. 5.16   Cylindrical and spherical polar coordinates, (ρ, ϕ, z) and (r, θ, ϕ) respectively

so that the Jacobian of the transformation from (x, y, z) to (r, θ, ϕ) is

$$\frac{\partial(x, y, z)}{\partial(r, \theta, \phi)} = \begin{vmatrix} \sin\theta\cos\phi & \sin\theta\sin\phi & \cos\theta \\ r\cos\theta\cos\phi & r\cos\theta\sin\phi & -r\sin\theta \\ -r\sin\theta\sin\phi & r\sin\theta\cos\phi & 0 \end{vmatrix} = r^2 \sin\theta.$$

Hence

$$\iiint\limits_{\mathscr{V}} f(x, y, z)\,dx\,dy\,dz = \iiint\limits_{\mathscr{V}'} F(r, \theta, \phi) r^2 \sin\theta\,dr\,d\theta\,d\phi.$$

It is convenient to use spherical or cylindrical polar coordinates in problems in which $\mathscr{V}$ has some spherical or cylindrical symmetry, or if the integrand takes a simpler form when expressed in polar coordinates.

EXAMPLE 2

A solid tyre of outer radius $b + a$ has a circular cross-section of radius a, and consists of material of constant mass density σ. Evaluate its total mass M and the moment of inertia about its axis of revolution (i.e. the wheel axle).

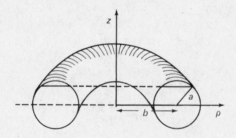

Fig. 5.17   Cross-section of 'tyre' at typical ϕ = constant

A typical cross-section, in a plane containing the axle, is shown in Fig. 5.17. It is convenient to use cylindrical polar coordinates ρ, ϕ, z with the z axis coincident with the axle. Since the density σ is constant, the total mass is

$$M = \sigma \iiint\limits_{\mathscr{V}} dV = \sigma \int_{-a}^{a} \int_{0}^{2\pi} \int_{b-(a^2-z^2)^{1/2}}^{b+(a^2-z^2)^{1/2}} \rho\,d\rho\,d\phi\,dz$$

$$= 2b\sigma \int_{-a}^{a} \int_{0}^{2\pi} (a^2 - z^2)^{1/2}\,d\phi\,dz = 2\pi^2 a^2 b\sigma.$$

The moment of inertia about the z axis is

$$I_z = \sigma \iiint_{\mathscr{V}} \rho^2 \, dV = \sigma \int_{-a}^{a} \int_{0}^{2\pi} \int_{b-(a^2-z^2)^{1/2}}^{b+(a^2-z^2)^{1/2}} \rho^3 \, d\rho \, d\phi \, dz$$

$$= 2\sigma \int_{-a}^{a} \int_{0}^{2\pi} \{b^3(a^2-z^2)^{1/2} + b(a^2-z^2)^{3/2}\} \, d\phi \, dz$$

$$= M(b^2 + \tfrac{3}{4} a^2).$$

Physical Applications

The tyre problem above is but one illustration of the occurrence of triple integrals in engineering applications. The most common examples relate to physical properties of a body occupying a region $\mathscr{V}$ in space.

The *volume* of a region $\mathscr{V}$ is

$$V = \iiint_{\mathscr{V}} dV \equiv \iiint_{\mathscr{V}} dx \, dy \, dz.$$

The *mass* of a body of density $\sigma(x, y, z)$ occupying $\mathscr{V}$ is

$$M = \iiint_{\mathscr{V}} \sigma(x, y, z) dV.$$

The coordinates of the *centre of mass* of such a body are

$$\bar{x} = \frac{1}{M} \iiint_{\mathscr{V}} \sigma(x, y, z) x \, dV, \quad \bar{y} = \frac{1}{M} \iiint_{\mathscr{V}} \sigma(x, y, z) y \, dV,$$

$$\bar{z} = \frac{1}{M} \iiint_{\mathscr{V}} \sigma(x, y, z) z \, dV.$$

The *moment of inertia* of the body about the x axis is

$$I_x = \iiint_{\mathscr{V}} \sigma(x, y, z)(y^2 + z^2) \, dV;$$

similar relations hold for the moments of inertia I_y, I_z about the y and z axes respectively.

The *momentum* of a fluid flowing through a region $\mathscr{V}$ has the component p_x in the x direction, where

$$p_x = \iiint_{\mathscr{V}} \sigma(x, y, z) u_x(x, y, z) dV,$$

with u_x denoting the component of velocity in the x direction. Similar relations hold for p_y and p_z in terms of u_y and u_z.

Exercises

1. Find by triple integration the volume of the ellipsoid

$$x^2/a^2 + y^2/b^2 + z^2/c^2 = 1.$$

2. The density $\sigma(r)$ of a sphere of radius R is $\sigma(r) = A + Br^n$, where r denotes distance from the centre of the sphere, and A, B and n are positive constants. Find the total mass of the sphere, and its moment of inertia about a diameter.

3. Show that for the triple integral

$$\int_0^h \int_{-z\,\tan\,\alpha}^{z\,\tan\,\alpha} \int_{-\sqrt{(z^2\,\tan^2\alpha - y^2)}}^{\sqrt{(z^2\,\tan^2\alpha - y^2)}} (x^2 + y^2)\,dx\,dy\,dz,$$

the region of integration is the region enclosed by a certain right circular cone. Express the integral in terms of cylindrical polar coordinates and hence evaluate the integral.

4. Find the centre of gravity of a homogeneous body bounded above by the sphere $r = a$ and below by the cone $\theta = \pi/6$, where r, θ, ϕ are spherical polar coordinates.

5.4 LINE INTEGRALS

From its definition in equation (2), the definite integral $\int_a^b g(t)\,dt$ could be described as the integral of $g(t)$ along the *straight line AB* joining $t = a$ and $t = b$. If $g(t)$ represented a force acting on a particle at a general position t on that line and in the direction of AB, then the integral would give the work done by that force as the particle moves from A to B.

In many engineering applications it is necessary to generalize the concept of an integral so as to include the integration of functions along *curved* lines in space. As an example, consider a particle moving from a point P to another point Q along a curve C and under the action of a variable force. If $F(x, y, z)$ denotes the component of the force in the direction of motion, then the work done by the force when the particle moves from P to Q is

$$\int_{s_P}^{s_Q} F(x, y, z)\,ds \equiv \lim_{n\to\infty} \sum_{i=1}^n F_i(s_i - s_{i-1}). \tag{23}$$

Here s denotes arc-length along C from some reference point on C, and $s_0 = s_P$ and $s_n = s_Q$ are the arc lengths at P and Q; F_i is the magnitude of the force at $s = s_i$.

The integral defined in equation (23) is called the *line integral* of the function $F(x, y, z)$ from P to Q along the curve C. Its definition is a generalization of the definition for ordinary integrals given by equation (2), and is independent of the physical context in which it has been introduced here.

If the equation of C can be expressed parametrically in terms of a parameter t, say, with

$$x = X(t), \quad y = Y(t), \quad z = Z(t),$$

then the line integral can be converted into an ordinary integral. Substituting for x, y and z in terms of t gives

$$F(x, y, z) = F(X(t), Y(t), Z(t)) \equiv F^*(t),$$

and

$$\delta s \simeq \{(\delta x)^2 + (\delta y)^2 + (\delta z)^2\}^{1/2}$$

so that

$$\frac{ds}{dt} = \left\{ \left(\frac{dX}{dt} \right)^2 + \left(\frac{dY}{dt} \right)^2 + \left(\frac{dZ}{dt} \right)^2 \right\}^{1/2}$$

Hence, if t_P and t_Q represent the values of t corresponding to P and Q, we obtain

$$\int_{s_P}^{s_Q} F(x, y, z) ds = \int_{t_P}^{t_Q} F^*(t) \left\{ \left(\frac{dX}{dt} \right)^2 + \left(\frac{dY}{dt} \right)^2 + \left(\frac{dZ}{dt} \right)^2 \right\}^{1/2} dt, \qquad (24)$$

which is an ordinary integral.

If the function F is expressed in terms of cylindrical polar coordinates (ρ, ϕ, z), then the line integral takes the form

$$\int_{s_P}^{s_Q} F(\rho, \phi, z) \, ds = \int_{t_P}^{t_Q} F^*(t) \left\{ \left(\frac{d\rho}{dt} \right)^2 + \rho^2 \left(\frac{d\phi}{dt} \right)^2 + \left(\frac{dz}{dt} \right)^2 \right\}^{1/2} dt, \qquad (25)$$

where the curve C is now defined parametrically by $\rho = \rho(t), \phi = \phi(t), z = z(t)$.

EXAMPLE 1

Determine the perimeter of the cardioid $\rho = a(1 - \cos \phi), z = 0$.

The arc length along any curve C is given by putting $F(\rho, \phi, z) = 1$ in equation (25). In this case the parametric representation of C is

$$\rho = a(1 - \cos t), \quad \phi = t, \quad z = 0, \quad 0 \leqslant t \leqslant 2\pi.$$

Hence the perimeter is

$$\int_0^{2\pi} \{a^2 \sin^2 t + a^2 (1 - \cos t)^2\}^{1/2} \, dt = \int_0^{2\pi} \{2a^2 (1 - \cos t)\}^{1/2} \, dt$$

$$= \int_0^{2\pi} 2a \sin \tfrac{1}{2} t \, dt = 8a.$$

Another type of line integral is obtained if we now consider the particle moving along C under an externally applied force $\mathbf{F}$ with components F_1, F_2, F_3 in the x, y, z directions respectively. Then the work done by the force as the particle moves a vector distance δs along C is $\mathbf{F} \cdot \delta s$ (see §6.2), which may be expressed as

$F_1 \delta x + F_2 \delta y + F_3 \delta z$ in terms of the components of **F** and δs. Hence the total work done in moving from P to Q is the line integral

$$\int_C \mathbf{F} \cdot d\mathbf{s} \equiv \int_C (F_1 \, dx + F_2 \, dy + F_3 \, dz)$$

$$= \int_{t_P}^{t_Q} \left(F_1^* \frac{dX}{dt} + F_2^* \frac{dY}{dt} + F_3^* \frac{dZ}{dt} \right) dt, \tag{26}$$

where $F_1^*(t) = F_1\{X(t), Y(t), Z(t)\}$, etc. Hence this type of line integral also can be evaluated as an ordinary integral.

EXAMPLE 2

A particle moves from the point P at $(0, 0, 0)$ to the point Q at $(1, 1, 1)$ along (a) the straight line $x = y = z$ or (b) the curve $y = x^2, z = x^3$. The force acting on the particle is given by

$$\mathbf{F} = (x^2 - y, y^2 - z, z^2 - x).$$

Determine the work done by the force in each case.

From equation (26), the work done can be written as

$$W = \int_C \left\{ (X^2 - Y)\frac{dX}{dt} + (Y^2 - Z)\frac{dY}{dt} + (Z^2 - X)\frac{dZ}{dt} \right\} dt,$$

where C is the path joining P and Q.

(a) An obvious parametric representation for the straight line is

$$x = t, \quad y = t, \quad z = t,$$

with P given by $t_P = 0$ and Q by $t_Q = 1$. Then

$$W = \int_0^1 \{(t^2 - t) + (t^2 - t) + (t^2 - t)\} dt = -\tfrac{1}{2}.$$

(b) The curve is given parametrically by

$$x = t, \quad y = t^2, \quad z = t^3,$$

with P again given by $t_P = 0$ and Q by $t_Q = 1$. Now we have

$$W = \int_0^1 \{(t^2 - t^2)(1) + (t^4 - t^3)(2t) + (t^6 - t)(3t^2)\} dt = -\tfrac{29}{60}.$$

Example 2 illustrates the fact that integrals evaluated between two points usually depend upon the path followed between those points. An important exception is the integration of conservative functions, which are treated in §6.5.

Green's Theorem in the Plane

Some line integrals can be related to double integrals by means of *Green's theorem in the plane.*

> THEOREM   Let $\mathscr{A}$ be a plane region bounded by a *closed* curve C. Then if $f(x, y), g(x, y), \partial f/\partial y$ and $\partial g/\partial x$ are continuous, single-valued functions in $\mathscr{A}$ and on C,

$$\iint_{\mathscr{A}} \left(\frac{\partial f}{\partial x} + \frac{\partial g}{\partial y} \right) dA = \oint_C (f\, dy - g\, dx). \tag{27}$$

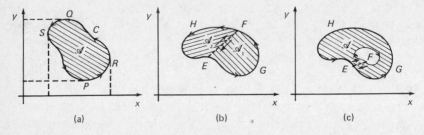

Fig. 5.18   Examples of simply-connected and multiply-connected regions

The notation $\oint_C$ simply indicates that C is a closed curve. The proof of the theorem is a straightforward exercise in double integration. Let the curve PRQ in Fig. 5.18(a) be described by $x = X_1(y)$ and PSQ by $x = X_2(y)$ for $c \leqslant y \leqslant d$. Then

$$\iint_{\mathscr{A}} \frac{\partial f}{\partial x}\, dA = \int_c^d \int_{X_2(y)}^{X_1(y)} \frac{\partial f}{\partial x}\, dx\, dy = \int_d^c \{f(X_1(y), y) - f(X_2(y), y)\}\, dy$$

$$= \int_c^d f(X_1(y), y)\, dy + \int_d^c f(X_2(y), y)\, dy$$

$$= \oint_C f\, dy. \tag{28}$$

Here we have adopted the standard sign convention that the positive direction of travel around a closed curve is such that the enclosed region is on the left of the curve. This is shown by the arrows in Fig. 5.18. By considering the two curves SPR and RQS we similarly obtain

$$\iint_{\mathscr{A}} \frac{\partial g}{\partial y}\, dA = \int_{SQR} g\, dx - \int_{SPR} g\, dx = -\oint_C g\, dx, \tag{29}$$

thus completing the proof.

It should be noted that the theorem actually involves two separate results, namely equations (28) and (29), concerning the two *independent* functions f and g.

The proof requires amendment if the boundary curve C is such that some line parallel to a coordinate axis cuts C in more than two points, as illustrated in Fig. 5.18(b). We then construct a line EF which divides the region $\mathscr{A}$ into two regions $\mathscr{A}_1$ and $\mathscr{A}_2$ of the type considered above. Then, in an obvious notation,

$$\iint_{\mathscr{A}} = \iint_{\mathscr{A}_1} + \iint_{\mathscr{A}_2} = \oint_{EGFE} + \oint_{EFHE} = \int_{EGF} + \int_{FE} + \int_{EF} + \int_{FHE}$$

$$= \int_{EGF} - \int_{EF} + \int_{EF} + \int_{FHE} = \int_{EGFHE} ,$$

thus proving that the theorem is true also for this more complicated region.

Both of the regions $\mathscr{A}$ considered above are termed *simply-connected*, which means that any closed curve lying in $\mathscr{A}$ can be continuously shrunk to a point without leaving $\mathscr{A}$; i.e. a simply-connected region does not contain any 'holes'. If a region does not have this property, it is termed *multiply-connected*.

Green's theorem is also true for multiply-connected regions $\mathscr{A}$. The proof is again accomplished by dividing $\mathscr{A}$ into suitable simply-connected subregions, as in Fig. 5.18(c).

EXAMPLE 3

Show that the area A of the region enclosed by a closed curve C is

$$\tfrac{1}{2}\oint_C (x\,\mathrm{d}y - y\,\mathrm{d}x) = \oint_C x\,\mathrm{d}y = -\oint_C y\,\mathrm{d}x.$$

The result is given immediately by putting $f = x$ and $g = y$ in equations (27), (28) and (29).

Exercises

1. Determine the value of $\int_C (x + 2y)\mathrm{d}s$ where C is the shorter elliptical path $x^2/a^2 + y^2/b^2 = 1$ in the x, y plane, joining $(a, 0)$ to $(0, b)$.

2. Evaluate $\int_C \{(x + y)\mathrm{d}x + xy\,\mathrm{d}y\}$ where C is the parabolic path $y = x^2$ between the points $(0, 0)$ and $(4, 16)$. Also evaluate the integral along the straight line joining the same end points.

3. If $\mathbf{F} = (2y + 3, 2xz, yz - x)$, evaluate $\int_C \mathbf{F} \cdot \mathrm{d}s$ along the following paths C:
   (a) $x = 2t^2, y = t, z = t^3$ from $t = 0$ to $t = 1$;
   (b)   the straight lines from $(0, 0, 0)$ to $(0, 0, 1)$ then to $(0, 1, 1)$ and then to $(2, 1, 1)$;
   (c)   the straight line joining $(0, 0, 0)$ and $(2, 1, 1)$.

5.5 SURFACE INTEGRALS

The basic ideas underlying line integrals can be extended and applied to the problem of integrating a function $f(x, y, z)$ over a *curved* surface $\mathscr{S}$. This occurs if we want to find, for example, the total electrostatic charge on a curved conductor or the mass of a curved shell of variable thickness. Such an integral is called the *surface integral* of f over $\mathscr{S}$ and is denoted by

$$\iint_{\mathscr{S}} f(x, y, z) \, dS,$$

where (x, y, z) is a typical point of $\mathscr{S}$. The integral is defined by the limiting process of dividing the surface into n subregions of area δS_i $(i = 1, 2, \ldots, n)$ surrounding the typical points (x_i, y_i, z_i), forming the sum

$$\sum_{i=1}^{n} f(x_i, y_i, z_i) \delta S_i,$$

and then letting $n \to \infty$ in such a way that each $\delta S_i \to 0$.

Surface integrals are evaluated by transforming them into double integrals. Let $\mathscr{A}$ be the projection of $\mathscr{S}$ onto the x, y plane, as shown in Fig. 5.2, and let δA be the projection of a typical surface element δS at (x, y, z). Then in the limit as $\delta S \to 0$, we have

$$\delta A / \delta S \to |\cos \alpha| = |\mathbf{n} \cdot \mathbf{k}|,$$

where α is the angle between the normal line to $\mathscr{S}$ and the positive z axis, and $\mathbf{n}$ and $\mathbf{k}$ are the unit vectors in those directions. If the equation of the surface is $z = Z(x, y)$, then it can be shown (see example 1 of §6.5) that $\mathbf{n}$ is given by

$$\mathbf{n} = \frac{\left(-\dfrac{\partial Z}{\partial x}, -\dfrac{\partial Z}{\partial y}, 1 \right)}{\left\{ \left(\dfrac{\partial Z}{\partial x} \right)^2 + \left(\dfrac{\partial Z}{\partial y} \right)^2 + 1 \right\}^{1/2}} .$$

Hence

$$\frac{\delta S}{\delta A} \to \left\{ \left(\frac{\partial Z}{\partial x} \right)^2 + \left(\frac{\partial Z}{\partial y} \right)^2 + 1 \right\}^{1/2}$$

as $\delta S \to 0$, so that

$$\iint f(x, y, z) \, dS = \iint_{\mathscr{A}} f(x, y, z) \left\{ \left(\frac{\partial Z}{\partial x} \right)^2 + \left(\frac{\partial Z}{\partial y} \right)^2 + 1 \right\}^{1/2} dA. \qquad (30)$$

The simplest application of equation (30) is in finding the *area of a curved surface*.

This is given by putting $f(x, y, z) = 1$, so that the area of $\mathscr{S}$ is

$$\iint_{\mathscr{S}} dS = \iint_{\mathscr{A}} \left\{ \left(\frac{\partial Z}{\partial x} \right)^2 + \left(\frac{\partial Z}{\partial y} \right)^2 + 1 \right\}^{1/2} dA. \tag{31}$$

EXAMPLE

Determine the surface area of the paraboloidal shell given by

$$z = x^2 + y^2, \quad 0 \leqslant z \leqslant 1.$$

If the mass per unit area of the shell is proportional to the height z, determine the total mass of the shell.

In this example, $Z(x, y) = x^2 + y^2$, so that equation (31) gives the surface area as

$$S = \iint_{\mathscr{A}} (4x^2 + 4y^2 + 1)^{1/2} \, dA$$

where $\mathscr{A}$ is the disc $x^2 + y^2 \leqslant 1$. Obviously in this example we should transform to polar coordinates r and θ giving

$$S = \int_0^{2\pi} \int_0^1 (4r^2 + 1)^{1/2} \, r \, dr \, d\theta = \int_0^{2\pi} \left[\frac{1}{12} (4r^2 + 1)^{3/2} \right]_0^1 d\theta$$

$$= \frac{\pi}{6} (5\sqrt{5} - 1).$$

The mass M of the shell is given by equation (30) with

$$f(x, y, z) = cz = c(x^2 + y^2),$$

where c is the constant of proportionality. Hence

$$M = \iint_{\mathscr{A}} c(x^2 + y^2)(4x^2 + 4y^2 + 1)^{1/2} \, dA$$

$$= \int_0^{2\pi} \int_0^1 cr^2 (4r^2 + 1)^{1/2} \, r \, dr \, d\theta = \frac{\pi c}{12} \left(5\sqrt{5} + \frac{1}{5} \right).$$

Exercises

1. Find the surface area of that part of the cone $z^2 = x^2 + y^2$ which lies inside the circular cylinder $x^2 + y^2 = 2x$.

2. A shell roof has the form of the hyperbolic paraboloid $z = kxy$ and covers the region enclosed by the planes $x = 0$, $x = a$, $y = 0$ and $y = b$. If the mass of unit area of the roof is cxy at a typical point (x, y, z), find the total mass.

PROBLEMS

1. Use polar coordinates to find the volume of the solid included between the x, y plane and the surface $\log(z/a) = -(x^2 + y^2)/b^2$, where a and b are constants.

2. Evaluate $\iint\limits_{\mathscr{A}} \cos \theta \, dA$ over the region $\mathscr{A}$ enclosed by the circle $r = c \cos \theta$.

3. Determine and sketch the region of integration of the integral

$$\int_0^1 \int_{-\sqrt{(1-x)}}^{x-1} (1 - 2y) e^{x+y} \, dy \, dx,$$

and write down the limits when the order of integration is reversed. Hence, or otherwise, evaluate the integral.

4. By introducing polar coordinates, evaluate $\iint\limits_{\mathscr{A}} (1 + x^2 + y^2)^{-2} \, dA$ where the the region of integration $\mathscr{A}$ is the right-hand loop of the lemniscate $(x^2 + y^2)^2 = x^2 - y^2$.

5. Determine the Jacobian $\partial(u, v)/\partial(x, y)$ of the transformation defined by $u = x/a$, $v = y/b$, where a and b are constants.

Express the integral $\int_0^b \int_0^{a\sqrt{(1-y^2/b^2)}} xy(b^2 x^2 + a^2 y^2) \, dx \, dy$ in terms of u and v,

and show in a figure the region of integration in the u, v plane. By making a further change of variable to polar coordinates, or otherwise, evaluate the integral.

6. Find the centroid of the smaller of the two regions into which the circle $x^2 + y^2 = 2a^2$ is divided by the line $x = a$.

7. Change the order of integration and then evaluate $\int_0^1 \int_y^{2y} f(x) \, dx \, dy$ where

$$f(x) = \begin{cases} x^{-1/2} & 0 \leqslant x \leqslant 1 \\ (2 - x)^{-1/2} & 1 \leqslant x \leqslant 2. \end{cases}$$

8. A solid sphere of radius a and uniform density σ is enclosed by a concentric layer $a \leqslant r \leqslant b$ of variable density $r\sigma/a$, where r denotes distance from the centre of the sphere. Find the mass of the composite sphere, and its moment of inertia about a diameter.

9. Sketch the regions of integration and evaluate the following integrals:

(a) $\int_0^a \int_0^{\sqrt{(a^2-y^2)}} (x^2 + y^2) \tan^{-1}(y/x) \, dx \, dy,$

where a is a constant;

(b) $\displaystyle\int_0^{2\pi} \int_0^{\alpha} \int_0^{h\,\sec\theta} r^2 \sin\theta \; dr \; d\theta \; d\phi,$

where α and h are constants.

10. A helter-skelter is in the form of a helix with parametric equations

$$x = a \sin\theta, \quad y = a \cos\theta, \quad z = b\theta, \quad 0 \leqslant \theta \leqslant 6\pi.$$

A body of mass m slides down the helter-skelter. Calculate (i) the work done by gravity in the descent, (ii) the work done against a resistance R which is constant in magnitude and always directly opposes the motion.

Show that the work done by gravity is the same as the work that would be done by gravity in the vertical free fall of the body.

11. Find the work done by the force field $\mathbf{F} = (3x^2, 2xz - y, z)$ in moving a particle of mass m along the following paths:

   (a)   the straight line from $(0, 0, 0)$ to $(2, 1, 3)$,
   (b)   the curve $x = 2t^2, y = t, z = 4t^2 - t$ from $t = 0$ to $t = 1$,
   (c)   the curve defined by $x^2 = 4y, 3x^3 = 8z$ from $x = 0$ to $x = 2$.

12. Determine the area of the part of the paraboloid $x^2 + y^2 = 2z$ which lies inside the cylinder $x^2 + y^2 = a^2$ and for which x is positive.

13. Calculate the surface area of the part of the surface $z^2 = x^2 - y^2$ lying above the triangle in the x, y plane enclosed by the lines $y = x, y = -x$ and $x = 1$.

14. A thin shell roof has the form of the hyperbolic paraboloid $z = h + kxy$ and covers the circular region $x^2 + y^2 \leqslant a^2$. If the mass per unit surface area of the roof is $\sigma(x, y)$ at the point (x, y, z), find an expression for the total mass of the roof. Determine the total mass of the roof when $\sigma(x, y) = \sigma_0$, a constant.

15. A cross-section of a uniform circular beam is represented in the x, y plane by the circle $x^2 + y^2 = a^2$. A crack in the plane of this cross-section extends over that part of the cross-section which lies within the circle $(x - a)^2 + y^2 = a^2$. Find (i) the area and (ii) the second moment of area about the y axis of the part of the cross-section which is *not* covered by the crack (i.e. the *larger* part of the circle $x^2 + y^2 = a^2$ cut off by the arc $(x - a)^2 + y^2 = a^2$).

BIBLIOGRAPHY

[1]   Courant, R. *Differential and Integral Calculus*, Vols I and II, Blackie, Glasgow (1937).

[2]   Courant, R. and F. John, *Introduction to Calculus and Analysis*, Vol. I, Interscience, New York (1965).

[3]   Dwight, H. B. *Tables of Integrals and Other Mathematical Data*, Macmillan, New York (1961).

CHAPTER 6

Vector Analysis

6.1 INTRODUCTION

In many problems, familiar physical quantities such as temperature, density, velocity and magnetic field vary with position. At a point having cartesian coordinates (x, y, z), the temperature θ and density ρ at time t are scalar valued quantities which may be expressed as the scalar functions $\theta = \theta(x, y, z, t)$ and $\rho = \rho(x, y, z, t)$ respectively. Such functions constitute *scalar fields* since they associate a scalar number with each position at each instant. However, fluid velocity $\mathbf{v}$ and magnetic field $\mathbf{B}$ each possess both direction and magnitude. The corresponding functions $\mathbf{v} = \mathbf{v}(x, y, z, t)$ and $\mathbf{B} = \mathbf{B}(x, y, z, t)$ which associate a vector with each position at each instant are examples of *vector fields*. Any field in which the value at each position (x, y, z) does not vary with time is said to be *steady*, whilst a field which is the same at all positions within some regions is said to be *uniform* over that region. For example, the temperature distribution through a furnace wall is a scalar field which may well be steady for many hours. A varying electric current in a coil produces a magnetic field which is an unsteady non-uniform vector field, whilst a steady current passing through a long solenoid produces a steady magnetic field, which, inside the solenoid, is approximately uniform.

Scalar and vector fields are natural mathematical tools for the analysis of fluid flow, heat and mass transfer, electromagnetism, etc. This chapter shows that certain combinations of partial derivatives (see Chapter 4) of these fields occur frequently as measures of the variation of these fields, and that certain multiple integrals (see Chapter 5) are also important. The chapter also gives procedures by which basic physical laws such as mass conservation, energy balance and charge conservation may be converted into partial differential equations (see Chapter 7).

Notation

The reader is reminded of the basic rules of addition, scalar (or dot) multiplication and vector (or cross) multiplication, by which two vectors may be combined.

Let $\mathbf{i}, \mathbf{j}$ and $\mathbf{k}$ be the unit vectors along the x, y and z axes of a right-handed cartesian coordinate system. Then any two vectors $\mathbf{a}$ and $\mathbf{b}$ may be resolved into component vectors parallel to these *base vectors* as

$$\mathbf{a} = a_1\mathbf{i} + a_2\mathbf{j} + a_3\mathbf{k} \quad \text{and} \quad \mathbf{b} = b_1\mathbf{i} + b_2\mathbf{j} + b_3\mathbf{k},$$

so that their sum, scalar product and vector product are given by

$$a + b = (a_1 + b_1)i + (a_2 + b_2)j + (a_3 + b_3)k,$$

$$a \cdot b = b \cdot a = a_1b_1 + a_2b_2 + a_3b_3,$$

$$a \times b = -b \times a = (a_2b_3 - a_3b_2)i + (a_3b_1 - a_1b_3)j + (a_1b_2 - a_2b_1)k$$

respectively. These rules may be extended to more than two vectors by use of the associative and distributive laws

$$a + (b + c) = (a + b) + c, \quad a \cdot (b + c) = a \cdot b + a \cdot c, \quad a \times (b + c) = a \times b + a \times c.$$

The magnitude, or *modulus*, $|a| \equiv (a_1^2 + a_2^2 + a_3^2)^{1/2}$ of the vector a may be determined from $a \cdot a = |a|^2$, whilst the formula for the vector product $a \times b$ may be memorized as the determinant

$$a \times b = \begin{vmatrix} i & j & k \\ a_1 & a_2 & a_3 \\ b_1 & b_2 & b_3 \end{vmatrix}. \tag{1}$$

Similarly, the *scalar triple product* defined by

$$(a, b, c) \equiv (a \times b) \cdot c = (a_2b_3 - a_3b_2)c_1 + (a_3b_1 - a_1b_3)c_2 + (a_1b_2 - a_2b_1)c_3$$

may be shown to be the value of the determinant

$$(a, b, c) = \begin{vmatrix} a_1 & a_2 & a_3 \\ b_1 & b_2 & b_3 \\ c_1 & c_2 & c_3 \end{vmatrix}, \tag{2}$$

from which the usual identities

$$(a \times b) \cdot c = a \cdot (b \times c), \quad (a, b, c) = (b, c, a) = (c, a, b),$$

$$(c, b, a) = (b, a, c) = (a, c, b) = -(a, b, c) \tag{3}$$

follow. The *vector triple product* $a \times (b \times c)$ may be computed by use of equation (1) and may be put into the form

$$a \times (b \times c) = (a \cdot c)b - (a \cdot b)c. \tag{4}$$

It should be noted that the carat symbol $\wedge$ is often used instead of $\times$ to denote vector multiplication.

EXAMPLE

Show that $(a \times b) \cdot (c \times d) = (a \cdot c)(b \cdot d) - (a \cdot d)(b \cdot c)$.

The left-hand side may be rearranged, with the aid of the identities (3), as $(a \times b) \cdot (c \times d) = a \cdot \{b \times (c \times d)\}$, and equation (4) may then be used to equate this to

$$a \cdot \{(b \cdot d)c - (b \cdot c)d\} = (a \cdot c)(b \cdot d) - (a \cdot d)(b \cdot c).$$

Exercises

1. If $a = i + 2j - 3k$ and $b = i + j + k$, find

    (a) $a + b$,   (b) $a \cdot b$,   (c) $a \times b$,   (d) $|a|$ and
    (e) $(a \times b) \times a$.

2. Show that, for any vectors a and b, $|a|^2 |b|^2 = (a \cdot b)^2 + (a \times b) \cdot (a \times b)$.

3. A vector b may be resolved into component vectors along and perpendicular to a in the form $b = \lambda a + \mu(a \times b) \times a$.

Deduce that $\lambda = \dfrac{a \cdot b}{|a|^2}$ and $\mu = \dfrac{1}{|a|^2}$, and verify these formulae when a and b are as in exercise 1.

6.2 VECTOR FUNCTIONS OF ONE VARIABLE

Derivatives of Vectors

Suppose that the position vector $r = ix + jy + kz$ measures the position of a representative point P of some object (a particle, electron or vehicle). If the object is in motion, the vector r changes with time t and is given by the *vector function*

$$r = r(t) \equiv ix(t) + jy(t) + kz(t)$$

of the single variable t. The velocity $v = v(t)$ of P also is a function of the single variable t. It is the derivative of $r(t)$ and is given by

$$v = \dot{r}(t) = \frac{dr}{dt} = \lim_{\delta t \to 0} \left(\frac{r(t + \delta t) - r(t)}{\delta t} \right) = \lim_{\delta t \to 0} \frac{\delta r}{\delta t}$$

$$= \lim_{\delta t \to 0} \left(\frac{i\delta x + j\delta y + k\delta z}{\delta t} \right)$$

$$= i\frac{dx}{dt} + j\frac{dy}{dt} + k\frac{dz}{dt},$$

where δr is the small displacement shown in Fig. 6.1. The velocity vector at time t is tangential to the trajectory at the point P, and its modulus is the speed of the object.

The derivative of a general vector function

$$F(\eta) = iu(\eta) + jv(\eta) + kw(\eta) \tag{5}$$

of any scalar quantity η is related to derivatives of the components u, v and w by

$$F'(\eta) \equiv \frac{dF}{d\eta} = i\frac{du}{d\eta} + j\frac{dv}{d\eta} + k\frac{dw}{d\eta}. \tag{6}$$

Higher order derivatives are given by repeated differentiation as

$$F^{(n)}(\eta) \equiv \frac{d^n F}{d\eta^n} = i\frac{d^n u}{d\eta^n} + j\frac{d^n v}{d\eta^n} + k\frac{d^n w}{d\eta^n}.$$

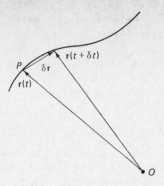

Fig. 6.1 The trajectory $\mathbf{r} = \mathbf{r}(t)$ of the point P, showing the displacement $\delta\mathbf{r}$ in the time increment δt

Furthermore, if $\mathbf{F}(\eta)$ and $\mathbf{G}(\eta)$ are differentiable vector functions, and $h(\eta)$ is a differentiable scalar function, it may be verified that

$$\frac{d}{d\eta}\{h(\eta)\mathbf{F}(\eta)\} = \frac{dh}{d\eta}\mathbf{F}(\eta) + h(\eta)\frac{d\mathbf{F}}{d\eta}, \tag{7}$$

$$\frac{d}{d\eta}\{\mathbf{F}(\eta)\cdot\mathbf{G}(\eta)\} = \frac{d\mathbf{F}}{d\eta}\cdot\mathbf{G}(\eta) + \mathbf{F}(\eta)\cdot\frac{d\mathbf{G}}{d\eta}, \tag{8}$$

$$\frac{d}{d\eta}\{\mathbf{F}(\eta)\times\mathbf{G}(\eta)\} = \frac{d\mathbf{F}}{d\eta}\times\mathbf{G}(\eta) + \mathbf{F}(\eta)\times\frac{d\mathbf{G}}{d\eta}. \tag{9}$$

The order of the vectors within each cross product in equation (9) should be carefully observed.

EXAMPLE 1
If a vector $\mathbf{F}(\eta)$ has magnitude $F(\eta) = |\mathbf{F}(\eta)|$, show that

$$\frac{dF}{d\eta} = \frac{1}{F}\mathbf{F}(\eta)\cdot\frac{d\mathbf{F}}{d\eta}.$$

Differentiate the identity $F^2(\eta) = \mathbf{F}(\eta)\cdot\mathbf{F}(\eta)$ to obtain

$$2F\frac{d\mathbf{F}}{d\eta} = \frac{d\mathbf{F}}{d\eta}\cdot\mathbf{F} + \mathbf{F}\cdot\frac{d\mathbf{F}}{d\eta} = 2\mathbf{F}\cdot\frac{d\mathbf{F}}{d\eta}.$$

Division by $2F$ then gives the required formula.

Integrals of Vectors

Since the velocity $\mathbf{v}(t)$ is the derivative of $\mathbf{r}(t)$, it is natural to regard $\mathbf{r}(t)$ as an integral of $\mathbf{v}(t)$. Indeed

$$\mathbf{r}(t_1) - \mathbf{r}(t_0) = \int_{t_0}^{t_1}\left(\mathbf{i}\frac{dx}{dt} + \mathbf{j}\frac{dy}{dt} + \mathbf{k}\frac{dz}{dt}\right)dt = \int_{t_0}^{t_1}\mathbf{v}(t)dt \tag{10}$$

defines the definite integral of $\mathbf{v}(t)$ with respect to t. More generally, whenever a vector function $\mathbf{G}(\eta)$ has derivative $\mathbf{G}'(\eta) = \mathbf{F}(\eta)$, it is said to be an indefinite integral of $\mathbf{F}(\eta)$ and is written as

$$\mathbf{G}(\eta) = \int \mathbf{F}(\eta) d\eta. \tag{11}$$

Notice that if $\mathbf{G}_1(\eta)$ and $\mathbf{G}_2(\eta)$ are each indefinite integrals of $\mathbf{F}(\eta)$, their difference $\mathbf{G}_2 - \mathbf{G}_1$ is a constant vector.

Other integrals of vector functions have important physical significance. For example, a force $\mathbf{F}$ does work $\mathbf{F} \cdot \delta \mathbf{r}$ when its point of application is displaced through $\delta \mathbf{r}$. Consequently the total work W performed during a time interval $t_0 \leqslant t \leqslant t_1$, in which the point of application moves from $\mathbf{r}_0 = \mathbf{r}(t_0)$ to $\mathbf{r}_1 = \mathbf{r}(t_1)$, is given by the line integral

$$W = \int_{\mathbf{r}_0}^{\mathbf{r}_1} \mathbf{F} \cdot d\mathbf{r} = \int_{t_0}^{t_1} \mathbf{F} \cdot \frac{d\mathbf{r}}{dt} dt = \int_{t_0}^{t_1} (\mathbf{F} \cdot \mathbf{v}) dt. \tag{12}$$

As another example, consider the resultant force on a wire carrying an electric current I, and whose shape is given parametrically as $\mathbf{r} = \mathbf{r}(\eta)$. It is known that in a magnetic field $\mathbf{B}$ a portion $\delta \mathbf{r}$ of the wire experiences a 'Lorentz force' $(I\delta \mathbf{r}) \times \mathbf{B} = -I\mathbf{B} \times \delta \mathbf{r}$, so that the resultant force on the portion of wire $\eta_0 \leqslant \eta \leqslant \eta_1$ is

$$\int_{\mathbf{r}_0}^{\mathbf{r}_1} (-I\mathbf{B}) \times \delta \mathbf{r} = -I \int_{\eta_0}^{\eta_1} \mathbf{B} \times \frac{d\mathbf{r}}{d\eta} d\eta, \tag{13}$$

where $\mathbf{r}_0 = \mathbf{r}(\eta_0)$ and $\mathbf{r}_1 = \mathbf{r}(\eta_1)$.

Notice that in both equation (12) and equation (13) integrals along a curve are evaluated by introduction of suitable parameters, t and η respectively.

EXAMPLE 2
A current I flows around a loop of wire situated in a uniform magnetic field. Show that there is no resultant force on the wire.

Represent the loop parametrically in the form $\mathbf{r} = \mathbf{r}(\eta)$ for $\eta_0 \leqslant \eta \leqslant \eta_1$, where $\mathbf{r}(\eta_1) = \mathbf{r}(\eta_0)$ because the loop is closed. The resultant force is

$$-I \int_{\eta_0}^{\eta_1} \mathbf{B} \times \frac{d\mathbf{r}}{d\eta} d\eta = -I\mathbf{B} \times \left(\int_{\eta_0}^{\eta_1} \frac{d\mathbf{r}}{d\eta} d\eta \right),$$

since $\mathbf{B}$ is independent of η. This force vanishes since the bracketed term has the value $\mathbf{r}(\eta_1) - \mathbf{r}(\eta_0) = \mathbf{0}$.

Curvature and Torsion

Unless a curve lies entirely in one plane it is said to be twisted. The measure of twist is the torsion.

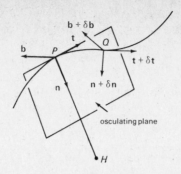

Fig. 6.2 The moving triads at two neighbouring points P, Q of a curve

Let the position vector $\mathbf{r}$ of a typical point P of the curve be given parametrically as $\mathbf{r} = \mathbf{r}(\eta)$, where the function $\mathbf{r}(\eta)$ is differentiable. If s is the distance measured along the curve from some reference point to P, then

$$\frac{ds}{d\eta} = \left| \frac{d\mathbf{r}}{d\eta} \right| = |\mathbf{r}'(\eta)|.$$

At P the *unit tangent* $\mathbf{t}$ to the curve is given by

$$\mathbf{t} = \lim_{\delta s \to 0} \frac{\vec{PQ}}{\delta s} = \lim_{\delta s \to 0} \frac{\delta \mathbf{r}}{\delta s} = \frac{d\mathbf{r}}{ds} = \frac{\mathbf{r}'(\eta)}{|\mathbf{r}'(\eta)|}, \tag{14}$$

where Q is the point $\mathbf{r} = \mathbf{r}(\eta + \delta\eta)$, as in Fig. 6.2. The rate at which this unit tangent turns is known as the *curvature* κ at the point P and is given by

$$\kappa \equiv \left| \frac{d\mathbf{t}}{ds} \right|. \tag{15}$$

This definition agrees with the definition of curvature for plane curves. Differentiation of the identity $\mathbf{t} \cdot \mathbf{t} = 1$ shows that the vector $d\mathbf{t}/ds$ is normal to the tangent $\mathbf{t}$. The unit vector parallel to $d\mathbf{t}/ds$ is known as the *unit principal normal* $\mathbf{n}$, and is defined by

$$\kappa\mathbf{n} = \frac{d\mathbf{t}}{ds} = \frac{d^2\mathbf{r}}{ds^2}, \quad \text{with } \mathbf{n} \cdot \mathbf{n} = 1. \tag{16}$$

The plane through P containing both of the vectors $\mathbf{t}$ and $\mathbf{n}$ is called the *plane of curvature*, or *osculating plane* at P, and is the limit as Q approaches P of the plane containing both the tangent $\mathbf{t}$ at P and the point Q. The point H such that $\vec{PH} = \kappa^{-1}\mathbf{n}$ is the *centre of curvature* corresponding to P, and it can be shown that the circle lying in the osculating plane, having H as centre and having radius κ^{-1} is the circle which most closely approximates the curve near P.

The axis about which $\mathbf{t}$ is instantaneously rotating at P is given by the *unit binormal* $\mathbf{b} = \mathbf{t} \times \mathbf{n}$. The vectors $\mathbf{t}$, $\mathbf{n}$ and $\mathbf{b}$ form a right-handed system known as the *moving triad* at P. When the curve is a plane curve the unit binormal has fixed direction, perpendicular to the plane of the curve. Generally, the rate at which **b** rotates with s determines the *torsion* λ of the curve. However, since $\mathbf{b} \cdot \mathbf{t} = 0$ and $\mathbf{b} \cdot \mathbf{b} = 1$ it follows from equation (16) that

$$0 = \frac{d}{ds}(\mathbf{b} \cdot \mathbf{t}) = \frac{d\mathbf{b}}{ds} \cdot \mathbf{t} + \mathbf{b} \cdot \frac{d\mathbf{t}}{ds} = \frac{d\mathbf{b}}{ds} \cdot \mathbf{t}$$

and that

$$0 = \frac{d}{ds}(\mathbf{b} \cdot \mathbf{b}) = 2\frac{d\mathbf{b}}{ds} \cdot \mathbf{b}.$$

Consequently $d\mathbf{b}/ds$ is parallel to **n** and may be written as

$$\frac{d\mathbf{b}}{ds} = -\lambda\mathbf{n}, \tag{17}$$

the sign being chosen so that a right-handed corkscrew has positive torsion. Notice that although λ may be positive or negative, the curvature κ is never negative.

Differentiation of the identity $\mathbf{n} = \mathbf{b} \times \mathbf{t}$ gives $d\mathbf{n}/ds = \lambda\mathbf{b} - \kappa\mathbf{t}$. This, together with equations (16) and (17), comprises the *Serret–Frenet formulae*

$$\frac{d\mathbf{t}}{ds} = \kappa\mathbf{n}, \qquad \frac{d\mathbf{n}}{ds} = \lambda\mathbf{b} - \kappa\mathbf{t}, \qquad \frac{d\mathbf{b}}{ds} = -\lambda\mathbf{n}. \tag{18}$$

EXAMPLE 3
A helix is given parametrically by $\mathbf{r} = \mathbf{r}(\eta) \equiv i a \cos \eta + j a \sin \eta + k b \eta$, where a and b are constants. Find its curvature and torsion.

The vector $\dfrac{d\mathbf{r}}{d\eta} = -i a \sin \eta + j a \cos \eta + k b$ is tangential to the helix. Its modulus is $ds/d\eta = |\,d\mathbf{r}/d\eta\,| = (a^2 + b^2)^{1/2} =$ constant, so that the unit tangent is $\mathbf{t} = (a^2 + b^2)^{-1/2}(-i a \sin \eta + j a \cos \eta + k b)$. Then

$$\kappa\mathbf{n} = \frac{d\mathbf{t}}{ds} = (a^2 + b^2)^{-1/2}\frac{d\mathbf{t}}{d\eta} = (a^2 + b^2)^{-1}(-i a \cos \eta - j a \sin \eta),$$

which shows that the *curvature* κ is $\kappa = a(a^2 + b^2)^{-1}$, and the unit principal normal is $\mathbf{n} = -i \cos \eta - j \sin \eta$. The unit binormal is then found to be $\mathbf{b} = \mathbf{t} \times \mathbf{n} = (a^2 + b^2)^{-1/2}(i b \sin \eta - j b \cos \eta + k a)$, so that

$$\frac{d\mathbf{b}}{ds} = (a^2 + b^2)^{-1/2}\frac{d\mathbf{b}}{d\eta} = (a^2 + b^2)^{-1}(i b \cos \eta + j b \sin \eta) = \frac{-b}{a^2 + b^2}\mathbf{n}.$$

Consequently the *torsion* is $\lambda = b(a^2 + b^2)^{-1}$ and is positive for $b > 0$ as illustrated in Fig. 6.3.

It is readily checked that $d\mathbf{n}/ds = (i \sin \eta - j \cos \eta)d\eta/ds = \lambda\mathbf{b} - \kappa\mathbf{t}$, so that all three of the Serret–Frenet formulae (18) are satisfied.

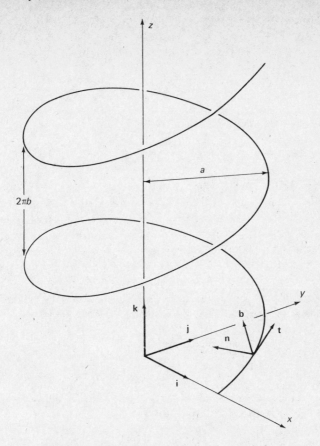

Fig. 6.3   The right-handed helix of example 3

Exercises

1. If $\mathbf{r} = \mathbf{i}t + \mathbf{j}(t^2 - t) + \mathbf{k}\sin \pi t$ and $\mathbf{F} = \mathbf{i}a - \mathbf{r}b$, find $d\mathbf{r}/dt$, $d^2\mathbf{r}/dt^2$ and $\displaystyle\int_{t=0}^{t=1} \mathbf{F} \cdot d\mathbf{r}$.

2. A particle of mass m, at position $\mathbf{r}(t)$ and subject to a force $\mathbf{F}$ moves according to Newton's Laws which imply that

$$m \frac{d^2\mathbf{r}}{dt^2} = \mathbf{F}.$$

Show that, in any motion, the work W performed by the force $\mathbf{F}$ equals the change in the *kinetic energy* $\frac{1}{2}mv^2$, where $v = |\mathbf{v}|$ and $\mathbf{v} = d\mathbf{r}/dt$.

3. The 'Lorentz force' on an electron of mass m and charge e moving with velocity $\mathbf{v}$ in a magnetic field $\mathbf{B}$ is $\mathbf{F} = -e\,\mathbf{B} \times \mathbf{v}$. If this is the only force acting on the electron, deduce from Newton's Laws that the speed $v = |\mathbf{v}|$ is constant throughout the motion.

4. The acceleration $\mathbf{a}(t)$ of a point P at position $\mathbf{r}(t)$ relative to a fixed point O and having velocity $\mathbf{v}(t) = \dot{\mathbf{r}}(t)$ is $\mathbf{a} = \dot{\mathbf{v}}(t) = d^2\mathbf{r}/dt^2$. If the distance $OP = L$ is fixed, differentiate the identity $\mathbf{r} \cdot \mathbf{r} = L^2$ and so show that the component of acceleration directed towards O is v^2/L, where $v = |\mathbf{v}|$.

6.3 SCALAR AND VECTOR FIELDS

Gradient of a Scalar

It is common experience that heat flows from hot regions to cold ones. Similarly, a gas diffuses away from regions of high concentration, towards regions of low concentration. The flow rates in these examples are vector fields, which must be related to the spatial variations of the (scalar) temperature and concentration fields respectively. By considering the directional derivative of a typical scalar field $f(x, y, z, t) = f(\mathbf{r}, t)$ we shall introduce a vector field which involves the spatial partial derivatives of f, and which is known as the *gradient* of f.

At any point P having position vector $\mathbf{r} = \mathbf{i}x + \mathbf{j}y + \mathbf{k}z$, consider any smooth curve passing through P. If s measures distance along the curve, the unit tangent $\mathbf{t}$ to the curve at P is given by

$$\mathbf{t} \equiv \frac{d\mathbf{r}}{ds} = \mathbf{i}\frac{dx}{ds} + \mathbf{j}\frac{dy}{ds} + \mathbf{k}\frac{dz}{ds}, \tag{19}$$

where $\mathbf{t}$ should not be confused with the time t. The rate of change of f with respect to distance s is given by the chain rule of §4.2 as

$$\frac{df}{ds} = \frac{\partial f}{\partial x}\frac{dx}{ds} + \frac{\partial f}{\partial y}\frac{dy}{ds} + \frac{\partial f}{\partial z}\frac{dz}{ds}, \tag{20}$$

which generalizes to three dimensions the *directional derivative* defined in §4.3. It may be seen from equation (20) that df/ds is the scalar product of the unit tangent vector $\mathbf{t}$ with the vector

$$\mathbf{i}\frac{\partial f}{\partial x} + \mathbf{j}\frac{\partial f}{\partial y} + \mathbf{k}\frac{\partial f}{\partial z}.$$

This vector does not depend on the choice of curve through P, but depends only on the spatial partial derivatives of $f(x, y, z, t)$ at P. It is known as the *gradient* of f at P and may be written in various forms as

$$\text{grad } f \equiv \mathbf{i}\frac{\partial f}{\partial x} + \mathbf{j}\frac{\partial f}{\partial y} + \mathbf{k}\frac{\partial f}{\partial z} = \mathbf{i}f_x + \mathbf{j}f_y + \mathbf{k}f_z = (f_x, f_y, f_z). \tag{21}$$

The gradient grad f of any scalar f has the property that

$$\mathbf{t} \cdot \text{grad } f$$

is the directional derivative of f in the direction of an arbitrary unit vector $\mathbf{t}$.

EXAMPLE 1
Find the gradient of the scalar functions:

(a) $f = x^2 y - z \sin y$,   (b) $f(x, y, z, t) = \exp\{-(x^2 + y^2 + z^2)/t\}$.

(a) Since $f_x = 2xy, f_y = x^2 - z \cos y$ and $f_z = -\sin y$, the gradient of f is the vector $\operatorname{grad} f = \mathbf{i}2xy + \mathbf{j}(x^2 - z \cos y) - \mathbf{k} \sin y$.

(b) Since $f_x = -(2x/t) \exp\{-(x^2 + y^2 + z^2)/t\}$, and the expressions for f_y and f_z are similar, $\operatorname{grad} f$ is given by

$$\operatorname{grad} f = -\{\mathbf{i}2x/t + \mathbf{j}2y/t + \mathbf{k}2z/t\} \exp\{-(x^2 + y^2 + z^2)/t\}$$
$$= -2t^{-1} \mathbf{r}f(x, y, z, t).$$

Geometric Properties of the Gradient

It can be seen from the definition (21), and verified from example 1(b), that the gradient of a scalar does not involve time-derivatives. Consequently, its geometric properties may be illustrated by consideration of steady fields $f(x, y, z) = f(\mathbf{r})$. Thus,

(a) $\operatorname{grad} f$ is normal to surfaces of constant f,
(b) $\operatorname{grad} f$ points in the direction in which f *increases* most rapidly,
(c)   this maximum value of the directional derivative is $| \operatorname{grad} f |$.

To prove properties (a), (b) and (c), consider the directional derivative

$$\frac{df}{ds} = \mathbf{t} \cdot \operatorname{grad} f = | \operatorname{grad} f | \cos \alpha$$

along any curve passing through a point P, with unit tangent $\mathbf{t}$ at inclination α to the vector $\operatorname{grad} f$. Whenever the curve lies in the surface $f = $ constant, $df/ds = 0$ so that $\alpha = \pi/2$. Hence, all vectors tangential to the surface at P are perpendicular to $\operatorname{grad} f$. This proves result (a). To verify (b) and (c), note that df/ds takes its maximum value $| \operatorname{grad} f |$ when $\alpha = 0$, so that $\mathbf{t}$ is parallel to $\operatorname{grad} f$.

Any surface on which $f(x, y, z)$ is constant is called a *level surface* of f. Thus, $\operatorname{grad} f$ is everywhere perpendicular to the corresponding level surface of f.

EXAMPLE 2
Find $\operatorname{grad} f$ and $| \operatorname{grad} f |$ for (a) $f = Ax$ and (b) $f = x^2 + y^2 + z^2 = r^2$. In each case verify that $\operatorname{grad} f$ is normal to the surface $f = $ constant.

(a) $f_x = A, f_y = 0, f_z = 0$ so that $\operatorname{grad} f = A\mathbf{i}$ and $| \operatorname{grad} f | = | A |$. The level surfaces of f are the planes $x = $ constant. Each has normal $\mathbf{i}$, which is everywhere parallel to $\operatorname{grad} f$.

(b)   The gradient is

$$\operatorname{grad} f = \mathbf{i}2x + \mathbf{j}2y + \mathbf{k}2z = 2\mathbf{r},$$

so that $| \operatorname{grad} f | = 2 | \mathbf{r} | = 2r$. Since $\operatorname{grad} f$ is everywhere directed radially outwards it is normal to the spheres $r = $ constant which are the level surfaces of f.

Flux of a Vector Field

Suppose that at a point P a fluid has density ρ and flows with velocity $\mathbf{v}$, and consider
the rate at which mass is transported across a typical surface element at P. If the
element has area dS and unit normal $\mathbf{n}$, only the normal component $\mathbf{v} \cdot \mathbf{n}$ of velocity
accounts for any mass transport. Consequently the rate of mass flow through the
surface element is

$$\rho \, \mathbf{v} \cdot \mathbf{n} \, dS.$$

The quantity $\mathbf{n} \, dS$ is often denoted by $d\mathbf{S}$ and called a *vector* (or *oriented*) *element of
area*. The vector field $\rho\mathbf{v}$ is called the *mass flux vector* of the fluid flow, and has the
property that its scalar product with $\mathbf{n}dS$ measures the rate of mass flow through the
area dS having unit normal $\mathbf{n}$.

   More generally, the flux of any vector field $\mathbf{F} = \mathbf{F}(x, y, z, t) = \mathbf{F}(\mathbf{r}, t)$ through a
surface element $d\mathbf{S} = \mathbf{n} \, dS$ is given by

$$\mathbf{F} \cdot d\mathbf{S} = \mathbf{F} \cdot \mathbf{n} \, dS.$$

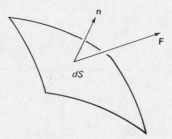

Fig. 6.4   A surface element

For example, the rate at which electric charge crosses the surface element may be
written as $\mathbf{J} \cdot d\mathbf{S} = \mathbf{J} \cdot \mathbf{n} \, dS$, where $\mathbf{J} = \mathbf{J}(\mathbf{r}, t)$ is the *electric current vector*. Similarly
the rate at which heat is conducted across a surface element $d\mathbf{S}$ within a solid may be
written as $\mathbf{q} \cdot d\mathbf{S}$, where $\mathbf{q}$ is the *heat conduction vector*.

EXAMPLE 3
Find the flux across an area element $d\mathbf{S} = \mathbf{j} \, dS$ at $\mathbf{r} = 2\mathbf{i}$ of the vector field
$\mathbf{F} = \mathbf{i}y + \mathbf{j}x^2 \cos z + \mathbf{k}yz$.

   At $\mathbf{r} = 2\mathbf{i}$, $\mathbf{F} = 4\mathbf{j}$, since $x = 2$, $y = 0$ and $z = 0$. Consequently the flux is
$\mathbf{F} \cdot d\mathbf{S} = 4\mathbf{j} \cdot \mathbf{j} \, dS = 4dS$.

EXAMPLE 4
Fourier's Law of heat conduction states that the heat conduction vector $\mathbf{q}$ within a
solid is given by $\mathbf{q} = -K$ grad θ, where $\theta = \theta(x, y, z, t)$ is the temperature and K is the
thermal conductivity of the solid. Verify that this law is consistent with the
experimental observation that the rate at which heat is conducted across an element of

area within the solid is proportional to the directional derivative of θ normal to that element of area.

If $dS = \mathbf{n}\,dS$ is an arbitrary area element at some point P of the solid, $\mathbf{n} \cdot \operatorname{grad} \theta$ is the directional derivative of temperature in the direction normal to that element. The rate of heat conduction across that element is

$$\mathbf{q} \cdot \mathbf{n}\,dS = -K \operatorname{grad} \theta \cdot \mathbf{n}\,dS = -K(\mathbf{n} \cdot \operatorname{grad} \theta)\,dS,$$

and so the rate of heat conduction across unit area is proportional to $\mathbf{n} \cdot \operatorname{grad} \theta$.

Divergence

The total outward heat flux through the boundary surface of any material region is the rate of heat loss from that region (and affects the rate of cooling). In this, and many other, physical situations the total outward flux of a vector field across the boundary surface of a typical region is an important quantity. It leads us to introduce the concept of *divergence*, which is the outward flux of the vector field per unit volume.

Consider an elementary rectangular box centred at the point (x, y, z) within a general vector field

$$\mathbf{F} = \mathbf{i}u(x, y, z) + \mathbf{j}v(x, y, z) + \mathbf{k}w(x, y, z). \tag{22}$$

Let the box have edges of lengths δx, δy and δz, and volume $\delta V = \delta x \delta y \delta z$ as in Fig. 6.5. The outward flux $\delta\Phi$ of the field $\mathbf{F}$ from this box is the sum of contributions from each of the six faces. Over the faces $ABCD$ and $A'B'C'D'$ the outward normal components of $\mathbf{F}$ are respectively $\mathbf{F} \cdot \mathbf{i} = u$ and $\mathbf{F} \cdot (-\mathbf{i}) = -u$. The values $u(x + \tfrac{1}{2}\delta x, y, z)$ and $-u(x - \tfrac{1}{2}\delta x, y, z)$ at the centres of the respective rectangular faces approximate to the corresponding mean values, so that the sum of the outward fluxes through the two faces is approximately

$$u(x + \tfrac{1}{2}\delta x, y, z)\delta y \delta z - u(x - \tfrac{1}{2}\delta x, y, z)\delta y \delta z = \{u(x + \tfrac{1}{2}\delta x, y, z) \\ - u(x - \tfrac{1}{2}\delta x, y, z)\}\delta y \delta z,$$

since both faces have area $\delta y \delta z$. By use of the mean value theorem (6) of §4.2, this

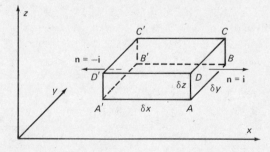

Fig. 6,5   An elementary rectangular box

sum may be written as

$$\frac{\partial u}{\partial x}(x', y, z)\,\delta x \delta y \delta z = \frac{\partial u}{\partial x}(x', y, z)\,\delta V$$

for some x' in the range $x - \frac{1}{2}\delta x < x' < x + \frac{1}{2}\delta x$. Similarly the flux contributions from the pairs of faces $y = $ constant and $z = $ constant are approximately

$$\frac{\partial v}{\partial y}(x, y', z)\,\delta V \quad \text{and} \quad \frac{\partial w}{\partial z}(x, y, z')\,\delta V$$

for some y' and z' satisfying $y - \frac{1}{2}\delta y < y' < y + \frac{1}{2}\delta y$ and $z - \frac{1}{2}\delta z < z' < z + \frac{1}{2}\delta z$. Using these approximations gives

$$\delta \Phi = \left\{ \frac{\partial u}{\partial x}(x', y, z) + \frac{\partial v}{\partial y}(x, y', z) + \frac{\partial w}{\partial z}(x, y, z') \right\} \delta V.$$

Dividing by δV and taking the limit $\delta x \to 0$, $\delta y \to 0$, $\delta z \to 0$, in which $x' \to x$, $y' \to y$ and $z' \to z$, gives

$$\lim_{\delta V \to 0} \left(\frac{\delta \Phi}{\delta V} \right) = \frac{\partial u}{\partial x} + \frac{\partial v}{\partial y} + \frac{\partial w}{\partial z}.$$

This scalar quantity is known as the *divergence* of the field **F**, and is written as

$$\text{div }\mathbf{F} \equiv \frac{\partial u}{\partial x} + \frac{\partial v}{\partial y} + \frac{\partial w}{\partial z}. \tag{23}$$

It measures the outward flux of **F** per unit volume from a small rectangular volume element situated at (x, y, z).

The Operator ∇

Equation (21) is a formula for calculation of a vector field grad f associated with a given scalar field $f(x, y, z, t)$. It involves the components f_x, f_y and f_z of grad f resolved along the base vectors **i**, **j** and **k** of the (x, y, z) coordinate system. Although in a new coordinate system the formula will involve different partial derivatives (see Problem 15), the vector itself must be unchanged as it measures the same physical and geometric quantities. Thus, just as 'differentiation' of a function $g(x)$ of one variable x is an operation producing a different function $g'(x)$, 'taking the gradient' may be regarded as an *operation* producing a vector field grad f related to the scalar field f. The vector grad f may be concisely written using the *vector operator* ∇ (pronounced 'del', but sometimes 'nabla') defined by

$$\nabla \equiv \mathbf{i}\frac{\partial}{\partial x} + \mathbf{j}\frac{\partial}{\partial y} + \mathbf{k}\frac{\partial}{\partial z} \tag{24}$$

as

$$\text{grad }f = \nabla f \equiv \left(\mathbf{i}\frac{\partial}{\partial x} + \mathbf{j}\frac{\partial}{\partial y} + \mathbf{k}\frac{\partial}{\partial z} \right) f = \mathbf{i}\frac{\partial f}{\partial x} + \mathbf{j}\frac{\partial f}{\partial y} + \mathbf{k}\frac{\partial f}{\partial z}. \tag{25}$$

Moreover, the scalar field div **F** derived from a vector field **F** may conveniently be written in terms of the same symbol ∇ as

$$\text{div } \mathbf{F} = \nabla \cdot \mathbf{F} \equiv \left(\mathbf{i} \frac{\partial}{\partial x} + \mathbf{j} \frac{\partial}{\partial y} + \mathbf{k} \frac{\partial}{\partial z} \right) \cdot (iu + jv + kw)$$

$$= \frac{\partial u}{\partial x} + \frac{\partial v}{\partial y} + \frac{\partial w}{\partial z}. \tag{26}$$

The operator ∇ also provides a ready means for writing out the properties

(a) $\nabla(kf) = k\nabla f,$ (b) $\nabla(f + g) = \nabla f + \nabla g,$

(c) $\nabla(fg) = f\nabla g + g \nabla f,$ (d) $\nabla\{\phi(f)\} = \phi'(f)\nabla f,$

(e) $\text{div}(f\mathbf{F}) = \nabla \cdot (f\mathbf{F}) = \nabla f \cdot \mathbf{F} + f \nabla \cdot \mathbf{F} = \mathbf{F} \cdot \text{grad } f + f \text{ div } \mathbf{F},$ (27)

where f and g are arbitrary scalar fields, $\phi(f)$ is any scalar function of f, **F** is a vector field, and k is a constant. The proofs of the identities (27), using the definitions (21) and (23) for gradient and divergence respectively, are left as exercises.

Curl of a Vector Field

Just as the scalar product of the operator ∇ with a vector field **F** yields a scalar field div **F** associated with the local outflow or 'source strength' of **F**, the vector product $\nabla \times \mathbf{F}$ gives a vector field having physical significance. It is called the *curl* of the field, and measures the local curling, swirl or rotation of the field – much as the angular velocity vector measures the rate of rotation of a rigid body. The curl of the field **F** may be resolved into **i**, **j** and **k** components as

$$\text{curl } \mathbf{F} \equiv \nabla \times \mathbf{F} = \left(\mathbf{i} \frac{\partial}{\partial x} + \mathbf{j} \frac{\partial}{\partial y} + \mathbf{k} \frac{\partial}{\partial z} \right) \times (iu + jv + kw)$$

$$= \mathbf{i} \left(\frac{\partial w}{\partial y} - \frac{\partial v}{\partial z} \right) + \mathbf{j} \left(\frac{\partial u}{\partial z} - \frac{\partial w}{\partial x} \right) + \mathbf{k} \left(\frac{\partial v}{\partial x} - \frac{\partial u}{\partial y} \right). \tag{28}$$

Note that curl **F** involves the six partial derivatives which do not appear in div **F**, and that the component of curl **F** in one coordinate direction involves neither the corresponding component of **F**, nor any partial derivatives with respect to that coordinate. A mnemonic for memorizing the formula (28) is

$$\text{curl } \mathbf{F} = \nabla \times \mathbf{F} = \begin{vmatrix} \mathbf{i} & \mathbf{j} & \mathbf{k} \\ \partial/\partial x & \partial/\partial y & \partial/\partial z \\ u & v & w \end{vmatrix},$$

since the rule for expansion of a determinant by its first row reproduces the last line of equation (28). However, the expression is not a true determinant, and manipulations involving whole rows and columns should not be attempted.

Further physical interpretation of curl **F** is left to §6.5 where it becomes clear that the right-hand side of equation (28) defines a physical vector, independent of the choice of base vectors **i**, **j** and **k**.

EXAMPLE 5

Find both div $\mathbf{F}$ and curl $\mathbf{F}$ when $\mathbf{F} = -\mathbf{i}yx + \mathbf{j}zx + \mathbf{k}xy$.

$$\text{div } \mathbf{F} = \frac{\partial}{\partial x}(-yx) + \frac{\partial}{\partial y}(zx) + \frac{\partial}{\partial z}(xy) = -y + 0 + 0 = -y,$$

whilst

$$\text{curl } \mathbf{F} = \mathbf{i}\left\{\frac{\partial}{\partial y}(xy) - \frac{\partial}{\partial z}(zx)\right\} + \mathbf{j}\left\{\frac{\partial}{\partial z}(-yx) - \frac{\partial}{\partial x}(xy)\right\}$$

$$+ \mathbf{k}\left\{\frac{\partial}{\partial x}(zx) - \frac{\partial}{\partial y}(-yx)\right\}$$

$$= \mathbf{i}(x - x) + \mathbf{j}(0 - y) + \mathbf{k}(z + x) = -\mathbf{j}y + \mathbf{k}(x + z).$$

EXAMPLE 6

When a rigid body spins about a fixed point O with angular velocity $\mathbf{\Omega} = \omega_1\mathbf{i} + \omega_2\mathbf{j} + \omega_3\mathbf{k}$, the velocity at the point with instantaneous position $\mathbf{r} = x\mathbf{i} + y\mathbf{j} + z\mathbf{k}$ relative to O is $\mathbf{v} = \mathbf{\Omega} \times \mathbf{r}$. Show that curl $\mathbf{v} = 2\mathbf{\Omega}$.

Since

$$\mathbf{v} = (\omega_1\mathbf{i} + \omega_2\mathbf{j} + \omega_3\mathbf{k}) \times (x\mathbf{i} + y\mathbf{j} + z\mathbf{k})$$

$$= (\omega_2 z - \omega_3 y)\mathbf{i} + (\omega_3 x - \omega_1 z)\mathbf{j} + (\omega_1 y - \omega_2 x)\mathbf{k},$$

$$\text{curl } \mathbf{v} = \mathbf{i}\{\omega_1 - (-\omega_1)\} + \mathbf{j}\{\omega_2 - (-\omega_2)\} + \mathbf{k}\{\omega_3 - (-\omega_3)\} = 2\mathbf{\Omega}$$

Example 6 illustrates the fact that ½ curl $\mathbf{F}$ measures the local 'spin' or 'rotation rate' of the field $\mathbf{F}$. For this reason, a field $\mathbf{F}$ is said to be *irrotational* in any region in which curl $\mathbf{F} = \mathbf{0}$. Such fields are important in fluid dynamics and electrostatics.

The Laplacian ∇^2

In many situations, a physical vector field $\mathbf{F}$ is the gradient of a scalar f, so that its divergence is related to f by

$$\text{div } \mathbf{F} = \text{div (grad } f) = \nabla \cdot \nabla f.$$

The combination of operators div grad $= \nabla \cdot \nabla$ is a scalar operator known as the *Laplacian*, written as ∇^2, and pronounced 'del squared'. It occurs in many partial differential equations, as is discussed in Chapter 7. For any function f the Laplacian of f is given by

$$\nabla^2 f = \nabla \cdot \nabla f = \text{div grad } f = \frac{\partial^2 f}{\partial x^2} + \frac{\partial^2 f}{\partial y^2} + \frac{\partial^2 f}{\partial z^2}. \tag{29}$$

The partial differential equation

$$\nabla^2 f = 0 \tag{30}$$

is *Laplace's equation* for f (see §7.5), and any solution of Laplace's equation is called a *harmonic function*.

EXAMPLE 7

If $r = (x^2 + y^2 + z^2)^{1/2}$, show that $\nabla^2(1/r) = 0$ except possibly at $r = 0$.

Using equation (27d) and the result $\mathrm{grad}(r^2) = 2\mathbf{r}$ of example 2(b) we find that $\mathrm{grad}(1/r) = \mathrm{grad}(r^2)^{-1/2} = -\tfrac{1}{2}(r^2)^{-3/2}\,\mathrm{grad}(r^2) = -r^{-3}\mathbf{r}$. Then $\nabla^2(1/r) = \mathrm{div}(\mathrm{grad}\ 1/r) = -\mathrm{div}(r^{-3}\mathbf{r}) = -\mathbf{r}\cdot\mathrm{grad}(r^{-3}) - r^{-3}\ \mathrm{div}\ \mathbf{r}$, using equation (27e). But div $\mathbf{r}$ $= \mathrm{div}(\mathbf{i}x + \mathbf{j}y + \mathbf{k}z) = 1 + 1 + 1 = 3$, and $\mathrm{grad}(r^{-3}) = -\tfrac{3}{2}(r^2)^{-5/2}\ \mathrm{grad}\ (r^2) = -3r^{-5}\mathbf{r}$. Consequently

$$\nabla^2\left(\frac{1}{r}\right) = \mathbf{r}\cdot(3r^{-5}\mathbf{r}) - 3r^{-3} = 0,$$

except possibly at the origin $\mathbf{r} = \mathbf{0}$ (see problem 10).

Vector Identities

There are many identities involving the operators grad, div, curl and ∇^2, some of which are logical extensions of rules involving scalar and vector products. An important example is the rule

$$\mathrm{curl}(\mathrm{grad}\ f) = \nabla \times \nabla f = \mathbf{0}, \tag{31}$$

which states that the gradient of *any* scalar f is irrotational. The identity may be proved, assuming only that all necessary partial derivatives are continuous, by noting that

$$\mathrm{curl\ grad}\ f = \mathbf{i}\left\{\frac{\partial}{\partial y}\left(\frac{\partial f}{\partial z}\right) - \frac{\partial}{\partial z}\left(\frac{\partial f}{\partial y}\right)\right\} + \mathbf{j}\left\{\frac{\partial}{\partial z}\left(\frac{\partial f}{\partial x}\right) - \frac{\partial}{\partial x}\left(\frac{\partial f}{\partial z}\right)\right\}$$

$$+ \mathbf{k}\left\{\frac{\partial}{\partial x}\left(\frac{\partial f}{\partial y}\right) - \frac{\partial}{\partial y}\left(\frac{\partial f}{\partial x}\right)\right\} = \mathbf{0}.$$

A second important identity is

$$\mathrm{div\ curl}\ \mathbf{F} = \nabla\cdot(\nabla\times\mathbf{F}) = 0, \tag{32}$$

which states that the curl of *any* vector field $\mathbf{F}$ has zero divergence. The proof, when $\mathbf{F}$ is sufficiently differentiable, is again straightforward. The rules (31) and (32) may be memorized by analogy with the identities $\mathbf{a}\times\mathbf{a} = \mathbf{0}$ and $\mathbf{a}\cdot(\mathbf{a}\times\mathbf{b}) = 0$ for fixed vectors $\mathbf{a}$ and $\mathbf{b}$. The converse results — that every irrotational vector field is the gradient of some scalar field, and that every *solenoidal* field (a vector field having divergence equal to zero) is the curl of some appropriate vector field — are important in fluid dynamics and electromagnetism, and are discussed in §6.5.

Some further vector identities are

(a) $\mathrm{curl}(f\mathbf{F}) = \nabla \times (f\mathbf{F}) = \nabla f \times \mathbf{F} + f\nabla \times \mathbf{F} = \mathrm{grad}\ f \times \mathbf{F} + f\ \mathrm{curl}\ \mathbf{F}$,

(b) $\mathrm{div}(\mathbf{F}\times\mathbf{G}) = \nabla\cdot(\mathbf{F}\times\mathbf{G}) = (\nabla\times\mathbf{F})\cdot\mathbf{G} - \mathbf{F}\cdot(\nabla\times\mathbf{G}) = \mathbf{G}\cdot\mathrm{curl}\ \mathbf{F} - \mathbf{F}\cdot\mathrm{curl}\ \mathbf{G}$,

(c) $\mathrm{curl}(\mathrm{curl}\ \mathbf{F}) = \nabla\times(\nabla\times\mathbf{F}) = \nabla(\nabla\cdot\mathbf{F}) - \nabla^2\mathbf{F} = \mathrm{grad}(\mathrm{div}\ \mathbf{F}) - \nabla^2\mathbf{F}.$ (33)

These (see Sowerby [1]) may be proved, like the identities (27), directly from the definitions (21), (22), (28) and (29). A ready, but non-rigorous, means for establishing these rules is to use equations (3) and (4), treating ∇ as a vector but remembering that it must operate on each quantity which it precedes, as in equation (33a).

EXAMPLE 8
Prove the identity (33c).

When $\mathbf{F} = iu + jv + kw$, its curl is given by equation (28) so that

$$\text{curl}(\text{curl } \mathbf{F}) = i\left\{\frac{\partial}{\partial y}\left(\frac{\partial v}{\partial x} - \frac{\partial u}{\partial y}\right) - \frac{\partial}{\partial z}\left(\frac{\partial u}{\partial z} - \frac{\partial w}{\partial x}\right)\right\}$$

$$+ j\left\{\frac{\partial}{\partial z}\left(\frac{\partial w}{\partial y} - \frac{\partial v}{\partial z}\right) - \frac{\partial}{\partial x}\left(\frac{\partial v}{\partial x} - \frac{\partial u}{\partial y}\right)\right\}$$

$$+ k\left\{\frac{\partial}{\partial x}\left(\frac{\partial u}{\partial z} - \frac{\partial w}{\partial x}\right) - \frac{\partial}{\partial y}\left(\frac{\partial w}{\partial y} - \frac{\partial v}{\partial z}\right)\right\}.$$

The i component of this vector may be rearranged as

$$\frac{\partial}{\partial x}\left(\frac{\partial v}{\partial y} + \frac{\partial w}{\partial z}\right) - \frac{\partial^2 u}{\partial y^2} - \frac{\partial^2 u}{\partial z^2} = \frac{\partial}{\partial x}\left(\frac{\partial u}{\partial x} + \frac{\partial v}{\partial y} + \frac{\partial w}{\partial z}\right) - \left(\frac{\partial^2 u}{\partial x^2} + \frac{\partial^2 u}{\partial y^2} + \frac{\partial^2 u}{\partial z^2}\right)$$

$$= \frac{\partial}{\partial x}(\text{div } \mathbf{F}) - \nabla^2 u.$$

The j and k components may be rearranged similarly, so that

$$\text{curl}(\text{curl } \mathbf{F}) = i\frac{\partial}{\partial x}(\text{div } \mathbf{F}) - i\nabla^2 u + j\frac{\partial}{\partial y}(\text{div } \mathbf{F}) - j\nabla^2 v + k\frac{\partial}{\partial z}(\text{div } \mathbf{F}) - k\nabla^2 w,$$

which is of the required form since i, j and k are constant, giving $\nabla^2 \mathbf{F} = i\nabla^2 u + j\nabla^2 v + k\nabla^2 w$.

Exercises

1. If $f(x, y, z) = 2x^2 y + 3xyz + e^x \sin y$, evaluate grad f and div grad f at the point $(0, \pi, 1)$.

2. If $f = \log(x^2 + y^2)$ and $\mathbf{F} = z\mathbf{k}$, find grad f, $\mathbf{F} \cdot$ grad f, $\mathbf{F} \times$ grad f, div $\mathbf{F}$, $\nabla^2 f$, and curl$(\mathbf{F} \times$ grad $f)$.

3. If $f(x, y, z) = xy^2 z + 2yz^2$, determine the unit normal to the level surface of f at $(-2, 1, 3)$.

4. Find div $\mathbf{F}$ and curl $\mathbf{F}$ where $\mathbf{F}$ is the vector field given by $\mathbf{F} = ixy + \frac{1}{2}jy^2 - 2kyz$.

5. If f and $\mathbf{F}$ are any scalar and vector fields show that div$(\mathbf{F} \times$ grad $f) =$ grad $f \cdot$ curl $\mathbf{F}$.

6. Show that the flux $\mathbf{F} \cdot \mathbf{n} \, dS$ of a vector field $\mathbf{F} = u\mathbf{i} + v\mathbf{j} + w\mathbf{k}$ through the surface element $\mathbf{n} \, dS$ may be evaluated as $\mathbf{F} \cdot \mathbf{n} \, dS = u \, dS_x + v \, dS_y + w \, dS_z$, where dS_x, dS_y and dS_z are the projections of the surface element onto the planes $x = 0$, $y = 0$ and $z = 0$ respectively.

6.4 THE DIVERGENCE THEOREM

Flux through a Surface

In this section the interpretation of div $\mathbf{F}$ as the outward flux of a vector field $\mathbf{F}$ per unit volume will be confirmed by showing that the flux of $\mathbf{F}$ through the bounding surface of *any* region equals the volume integral of div $\mathbf{F}$ through that region.

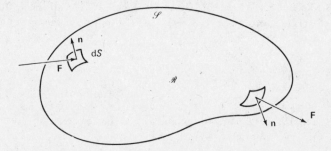

Fig. 6.6　Flux through elements of the surface $\mathscr{S}$ bounding a region $\mathscr{R}$

Let $\mathscr{R}$ be any region of three dimensional space bounded, as in Fig. 6.6, by a *single* closed surface labelled $\mathscr{S}$. Then if $\mathscr{S}$ is regarded as a collection of surface elements $\mathbf{n} \, dS$, where $\mathbf{n}$ is the unit outward normal to $\mathscr{S}$, the *flux of* $\mathbf{F}$ *from* $\mathscr{R}$ is the aggregate of contributions $\mathbf{F} \cdot \mathbf{n} \, dS$ from all elements, and so is given by the double integral

$$\iint_{\mathscr{S}} \mathbf{F} \cdot \mathbf{n} \, dS. \tag{34}$$

The integral (34) taken over the whole surface $\mathscr{S}$ is sometimes known as the *flux of* $\mathbf{F}$ *through* $\mathscr{S}$, and in practical examples it is evaluated using methods described in §5.5.

EXAMPLE 1
Find the flux of $\mathbf{F} = \mathbf{i}x + \mathbf{j}z$ through the sphere $\mathscr{S}$ having equation $x^2 + y^2 + z^2 = 1$.

$\mathscr{S}$ is defined by $f(x, y, z) \equiv x^2 + y^2 + z^2 - 1 = 0$. The unit outward normal $\mathbf{n}$ to $\mathscr{S}$ is parallel to grad f, so that $\mathbf{n} = \mathbf{i}x + \mathbf{j}y + \mathbf{k}z$. Then, at all points of $\mathscr{S}$, $\mathbf{F} \cdot \mathbf{n} = x^2 + yz$. To evaluate the integral (34) spherical polar coordinates may be introduced on the surface $\mathscr{S}$, so that

$$x = \sin\theta \cos\phi, \quad y = \sin\theta \sin\phi, \quad z = \cos\theta \quad \text{and} \quad dS = \sin\theta \, d\theta \, d\phi.$$

The flux of **F** through $\mathscr{S}$ is then given by

$$\iint_{\mathscr{S}} \mathbf{F} \cdot \mathbf{n}\, \mathrm{d}S = \int_0^{2\pi} \int_0^{\pi} (\sin^2 \theta \cos^2 \phi + \sin \theta \cos \theta \sin \phi)\sin \theta\, \mathrm{d}\theta\, \mathrm{d}\phi$$

$$= \int_0^{2\pi} \left[(-\cos \theta + \tfrac{1}{3} \cos^3 \theta)\cos^2 \phi + \tfrac{1}{3} \sin^3 \theta \sin \phi \right]_{\theta = 0}^{\theta = \pi} \mathrm{d}\phi$$

$$= \int_0^{2\pi} \tfrac{4}{3} \cos^2 \phi\, \mathrm{d}\phi = \tfrac{4}{3}\pi.$$

One of the most useful results in vector calculus is

THE DIVERGENCE THEOREM (GAUSS'S THEOREM)   If the vector field **F** has continuous first-order partial derivatives at all points of the region $\mathscr{R}$ bounded by the surface $\mathscr{S}$, then

$$\iiint_{\mathscr{R}} \operatorname{div} \mathbf{F}\, \mathrm{d}V = \iint_{\mathscr{S}} \mathbf{F} \cdot \mathbf{n}\, \mathrm{d}S, \qquad (35)$$

where $\mathrm{d}V$ and $\mathrm{d}S$ are elements of volume and of surface area respectively, and **n** is the unit outward normal to $\mathscr{S}$.

The theorem will be proved only for regions $\mathscr{R}$ with the special property that no line parallel to any one of the coordinate axes has more than one segment lying in $\mathscr{R}$. The methods for extending the proof to more general regions $\mathscr{R}$ will then be briefly indicated.

When **F** is expressed in terms of components as $\mathbf{F} = \mathbf{i}u + \mathbf{j}v + \mathbf{k}w$, equation (35) takes the form

$$\iiint_{\mathscr{R}} \left(\frac{\partial u}{\partial x} + \frac{\partial v}{\partial y} + \frac{\partial w}{\partial z} \right) \mathrm{d}V = \iint_{\mathscr{S}} (u\mathbf{n} \cdot \mathbf{i} + v\mathbf{n} \cdot \mathbf{j} + w\mathbf{n} \cdot \mathbf{k})\mathrm{d}S.$$

To prove the theorem it is clearly sufficient to prove the relationship

$$\iiint_{\mathscr{R}} \frac{\partial w}{\partial z}\, \mathrm{d}V = \iint_{\mathscr{S}} w\mathbf{n} \cdot \mathbf{k}\, \mathrm{d}S, \qquad (36)$$

and two similar relationships involving u and v respectively.

To prove equation (36), let $\mathscr{S}_z$ be the orthogonal projection of $\mathscr{S}$ onto the plane $z = 0$, as in Fig. 6.7. Then, on the line $x = $ constant, $y = $ constant passing through an interior point $(x, y, 0)$ of $\mathscr{S}_z$ there are just two points of $\mathscr{S}$. One belongs to the 'lower' portion $\mathscr{S}^-$ which may be written as $z = g(x, y)$, whilst the second point belongs to the 'upper' portion $\mathscr{S}^+$, on which $z = h(x, y)$. Let $\mathrm{d}A$ be an elementary

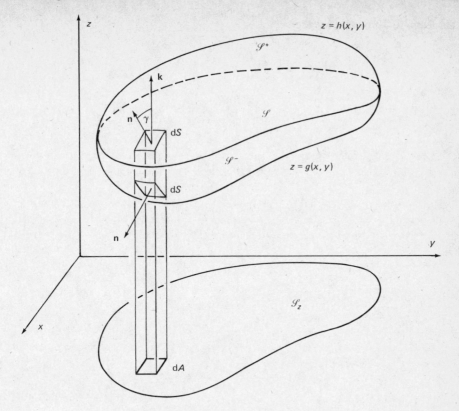

Fig. 6.7 The surface $\mathscr{S}$ considered in the proof of the divergence theorem

area of $\mathscr{S}_z$, and consider the cylinder of $\mathscr{R}$ which is parallel to the z axis, and which has projection dA onto $z = 0$. This cylinder extends from $z = g(x, y)$ to $z = h(x, y)$ and is comprised of volume elements $dV = dz\, dA$. Consequently the left-hand side of equation (36) may be evaluated as

$$\iiint\limits_{\mathscr{R}} \frac{\partial w}{\partial z}\, dV = \iint\limits_{\mathscr{S}_z} \left\{ \int_{g(x,y)}^{h(x,y)} \frac{\partial w}{\partial z}\, dz \right\} dA$$

$$= \iint\limits_{\mathscr{S}_z} \{ w(x, y, h(x, y)) - w(x, y, g(x, y)) \} dA.$$

In the first term w is evaluated on $\mathscr{S}^+$ where

$$dA = \mathbf{n} \cdot \mathbf{k}\, dS = \cos \gamma\, dS$$

is the element of projected area, whilst in the second term w is evaluated on $\mathscr{S}^-$ and the element of projected area is

$$dA = \mathbf{n} \cdot (-\mathbf{k})dS.$$

Substitution of these expressions gives

$$\iiint\limits_{\mathscr{R}} \frac{\partial w}{\partial z}\,dV = \iint\limits_{\mathscr{S}_1^+} w\mathbf{n} \cdot \mathbf{k}\,dS - \iint\limits_{\mathscr{S}_1^-} w\mathbf{n} \cdot (-\mathbf{k})dS = \iint\limits_{\mathscr{S}} w\mathbf{n} \cdot \mathbf{k}\,dS,$$

which proves equation (36). The identities involving u and v are proved by taking projections onto the planes $x = 0$ and $y = 0$ respectively. The divergence theorem (35) then follows.

The proof may be extended to regions $\mathscr{R}$ of more general shape by subdividing into regions having the previous special property. For example, when the region $\mathscr{R}$ needs be divided, as in Fig. 6.8(a), into just two parts $\mathscr{R}_1$, $\mathscr{R}_2$ of the required type we have

$$\iiint\limits_{\mathscr{R}} \operatorname{div} \mathbf{F}\,dV = \iiint\limits_{\mathscr{R}_1} \operatorname{div} \mathbf{F}\,dV + \iiint\limits_{\mathscr{R}_2} \operatorname{div} \mathbf{F}\,dV$$

$$= \iint\limits_{\mathscr{S}_1} \mathbf{F} \cdot \mathbf{n}_1\,dS + \iint\limits_{\overline{\mathscr{S}}} \mathbf{F} \cdot \mathbf{n}_1\,dS + \iint\limits_{\mathscr{S}_2} \mathbf{F} \cdot \mathbf{n}_2\,dS + \iint\limits_{\overline{\mathscr{S}}} \mathbf{F} \cdot \mathbf{n}_2\,dS$$

$$= \iint\limits_{\mathscr{S}_1} \mathbf{F} \cdot \mathbf{n}\,dS + \iint\limits_{\mathscr{S}_2} \mathbf{F} \cdot \mathbf{n}\,dS = \iint\limits_{\mathscr{S}} \mathbf{F} \cdot \mathbf{n}\,dS,$$

because $\mathbf{n}_1 = \mathbf{n}$ on $\mathscr{S}_1$, $\mathbf{n}_2 = \mathbf{n}$ on $\mathscr{S}_2$ and $\mathbf{n}_2 = -\mathbf{n}_1$ on $\overline{\mathscr{S}}$. Likewise, the divergence theorem may be proved for regions enclosing one or more holes, as in Fig. 6.8(b). In

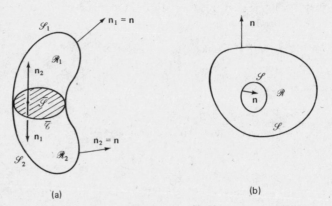

(a)   (b)

Fig. 6.8   (a) A region $\mathscr{R}$ divided into two parts $\mathscr{R}_1$, $\mathscr{R}_2$ by a surface $\mathscr{S}$ which meets $\mathscr{S}$ in a curve $\overline{\mathscr{C}}$ along which the normal $\mathbf{n}$ to $\mathscr{S}$ is perpendicular to $\mathbf{k}$. (b) A multiply-connected region $\mathscr{R}$ and the outward normal $\mathbf{n}$ on various portions of its boundary

such cases the bounding surface $\mathcal{S}$ possesses more than one portion, and it should be remembered that on *each* portion the unit normal $\mathbf{n}$ is directed away from $\mathcal{R}$.

EXAMPLE 2
Verify the divergence theorem for the sphere $\mathcal{S}$ and the vector field $\mathbf{F}$ of example 1.

Since div $\mathbf{F} = 1 + 0 + 0 = 1$ we have

$$\iiint_{\mathcal{R}} \text{div } \mathbf{F} \, dV = \iiint_{\mathcal{R}} dV = \tfrac{4}{3}\pi = \iint_{\mathcal{S}} \mathbf{F} \cdot \mathbf{n} \, dS,$$

using the result of example 1.

Some regions $\mathcal{R}$, such as the tetrahedron shown in Fig. 6.9, are bounded by surfaces with sharp edges. In such cases, the surface integral occurring in the divergence theorem must be evaluated as the sum of contributions from smooth portions of surface, such as the planes $\mathcal{S}_1$, $\mathcal{S}_2$, $\mathcal{S}_3$ and $\mathcal{S}_4$ in Fig. 6.9.

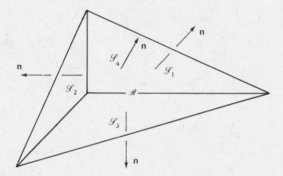

Fig. 6.9   A tetrahedron $\mathcal{R}$ bounded by the planes $\mathcal{S}_1$, $\mathcal{S}_2$, $\mathcal{S}_3$ and $\mathcal{S}_4$ with associated unit outward normals $\mathbf{n}$

Physical Interpretations of the Divergence Theorem

In any steady heat flow field $\mathbf{q}$, the heat flux Q from any region $\mathcal{R}$ may be expressed, using the divergence theorem, as

$$Q \equiv \iint_{\mathcal{S}} \mathbf{q} \cdot \mathbf{n} \, dS = \iiint_{\mathcal{R}} \text{div } \mathbf{q} \, dV.$$

In particular, if δQ is the heat flux from a region having volume δV and of such small dimensions that div $\mathbf{q}$ may be treated as constant throughout its interior, this equation may be approximated by

$\delta Q = $ Heat flux from the small region $\simeq$ div $\mathbf{q} \, \delta V$.

Whenever $\mathbf{q}$ is steady,

$$\operatorname{div} \mathbf{q} = \lim_{\delta V \to 0} \frac{\delta Q}{\delta V}$$

measures the *heat source intensity* or *heat production rate per unit volume*. Similarly, in a fluid flow with density ρ and velocity $\mathbf{v}$ the rate at which mass leaves a region $\mathscr{R}$ across its boundary $\mathscr{S}$ is

$$\iint_{\mathscr{S}} (\rho\mathbf{v}) \cdot \mathbf{n} \, \mathrm{d}S = \iiint_{\mathscr{R}} \operatorname{div}(\rho\mathbf{v}) \mathrm{d}V.$$

In steady flows $\operatorname{div}(\rho\mathbf{v})$ measures the *source strength*, or rate at which fluid mass is supplied to unit volume, for example by chemical reaction. In unsteady flows the rate of density decrease $-\partial\rho/\partial t$ also contributes to $\operatorname{div}(\rho\mathbf{v})$, as will be seen in equation (53).

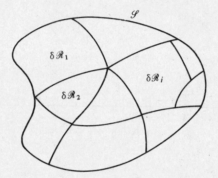

Fig. 6.10   Subdivision of a region $\mathscr{R}$ bounded by the surface $\mathscr{S}$

To interpret the divergence theorem for a general differentiable field $\mathbf{F}$ and a general region $\mathscr{R}$, suppose that $\mathscr{R}$ is regarded as a collection of smaller elements $\delta\mathscr{R}_1, \delta\mathscr{R}_2, \ldots$, as in Fig. 6.10. Let $\delta\Phi_1, \delta\Phi_2, \ldots$, be the fluxes of $\mathbf{F}$ through the surfaces of $\delta\mathscr{R}_1, \delta\mathscr{R}_2, \ldots$ respectively. Then $\Phi = \sum_i \delta\Phi_i$ is the flux of $\mathbf{F}$ from $\mathscr{R}$, since only the surface elements which are part of the boundary $\mathscr{S}$ contribute to the total flux from $\mathscr{R}$. All other flux contributions out of one element are flux contributions into a neighbouring element. Since the divergence theorem implies that $\Phi \simeq \sum_i \operatorname{div} \mathbf{F} \, \delta V_i$ whenever the volume δV_i of each element $\delta\mathscr{R}_i$ is sufficiently small, we conclude that the interpretation of $\operatorname{div} \mathbf{F}$ as

$$\operatorname{div} \mathbf{F} \equiv \lim_{\delta V \to 0} \frac{\text{Flux of } \mathbf{F} \text{ from the volume element } \delta V}{\delta V} \qquad (37)$$

applies to elements $\delta\mathscr{R}$ of arbitrary shape, and not solely to the rectangular boxes considered in Fig. 6.5. The foregoing physical examples provide illustrations of this assertion.

Green's Theorems

Green's theorem in the plane (see §5.4) is a special case of the divergence theorem, and may be deduced by considering the flux of the vector field $\mathbf{F} = V(x, y)\mathbf{i} - U(x, y)\mathbf{j}$ through the surface of a cylinder $0 \leq z \leq 1$ erected above the plane region $\mathscr{A}$ shown in Fig. 5.18(a). The proof is left as an exercise.

Other important results attributed to Green follow from the divergence theorem. They involve the idea of *normal derivative* of a scalar field.

> **DEFINITION** If $\mathbf{n}$ is the unit normal at a point P of a surface $\mathscr{S}$ the *normal derivative* $\partial f/\partial n$ of a scalar field f at P is
>
> $$\frac{\partial f}{\partial n} \equiv \mathbf{n} \cdot \operatorname{grad} f. \tag{38}$$

Notice that $\partial f/\partial n$ is the directional derivative of f in the direction of $\mathbf{n}$.

Let Φ and Ψ be scalar fields, and apply the divergence theorem to the vector field $\mathbf{F} \equiv \Phi \operatorname{grad} \Psi$, for which the component normal to the boundary $\mathscr{S}$ is

$$\mathbf{F} \cdot \mathbf{n} = (\Phi \operatorname{grad} \Psi) \cdot \mathbf{n} = \Phi \, \mathbf{n} \cdot \operatorname{grad} \Psi = \Phi \frac{\partial \Psi}{\partial n}.$$

Then, since

$$\operatorname{div} \mathbf{F} = \operatorname{div}(\Phi \operatorname{grad} \Psi) = \operatorname{grad} \Phi \cdot \operatorname{grad} \Psi + \Phi \nabla^2 \Psi,$$

equation (35) becomes

GREEN'S FIRST FORMULA

$$\iiint_{\mathscr{R}} (\Phi \nabla^2 \Psi + \operatorname{grad} \Phi \cdot \operatorname{grad} \Psi) \, dV = \iint_{\mathscr{S}} \Phi \frac{\partial \Psi}{\partial n} \, dS. \tag{39}$$

Interchange of Φ and Ψ in equation (39) gives the similar formula

$$\iiint_{\mathscr{R}} (\Psi \nabla^2 \Phi + \operatorname{grad} \Psi \cdot \operatorname{grad} \Phi) \, dV = \iint_{\mathscr{S}} \Psi \frac{\partial \Phi}{\partial n} \, dS.$$

The equation which arises when this is subtracted from equation (39) is

GREEN'S SECOND FORMULA

$$\iiint_{\mathscr{R}} (\Phi \nabla^2 \Psi - \Psi \nabla^2 \Phi) \, dV = \iint_{\mathscr{S}} \left(\Phi \frac{\partial \Psi}{\partial n} - \Psi \frac{\partial \Phi}{\partial n} \right) dS. \tag{40}$$

The formulae (39) and (40) together with statements that the appropriate vector fields $\Phi \operatorname{grad} \Psi$ and $\Psi \operatorname{grad} \Phi$ have continuous first-order partial derivatives in the interior $\mathscr{R}$ of the surface $\mathscr{S}$ are known respectively as the *first* and *second forms of Green's theorem.* They are important in the analysis of partial differential equations such as those discussed in Chapter 7. Two typical results are given in the following examples.

EXAMPLE 3

Suppose that $\Phi(x, y, z)$ satisfies Laplace's equation $\nabla^2 \Phi = 0$ everywhere within a region $\mathscr{R}$. Show that the flux of grad Φ from $\mathscr{R}$ vanishes.

Let $\mathscr{S}$ denote the boundary surface of $\mathscr{R}$. The flux of grad Φ from $\mathscr{R}$ may then be evaluated as

$$\iint_{\mathscr{S}} \frac{\partial \Phi}{\partial n} \, dS \equiv \iint_{\mathscr{S}} (\text{grad } \Phi) \cdot \mathbf{n} \, dS = \iiint_{\mathscr{R}} \text{div}(\text{grad } \Phi) \, dV = \iiint_{\mathscr{R}} \nabla^2 \Phi \, dV = 0,$$

using the divergence theorem and setting $\nabla^2 \Phi = 0$ at all points of $\mathscr{R}$.

The result may alternatively be derived from equation (40) by setting $\Psi = 1$ throughout $\mathscr{R}$.

EXAMPLE 4

Laplace's equation $\nabla^2 \theta = 0$ governs steady temperature distributions $\theta(x, y, z)$ within a region $\mathscr{R}$ of homogeneous material. Show that only one possible temperature distribution can exist within $\mathscr{R}$ if the temperature is specified as $\theta = \bar{\theta}(x, y, z)$ over some portions $\overline{\mathscr{S}}$ of the boundary surface $\mathscr{S}$, whilst the remaining portions $\hat{\mathscr{S}}$ are insulated so that $\partial \theta / \partial n = 0$ at points of $\hat{\mathscr{S}}$.

Suppose that $\theta_1(x, y, z)$ and $\theta_2(x, y, z)$ are two possible temperature distributions, so that $\theta_1 = \theta_2 = \bar{\theta}$ over $\overline{\mathscr{S}}$ and $\partial \theta_1 / \partial n = 0 = \partial \theta_2 / \partial n$ over $\hat{\mathscr{S}}$. Introduce the 'difference temperature' $\Theta(x, y, z) \equiv \theta_2 - \theta_1$. This satisfies Laplace's equation throughout $\mathscr{R}$, since

$$\nabla^2 \Theta = \nabla^2 (\theta_2 - \theta_1) = \nabla^2 \theta_2 - \nabla^2 \theta_1 = 0 - 0 = 0.$$

Now apply Green's first formula (39) with $\Phi \equiv \Psi \equiv \Theta(x, y, z)$ to obtain

$$\iiint_{\mathscr{R}} (\Theta \nabla^2 \Theta + \text{grad } \Theta \cdot \text{grad } \Theta) \, dV = \iint_{\mathscr{S}} \Theta \frac{\partial \Theta}{\partial n} \, dS.$$

Since $\Theta = 0$ over $\overline{\mathscr{S}}$, whilst $\partial \Theta / \partial n = \partial \theta_2 / \partial n - \partial \theta_1 / \partial n = 0$ over $\hat{\mathscr{S}}$, we obtain

$$\iint_{\mathscr{S}} \Theta \frac{\partial \Theta}{\partial n} \, dS = \iint_{\overline{\mathscr{S}}} \Theta \frac{\partial \Theta}{\partial n} \, dS + \iint_{\hat{\mathscr{S}}} \Theta \frac{\partial \Theta}{\partial n} \, dS = 0 + 0 = 0,$$

so that

$$\iiint_{\mathscr{R}} |\text{grad } \Theta|^2 \, dV = -\iiint_{\mathscr{R}} \Theta \nabla^2 \Theta \, dV = 0. \tag{41}$$

The integrand $|\text{grad } \Theta|^2$ is continuous and non-negative throughout $\mathscr{R}$, and so cannot be positive anywhere within $\mathscr{R}$ without violating equation (41). Thus grad $\Theta = \mathbf{0}$ throughout $\mathscr{R}$, showing that $\theta_2 - \theta_1 = \Theta = $ constant. Since $\Theta = 0$ at points of $\overline{\mathscr{S}}$, $\Theta = 0$ throughout $\mathscr{R}$, and the temperature distributions $\theta_1(x, y, z)$ and $\theta_2(x, y, z)$ are identical.

Example 4 is a *uniqueness theorem*. It shows that any procedure (as in example 1 of §7.6, where T is used in place of θ) for constructing a function $\theta(x, y, z)$ which satisfies both $\nabla^2\theta = 0$ within $\mathscr{R}$ and the given *boundary conditions* over $\mathscr{S}$ must yield the *unique solution* $\theta(x, y, z)$. Similar uniqueness theorems may be proved for many important *boundary value problems* for other partial differential equations, and they justify the construction of solutions by the methods of Chapter 7.

Exercises

1. If $\mathscr{S}$ is the sphere $x^2 + y^2 + z^2 = 1$ and $\mathscr{R}$ is its interior, evaluate $\iint\limits_{\mathscr{S}} \mathbf{F} \cdot \mathbf{n} \, dS$ and $\iiint\limits_{\mathscr{R}} \text{div } \mathbf{F} \, dV$, where $\mathbf{F} = x^2y^2\mathbf{i} + y^2z^2\mathbf{j} + x\mathbf{k}$. Verify that the two integrals are equal.

2. By applying the divergence theorem to the vector $\mathbf{c} \times \mathbf{F}$, where $\mathbf{c}$ is any constant vector, show that

$$\iiint\limits_{\mathscr{R}} \text{curl } \mathbf{F} \, dV = -\iint\limits_{\mathscr{S}} \mathbf{F} \times \mathbf{n} \, dS.$$

3. Verify the formula of exercise 2 for $\mathbf{F}$, $\mathscr{S}$ and $\mathscr{R}$ as in exercise 1.

4. Deduce Green's theorem in the plane as a special case of the divergence theorem.

6.5 STOKES'S THEOREM

Circulation around a Loop

If the vector field $\mathbf{F}(\mathbf{r})$ is defined everywhere within a region $\mathscr{R}$, and $\mathscr{C}$ is a three-dimensional closed curve, or *loop*, lying entirely within $\mathscr{R}$, the integral

$$\oint\limits_{\mathscr{C}} \mathbf{F} \cdot d\mathbf{r}$$

taken once around the loop $\mathscr{C}$ is called the *circulation of* $\mathbf{F}$ *around* $\mathscr{C}$. As a physical example consider a particle having position $\mathbf{r}$ and subject to a force $\mathbf{F}(\mathbf{r})$ due to either gravity, an electric field or a magnetic field. Then the circulation $\oint_{\mathscr{C}} \mathbf{F} \cdot d\mathbf{r}$ around any loop $\mathscr{C}$ is the work supplied by the field when the particle is taken once around $\mathscr{C}$. (This, like all other concepts in this section, applies also to unsteady vector fields).

The connection between circulation of $\mathbf{F}$ and curl $\mathbf{F}$ is provided by

STOKES'S THEOREM   If Σ is a portion of surface having unit normal $\mathbf{n}$ and bounded by the loop $\mathscr{C}$, then

$$\oint\limits_{\mathscr{C}} \mathbf{F} \cdot d\mathbf{r} = \iint\limits_{\Sigma} \text{curl } \mathbf{F} \cdot \mathbf{n} \, dS, \tag{42}$$

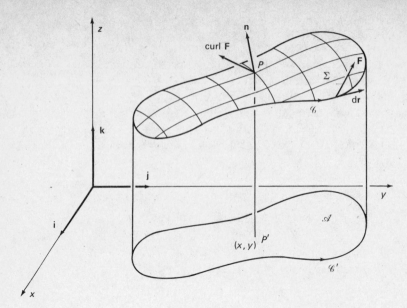

Fig. 6.11   A surface Σ, and its bounding loop $\mathscr{C}$ as they occur in Stokes's theorem

provided that the vector field **F** is continuous over Σ and $\mathscr{C}$, and that **F** possesses continuous first-order derivatives over Σ.

Notice that the right-hand side of equation (42) is the flux of curl **F** through Σ. Also, as in Fig. 6.11, the sense of **n** is related to the positive direction around $\mathscr{C}$ by the right-hand corkscrew rule. The theorem is proved by relating the integrals over $\mathscr{S}$ and $\mathscr{C}$ to certain integrals over their projections $\mathscr{A}$ and $\mathscr{C}'$ onto the plane $z = 0$ (see Sowerby [1]).

EXAMPLE 1
Verify Stokes's theorem for $\mathbf{F} = (x + y)\mathbf{i} + (y - z)\mathbf{j} - z^3\mathbf{k}$ when $\mathscr{C}$ is the circle $x^2 + y^2 = 1, z = 0$, and

(a) $\mathscr{C}$ is spanned by the hemisphere Σ_1 given by $z = (1 - x^2 - y^2)^{1/2}$,
(b) $\mathscr{C}$ is spanned by the disc Σ_2 given by $z = 0, x^2 + y^2 \leqslant 1$.

Represent the curve $\mathscr{C}$ parametrically as $x = \cos \phi, y = \sin \phi, z = 0$ for $0 \leqslant \phi \leqslant 2\pi$, so that $\mathbf{F} = (\cos \phi + \sin \phi)\mathbf{i} + \sin \phi\,\mathbf{j}$ and $d\mathbf{r} = (-\sin \phi\,\mathbf{i} + \cos \phi\,\mathbf{j})d\phi$ on $\mathscr{C}$. The loop integral then is

$$\oint_{\mathscr{C}} \mathbf{F} \cdot d\mathbf{r} = \int_0^{2\pi} (-\cos \phi \sin \phi - \sin^2\phi + \sin \phi \cos \phi)\,d\phi = -\pi.$$

The normal to any surface $z = Z(x, y)$ is parallel to
$\text{grad }(z - Z(x, y)) = - Z_x\mathbf{i} - Z_y\mathbf{j} + \mathbf{k}$, so that the unit normal is
$\mathbf{n} = (-Z_x\mathbf{i} - Z_y\mathbf{j} + \mathbf{k})/(Z_x^2 + Z_y^2 + 1)^{1/2}$. In case (a), the normal **n** to Σ_1 is $x\mathbf{i} + y\mathbf{j} + z\mathbf{k}$,

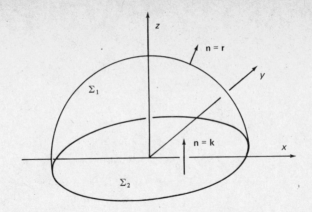

Fig. 6.12   The surfaces Σ_1, Σ_2 in example 1

so that

$$dxdy = \mathbf{n} \cdot \mathbf{k} \, dS = z \, dS = (1 - x^2 - y^2)^{1/2} \, dS.$$

Also, curl $\mathbf{F} = \mathbf{i} - \mathbf{k}$ everywhere. Over Σ_1, curl $\mathbf{F} \cdot \mathbf{n} = x - z$ so that curl $\mathbf{F} \cdot \mathbf{n} \, dS = (xz^{-1} - 1) \, dxdy$. Thus

$$\iint\limits_{\Sigma_2} \text{curl } \mathbf{F} \cdot \mathbf{n} \, dS = \int_{-1}^{1} \int_{-(1-y^2)^{1/2}}^{(1-y^2)^{1/2}} \left\{ \frac{x}{(1-x^2-y^2)^{1/2}} - 1 \right\} dxdy$$

$$= 0 - \pi = -\pi,$$

because the first integrand is an odd function of x whilst the region of integration is symmetric in $x = 0$.

In case (b), $\mathbf{n} = \mathbf{k}$, so that curl $\mathbf{F} \cdot \mathbf{n} = -1$. Then

$$\iint\limits_{\Sigma_2} \text{curl } \mathbf{F} \cdot \mathbf{n} \, dS = (-1) \iint\limits_{\Sigma_2} dS = -\pi,$$

so that, as in case (a), Stokes's theorem is verified.

Notice that Stokes's theorem equates the circulation of $\mathbf{F}$ around a loop $\mathscr{C}$ to the flux of curl $\mathbf{F}$ through *any* allowable surface spanning $\mathscr{C}$. As verified in example 1, the fluxes through two allowable surfaces Σ_1 and Σ_2 are equal.

Interpretation of Stokes's Theorem

Through any point $\mathbf{r}$ consider the plane having unit normal $\mathbf{n}$. Choose Σ to be a small portion of this plane containing the point $\mathbf{r}$ and having area δA. If $\delta K \equiv \oint_{\mathscr{C}} \mathbf{F} \cdot d\mathbf{r}$ is the circulation of $\mathbf{F}$ around the boundary $\mathscr{C}$ of Σ, then

$$\frac{\delta K}{\delta A} = \frac{1}{\delta A} \oint_{\mathscr{C}} \mathbf{F} \cdot d\mathbf{r} = \frac{1}{\delta A} \iint_{\Sigma} \text{curl } \mathbf{F} \cdot \mathbf{n} \, dS$$

$$= \mathbf{n} \cdot \left(\frac{1}{\delta A} \iint_{\Sigma} \text{curl } \mathbf{F} \, dS \right) \qquad (43)$$

is the average circulation per unit area of Σ. Now consider elements of area for which $\delta A \to 0$, so that the right-hand side of equation (43) tends to the value $\mathbf{n} \cdot \text{curl } \mathbf{F}$ evaluated at $\mathbf{r}$. This shows that curl $\mathbf{F}$ has the property that its scalar product with any unit vector $\mathbf{n}$ measures the circulation per unit area around sufficiently small plane loops enclosing $\mathbf{r}$ and having unit normal $\mathbf{n}$, since

$$\mathbf{n} \cdot \text{curl } \mathbf{F} = \lim_{\delta A \to 0} \frac{\delta K}{\delta A} = \lim_{\delta A \to 0} \left(\frac{1}{\delta A} \oint_{\mathscr{C}} \mathbf{F} \cdot d\mathbf{r} \right). \qquad (44)$$

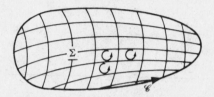

Fig. 6.13   A mesh covering a surface Σ

Equation (44) is sometimes used as the definition of curl $\mathbf{F}$, and the component form (27) is deduced as a consequence. It also provides a useful interpretation of Stokes's theorem. Suppose that any surface Σ bounded by a loop $\mathscr{C}$ is covered by a fine mesh, as in Fig. 6.13. The circulation K of $\mathbf{F}$ around $\mathscr{C}$ then equals the aggregate of the circulations around all the mesh line exactly cancel. Thus, if δK_i is the circulation each internal segment of mesh line exactly cancel. Thus, if δK_i is the circulation around the ith mesh element,

$$K = \sum_{i} \delta K_i. \qquad (45)$$

As the mesh is drawn ever more finely the area of each mesh element becomes infinitesimal and the sum in equation (45) tends to the limiting form given by the integral

$$\oint_{\mathscr{C}} \mathbf{F} \cdot d\mathbf{r} \equiv K = \iint_{\Sigma} dK = \iint_{\Sigma} \lim_{\delta A \to 0} \frac{\delta K}{\delta A} \, dS.$$

Stokes's theorem (42) then shows that $\mathbf{n} \cdot \text{curl } \mathbf{F} \, dS$ is the contribution to circulation from the element dS of Σ, so confirming the property (44) of curl $\mathbf{F}$.

Irrotational Fields

In §6.3 it is shown that the gradient grad $f \equiv \mathbf{F}$ of any scalar field f is *irrotational* (curl $\mathbf{F} = \mathbf{0}$). The converse result, that every irrotational field is the gradient of a scalar, is often useful. Indeed, a vector field $\mathbf{F}$ which is *irrotational* throughout some connected region $\mathcal{R}$ is expressible as the gradient of the scalar field $f(\mathbf{r})$ defined by the integral

$$f(\mathbf{r}) \equiv \int_{\mathbf{r}_0}^{\mathbf{r}} \mathbf{F}(\hat{\mathbf{r}}) \cdot d\hat{\mathbf{r}} \tag{46}$$

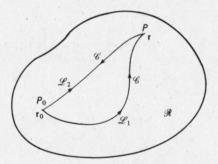

Fig. 6.14   Two paths $\mathcal{L}_1$, $\mathcal{L}_2$ from $\mathbf{r}_0$ to $\mathbf{r}$

In equation (46) the path of integration is *any* curve joining the reference point $\mathbf{r}_0$ to $\mathbf{r}$ and lying entirely within $\mathcal{R}$. For, if $\mathcal{L}_1$ and $\mathcal{L}_2$ are two distinct paths, as shown in Fig. 6.14, they together form a closed loop $\mathcal{C}$. The difference in the values of the integral (46) evaluated along the two paths is given by

$$\int_{\mathcal{L}_1} \mathbf{F} \cdot d\mathbf{r} - \int_{\mathcal{L}_2} \mathbf{F} \cdot d\mathbf{r} = \oint_{\mathcal{C}} \mathbf{F} \cdot d\mathbf{r},$$

which vanishes in consequence of Stokes's theorem, provided that the loop $\mathcal{C}$ may be spanned by a surface lying *entirely* in the region $\mathcal{R}$ of vanishing curl $\mathbf{F}$. To verify that grad $f = \mathbf{F}$, notice that the directional derivative of f in any direction $\mathbf{t}$ at P may be calculated from equation (46) as

$$\mathbf{t} \cdot \text{grad} f = \frac{df}{ds} = \mathbf{F}(\mathbf{r}) \cdot \frac{d\mathbf{r}}{ds} = \mathbf{t} \cdot \mathbf{F}.$$

Since this identity holds for all choices of $\mathbf{t}$, we deduce that grad $f = \mathbf{F}$.

In equation (46) the reference point $\mathbf{r}_0$ may be changed, but this merely alters $f(\mathbf{r})$ by the addition of a constant.

EXAMPLE 2
Verify that the vector field $\mathbf{F} = \mathbf{i}y + \mathbf{j}(x + z \cos y) + \mathbf{k} \sin y$ is irrotational, and find a scalar function $f(x, y, z)$ for which $\mathbf{F} = \text{grad} f$.

Since

$$\text{curl } \mathbf{F} = \mathbf{i} \left\{ \frac{\partial}{\partial y} (\sin y) - \frac{\partial}{\partial z} (x + z \cos y) \right\} + \mathbf{j} \left\{ \frac{\partial y}{\partial z} - \frac{\partial(\sin y)}{\partial x} \right\}$$

$$+ \mathbf{k} \left\{ \frac{\partial}{\partial x} (x + z \cos y) - \frac{\partial y}{\partial y} \right\} = \mathbf{0},$$

the field $\mathbf{F}$ is irrotational and may be written as $\mathbf{F} = \text{grad } f$ where

$$\frac{\partial f}{\partial x} = y, \quad \frac{\partial f}{\partial y} = x + z \cos y, \quad \text{and} \quad \frac{\partial f}{\partial z} = \sin y.$$

Integration of the first equation gives $f = xy + p(y, z)$, so that $\partial f/\partial y = x + \partial p/\partial y$ for some choice of function $p(y, z)$. Thus $\partial p/\partial y = z \cos y$, so that $p(y, z) = z \sin y + q(z)$ for some choice of function $q(z)$. This agrees with $\partial f/\partial z = \sin y$ only when $dq/dz = 0$. Consequently $q(z) = C = \text{constant}$, and $f(x, y, z) = xy + z \sin y + C$ is the general scalar field such that $\mathbf{F} = \text{grad } f$.

Some irrotational fields are the gradients of scalars which are multivalued. Consider, for example, the field

$$\mathbf{F} = (x^2 + y^2)^{-1} (-y\mathbf{i} + x\mathbf{j}) \quad \text{for} \quad (x, y) \neq (0, 0) \tag{47}$$

which occurs as the fluid velocity due to a 'line vortex' on the z axis, and as the magnetic field due to a steady current flowing along a long wire situated on the z axis. It is irrotational and may be expressed as $\mathbf{F} = \text{grad } \phi$, where ϕ is the azimuthal angle of cylindrical polar coordinates. However, the circulation around any loop $\mathscr{C}$ enclosing the z axis is

$$\oint_{\mathscr{C}} \mathbf{F} \cdot d\mathbf{r} = \pm 2\pi,$$

the sign depending on the positive sense of $\mathscr{C}$. This result does not violate Stokes's theorem since no surface Σ can span $\mathscr{C}$ without cutting the z axis, and $\mathbf{F}$ is not differentiable on that axis. Although $\mathbf{F}$ is the gradient of a scalar, the scalar ϕ is multivalued.

Potentials

A particle of unit mass in a gravitational field experiences a force which may be represented by a vector field $\mathbf{F}(\mathbf{r})$. Gravitational fields $\mathbf{F}$ must be irrotational; otherwise energy could be extracted from the field by taking the particle around a loop for which the circulation of $\mathbf{F}$ is positive, and so a perpetual motion machine could be devised. For similar reasons electrostatic fields are irrotational. It is conventional to express irrotational force fields $\mathbf{F}$ as $\mathbf{F} = -\text{grad } V$, where $V = V(\mathbf{r})$ is known as a *potential* for $\mathbf{F}$. Similarly $V(\mathbf{r}) - V(\mathbf{r}_0)$ is a potential, for any choice of reference point $\mathbf{r}_0$, and measures the energy given up by the field when a particle is moved from $\mathbf{r}$ to $\mathbf{r}_0$. Consequently $V(\mathbf{r})$ measures the ability of the field to supply energy. Irrotational force fields are often called *conservative* since the total work required in moving a particle around any loop is always zero.

EXAMPLE 3

Find a potential $V(\mathbf{r})$ for the electrostatic force field $\mathbf{E} = Q\mathbf{r}/4\pi\epsilon_0 r^3$ due to an electric charge Q situated at the origin, where $r = |\mathbf{r}|$, and ϵ_0 is the permittivity of free space.

The radial field $-Qr^{-3}\mathbf{r} = -4\pi\epsilon_0 \mathbf{E} = 4\pi\epsilon_0 \text{ grad } V$ is everywhere normal to the level surfaces of V. Consequently these surfaces are the spheres $r = $ constant, so that $V = f(r)$ for some function $f(r)$. Then $4\pi\epsilon_0 r^{-1} f'(r)\mathbf{r} = 4\pi\epsilon_0 \text{ grad } V = -Qr^{-3}\mathbf{r}$, so that $f'(r) = -Q/4\pi\epsilon_0 r^2$ and

$$V(\mathbf{r}) = \frac{Q}{4\pi\epsilon_0 r} + C = \frac{Q}{4\pi\epsilon_0 |\mathbf{r}|} + C, \quad \text{where } C \text{ is constant.}$$

(It is conventional to set $C = 0$. Then $V(\mathbf{r})$ measures the work stored when a unit charge is brought to $\mathbf{r}$ from infinitely large distances.)

Exercises

1. If $\mathbf{F} = \mathbf{i}xy + \mathbf{j}(y^3 - x) + 3\mathbf{k}z^2 y$, find $\oint_\mathscr{C} \mathbf{F} \cdot d\mathbf{r}$ where the loop $\mathscr{C}$ is given parametrically as $\mathbf{r} = \mathbf{i} \cos\theta + \mathbf{j} \sin\theta + \mathbf{k} \sin 2\theta$, for $0 \leqslant \theta \leqslant 2\pi$.

2. Find curl $\mathbf{F}$, where $\mathbf{F} = \mathbf{i}xy + \frac{1}{2}\mathbf{j}y^2 - 2\mathbf{k}yz$. Verify Stokes's theorem for this vector field $\mathbf{F}$ when $\mathscr{C}$ is the circle $x = 0, y^2 + z^2 = 1$, and Σ is the hemisphere $x^2 + y^2 + z^2 = 1, x \geqslant 0$.

3. Show that $\mathbf{F} = xy\mathbf{i} + (\frac{1}{2}x^2 + z \cos yz)\mathbf{j} + (e^z + y \cos yz)\mathbf{k}$ is irrotational, and find the most general scalar field f such that $\mathbf{F} = \text{grad } f$.

4. Show that when the surface Σ and curve $\mathscr{C}$ both lie in the plane $z = 0$ Stokes's theorem reduces to Green's theorem in the plane.

5. Let $\mathbf{F} = u\mathbf{i} + v\mathbf{j} + w\mathbf{k}$ be any *solenoidal* vector field. Show that it is possible to choose functions $A(x, y, z)$ and $B(x, y, z)$ in such a way that

$$u = -\frac{\partial B}{\partial z}, \quad v = \frac{\partial A}{\partial z}.$$

Use the condition div $\mathbf{F} = 0$ to deduce that w may be simultaneously expressed as

$$w = \frac{\partial B}{\partial x} - \frac{\partial A}{\partial y}.$$

Hence deduce that any solenoidal field $\mathbf{F}$ may be written as $\mathbf{F} = \text{curl } \mathbf{A}$, for many choices of vector field $\mathbf{A}$.

6.6 THE FORMULATION OF PARTIAL DIFFERENTIAL EQUATIONS

Conservation and Balance Laws

In a fluid flow, the rate of mass flux through the boundary surface $\mathscr{S}$ of any region $\mathscr{R}$ must equal the rate of decrease of mass within $\mathscr{R}$, since mass is neither created nor destroyed. The corresponding equation

$$\iint_{\mathscr{S}} (\rho \mathbf{v}) \cdot \mathbf{n} \, dS = -\frac{d}{dt} \iiint_{\mathscr{R}} \rho \, dV, \tag{48}$$

in which ρ is density and $\mathbf{v}$ is velocity, as in §6.3, is the *law of conservation of mass*. It is an example of a *balance law*, and, as will be shown in this section, it is equivalent to a partial differential equation involving ρ and the components of $\mathbf{v}$. Similar *balance laws* may be derived for the rate of storage of any physical quantity within an arbitrary surface $\mathscr{S}$, which is sometimes called a *control surface*. The balance must take into account all the means of supply or removal of the quantity from the interior region $\mathscr{R}$, and the total rate of flow through $\mathscr{S}$.

EXAMPLE 1
Heat conduction.   If a solid has *thermal capacity c*, the amount of heat stored by an element having volume δV when the temperature rises by $\delta \theta$ is $c \, \delta \theta \, \delta V$. Thus the rate of storage of heat within $\mathscr{R}$ is

$$\iiint_{\mathscr{R}} c \frac{\partial \theta}{\partial t} \, dV.$$

The rate of heat loss through the boundary $\mathscr{S}$ is

$$\iint_{\mathscr{S}} \mathbf{q} \cdot \mathbf{n} \, dS,$$

where $\mathbf{q}$ is the heat conduction vector. In the absence of radiation and of heat sources such as chemical or nuclear reactions these two effects must balance, giving the thermal balance law

$$\iint_{\mathscr{S}} \mathbf{q} \cdot \mathbf{n} \, dS = - \iiint_{\mathscr{R}} c \frac{\partial \theta}{\partial t} \, dV. \tag{49}$$

EXAMPLE 2
Electric currents.   The *electric current vector* $\mathbf{J}$ of §6.3 measures the rate of flow of electric charge. If $\rho_e(\mathbf{r}, t)$ is the *electric charge density*, the balance between rate of charge flow through $\mathscr{S}$ and the rate of decrease of charge within $\mathscr{R}$ is expressed as the *principle of charge conservation*:

$$\iint_{\mathscr{S}} \mathbf{J} \cdot \mathbf{n} \, dS = -\frac{d}{dt} \iiint_{\mathscr{R}} \rho_e \, dV. \tag{50}$$

Reduction to a Partial Differential Equation

The balance laws (48), (49) and (50) are similar in form, since each involves a volume integral and a surface flux integral. Such laws may be rearranged as a single volume integral, by use of the divergence theorem and the identity

$$\frac{d}{dt} \iiint_{\mathscr{R}} f(\mathbf{r}, t)\, dV = \iiint_{\mathscr{R}} \frac{\partial f}{\partial t}\, dV, \tag{51}$$

which applies to any scalar f when the region of integration $\mathscr{R}$ does not vary with time. For example, the divergence theorem gives

$$\iint_{\mathscr{S}} \rho \mathbf{v} \cdot \mathbf{n}\, dS = \iiint_{\mathscr{R}} \operatorname{div}(\rho \mathbf{v})\, dV,$$

and so equation (48) may be expressed as

$$\iiint_{\mathscr{R}} \left(\operatorname{div}(\rho \mathbf{v}) + \frac{\partial \rho}{\partial t} \right) dV = 0. \tag{52}$$

Equation (52) applies for arbitrary choice of the region $\mathscr{R}$. If $\operatorname{div}(\rho \mathbf{v})$ and $\partial \rho / \partial t$ are continuous functions the integrand of equation (52) must not be positive anywhere. For, suppose that it is positive at $\mathbf{r}_0$. Then choose $\mathscr{R}$ as any neighbourhood of $\mathbf{r}_0$ in which the integrand remains positive, so that the left-hand side of equation (52) is also positive. This leads to a contradiction. Similarly the integrand cannot be negative anywhere, so that equation (52) implies that ρ and $\mathbf{v}$ satisfy the *continuity equation*

$$\operatorname{div}(\rho \mathbf{v}) + \frac{\partial \rho}{\partial t} = 0. \tag{53}$$

Similarly the balance laws (49) and (50) may be written as

$$\iiint_{\mathscr{R}} \left(\operatorname{div} \mathbf{q} + c\, \frac{\partial \theta}{\partial t} \right) dV = 0,$$

$$\iiint_{\mathscr{R}} \left(\operatorname{div} \mathbf{J} + \frac{\partial \rho_e}{\partial t} \right) dV = 0,$$

which lead to the respective *partial differential equations*

$$\operatorname{div} \mathbf{q} + c\, \frac{\partial \theta}{\partial t} = 0, \tag{54}$$

$$\operatorname{div} \mathbf{J} + \frac{\partial \rho_e}{\partial t} = 0. \tag{55}$$

Applications of Stokes's Theorem

Electric and magnetic fields are related by physical laws involving circulations around arbitrary loops. By use of Stokes's theorem (42), these laws may be recast as partial differential equations.

(a) *Ampère's law.*   The results of many experiments may be summarized by the statement that, around any loop, the circulation of the magnetic field **B** excited by any steady distribution of electric current is proportional to the flux of current threading that loop. This is Ampère's law, which may be written as

$$\oint_{\mathscr{C}} \mathbf{B} \cdot d\mathbf{r} = \mu \iint_{\Sigma} \mathbf{J} \cdot \mathbf{n} \, dS, \tag{56}$$

where Σ is any surface spanning the arbitrary loop $\mathscr{C}$, and μ is a physical constant known as the *permeability*.

Application of Stokes's theorem to the left-hand side of equation (56), followed by suitable rearrangement, then leads to the equation

$$\iint_{\Sigma} (\operatorname{curl} \mathbf{B} - \mu \, \mathbf{J}) \cdot \mathbf{n} \, dS = 0.$$

Since the surface Σ is arbitrary, the integrand $(\operatorname{curl} \mathbf{B} - \mu \, \mathbf{J}) \cdot \mathbf{n}$ must vanish at all points, for all orientations of **n**. Consequently, Ampère's law may be expressed as the partial differential equation

$$\operatorname{curl} \mathbf{B} = \mu \mathbf{J}. \tag{57}$$

(b) *Faraday's law of induction.*   This law may be written as

$$\oint_{\mathscr{C}} \mathbf{E} \cdot d\mathbf{r} = -\frac{d}{dt} \iint_{\Sigma} \mathbf{B} \cdot \mathbf{n} \, dS, \tag{58}$$

and states that a varying flux of magnetic field through any loop $\mathscr{C}$ produces a 'potential difference', or circulation of the electric field **E**. By using equation (51) and manipulations similar to those in (a), equation (58) may be replaced by the partial differential equation

$$\operatorname{curl} \mathbf{E} = -\frac{\partial \mathbf{B}}{\partial t}. \tag{59}$$

EXAMPLE 3

Kelvin's circulation theorem (see Curle and Davies [2]) states that, in a region $\mathscr{R}$ of incompressible fluid which has flowed from a uniform stream and in which viscosity may be neglected, the circulation of velocity **v** around any loop $\mathscr{C}$ vanishes. Deduce that the flow is irrotational within $\mathscr{R}$.

Let Σ be any surface lying within $\mathscr{R}$ and spanning an arbitrary loop $\mathscr{C}$. Since the circulation of $\mathbf{v}$ around $\mathscr{C}$ vanishes, Stokes's theorem implies that

$$\iint_{\Sigma} \text{curl } \mathbf{v} \cdot \mathbf{n} \, dS = 0. \tag{60}$$

Since the choice of Σ and its unit normal $\mathbf{n}$ is entirely arbitrary within $\mathscr{R}$, equation (60) implies that curl $\mathbf{v} = \mathbf{0}$ throughout $\mathscr{R}$. Hence the flow velocity $\mathbf{v}$ is irrotational within $\mathscr{R}$.

The Heat Conduction Equation and Laplace's Equation

The equations (53), (54), (55) which result from the balance laws contain no information about the physical mechanisms which cause the corresponding flows. For example, the full equations governing fluid flow must relate fluid acceleration to the gradient of pressure. Similarly the heat conduction vector $\mathbf{q}$ and the temperature gradient grad θ which occur in equation (54) must be connected — usually they are related by *Fourier's law of heat conduction*

$$\mathbf{q} = -K \text{ grad } \theta.$$

When this is substituted into equation (54) a single partial differential equation is obtained for $\theta(x, y, z, t)$. In regions where K and c are uniform this equation is the *heat conduction equation*

$$\nabla^2 \theta = \frac{1}{\kappa} \frac{\partial \theta}{\partial t}, \quad \text{where } \kappa = \frac{K}{c}. \tag{61}$$

Methods for solution of equation (61) are discussed in §7.5. When the temperature θ is steady, equation (61) reduces to $\nabla^2 \theta = 0$ which is Laplace's equation (30) and which is analysed in §§7.6–7 and in §7.6 of Volume 2. It is important because it governs many phenomena besides steady heat conduction.

EXAMPLE 4

(a) *Irrotational, incompressible fluid flow.* The velocity field in an inviscid fluid is often irrotational (see example 3), and so may be written as $\mathbf{v} = \text{grad } \Phi$, where Φ is known as the velocity potential. If the density ρ is uniform in such a flow the continuity equation (53) becomes div $\mathbf{v} = 0$, so that Φ satisfies Laplace's equation

$$\text{div (grad } \Phi) = \nabla^2 \Phi = 0.$$

(b) *Steady electric currents.* Within an electric conductor *Ohm's law* relates the *current vector* $\mathbf{J}$ and *electric field* $\mathbf{E}$ by $\mathbf{J} = \sigma \mathbf{E}$, where σ is the conductivity of the material. When $\mathbf{B}$ vanishes or is steady, equation (59) allows us to write $\mathbf{E} = -\text{grad } V_e$, where V_e is the 'electric potential'. When currents are steady, equation (55) reduces to div $\mathbf{J} = 0$, and so V_e satisfies

$$\text{div } (\sigma \text{ grad } V_e) = 0.$$

Thus, in regions where the conductivity σ is uniform V_e satisfies Laplace's equation.

(c) *Steady magnetic fields.* In regions where no electric current flows, Ampère's law (57) implies that **B** is irrotational and so may be written as $\mathbf{B} = -\text{grad } V_m$. Moreover it is known that in *all* magnetic fields div **B** = 0, so that the *magnetic potential* V_m satisfies $\nabla^2 V_m = 0$.

Exercises

1. Heat is conducted through a solid having thermal capacity c, and thermal conductivity K according to Fourier's law of heat conduction. If a chemical reaction releases heat to a volume element dV at rate $\dot{\mu}\, dV$, obtain the balance law for heat content within an arbitrary control surface. Derive the partial differential equation governing the temperature $\theta(\mathbf{r}, t)$ in the case $\dot{\mu} = ke^{\beta\theta}$.

2. Within a porous medium *Fick's law of diffusion* states that fluid diffuses with a mass flux vector $\mathbf{V} = -\nu\, \text{grad } C$, where C is the fluid mass per unit volume. Derive the balance law for fluid content within a control surface $\mathscr{S}$, and so show that C satisfies the equation

$$\nu \nabla^2 C = \partial C / \partial t.$$

(This is the 'diffusion equation', and has the same form as the heat conduction equation (61) with κ replaced by ν; see §7.5.)

6.7 ORTHOGONAL CURVILINEAR COORDINATES

Change of Coordinates

Orthogonal cartesian coordinates and the corresponding vector components have been frequently used in the preceding sections. However, it is more natural in problems with spherical boundaries to use spherical polar coordinates, and in problems with circular cylindrical boundaries to use cylindrical polar coordinates. The corresponding formulae for gradient, divergence and curl will here be derived by considering general 'curvilinear coordinates'.

If (x, y, z) are the cartesian coordinates of a point P, the three functions $q_1 = q_1(x, y, z), q_2 = q_2(x, y, z)$ and $q_3 = q_3(x, y, z)$ determine the set of numbers (q_1, q_2, q_3) at P. Conversely it can be shown that, in a region throughout which the Jacobian (see §5.3),

$$\frac{\partial(q_1, q_2, q_3)}{\partial(x, y, z)} \equiv \nabla q_1 \cdot (\nabla q_2 \times \nabla q_3) \tag{62}$$

is non-zero, the set of values (q_1, q_2, q_3) can serve as coordinates which determine position. They specify P as the point of intersection of three loci q_i = constant $(i = 1, 2, 3)$, and this point of intersection is unique since the surfaces have normals $\nabla q_1, \nabla q_2$ and ∇q_3 which are non-zero and not coplanar. Since each surface q_i = constant is generally curved, the coordinates (q_1, q_2, q_3) are called *curvilinear*

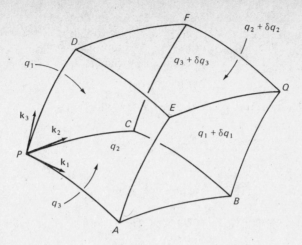

Fig. 6.15   An elementary volume bounded by curvilinear coordinate surfaces

coordinates. For simplicity, coordinate systems in which the coordinate surfaces intersect orthogonally are usually chosen. Analysis will here be confined to such systems of *orthogonal curvilinear coordinates.*

At any point P, let k_1, k_2 and k_3 be the unit vectors which are positive multiples of the normals ∇q_1, ∇q_2 and ∇q_3 to the respective level surfaces. When they satisfy

$$k_1 = k_2 \times k_3, \quad k_2 = k_3 \times k_1 \quad \text{and} \quad k_3 = k_1 \times k_2 \tag{63}$$

as in Fig. 6.15, the coordinates (q_1, q_2, q_3) form a right-handed orthogonal system, and the vectors k_1, k_2 and k_3 form the corresponding basis. Then, k_1 is tangential at P to the curve in which the level surfaces of q_2 and q_3 intersect. This curve is the *coordinate curve* of q_1, and similarly k_2 and k_3 are tangential to the coordinate curves of q_2 and q_3 respectively. If r is the position vector of P the vector $\partial r/\partial q_i$ is parallel to k_i for each $i = 1, 2, 3$, and so may be written as

$$\frac{\partial r}{\partial q_i} = h_i k_i.$$

The quantities h_i defined by

$$h_i = \left| \frac{\partial r}{\partial q_i} \right| \qquad (i = 1, 2, 3) \tag{64}$$

are known as the *scale factors*, and each measures the rate of change of distance with q_i along the corresponding coordinate curve at P.

EXAMPLE 1
Spherical polar coordinates (r, θ, ϕ) are related to x, y and z by $x = r \sin \theta \cos \phi$, $y = r \sin \theta \sin \phi$, $z = r \cos \theta$ (see Fig. 5.16). Find the unit base vectors k_r, k_θ and k_ϕ along the coordinate curves of r, θ and ϕ, and so verify that the coordinates form a

right-handed orthogonal system. (In spherical polar coordinates (r, θ, ϕ) it is unnecessary to introduce the notation (q_1, q_2, q_3) explicitly. The base vectors and scale factors are normally denoted by $\mathbf{k}_r, \mathbf{k}_\theta, \mathbf{k}_\phi$ and h_r, h_θ, h_ϕ instead of $\mathbf{k}_1, \mathbf{k}_2, \mathbf{k}_3$ and h_1, h_2, h_3. Similar conventions apply in cylindrical polar coordinates, see example 2.)

Since the position vector $\mathbf{r}$ is $\mathbf{r} = x\mathbf{i} + y\mathbf{j} + z\mathbf{k}$, it follows that

$$h_r \mathbf{k}_r \equiv \frac{\partial \mathbf{r}}{\partial r} = \sin \theta \cos \phi \mathbf{i} + \sin \theta \sin \phi \mathbf{j} + \cos \theta \mathbf{k},$$

$$h_\theta \mathbf{k}_\theta \equiv \frac{\partial \mathbf{r}}{\partial \theta} = r \cos \theta \cos \phi \mathbf{i} + r \cos \theta \sin \phi \mathbf{j} - r \sin \theta \mathbf{k},$$

$$h_\phi \mathbf{k}_\phi \equiv \frac{\partial \mathbf{r}}{\partial \phi} = -r \sin \theta \sin \phi \mathbf{i} + r \sin \theta \cos \phi \mathbf{j}.$$

Thus the scale factors h_r, h_θ and h_ϕ are given by

$$h_r = \left| \frac{\partial \mathbf{r}}{\partial r} \right| = 1, \quad h_\theta = \left| \frac{\partial \mathbf{r}}{\partial \theta} \right| = r, \quad h_\phi = \left| \frac{\partial \mathbf{r}}{\partial \phi} \right| = r \sin \theta,$$

so that the base vectors are

$$\mathbf{k}_r = \sin \theta \, (\cos \phi \mathbf{i} + \sin \phi \mathbf{j}) + \cos \theta \mathbf{k},$$

$$\mathbf{k}_\theta = \cos \theta \, (\cos \phi \mathbf{i} + \sin \phi \mathbf{j}) - \sin \theta \mathbf{k}, \quad \mathbf{k}_\phi = -\sin \phi \mathbf{i} + \cos \phi \mathbf{j}.$$

Consequently, spherical polar coordinates form a right-handed orthogonal system, since

$$\mathbf{k}_r = \mathbf{k}_\theta \times \mathbf{k}_\phi, \quad \mathbf{k}_\theta = \mathbf{k}_\phi \times \mathbf{k}_r \quad \text{and} \quad \mathbf{k}_\phi = \mathbf{k}_r \times \mathbf{k}_\theta.$$

Elements of Length

Consider any curve through P given parametrically as

$$q_1 = q_1(\eta), \quad q_2 = q_2(\eta) \quad \text{and} \quad q_3 = q_3(\eta).$$

At P, the derivative of $\mathbf{r}$ with respect to η is a vector tangential to the curve, and is given by

$$\frac{d\mathbf{r}}{d\eta} = \sum_{i=1}^{3} \frac{\partial \mathbf{r}}{\partial q_i} \frac{dq_i}{d\eta} = \sum_{i=1}^{3} h_i \mathbf{k}_i \frac{dq_i}{d\eta}.$$

If s denotes distance along the curve, its derivative with respect to η is given by the formula

$$\left(\frac{ds}{d\eta} \right)^2 = \left| \frac{d\mathbf{r}}{d\eta} \right|^2 = h_1^2 \left(\frac{dq_1}{d\eta} \right)^2 + h_2^2 \left(\frac{dq_2}{d\eta} \right)^2 + h_3^2 \left(\frac{dq_3}{d\eta} \right)^2, \tag{65}$$

since $\mathbf{k}_1, \mathbf{k}_2$ and $\mathbf{k}_3$ are orthogonal unit vectors. Equation (65) is frequently rewritten to relate the *differential displacement* ds to the differentials dq_1, dq_2, dq_3 as

$$(ds)^2 = h_1^2(dq_1)^2 + h_2^2(dq_2)^2 + h_3^2(dq_3)^2, \tag{66}$$

and may be recognized as the limiting form of Pythagoras's theorem for the calculation of the diagonal $PQ \simeq \delta s$ of the approximately rectangular region in Fig. 6.15.

Gradient

Any vector $\mathbf{F}$ at P may be resolved into components as

$$\mathbf{F} = F_1\mathbf{k}_1 + F_2\mathbf{k}_2 + F_3\mathbf{k}_3, \tag{67}$$

where

$$F_i = \mathbf{F} \cdot \mathbf{k}_i = \mathbf{k}_i \cdot \mathbf{F} \quad \text{for each } i = 1, 2, 3,$$

and it should be remembered that $\mathbf{k}_1, \mathbf{k}_2$ and $\mathbf{k}_3$ may vary with (q_1, q_2, q_3). The gradient ∇f of any scalar $f(q_1, q_2, q_3)$ has components $\mathbf{k}_i \cdot \nabla f (i = 1, 2, 3)$ each of which is the directional derivative of f along the corresponding coordinate curve. Consequently

$$\mathbf{k}_i \cdot \nabla f = \frac{\partial f}{\partial q_i} \frac{dq_i}{ds} = \frac{1}{h_i} \frac{\partial f}{\partial q_i},$$

in view of equation (65). The formula for grad f in curvilinear coordinates is

$$\operatorname{grad} f \equiv \nabla f = \frac{1}{h_1} \frac{\partial f}{\partial q_1} \mathbf{k}_1 + \frac{1}{h_2} \frac{\partial f}{\partial q_2} \mathbf{k}_2 + \frac{1}{h_3} \frac{\partial f}{\partial q_3} \mathbf{k}_3. \tag{68}$$

Notice that equation (68) confirms that $\mathbf{k}_1, \mathbf{k}_2$ and $\mathbf{k}_3$ are normal to the coordinate surfaces, since

$$\operatorname{grad} q_1 = \frac{\mathbf{k}_1}{h_1}, \quad \operatorname{grad} q_2 = \frac{\mathbf{k}_2}{h_2} \quad \text{and} \quad \operatorname{grad} q_3 = \frac{\mathbf{k}_3}{h_3}.$$

Also, equation (68) gives a direct procedure for calculation of the scale factors when the curvilinear coordinates are specified by formulae $q_i = q_i(x, y, z)$, since

$$h_i = |\operatorname{grad} q_i|^{-1}, \quad \text{for } i = 1, 2, 3. \tag{69}$$

EXAMPLE 2

Find the scale factors and coordinate base vectors for cylindrical polar coordinates (ρ, ϕ, z) defined by $\rho = (x^2 + y^2)^{1/2}$, $\phi = \tan^{-1} y/x$ and $z = z$, and illustrated in Fig. 5.16.

Since grad $\rho = (x^2 + y^2)^{-1/2}(x\mathbf{i} + y\mathbf{j})$, grad $\phi = (x^2 + y^2)^{-1}(-y\mathbf{i} + x\mathbf{j})$, grad $z = \mathbf{k}$ the scale factors are

$$h_\rho = |\operatorname{grad} \rho|^{-1} = 1, \quad h_\phi = |\operatorname{grad} \phi|^{-1} = \rho \quad \text{and} \quad h_z = |\mathbf{k}|^{-1} = 1,$$

and the corresponding base vectors are

$$\mathbf{k}_\rho = \rho^{-1}(x\mathbf{i} + y\mathbf{j}) = \mathbf{i} \cos \phi + \mathbf{j} \sin \phi, \quad \mathbf{k}_\phi = \rho^{-1}(-y\mathbf{i} + x\mathbf{j}) = -\mathbf{i} \sin \phi + \mathbf{j} \cos \phi$$

$$\mathbf{k}_z = \mathbf{k}.$$

It is readily verified that these form a right-handed orthogonal system.

Elements of Area and Volume

The curvilinear block in Fig. 6.15 has edges which are approximately straight, orthogonal and of lengths $h_1 \delta q_1$, $h_2 \delta q_2$ and $h_3 \delta q_3$, so that its faces are approximately plane and rectangular. For example the face *ABQE* is approximately plane with vector area given by

$$\mathbf{n} \, \delta S = \delta \mathbf{S} \simeq (\mathbf{k}_2 h_2 \delta q_2) \times (\mathbf{k}_3 h_3 \delta q_3) = \mathbf{k}_1 h_2 h_3 \delta q_2 \delta q_3,$$

and the areas of the other faces are computed similarly. The volume of the block is correspondingly given by

$$\delta V \simeq (\mathbf{k}_1 h_1 \delta q_1) \cdot (\mathbf{k}_2 h_2 \delta q_2 \times \mathbf{k}_3 h_3 \delta q_3) = h_1 h_2 h_3 \delta q_1 \delta q_2 \delta q_3.$$

Consequently the differential elements of volume and of projected area in curvilinear coordinates are given by

$$dV = h_1 h_2 h_3 \, dq_1 \, dq_2 \, dq_3, \tag{70}$$

and

$$\mathbf{k}_1 \cdot d\mathbf{S} = h_2 h_3 \, dq_2 \, dq_3, \quad \mathbf{k}_2 \cdot d\mathbf{S} = h_3 h_1 \, dq_3 \, dq_1, \quad \mathbf{k}_3 \cdot d\mathbf{S} = h_1 h_2 \, dq_1 \, dq_2. \tag{71}$$

Divergence

To obtain the formula for div $\mathbf{F}$ in curvilinear coordinates the formula (37) should be applied to the elementary block in Fig. 6.15. Then the fluxes of $\mathbf{F}$ through the faces *ABQE* and *PCFD* are given approximately by

$$F_1 h_2 h_3 \delta q_2 \delta q_3 \quad \text{and} \quad -F_1 h_2 h_3 \delta q_2 \delta q_3,$$

evaluated at the centres $(q_1 + \delta q_1, q_2 + \tfrac{1}{2}\delta q_2, q_3 + \tfrac{1}{2}\delta q_3)$ and $(q_1, q_2 + \tfrac{1}{2}\delta q_2, q_3 + \tfrac{1}{2}\delta q_3)$ of the respective faces. The sum of these fluxes may be written, after use of the mean value theorem, as

$$\frac{\partial(F_1 h_2 h_3)}{\partial q_1} \delta q_1 \delta q_2 \delta q_3 = \frac{1}{h_1 h_2 h_3} \frac{\partial(h_2 h_3 F_1)}{\partial q_1} \delta V,$$

where all quantities are evaluated at some interior point of the block. The contributions to equation (37) from the remaining two pairs of faces may be expressed similarly. When the limit $\delta V \to 0$ is then taken, the formula for div $\mathbf{F}$ is found as

$$\operatorname{div} \mathbf{F} = \frac{1}{h_1 h_2 h_3} \left\{ \frac{\partial}{\partial q_1}(h_2 h_3 F_1) + \frac{\partial}{\partial q_2}(h_3 h_1 F_2) + \frac{\partial}{\partial q_3}(h_1 h_2 F_3) \right\}. \tag{72}$$

The explicit formulae for div **F** in spherical and cylindrical polar coordinates are given in table 6.1.

The Laplacian ∇^2

It has been shown that the *Laplacian operator* $\nabla^2 \equiv \text{div grad}$ occurs in many partial differential equations. In orthogonal curvilinear coordinates (q_1, q_2, q_3) the formula for $\nabla^2 f$ follows from equations (68) and (72) as

$$\nabla^2 f = \text{div grad } f = \frac{1}{h_1 h_2 h_3} \left\{ \frac{\partial}{\partial q_1} \left(\frac{h_2 h_3}{h_1} \frac{\partial f}{\partial q_1} \right) + \frac{\partial}{\partial q_2} \left(\frac{h_3 h_1}{h_2} \frac{\partial f}{\partial q_2} \right) \right.$$

$$\left. + \frac{\partial}{\partial q_3} \left(\frac{h_1 h_2}{h_3} \frac{\partial f}{\partial q_3} \right) \right\}, \tag{73}$$

and is given explicitly for both spherical and cylindrical polar coordinates in table 6.1.

Curl

The formula giving curl **F** in (q_1, q_2, q_3) coordinates is obtained by applying Stokes's theorem to portions of coordinate surfaces. For example, by considering the circulation around an elementary portion $dS = h_2 h_3 \, dq_2 \, dq_3$ of a surface $q_1 = \text{constant}$, we deduce that

$$(\text{curl } \mathbf{F}) \cdot \mathbf{k}_1 h_2 h_3 = \frac{\partial}{\partial q_2} (h_3 F_3) - \frac{\partial}{\partial q_3} (h_2 F_2).$$

Similar formulae determine the remaining components of curl **F**, so that

$$\text{curl } \mathbf{F} = \frac{1}{h_1 h_2 h_3} \left[h_1 \mathbf{k}_1 \left\{ \frac{\partial}{\partial q_2} (h_3 F_3) - \frac{\partial}{\partial q_3} (h_2 F_2) \right\} \right.$$

$$+ h_2 \mathbf{k}_2 \left\{ \frac{\partial}{\partial q_3} (h_1 F_1) - \frac{\partial}{\partial q_1} (h_3 F_3) \right\}$$

$$\left. + h_3 \mathbf{k}_3 \left\{ \frac{\partial}{\partial q_1} (h_2 F_2) - \frac{\partial}{\partial q_2} (h_1 F_1) \right\} \right]. \tag{74}$$

This formula, like equation (28), may be put into mnemonic form as

$$\text{curl } \mathbf{F} = \frac{1}{h_1 h_2 h_3} \begin{vmatrix} h_1 \mathbf{k}_1 & h_2 \mathbf{k}_2 & h_3 \mathbf{k}_3 \\ \dfrac{\partial}{\partial q_1} & \dfrac{\partial}{\partial q_2} & \dfrac{\partial}{\partial q_3} \\ h_1 F_1 & h_2 F_2 & h_3 F_3 \end{vmatrix}, \tag{75}$$

and for spherical and cylindrical polar coordinates the explicit formulae are given in table 6.1.

TABLE 6.1   Vector formulae in spherical and cylindrical polar coordinates (see Fig. 5.16)

	Spherical polars (r, θ, ϕ)	*Cylindrical polars* (ρ, ϕ, z)
	$x = r \sin \theta \cos \phi, y = r \sin \theta \sin \phi, z = r \cos \theta$	$x = \rho \cos \phi, y = \rho \sin \phi, z = z$
Scale factors	$h_r = 1, h_\theta = r, h_\phi = r \sin \theta$	$h_\rho = 1, h_\phi = \rho, h_z = 1$
Base vectors	$\mathbf{k}_r = \sin \theta (\mathbf{i} \cos \phi + \mathbf{j} \sin \phi) + \mathbf{k} \cos \theta$	$\mathbf{k}_\rho = \mathbf{i} \cos \phi + \mathbf{j} \sin \phi$
	$\mathbf{k}_\theta = \cos \theta (\mathbf{i} \cos \phi + \mathbf{j} \sin \phi) - \mathbf{k} \sin \theta$	$\mathbf{k}_\phi = -\mathbf{i} \sin \phi + \mathbf{j} \cos \phi$
	$\mathbf{k}_\phi = -\mathbf{i} \sin \phi + \mathbf{j} \cos \phi$	$\mathbf{k}_z = \mathbf{k}$
Components	$F_r = \mathbf{F} \cdot \mathbf{k}_r, F_\theta = \mathbf{F} \cdot \mathbf{k}_\theta, F_\phi = \mathbf{F} \cdot \mathbf{k}_\phi$	$F_\rho = \mathbf{F} \cdot \mathbf{k}_\rho, F_\phi = \mathbf{F} \cdot \mathbf{k}_\phi, F_z = \mathbf{F} \cdot \mathbf{k}_z$
grad f	$\dfrac{\partial f}{\partial r} \mathbf{k}_r + \dfrac{1}{r} \dfrac{\partial f}{\partial \theta} \mathbf{k}_\theta + \dfrac{1}{r \sin \theta} \dfrac{\partial f}{\partial \phi} \mathbf{k}_\phi$	$\dfrac{\partial f}{\partial \rho} \mathbf{k}_\rho + \dfrac{1}{\rho} \dfrac{\partial f}{\partial \phi} \mathbf{k}_\phi + \dfrac{\partial f}{\partial z} \mathbf{k}_z$
div $\mathbf{F}$	$\dfrac{1}{r^2} \dfrac{\partial}{\partial r}(r^2 F_r) + \dfrac{1}{r \sin \theta} \dfrac{\partial}{\partial \theta}(\sin \theta F_\theta) + \dfrac{1}{r \sin \theta} \dfrac{\partial F_\phi}{\partial \phi}$	$\dfrac{1}{\rho} \dfrac{\partial}{\partial \rho}(\rho F_\rho) + \dfrac{1}{\rho} \dfrac{\partial F_\phi}{\partial \phi} + \dfrac{\partial F_z}{\partial z}$
$\nabla^2 f$	$\dfrac{1}{r^2} \dfrac{\partial}{\partial r}\left(r^2 \dfrac{\partial f}{\partial r}\right) + \dfrac{1}{r^2 \sin \theta} \dfrac{\partial}{\partial \theta}\left(\sin \theta \dfrac{\partial f}{\partial \theta}\right) + \dfrac{1}{r^2 \sin^2 \theta} \dfrac{\partial^2 f}{\partial \phi^2}$	$\dfrac{1}{\rho} \dfrac{\partial}{\partial \rho}\left(\rho \dfrac{\partial f}{\partial \rho}\right) + \dfrac{1}{\rho^2} \dfrac{\partial^2 f}{\partial \phi^2} + \dfrac{\partial^2 f}{\partial z^2}$
curl $\mathbf{F}$	$\dfrac{\mathbf{k}_r}{r \sin \theta}\left\{\dfrac{\partial}{\partial \theta}(\sin \theta F_\phi) - \dfrac{\partial F_\theta}{\partial \phi}\right\} + \dfrac{\mathbf{k}_\phi}{r}\left\{\dfrac{\partial(r F_\theta)}{\partial r} - \dfrac{\partial F_r}{\partial \theta}\right\}$ $+ \dfrac{\mathbf{k}_\theta}{r \sin \theta}\left\{\dfrac{\partial F_r}{\partial \phi} - \sin \theta \dfrac{\partial(r F_\phi)}{\partial r}\right\}$	$\dfrac{\mathbf{k}_\rho}{\rho}\left\{\dfrac{\partial F_z}{\partial \phi} - \rho \dfrac{\partial F_\phi}{\partial z}\right\} + \mathbf{k}_\phi\left\{\dfrac{\partial F_\rho}{\partial z} - \dfrac{\partial F_z}{\partial \rho}\right\}$ $+ \dfrac{\mathbf{k}_z}{\rho}\left\{\dfrac{\partial}{\partial \rho}(\rho F_\phi) - \dfrac{\partial F_\rho}{\partial \phi}\right\}$

Exercises

1. Oblate spheroidal coordinates (u, v, ϕ) are defined by $x = \cosh u \sin v \cos \phi$, $y = \cosh u \sin v \sin \phi$, $z = \sinh u \cos v$, for $0 \leqslant u < \infty, 0 \leqslant v \leqslant \pi$ and $0 \leqslant \phi < 2\pi$. Verify that the surfaces of constant u and of constant v are hyperboloids and ellipsoids respectively.

   Show that the vectors $\partial r/\partial u$, $\partial r/\partial v$ and $\partial r/\partial \phi$ are mutually orthogonal. Find the corresponding scale factors h_u, h_v and h_ϕ and the unit base vectors k_u, k_v and k_ϕ.

2. Find div $\mathbf{F}$ if $\mathbf{F} = k_\rho \rho \sin \phi + k_\phi \rho \cos \phi + k_z z \cos \phi$, where k_ρ, k_ϕ and k_z are the unit base vectors for cylindrical polar coordinates (ρ, ϕ, z). Check this calculation by using cartesian coordinates.

3. If r, θ and ϕ are the usual spherical polar coordinates find the components F_r, F_θ and F_ϕ of $\mathbf{F} = r^{-2}k \times \mathbf{r}$.

   Calculate div $\mathbf{F}$ and curl $\mathbf{F}$. If $\mathscr{C}$ is any loop $\theta = \theta_0, r = r_0, 0 \leqslant \phi < 2\pi$, evaluate $\oint_\mathscr{C} \mathbf{F} \cdot d\mathbf{r}$ and verify Stokes's theorem when Σ is chosen as the spherical cap $r = r_0$, $0 \leqslant \theta < \theta_0$.

PROBLEMS

1. If $\mathbf{r}(t)$ denotes the position of a particle at time t, show that

   (a) $\dfrac{d}{dt}(\mathbf{r} \times \dot{\mathbf{r}}) = \mathbf{r} \times \ddot{\mathbf{r}}$ and   (b) $\dfrac{d}{dt}\{V(r)\} = \dfrac{dV}{dr}\dfrac{\mathbf{r} \cdot \dot{\mathbf{r}}}{r}$,

   where $r = |\mathbf{r}|$ and dots denote time derivatives.

   A particle of mass m moves subject to a force directed radially towards the origin $\mathbf{r} = \mathbf{0}$ and of magnitude dV/dr, so that

   $$m\ddot{\mathbf{r}} = -\frac{dV}{dr}\frac{\mathbf{r}}{r}.$$

   Use (a) and (b) to deduce that $\mathbf{r} \times \dot{\mathbf{r}}$ and $\frac{1}{2}m\dot{\mathbf{r}} \cdot \dot{\mathbf{r}} + V(r)$ are each constant throughout the motion.

2. The points of a twisted curve are given parametrically as

   $$\mathbf{r}(\eta) = \tfrac{1}{2}i\eta^2 + j(\eta \sin \eta + \cos \eta) + k(\eta \cos \eta - \sin \eta).$$

   Find the *unit tangent* $t(\eta)$, the *principal normal* $n(\eta)$ and the *binormal* $b(\eta)$, and so show that the *curvature* is $\kappa = 1/2\eta$ and that the *torsion* is $\lambda = -1/2\eta$. Show also that the arc length of curve between $\eta = 0$ and $\eta = \eta_1$ is $2^{-1/2}\eta_1^2$.

3. Find the directional derivatives of the following functions in the direction of $i + 2j - 2k$ at a typical point $\mathbf{r} = xi + yj + zk$:

   (a) $f = 3x^2 + xy^2 + yz$,   (b) $g = \cosh xyz$.

4. If $f(\mathbf{r})$ and $g(\mathbf{r})$ are two scalar fields, show that the related scalar field $F = F(f, g)$ has gradient

$$\frac{\partial F}{\partial f} \text{ grad } f + \frac{\partial F}{\partial g} \text{ grad } g.$$

Use this result to find the gradient of $\sin\left(r + \dfrac{x}{r}\right)$, where $r = (x^2 + y^2 + z^2)^{1/2}$

5. Find the divergence and the curl of $\mathbf{F} = xz^2\mathbf{i} + y(x^2 - z^2)\mathbf{j} - xyz\,\mathbf{k}$, and verify that $\text{div(curl } \mathbf{F}) = 0$.

6. The vectors $\mathbf{u}$ and $\mathbf{v}$ are given by

$$\mathbf{u} = x\mathbf{i} + 3y\mathbf{j} + 4z\mathbf{k}, \quad \mathbf{v} = (y + 2z)\mathbf{i} + (x + 3z)\mathbf{j} + (2x + 3y)\mathbf{k}.$$

Verify that curl $\mathbf{u} = \mathbf{0}$, and curl $\mathbf{v} = \mathbf{0}$. Find $\mathbf{u} \times \mathbf{v}$ and calculate its divergence.

7. If $\mathbf{r} = x\mathbf{i} + y\mathbf{j} + z\mathbf{k}$, $r = |\mathbf{r}|$ and $\mathbf{a}$ is any constant vector, show that

(a)   div $\mathbf{r} = 3$,   (b) $\text{grad}(\mathbf{a} \cdot \mathbf{r}) = \mathbf{a}$,   (c) $(\mathbf{a} \cdot \text{grad})\mathbf{r} = \mathbf{a}$

(d)   curl $\mathbf{r} = \mathbf{0}$,   (e) $\text{div}(\mathbf{a} \times \mathbf{r}) = 0$,   and   (f) $\text{div}\left(\dfrac{\mathbf{r}}{r^n}\right) = \dfrac{3 - n}{r^n}$.

8. In a particular fluid motion the velocity field $\mathbf{v}$ is given in terms of a velocity potential Φ by $\mathbf{v} = \text{grad } \Phi$, where

$$\Phi = s \log(x^2 + y^2) + c \tan^{-1} y/x \quad \text{for } (x, y) \neq (0, 0)$$

and c and s are constants. Evaluate $\mathbf{v}$ and confirm that div $\mathbf{v} = 0$. Similarly confirm that the *vorticity* curl $\mathbf{v}$ is zero.

9. If ψ is any scalar field apply the divergence theorem to $\mathbf{a}\psi$, where $\mathbf{a}$ is any constant vector, and so deduce that

$$\iint_{\mathscr{S}} \psi \mathbf{n} \, dS = \iiint_{\mathscr{R}} \text{grad } \psi \, dV,$$

where $\mathscr{R}$ is any region, $\mathscr{S}$ is its boundary surface and $\mathbf{n}$ is the unit outward normal to $\mathscr{S}$.

10. Find the flux of the vector field $\mathbf{F} = \mathbf{r}/r^3$ through any sphere $r = a$. Hence, by using the divergence theorem show that for any closed surface $\mathscr{S}$ having unit outward normal $\mathbf{n}$

$$\iint_{\mathscr{S}} \frac{\mathbf{r}}{r^3} \cdot \mathbf{n} \, dS = \begin{cases} 0 & \text{if the origin } \mathbf{r} = \mathbf{0} \text{ is outside } \mathscr{S}, \\ 4\pi & \text{if the origin } \mathbf{r} = \mathbf{0} \text{ is within } \mathscr{S}. \end{cases}$$

11. In the plane $z = 0$ consider the two paths $\mathscr{C}_1$ and $\mathscr{C}_2$ joining the origin to the point $(2, 2, 0)$. $\mathscr{C}_1$ is part of the line $y = x$, whilst $\mathscr{C}_2$ comprises parts of $y = 0$ and of

$x = 2$. If $F = i(x^2 - 3z) + j(y^2 - x) + kxy$, evaluate the integrals

$$I_1 = \oint_{\mathscr{C}_1} F \cdot dr, \quad I_2 = \oint_{\mathscr{C}_2} F \cdot dr \quad \text{and} \quad J = \iint_{\mathscr{S}} \text{curl } F \cdot k \, dx \, dy,$$

where $\mathscr{S}$ is the triangle bounded by $\mathscr{C}_1$ and $\mathscr{C}_2$, and verify that

$$J = I_2 - I_1.$$

12. If (r, θ, ϕ) are spherical polar coordinates calculate $\nabla \cdot F$ when $F = r^2 r + \nabla \times r^2 i$. Hence, or otherwise, show that

$$\iint_{\mathscr{S}} F \cdot n \, dS = 2\pi a^5,$$

where $\mathscr{S}$ is the curved surface and n the unit outward normal of the hemisphere $r = a$, $0 \leqslant \theta \leqslant \frac{1}{2}\pi$. (State any vector theorems you may require.)

13. Find (a) the cartesian components, and (b) the spherical polar components of $F = r^{-2}\{r \cdot (r - ak)\}r$.
   Calculate div F using each coordinate system, and check that the answers agree.

14. The cartesian coordinate system $(\bar{x}, \bar{y}, \bar{z})$, having base vectors k_1, k_2 and k_3 is obtained from the (x, y, z) system by a rotation about 0. Determine the scale factors h_1, h_2, h_3 of the $(\bar{x}, \bar{y}, \bar{z})$ system, and so write down the expression for grad f in this coordinate system. Verify that this formula agrees with $i \cdot \text{grad } f = \partial f/\partial x$. (You may use the identity $xi + yj + zk = \bar{x}k_1 + \bar{y}k_2 + \bar{z}k_3$ to determine $\partial\bar{x}/\partial x$, $\partial\bar{y}/\partial x$ and $\partial\bar{z}/\partial x$).

15. The system of cartesian coordinates $(\bar{x}, \bar{y}, \bar{z})$ is obtained by rotation through an angle $\frac{1}{3}\pi$ about the z axis of the (x, y, z) coordinate system. Express the coordinates and base vectors of the (x, y, z) system in terms of those for the $(\bar{x}, \bar{y}, \bar{z})$ system, and conversely. Express the vector field $F = (x + y)i + (x - y)j + zk$ in terms of the coordinates $(\bar{x}, \bar{y}, \bar{z})$ and the corresponding base vectors. Verify that the divergence and curl of F are the same in both systems.

16. An equation governing diffusion of a chemically reacting fluid is sought. It is assumed that at any point r the mass flow rate per unit area is $q = -K$ grad C, where C is the concentration of the fluid. The rate at which fluid is removed from unit volume by chemical reaction is assumed to be proportional to C, and so is given by αC.
   Show, by considering an arbitrary fixed region $\mathscr{R}$, that the required equation is

$$\frac{\partial C}{\partial t} + \alpha C = K\nabla^2 C.$$

17. A fluid of uniform density ρ is at rest subject to a gravitational force $-\rho gk$ per unit volume, and subject to a hydrostatic pressure p. By considering the equilibrium of the fluid within an arbitrary closed surface $\mathscr{S}$, and using the result of problem 9, show that

$$\frac{\partial p}{\partial x} = 0, \quad \frac{\partial p}{\partial y} = 0 \quad \text{and} \quad \frac{\partial p}{\partial z} = -\rho g.$$

By applying a similar procedure to the region occupied by an immersed solid object of volume V and mass M, verify *Archimedes' principle* that the apparent weight is $(M - \rho V)g$.

BIBLIOGRAPHY

[1]   Sowerby, L. *Vector Field Theory with Applications*, Longmans, London (1974).
[2]   Curle, N. and H. J. Davies, *Modern Fluid Dynamics*, Vol. 1, Van Nostrand, London (1968).

CHAPTER 7

Partial Differential Equations

7.1 INTRODUCTION

Most physical phenomena in continuous media can be described in terms of *fields* (see §6.1). Mathematically a field is just a function of position and time. The temperature field in a given body depends upon the point of measurement, which may be defined by cartesian coordinates x, y, z, and the time of measurement t. If the temperature is denoted by θ, then the temperature field can be expressed mathematically as $\theta = \theta(x, y, z, t)$. Other fields which are frequently encountered are the electrostatic potential, the gravitational potential, the velocity potential and the stream function in fluid flow. The three cartesian components of the displacement vector in mechanics form three scalar fields.

A physical quantity which can be represented by a field is normally related from point to point and time to time by a partial differential equation. In this context the partial differential equation is the mathematical statement of the way in which the laws of nature govern the phenomenon. For example, the fundamental laws of Newtonian mechanics are Newton's laws of motion and the principles of conservation of mass and energy. The application of these laws to a mechanical phenomenon will lead to at least one partial differential equation.

This chapter is mainly concerned with the following important differential equations

$$\text{The Wave Equation} \qquad \frac{\partial^2 v}{\partial x^2} + \frac{\partial^2 v}{\partial y^2} + \frac{\partial^2 v}{\partial z^2} = \frac{1}{c^2} \frac{\partial^2 v}{\partial t^2}, \tag{1}$$

$$\text{The Heat Conduction Equation} \qquad \frac{\partial^2 \theta}{\partial x^2} + \frac{\partial^2 \theta}{\partial y^2} + \frac{\partial^2 \theta}{\partial z^2} = \frac{1}{\kappa} \frac{\partial \theta}{\partial t}, \tag{2}$$

$$\text{Laplace's Equation} \qquad \frac{\partial^2 T}{\partial x^2} + \frac{\partial^2 T}{\partial y^2} + \frac{\partial^2 T}{\partial z^2} = 0, \tag{3}$$

in which c^2 and κ are physical constants. Different field variables v, θ, T have been associated with these equations to prevent any ambiguity over which equation is being discussed in a particular case. Some engineering and physical applications of the equations are described in §§7.2, 7.4, 7.5 and 7.6.

Definitions

The order of a differential equation was defined in §1.1 to be the order of the highest derivative in the equation.

A partial differential equation is said to be *linear* if it is of the first degree in the field variable and its partial derivatives. The equation $\dfrac{\partial \theta}{\partial x} = \dfrac{\partial \theta}{\partial t}$ is linear, while $\dfrac{\partial \theta}{\partial x} = \left(\dfrac{\partial \theta}{\partial t}\right)^2$ is non-linear.

A linear partial differential equation is said to be *homogeneous* if every term in the equation contains either the field variable or one of its derivatives. Otherwise it is said to be *inhomogeneous*. The equation $\dfrac{\partial^2 \theta}{\partial x^2} = \dfrac{\partial \theta}{\partial t}$, is homogeneous, whereas the equation $\dfrac{\partial^2 \theta}{\partial x^2} = \dfrac{\partial \theta}{\partial t} + 3$ is inhomogeneous.

Each of equations (1), (2), (3) is a second-order linear homogeneous equation. The equation

$$\frac{\partial^4 v}{\partial x^4} = -\frac{1}{c^2} \frac{\partial^2 v}{\partial t^2} + h(x, t),$$

where $h(x, t)$ is a known non-zero function, is a fourth-order linear inhomogeneous equation. The methods described in this chapter may be applied to the important class of equations which are linear and homogeneous. Linear inhomogeneous equations are briefly discussed in §7.8. The methods of solution of linear equations are not easily extended to the non-linear case. For a discussion of non-linear partial differential equations see Ames [1].

Superposition of Solutions

If each of the n functions $v = v_1(x, y, z, t), v = v_2(x, y, z, t), \ldots, v = v_n(x, y, z, t)$ satisfies the wave equation (1), then it is easily verified by differentiation that the *linear combination*

$$v = c_1 v_1(x, y, z, t) + c_2 v_2(x, y, z, t) + \ldots + c_n v_n(x, y, z, t),$$

where $c_1, c_2, \ldots, c_n$ are arbitrary constants, also satisfies equation (1). Similarly it is possible to superpose solutions of any *linear homogeneous* differential equation. For example since $T = x^2 - y^2$, $T = xy$ are solutions of Laplace's equation, so is $T = 3(x^2 - y^2) + 4xy$. This superposition property is of fundamental importance because it allows a set of simple solutions of a given linear homogeneous equation to be combined by addition to form a more general solution of the same equation.

Each of the partial differential equations (1), (2) and (3) has a wide variety of solutions. For example, Laplace's equation (3) in two variables x and y is

$$\frac{\partial^2 T}{\partial x^2} + \frac{\partial^2 T}{\partial y^2} = 0, \tag{4}$$

and the reader will easily confirm that this has the solutions

$$T = Ax + By, \quad T = A(x^2 - y^2), \quad T = Ae^{-x} \cos y,$$

where A and B are arbitrary constants. These solutions are entirely different from each other.

Arbitrary Functions of Integration

It was shown in §4.5 that if u is a function of two independent variables x and y, then the solution of

$$\frac{\partial u}{\partial x} = 0$$

is $u = F(y)$, where $F(y)$ is an arbitrary function of y. This illustrates a fundamental difference between general solutions of ordinary differential equations and of partial differential equations, namely that whereas solutions of ordinary differential equations involve arbitrary *constants*, solutions of partial differential equations involve arbitrary *functions*.

As a further example, suppose that v is a function of x and y and satisfies the equation

$$\frac{\partial^2 v}{\partial x \partial y} \equiv \frac{\partial}{\partial x}\left(\frac{\partial v}{\partial y}\right) = 0.$$

Integration with respect to x shows that $\partial v/\partial y$ must be an arbitrary function of y which for convenience is written as

$$\frac{\partial v}{\partial y} = F'(y).$$

On integrating with respect to y, we find the solution

$$v = \int F'(y)\,dy + G(x) = F(y) + G(x),$$

where $F(y)$ and $G(x)$ are arbitrary functions of the named variables.

In general, while the general solution of an nth-order ordinary differential equation contains n arbitrary constants, the general solution of an nth-order partial differential equation may be regarded as containing n arbitrary functions.

Uniqueness

A typical *boundary value problem* for Laplace's equation consists of finding a function T which satisfies equation (3) at all points in a given region R in space subject to specified boundary values $T = f(x, y, z)$ at each point of the boundary of the region R, where $f(x, y, z)$ is a known function. Thus the problem in partial differential equations does not just consist of finding solutions to a differential equation, but of determining how to combine known solutions of the differential equation to match with the given function $f(x, y, z)$ on the boundary of the region R. It was proved in §6.4 that there is only one solution of Laplace's equation which takes specified values on the boundary of R. This is an example of a *uniqueness theorem*. There exist many uniqueness theorems for the partial differential equations considered in this chapter. We shall not discuss them further, but remark that in practice the solutions of physically meaningful problems for these equations are nearly always unique. This means that if we can find *a* solution (which satisfies all the conditions) to such a problem, then it is probably *the* solution.

Separable Solutions

Before starting to consider the solution of boundary value problems such as the one
just described, it is useful to build up a 'catalogue' of simple solutions of the linear
partial differential equations under consideration. Although individually these
solutions will only satisfy very special boundary conditions, we shall show that sets of
them can often be combined to solve quite general problems.

For illustration, suppose that T is a function of two independent variables x and y
and satisfies Laplace's equation (4) in two variables

$$\frac{\partial^2 T}{\partial x^2} + \frac{\partial^2 T}{\partial y^2} = 0.$$

First let us look for a trial solution of the form $T = X(x) + Y(y)$ where $X(x)$, $Y(y)$ are
functions of the named variables. Then the equation becomes

$$X''(x) + Y''(y) = 0. \tag{5}$$

Since x and y are independent variables, y may be held fixed and x allowed to vary.
As y is fixed, $Y''(y)$ is a constant. Equation (5) then implies that $X''(x)$ remains
constant for varying values of x. Hence the only possible solutions of this form must
satisfy

$$X''(x) = \text{a constant} = -Y''(y).$$

If the constant is denoted by A, then these solutions are

$$X(x) = \tfrac{1}{2}Ax^2 + Bx + C, \quad Y(y) = -\tfrac{1}{2}Ay^2 + Dy + E,$$

where A, B, C, D, E are arbitrary constants. Thus the most general solution of (4) of
the type $T = X(x) + Y(y)$ is

$$T = \tfrac{1}{2}A(x^2 - y^2) + Bx + Dy + C + E. \tag{6}$$

This is a rather narrow class of solutions and will not be considered further.

A much more interesting class of solutions is produced if we seek solutions which
separate into products of the form

$$T = X(x)Y(y). \tag{7}$$

This trial representation is the basis of the method of separation of variables which is
the main technique which will be employed in this chapter. When equation (7) is
substituted into equation (4), the differential equation becomes

$$X''(x)Y(y) + X(x)Y''(y) = 0$$

which is equivalent to

$$\frac{X''(x)}{X(x)} = -\frac{Y''(y)}{Y(y)}, \tag{8}$$

whenever $T = X(x)Y(y)$ is non-zero. Now, by holding y constant and allowing x to
vary and applying the arguments used on equation (5), we can conclude that $X(x)$ and

$Y(y)$ must satisfy the equations

$$\frac{X''(x)}{X(x)} = \text{a constant} = -\frac{Y''(y)}{Y(y)}. \tag{9}$$

The constant occurring in these relations is arbitrary and may be positive, negative or zero. We examine each case separately.

When the constant is positive it can be written as p^2, where p is an arbitrary positive constant, and equations (9) become

$$X''(x) = p^2 X(x), \quad Y''(y) = -p^2 Y(y).$$

These are homogeneous linear second-order ordinary differential equations with the solutions (see §1.5)

$$X(x) = ae^{px} + be^{-px}, \quad Y(y) = c \cos py + d \sin py$$

where a, b, c, d are arbitrary constants. Hence from the assumption that $T = X(x)Y(y)$ we see that possible forms for $T(x, y)$ are

$$e^{px} \cos py, \quad e^{px} \sin py, \quad e^{-px} \cos py, \quad e^{-px} \sin py$$

where each term may be multiplied by an arbitrary constant. These solutions display an exponential increase or decrease in the x variable and a periodic behaviour in the y variable. Since Laplace's equation is linear and homogeneous, a linear combination of these solutions

$$T = Ae^{px} \cos py + Be^{px} \sin py + Ce^{-px} \cos py + De^{-px} \sin py \tag{10}$$

where A, B, C, D are arbitrary constants, is also a solution of Laplace's equation.

When the constant is negative it can be written as $-p^2$ and equations (9) become

$$X''(x) = -p^2 X(x), \quad Y''(y) = p^2 Y(y),$$

leading to solutions of the form

$$T = \cos px(Ae^{py} + Be^{-py}) + \sin px(Ce^{py} + De^{-py}), \tag{11}$$

where A, B, C, D are arbitrary constants. These solutions are periodic in x and exponential in y.

When the constant in equation (9) is zero the basic equations are simply $X''(x) = 0$, $Y''(y) = 0$. Then $X(x) = ax + b$, $Y(y) = cy + d$ and the linear combination of these solutions is of the form

$$T = Axy + Bx + Cy + D \tag{12}$$

where A, B, C, D are arbitrary constants.

Thus, the assumption that the solution separates into a product yields the broad classes of solutions to equation (4) given in equations (10), (11) and (12). It is important to note that not only are A, B, C, D arbitrary constants, but p also is an arbitrary positive constant and may be chosen to satisfy the boundary conditions in a particular problem. These solutions are further examined in §7.6, which discusses Laplace's equation.

Exercises

1. Classify the following differential equations, giving their order and stating whether they are linear or non-linear, homogeneous or inhomogeneous:

(a) $\dfrac{\partial^2 \theta}{\partial x^2} = 3 \dfrac{\partial \theta}{\partial t}$,

(b) $\dfrac{\partial^2 \theta}{\partial x^2} = 4\theta \dfrac{\partial \theta}{\partial t}$,

(c) $\dfrac{\partial^2 \theta}{\partial x^2} = 3 \dfrac{\partial \theta}{\partial t} + f(x, t)$,

(d) $\dfrac{\partial^2 \theta}{\partial x^2} = 4x \dfrac{\partial \theta}{\partial t}$,

(e) $\left(\dfrac{\partial^2 \theta}{\partial x \partial t} \right)^3 = \theta + f(x, t)$,

where $f(x, t)$ is a known function.

2. Find the separable solutions of the following equations

(a) $\dfrac{\partial \theta}{\partial x} = k \dfrac{\partial \theta}{\partial t}$,

(b) $\dfrac{\partial^2 \theta}{\partial x^2} = \dfrac{\partial \theta}{\partial t}$,

(c) $\dfrac{\partial^2 v}{\partial x^2} = \dfrac{1}{c^2} \dfrac{\partial^2 v}{\partial t^2}$.

7.2 THE ONE-DIMENSIONAL WAVE EQUATION

When the field variable v in the wave equation (1) depends on only one space variable x and on the time t, equation (1) reduces to

$$\frac{\partial^2 v}{\partial x^2} = \frac{1}{c^2} \frac{\partial^2 v}{\partial t^2}. \tag{13}$$

This is referred to as the *one-dimensional wave equation*. It governs both the vibrations in, and the propagation of small amplitude plane waves through uniform solids, liquids and gases, plane electromagnetic waves and numerous other wave phenomena. We shall show only that the equation governs the transverse vibrations of a stretched flexible string. The other interpretations may be found in Coulson [2] and in more specialized texts. In formulating the differential equation corresponding to a particular problem it is necessary to make simplifying assumptions — 'idealizations' — to prevent the resulting equation becoming too complicated. These idealizations should be sufficiently strong to produce a fairly simple differential equation, but sufficiently weak so that the model is still closely related to the physical problem. The simplifying assumptions should also be self-consistent.

For the transverse vibrations of a stretched flexible string, the following assumptions are made:

(a) The mass per unit length of the string is constant and denoted by σ.

(b) The string is elastic but offers no resistance to bending.

(c) The string is stretched between its end points under a sufficiently large tension T_0 so that gravitational effects can be neglected. This tension is assumed to remain constant throughout any vibration.

(d) If the string is taken to be stretched along the x axis between $x = 0$ and $x = a$, then the point of the string at $(x, 0, 0)$ is assumed to be displaced transversely to the positions $(x, v(x, t), 0)$ during the motion. We shall assume that both the transverse displacement $v(x, t)$ and the slope $\partial v/\partial x$ at any point of the string are sufficiently small so that their squares and products may be neglected.

These assumptions are such that we might expect the resulting equations to model adequately the small transverse vibrations of a flexible string under a large tension. If some or all of these idealizations do not hold even approximately, the resulting equations will be inappropriate.

Consider the equations of motion of a small portion of the string that originally lay along the x axis between x and $x + \delta x$, as shown in Fig. 7.1. For the purely transverse motion, the equations of motion in the y and x directions give

$$-T_1 \sin \psi + T_2 \sin(\psi + \delta \psi) = \sigma \, \delta x \, \frac{\partial^2 v}{\partial t^2},$$

$$-T_1 \cos \psi + T_2 \cos(\psi + \delta \psi) = 0.$$

The non-zero right-hand side is the mass of the element multiplied by the acceleration (neglecting product terms). Since $\tan \psi = \partial v/\partial x$, by assumption (d),

$$\cos \psi = \left\{1 + \left(\frac{\partial v}{\partial x}\right)^2\right\}^{-1/2} \simeq 1, \quad \sin \psi = \frac{\partial v}{\partial x} \left\{1 + \left(\frac{\partial v}{\partial x}\right)^2\right\}^{-1/2} \simeq \frac{\partial v}{\partial x}(x, t),$$

and

$$\cos(\psi + \delta \psi) \simeq 1, \quad \sin(\psi + \delta \psi) \simeq \frac{\partial v}{\partial x}(x + \delta x, t),$$

to within second degree terms in $\partial v/\partial x$. Thus the second equation of motion becomes

$$-T_1 + T_2 = 0.$$

This result is consistent with assumption (c). Putting $T_1 = T_2 = T_0$, the first equation

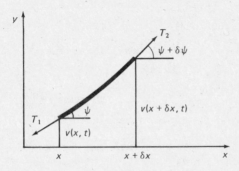

Fig. 7.1   Forces acting on an element of a vibrating string

becomes

$$T_0 \left(\frac{\partial v}{\partial x}(x + \delta x, t) - \frac{\partial v}{\partial x}(x, t) \right) = \sigma \, \delta x \, \frac{\partial^2 v}{\partial t^2} \, .$$

On dividing by δx and taking the limit as $\delta x \to 0$, we obtain the equation

$$T_0 \frac{\partial^2 v}{\partial x^2} = \sigma \frac{\partial^2 v}{\partial t^2} \, .$$

Thus the transverse displacement $v(x, t)$ of a stretched string is governed by the one-dimensional wave equation (13) in which the wave speed c is equal to $(T_0/\sigma)^{1/2}$. That is, the wave speed depends upon the tension in the string divided by its mass per unit length.

Standing Waves

There are two main methods of solution of the wave equation. The method of separation of variables yields *standing wave* solutions and is considered first. A general solution of the wave equation can also be found in terms of propagating waves and this will be considered later. It should be appreciated that a properly posed problem will yield a unique solution no matter which technique is followed.

Let us look for a separated solution of the wave equation

$$\frac{\partial^2 v}{\partial x^2} = \frac{1}{c^2} \frac{\partial^2 v}{\partial t^2} \tag{14}$$

of the form $v = X(x)T(t)$, where $X(x)$ and $T(t)$ are functions of x and t respectively. Substitution into equation (14) gives

$$\frac{X''(x)}{X(x)} = \frac{1}{c^2} \frac{T''(t)}{T(t)} \, .$$

By arguing that the right-hand side is a function of t and hence remains constant as the independent variable x changes, we obtain

$$\frac{X''(x)}{X(x)} = \text{a constant} = \frac{1}{c^2} \frac{T''(t)}{T(t)} \, . \tag{15}$$

If the constant is given the positive value p^2, the equations for $X(x)$ and $T(t)$ are

$$X''(x) = p^2 X(x), \qquad T''(t) = c^2 p^2 T(t).$$

These ordinary differential equations have the exponential solutions

$$X(x) = A e^{px} + B e^{-px}, \qquad T(t) = C e^{cpt} + D e^{-cpt}, \tag{16}$$

where A, B, C, D are arbitrary constants. Such solutions are not too realistic in vibration problems as they imply that $v = X(x)T(t)$ behaves exponentially in both the distance x and the time t.

If the constant is given the negative value $-p^2$, equations (15) become

$$X''(x) = -p^2 X(x), \quad T''(t) = -p^2 c^2 T(t).$$

These equations yield the periodic solutions

$$X(x) = A \cos px + B \sin px, \quad T(t) = C \cos pct + D \sin pct \qquad (17)$$

where A, B, C, D are arbitrary constants. In this case $v = X(x)T(t)$ is periodic in both the distance x and the time t.

The constant p in solutions (16) and (17) may be restricted to be positive without loss of generality.

The case when the constant in (15) is zero yields the solutions

$$X(x) = Ax + B, \quad T(t) = Ct + D. \qquad (18)$$

Vibrations of a Stretched String

Let us now use these solutions to determine the transverse displacement $v(x, t)$ of a stretched string with its ends $x = 0$ and $x = a$ held fixed so that $v = 0$ at both $x = 0$ and $x = a$ for all time t. Suppose that the string is held at rest in the displaced configuration

$$v = f(x), \quad 0 \leqslant x \leqslant a$$

for times $t < 0$ and at $t = 0$ is released from rest in this position. The mathematical problem consists of solving the wave equation (14) subject to the boundary conditions

$$v(0, t) = 0, \quad v(a, t) = 0, \quad \text{for all} \quad t \geqslant 0, \qquad (19)$$

on the ends of the string, and the initial conditions which hold at $t = 0$:

$$v(x, 0) = f(x) \quad \text{(given initial displacement)},$$
$$\frac{\partial v}{\partial t}(x, 0) = 0 \quad \text{(zero initial velocity)}. \qquad (20)$$

Separable solutions $v = X(x)T(t)$ satisfy the boundary conditions (19) when

$$X(0)T(t) = 0, \quad X(a)T(t) = 0$$

for all values of t, which can imply only that

$$X(0) = 0, \quad X(a) = 0. \qquad (21)$$

Let us see which of the possible sets of solutions (16), (17) or (18) can be made to satisfy the separated boundary conditions (21). Substituting $X(x)$ from (16) gives

$$A + B = 0, \quad Ae^{pa} + Be^{-pa} = 0.$$

Since $e^{pa} - e^{-pa}$ is always non-zero for $p \neq 0$, these equations imply that $A = 0$ and $B = 0$ and hence $X(x) \equiv 0$. Also, substituting $X(x)$ from (18) into (21) again yields $A = 0, B = 0$ and hence $X(x) \equiv 0$. Consequently, as suspected, solutions (16) and (18) are useless in this vibration problem.

The remaining solution is equation (17). On substituting it into equation (21) we find that $A = 0$, $B \sin pa = 0$. Clearly, if B is taken to be zero, the solution degenerates to $X(x) \equiv 0$. Consequently a non-zero solution is possible only if the arbitrary positive constant p is chosen to satisfy the equation

$$\sin pa = 0. \tag{22}$$

The only positive solutions of this equation are

$$pa = 0, \quad \pi, \quad 2\pi, \quad \ldots,$$

that is

$$pa = n\pi \quad \text{where } n \text{ is an integer.} \tag{23}$$

The equation (22) is usually referred to as the *eigenvalue equation* for the problem and the values of p given by equation (23) are termed the *eigenvalues* of the problem. However, the terms *characteristic equation* and *characteristic roots* are sometimes used. Corresponding to the eigenvalue $p = n\pi/a$, the solution (17) is

$$X(x) = B \sin \frac{n\pi x}{a}, \quad T(t) = C \cos \frac{n\pi ct}{a} + D \sin \frac{n\pi ct}{a}$$

and the displacement $v = X(x)T(t)$ becomes

$$v = \sin \frac{n\pi x}{a} \left(BC \cos \frac{n\pi ct}{a} + BD \sin \frac{n\pi ct}{a} \right).$$

Obviously for each integer n there are only two arbitrary constants BC and BD in this expression. For clarity, these constants may be denoted by C_n and D_n, where the suffix n indicates that these arbitrary constants may take different values for $n = 1, 2, 3$, etc. Thus each of the functions

$$v = v_n(x, t) = \sin \frac{n\pi x}{a} \left(C_n \cos \frac{n\pi ct}{a} + D_n \sin \frac{n\pi ct}{a} \right) \tag{24}$$

for $n = 1, 2, 3, \ldots$, is a possible mode of vibration of the string. The displacement (24) is referred to as the *n*th *eigenfunction* or *n*th *normal mode* of the vibrating string. Note that the normal mode corresponding to $n = 0$ is $v = 0$ and the normal modes corresponding to negative integers can be omitted as they are identical to those which correspond to the positive integers.

The *n*th normal mode vibrates with a period of $2a/nc$ seconds which corresponds to a frequency of $nc/2a$ cycles per second. Since $c^2 = T_0/\sigma$, the frequency is

$$\frac{n}{2a} \left(\frac{T_0}{\sigma} \right)^{1/2}.$$

Hence, if a string on a musical instrument is vibrating in a normal mode, its pitch may be sharpened (frequency increased) by either decreasing the length a of the string or increasing the tension T_0 in the string. The first normal mode $n = 1$ vibrates with the lowest frequency $T_0^{1/2}/2a\sigma^{1/2}$ and this is called the *fundamental* frequency of the string. If the string can be made to vibrate in a higher normal mode the frequency is increased by an integer multiple; this corresponds to the production of a musical harmonic or overtone.

For a given normal mode at the instant $t = t_0$, the shape of the string is the sine curve represented by equation (24) with t replaced by t_0. The shape functions of the first four normal modes, together with their frequencies, are shown in Fig. 7.2. Also,

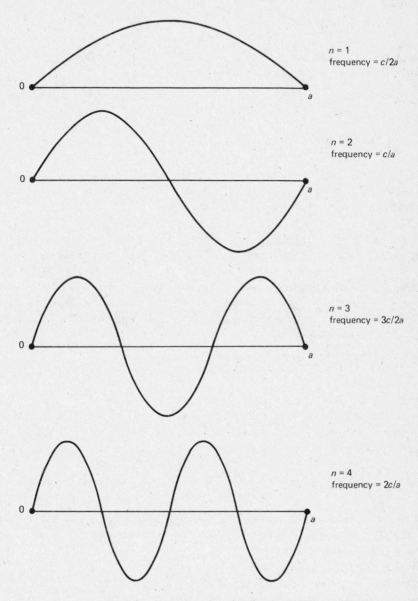

$n = 1$
frequency $= c/2a$

$n = 2$
frequency $= c/a$

$n = 3$
frequency $= 3c/2a$

$n = 4$
frequency $= 2c/a$

Fig. 7.2   Normal modes of a vibrating string

equation (24) shows that the point $x = x_0$ of the string undergoes a periodic transverse oscillation with amplitude $(C_n^2 + D_n^2)^{1/2} \sin(n\pi x_0/a)$.

Clearly, a single normal mode $v_n(x, t)$ does not contain sufficient generality to satisfy the initial conditions (20). However, the wave equation is linear and homogeneous so that a sum of a finite number of normal modes will also satisfy the wave equation (14) and the boundary conditions (19). Consider the infinite sum of all normal modes

$$v(x, t) = \sum_{n=1}^{\infty} v_n(x, t) = \sum_{n=1}^{\infty} \left(C_n \cos \frac{n\pi ct}{a} + D_n \sin \frac{n\pi ct}{a} \right) \sin \frac{n\pi x}{a}. \tag{25}$$

If this is to match the initial conditions, then the constants C_n and D_n must satisfy the equations corresponding to the initial displacement (20)

$$v(x, 0) = \sum_{n=1}^{\infty} C_n \sin \frac{n\pi x}{a} = f(x), \quad 0 \leqslant x \leqslant a, \tag{26}$$

and the initial velocity

$$\frac{\partial v}{\partial t}(x, 0) = \sum_{n=1}^{\infty} \frac{n\pi c}{a} D_n \sin \frac{n\pi x}{a} = 0, \quad 0 \leqslant x \leqslant a.$$

Clearly the second equation may be satisfied by putting $D_n = 0$ for $n = 1, 2, 3, \ldots$. The first equation can be satisfied only if it is possible to represent the known function $f(x)$ over the range $0 \leqslant x \leqslant a$ by the series in equation (26). This series has the form of a half-range Fourier sine series (see §2.4). Now $f(x)$ is the initial displacement of the string and so is defined and continuous in $0 \leqslant x \leqslant a$, and satisfies the boundary conditions $f(0) = 0$, $f(a) = 0$. The theory of Fourier series described in Chapter 2 shows that it is possible to represent $f(x)$ by the series in equation (26). In addition the constants C_n may be found by applying the Euler formulae (equations (18) of §2.4), and are given by

$$C_n = \frac{2}{a} \int_0^a f(x) \sin \frac{n\pi x}{a} dx, \quad n = 1, 2, 3, \ldots . \tag{27}$$

Thus the displacement of the string at all times $t \geqslant 0$ is

$$v = \sum_{n=1}^{\infty} C_n \sin \frac{n\pi x}{a} \cos \frac{n\pi ct}{a} \tag{28}$$

where the C_n are given by equation (27).

Of course, this solution is formal and the convergence of the series in equation (28) and of its partial derivatives must be examined before it can be proved that equation (28) satisfies equation (14), and that it is the only solution of the wave equation (14) subject to the boundary conditions (19) and the initial conditions (20). It can be shown that if the second derivatives of the initial shape $f(x)$ exist in $0 \leqslant x \leqslant a$, the solution is valid. In fact, even if $f''(x)$ does not exist at certain points, for example where the string has kinks, the solution is still 'good' but care should be exercised when manipulating the differentiated Fourier series.

It is interesting to observe that we can sum the series in equation (28). Since, for any angles A and B,

$$2 \sin A \cos B = \sin(A + B) + \sin(A - B),$$

the series becomes

$$v = \sum_{n=1}^{\infty} \tfrac{1}{2} C_n \sin \frac{n\pi(x + ct)}{a} + \sum_{n=1}^{\infty} \tfrac{1}{2} C_n \sin \frac{n\pi(x - ct)}{a}.$$

As C_n satisfies equation (27), it is clear that each of these series is simply the Fourier sine series for the function $\tfrac{1}{2} f$ evaluated at $x + ct$ and $x - ct$ respectively. Hence the solution is

$$v = \tfrac{1}{2} [f(x + ct) + f(x - ct)].$$

Again this is a formal solution because the function f is not defined at $x + ct$ and $x - ct$ for values of $x \pm ct$ outside the range $0 \leqslant x \pm ct \leqslant a$. However, the half-range Fourier sine series in equation (26) generates the odd periodic extension of $f(x)$ of period $2a$ (see §2.4), denoted by $f_0(x)$ and illustrated on Fig. 7.3. Consequently the solution for all x and t in $0 \leqslant x \leqslant a$, $t \geqslant 0$ is simply

$$v = \tfrac{1}{2} [f_0(x + ct) + f_0(x - ct)]. \tag{29}$$

An interpretation of this neat solution will be given later.

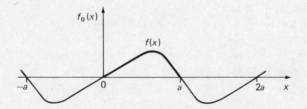

Fig. 7.3   Odd periodic extension of $f(x)$

EXAMPLE 1
Suppose the string is released from rest in the displaced configuration $f(x) = x(a - x)$, then it is easily confirmed by an integration by parts that equation (27) gives

$$C_n = \frac{4a^2}{n^3 \pi^3} \{1 - (-1)^n\}.$$

Hence the solution is

$$v = \sum_{n=1}^{\infty} \frac{4a^2 \{1 - (-1)^n\}}{n^3 \pi^3} \sin \frac{n\pi x}{a} \cos \frac{n\pi ct}{a}$$

$$= \frac{8a^2}{\pi^3} \left(\sin \frac{\pi x}{a} \cos \frac{\pi ct}{a} + \frac{1}{27} \sin \frac{3\pi x}{a} \cos \frac{3\pi ct}{a} + \frac{1}{125} \sin \frac{5\pi x}{a} \cos \frac{5\pi ct}{a} + \ldots \right).$$

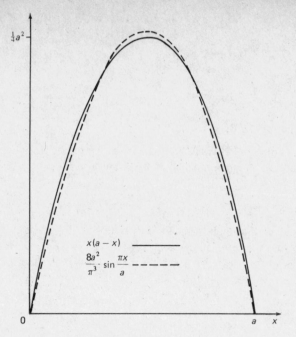

Fig. 7.4   Comparison of $x(a - x)$ and $\dfrac{8a^2}{\pi^3} \sin \dfrac{\pi x}{a}$

It is evident that the first term has an appreciably larger amplitude than the other terms. Hence the response of the string is dominated by the first term, so that the string almost adopts the shape $\sin \pi x/a$ and oscillates with the fundamental frequency $2a/c$, as indicated in Fig. 7.4.

Boundary Conditions and Initial Conditions

It will be appreciated that the boundary conditions (19) and the initial conditions (20) are independent of each other and influence the solution in quite distinct ways. The boundary conditions alone determine the form of the normal modes (eigenfunctions) and the natural frequencies (eigenvalues) of the system. For example, let us replace the boundary conditions (19) by

$$v(0, t) = 0, \quad \frac{\partial v}{\partial x}(a, t) = 0, \quad \text{all } t \geqslant 0, \tag{30}$$

so that the string is held fixed at $x = 0$ but vibrates with a horizontal tangent at $x = a$. [This could be achieved by attaching the end $x = a$ by a ring to a frictionless wire held parallel to the y axis at $x = a$, see Fig. 7.5] On looking for a separated solution $v = X(x)T(t)$ of the wave equation and these new boundary conditions, we find that $X(x)$ must satisfy the conditions

$$X(0) = 0 \quad \text{and} \quad X'(a) = 0.$$

Fig. 7.5   Boundary conditions $v(0, t) = 0$ and $\dfrac{\partial v}{\partial x}(a, t) = 0$

Of the set of separated solutions (16), (17) and (18), only equations (17) yield a non-zero solution for $X(x)$. In this case the constants satisfy $A = 0$ and $Bp \cos pa = 0$. Hence, for a non-zero solution, p must satisfy the eigenvalue equation $\cos pa = 0$. This has the positive solutions

$$pa = \pi/2, 3\pi/2, 5\pi/2, \ldots,$$

so that $p = (2n + 1)\pi/2a$, where n is an integer. Thus the normal modes are

$$v = \sin \frac{(2n + 1)\pi x}{2a} \left(C_n \cos \frac{(2n + 1)\pi ct}{2a} + D_n \sin \frac{(2n + 1)\pi ct}{2a} \right), \tag{31}$$

where n is an integer. It will be appreciated that these normal modes are of a different functional form from the normal modes (24) which correspond to the different boundary conditions (19). The frequencies $(2n + 1)c/4a$ of equation (31) also differ from the frequencies of equation (24), the fundamental being $c/4a$ as compared with a fundamental of $c/2a$ for equation (24). The form of each normal mode depends entirely on the boundary conditions and is independent of the initial conditions.

In the original problem specified by equations (19) and (20), the initial conditions (20) merely determined the constants C_n, D_n which occurred in the sum of the normal modes (25). If the displacement v is regarded as being a sum of normal modes with shape functions $\sin(n\pi x/a)$ and periodic time-dependent amplitudes

$$C_n \cos \frac{n\pi ct}{a} + D_n \sin \frac{n\pi ct}{a},$$

then the initial conditions specify the amplitude factors.

So far we have considered only initial conditions of the form (20) in which the initial displacement is taken to be non-zero and the initial velocity is zero. It is apparent that if the initial velocity is non-zero, say $\partial v/\partial t = g(x)$ when $t = 0$, the mathematical difficulties are not increased but the constants D_n, instead of being zero, satisfy

$$\sum_{n=1}^{\infty} \frac{n\pi c}{a} D_n \sin \frac{n\pi x}{a} = g(x), \quad 0 \leqslant x \leqslant a.$$

Again, this is a half-range Fourier sine series representation for $g(x)$ with the constants D_n given by

$$\frac{n\pi c}{a} D_n = \frac{2}{a} \int_0^a g(x) \sin \frac{n\pi x}{a} \, dx. \tag{32}$$

The complete solution may now be determined from the sum of normal modes (25), with the C_n depending on the initial displacement as in equation (27) and the D_n depending on the initial velocity as in equation (32).

Particular examples are given in the exercises at the end of this section.

D'Alembert's Solution

The wave equation (13) may be written in operator notation as

$$\frac{\partial^2 v}{\partial x^2} - \frac{1}{c^2}\frac{\partial^2 v}{\partial t^2} \equiv \left(\frac{\partial}{\partial x} - \frac{1}{c}\frac{\partial}{\partial t}\right)\left(\frac{\partial v}{\partial x} + \frac{1}{c}\frac{\partial v}{\partial t}\right) = 0. \tag{33}$$

This suggests that the combinations $x - ct$ and $x + ct$ may be the natural variables for the solution of this equation. The solution (29) also emphasizes this suggestion. Let us define new variables

$$\xi = x - ct, \quad \eta = x + ct \tag{34}$$

and express the wave equation (33) in terms of them. Using the change of variable formulae from §4.2, equation (33) becomes

$$4\frac{\partial^2 v}{\partial \xi \partial \eta} = 0.$$

Its general solution was found in §7.1 to be

$$v = F(\xi) + G(\eta),$$

where $F(\xi)$ and $G(\eta)$ are arbitrary functions of ξ and η respectively. In terms of x and t this solution becomes

$$v = F(x - ct) + G(x + ct), \tag{35}$$

which is referred to as *D'Alembert's solution* of the wave equation.

The physical interpretation of these terms is quite interesting. Consider the solution $u = F(x - ct)$. If we take a photograph of the displacement $u = F(x)$ at $t = 0$ and compare it with a photograph taken at a subsequent time $t = t'$, then the second picture $u = F(x - ct')$ simply portrays the first picture $u = F(x)$ moved a distance ct' to the right (see Fig. 7.6). Hence $u = F(x - ct)$ represents a wave of profile $u = F(x)$ which is moving to the right along the string with a uniform speed c and an undistorting profile. Similarly the displacement $u = G(x + ct)$ is an undistorting wave moving to the left with speed c. Thus D'Alembert's solution (35) shows that the solution to the wave equation consists of two waves of (arbitrary) profiles $F(x)$ and $G(x)$ which move to the right and to the left with speed c and can pass through each other without distortion or interference. A similar effect is often observed in ripples on a pond. Figure 7.7 illustrates this for two approaching waves of opposite profiles.

D'Alembert's solution (35) is a very convenient representation for progressive waves which travel large distances along a string or through a uniform medium. Let us consider an infinitely long string $-\infty < x < \infty$ and suppose that both the displacement $v(x, 0) = f(x)$ and the velocity $\partial v/\partial t = g(x)$ are specified at the time $t = 0$. Then in

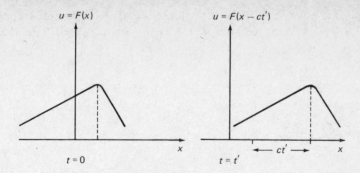

Fig. 7.6   A progressive wave

D'Alembert's solution (35) we find that

$$F(x) + G(x) = f(x)$$
$$- cF'(x) + cG'(x) = g(x)$$

for all values of x. Hence

$$-F(x) + G(x) = \frac{1}{c}\int_0^x g(\zeta)\,\mathrm{d}\zeta + A,$$

and so

$$F(x) = \tfrac{1}{2}\left\{ f(x) - \frac{1}{c}\int_0^x g(\zeta)\,\mathrm{d}\zeta - A \right\},$$

$$G(x) = \tfrac{1}{2}\left\{ f(x) + \frac{1}{c}\int_0^x g(\zeta)\,\mathrm{d}\zeta + A \right\}.$$

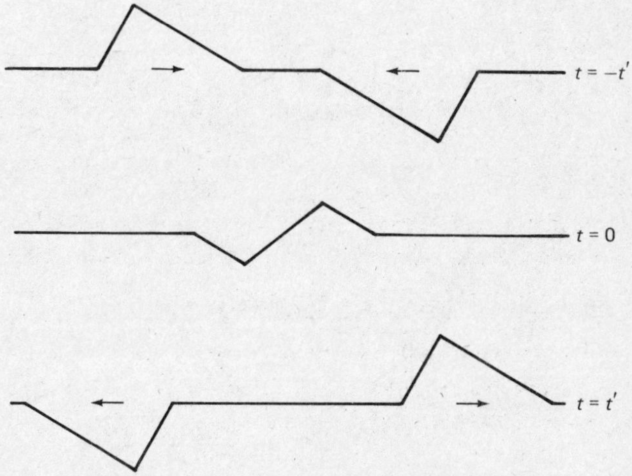

$t = -t'$

$t = 0$

$t = t'$

Fig. 7.7   Waves progressing in opposite directions

Inserting these expressions into equation (35) gives the displacement as

$$v(x, t) = \frac{1}{2}\left\{ f(x - ct) + f(x + ct)\right\} + \frac{1}{2c}\int_{x-ct}^{x+ct} g(\zeta)\, d\zeta. \tag{36}$$

This form enables us to trace how the initial conditions influence the solution. At the point $x = x'$ at time $t = t'$, the displacement $v(x', t')$ in equation (36) depends upon $f(x' - ct')$ and $f(x' + ct')$, which are the initial displacements at the points $x = x' - ct'$ and $x = x' + ct'$, and upon

$$\int_{x'-ct'}^{x'+ct'} g(\zeta)\, d\zeta$$

which is the integral of the velocity over the range $x' - ct' \leqslant x \leqslant x' + ct'$ in the initial conditions. Thus, as expected, the information provided by the initial conditions propagates with the speed c and hence at time $t = t'$ the point $x = x'$ has received the information only from the restricted range $x' - ct' \leqslant x \leqslant x' + ct'$ of the initial conditions. This is illustrated on a space-time diagram in Fig. 7.8.

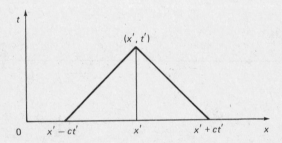

Fig. 7.8   Influence of the initial conditions in equation (36)

Boundary Conditions

Consider a wave $v = F(x - ct)$ propagating to the right along a semi-infinite string $x < 0$. Suppose the string is held at $x = 0$ so that $v = 0$ at $x = 0$ for all time. When the disturbance reaches $x = 0$, a reflected wave $v = G(x + ct)$ must be set up. What is the form of the reflected wave?

The composite wave on the string $x < 0$ is

$$v = F(x - ct) + G(x + ct).$$

The boundary condition at the end $x = 0$ of the string is

$$v(0, t) = F(-ct) + G(ct) = 0$$

for all values of t. Hence $G(\tau) = -F(-\tau)$. Thus the form of the reflected wave is $v = G(x + ct) = -F(-x - ct)$. The total disturbance in $x < 0$ is

$$v = F(x - ct) - F(-x - ct). \tag{37}$$

The exercises at the end of this section illustrate the effect of other boundary conditions on progressive waves.

For problems involving finite bodies and/or multiple reflections, D'Alembert's solution is not as convenient as the solutions produced by the method of separation of variables. Naturally the same solution will be obtained if either method is applied to a properly posed problem, although the algebraic forms in which the solution is expressed may differ. Expressions (28) and (29) illustrate this.

Vibrations of Beams

The basic difference between a beam and a string is that a beam is stiff and resists bending. One of the assumptions which led to the wave equation for transverse vibrations of a string was that there was no resistance to bending. It may be shown that the small bending vibrations of a uniform beam are governed by the fourth-order linear equation

$$\frac{\partial^4 v}{\partial x^4} = -\frac{1}{c^2}\frac{\partial^2 v}{\partial t^2}, \quad c^2 = \frac{EI}{\sigma A} \tag{38}$$

where the x axis lies along the length of the beam, the bending displacement v is in the y direction and the constant c^2 depends on Young's modulus E, the density σ, the cross-sectional area A of the beam, and the second moment of area I of the cross-section about the z direction through the centroid. Separable solutions $v = X(x)T(t)$ of equation (38) must satisfy

$$\frac{X''''(x)}{X(x)} = \text{constant} = -\frac{1}{c^2}\frac{T''(t)}{T(t)}.$$

If the solution is to be periodic in time, the constant must be positive so that

$$X''''(x) = p^4 X(x), \quad T''(t) = -c^2 p^4 T(t),$$

where for convenience the constant is put equal to p^4. Following the methods of Chapter 1, the solutions are found to be

$$X(x) = A \cosh px + B \sinh px + C \cos px + D \sin px,$$
$$T(t) = E \cos p^2 ct + F \sin p^2 ct, \tag{39}$$

where $A, \ldots, F$ are arbitrary constants.

Suppose the beam is of length a, and is 'built-in' at the ends $x = 0$ and $x = a$. Then the boundary conditions are

$$v(0, t) = 0, \quad \frac{\partial v}{\partial x}(0, t) = 0,$$

$$v(a, t) = 0, \quad \frac{\partial v}{\partial x}(a, t) = 0.$$

Substitution of $v = X(x)T(t)$ into these boundary conditions implies that

$$X(0) = 0, \quad X'(0) = 0,$$
$$X(a) = 0, \quad X'(a) = 0.$$

After substituting from equation (39), the following equations are produced:

$$
\begin{aligned}
A \qquad\qquad\qquad + C \qquad\qquad\qquad\qquad &= 0, \\
Bp \qquad\qquad\qquad + Dp \qquad &= 0, \\
A \cosh pa + B \sinh pa + C \cos pa + D \sin pa &= 0, \\
Ap \sinh pa + Bp \cosh pa - Cp \sin pa + Dp \cos pa &= 0.
\end{aligned}
\tag{40}
$$

The equations obtained by the elimination of C and D have a non-zero solution for A and B only if the determinant

$$
\begin{vmatrix}
\cosh pa - \cos pa & \sinh pa - \sin pa \\
\sinh pa + \sin pa & \cosh pa - \cos pa
\end{vmatrix}
$$

is zero (see §8.8). Hence p must be chosen so that

$$(\cosh pa - \cos pa)^2 - \sinh^2 pa + \sin^2 pa = 0,$$

that is

$$\cosh pa \cos pa = 1. \tag{41}$$

This is an eigenvalue equation and determines the values of p, and hence the natural frequencies cp^2 of vibration of the beam. Equation (41) has an infinite number of roots and must be solved numerically (see §9.4). A short table of eigenvalues of equation (41) is given in Abramowitz and Stegun [3], table 4.18. The shape functions for the beam are obtained by solving equation (40) and are

$$(\sinh pa - \sin pa)(\cosh px - \cos px) - (\cosh pa - \cos pa)(\sinh px - \sin px),$$

where p satisfies equation (41). Further information regarding vibrations of beams and plates may be found in the article by Stokey [4].

Exercises

1. A string is fixed at $x = 0$ and $x = a$ and lies initially along the x axis. If it is set in motion by giving all points $0 < x < a$ a constant transverse velocity $\partial v / \partial t = V_0$ at $t = 0$, use the expression (25) to show that the subsequent motion is given by

$$v = \sum_{n=1}^{\infty} \frac{2 V_0 a}{n^2 \pi^2 c} \{1 - (-1)^n\} \sin \frac{n \pi x}{a} \sin \frac{n \pi c t}{a}.$$

2. If the initial conditions for the string in exercise 1 are changed to

$$v(x, 0) = \begin{cases} \epsilon x & \text{in} \quad 0 \leqslant x \leqslant \tfrac{1}{4}a, \\ \epsilon(a - x) & \text{in} \quad \tfrac{1}{2}a \leqslant x \leqslant a, \end{cases}$$

and the string is released from rest in this position, determine the displacement at any subsequent time.

3. Show that the solutions of exercises 1 and 2 are identical when $\epsilon = V_0/c$ and the time in exercise 2 is measured from an instant $3a/2c$ seconds after the start of the motion.

   By using the solution (29), confirm that the string takes up the configurations shown in Fig. 7.9.

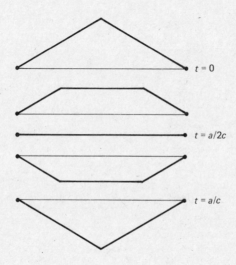

Fig. 7.9   The vibrating string of exercise 2

4. If the boundary conditions at the ends of a vibrating string are

$$\frac{\partial v}{\partial x}(0, t) = 0, \qquad \frac{\partial v}{\partial x}(a, t) = 0,$$

show that the normal modes are

$$\cos\frac{n\pi x}{a}\left(A_n \cos\frac{n\pi ct}{a} + B_n \sin\frac{n\pi ct}{a}\right)$$

where n is an integer.

5. (a)   If the wave

$$v = \begin{cases} a \sin m(x - ct), & x < ct, \\ \\ 0, & x \geqslant ct, \end{cases}$$

propagates along a semi-infinite string $-\infty \leqslant x < 0$ which is held so that $v = 0$ at $x = 0$ for all $t > 0$, find the form of the reflected wave.

(b)   If the boundary condition at $x = 0$ is $\partial v/\partial x = 0$ for all time, find the form of the reflected wave. Find the nearest point to the end $x = 0$ at which the string does not vibrate.

6. Equation (38) governs the transverse vibrations of a uniform cantilever beam. If the beam is clamped at $x = 0$ and free at $x = a$, the boundary conditions are

$$v(0, t) = 0, \qquad \frac{\partial v}{\partial x}(0, t) = 0,$$

$$\frac{\partial^2 v}{\partial x^2}(a, t) = 0, \qquad \frac{\partial^3 v}{\partial x^3}(a, t) = 0,$$

for all t. Show that the natural frequencies $m^2 c$ are determined by the roots of

$$\cosh ma \cos ma = -1.$$

By sketching $\cosh ma \cos ma$ as a function of m, show that this equation has an infinite number of positive roots.

7.3 THE METHOD OF SEPARATION OF VARIABLES

The method of separation of variables was introduced in §7.1 in connection with Laplace's equation in two variables, and was employed in §7.2 to obtain solutions to the one-dimensional wave equation. Since it is of great use in the solution of linear partial differential equations and will be employed later in this chapter it is worth enumerating its steps with reference to the example on the vibrations of a stretched string detailed in the previous section. The problem was to solve the wave equation (14) subject to the boundary conditions (19) and the initial conditions (20). The method consists of the following steps:

(a) Find all separated solutions of the basic equation in the chosen coordinate system. For equation (14) these are equations (16), (17) and (18).

(b) Match these solutions with the homogeneous boundary conditions (19). In general this will lead to an eigenvalue problem for one of the arbitrary constants and to the selection of a particular set of separated solutions, referred to as the eigenfunctions. In the case of equation (14) the boundary conditions (19) eliminated the separated solutions (16) and (18) and led to the eigenvalue equation (22) for the constant p occurring in the solution (17). As a consequence the set of eigenfunctions (normal modes) (24) were generated.

(c) Form a linear combination of the set of eigenfunctions and use this to match with the initial conditions (and/or any remaining boundary conditions). Usually it is this step which is the most difficult to perform mathematically. In §7.2 the linear combination of eigenfunctions is the series in equation (25), and matching with the initial conditions leads to the Fourier series determined by equation (26).

The method of separation of variables may be applied only to a *homogeneous* linear partial differential equation. The approach for inhomogeneous equations is outlined in §7.8. In addition, the boundary conditions should be linear in the dependent variable v and its derivatives. When a linear combination of v and its derivatives is specified to be non-zero on a part of the boundary, it is called an *inhomogeneous* boundary condition. When the linear combination is specified to be zero, it is called a *homogeneous* boundary condition. For example, the boundary condition $v + 2(\partial v/\partial x) = 0$ on $x = 0$ is homogeneous whilst the condition $v = 100$ on $x = 0$ is inhomogeneous. Linear homogeneous boundary conditions such as (19) are required to construct the eigenfunctions.

In problems for the wave equation or the heat conduction equation there is little difficulty in distinguishing the boundary conditions from the initial conditions and often the boundary conditions are homogeneous. If the boundary conditions are inhomogeneous, it is necessary to find a suitable particular solution in order to modify the problem so that it becomes one having homogeneous conditions. This technique is illustrated for the heat conduction equation in §7.5.

The natural problems for Laplace's equation involve boundary conditions specified at all boundary points and no initial conditions. In this case homogeneous boundary conditions over a part or parts of the boundary should be used to generate the eigenfunctions as in (b), and the remaining boundary conditions may then be satisfied as in (c). It is often necessary to split a problem into several subproblems to produce the homogeneous boundary conditions necessary to carry out this operation. Examples are given in §7.6.

For problems which involve two or three space dimensions it is possible to apply the method of separation of variables only to a linear problem in a suitably shaped region. It is necessary to choose a system of coordinates so that some coordinate lines or surfaces coincide with the boundary of the region, and look for separable solutions in terms of these coordinates. The natural coordinate system for a rectangular region is a cartesian coordinate system, and for a cylindrical or spherical region, cylindrical or spherical polar coordinates. Except in a few special cases, boundary-value problems for a region with a less regular shape may only be solved numerically. Some numerical methods are described in Chapter 7 of Volume 2.

7.4 THE WAVE EQUATION

Solutions of the three-dimensional wave equation (1)

$$\frac{\partial^2 v}{\partial x^2} + \frac{\partial^2 v}{\partial y^2} + \frac{\partial^2 v}{\partial z^2} = \frac{1}{c^2}\frac{\partial^2 v}{\partial t^2} \tag{42}$$

in cartesian coordinates x, y, z and time t have a behaviour and properties which are very similar to those of the one-dimensional wave equation discussed in §7.2. Equation (42) governs a wide variety of wave and vibration phenomena.

Plane Waves

It is natural to enquire whether the wave equation (42) possesses solutions similar to D'Alembert's general solution (35) of the one-dimensional wave equation. Consider $v = F(lx + my + nz - ct)$ where F is an arbitrary differentiable function, l, m, n are arbitrary constants and c is the wave speed. This form satisfies the wave equation (42) whenever

$$l^2 + m^2 + n^2 = 1,$$

so that l, m, n may be interpreted as direction cosines. Similarly it may be confirmed that $v = G(lx + my + nz + ct)$ also satisfies equation (42), when l, m, n are direction cosines. These solutions represent plane waves moving in opposite senses along the direction of the unit vector $\mathbf{n} = l\mathbf{i} + m\mathbf{j} + n\mathbf{k}$.

Consider the equation $lx + my + nz - p = 0$. This represents a plane with the unit normal $\mathbf{n} = l\mathbf{i} + m\mathbf{j} + n\mathbf{k}$. The line through the origin along the unit normal direction $\mathbf{n}$ intersects the plane at a distance p from the origin. Suppose the point of intersection moves along the normal line with a speed c and passed through the origin at $t = 0$, so that $p = ct$, then a plane moving along its fixed normal direction $\mathbf{n}$ with the speed c is given by the equation $lx + my + nz - ct = 0$. The surface $lx + my + nz - ct = \xi$, where ξ is a constant, represents the parallel plane (moving with speed c along the normal direction $\mathbf{n}$) which passed through the origin at the time $t = -\xi/c$.

Consider the solution

$$v = F(lx + my + nz - ct) = F(\xi).$$

We shall see that this corresponds to a wave of profile $F(\xi)$. The part of the wave corresponding to $\xi = \xi_0$ with the 'signal' $v = F(\xi_0)$ is carried by the surfaces $lx + my + nz - ct = \xi_0$. Consequently all points on the moving plane which passed through the origin at the time $t = -\xi_0/c$ and which moves along its normal direction $\mathbf{n}$ with the speed c, carry the same signal $v = F(\xi_0)$. This gives rise to the name plane waves.

At a fixed position (x_0, y_0, z_0) in space, the signals $v = F(lx_0 + my_0 + nz_0 - ct)$ are received as t varies. This corresponds to a wave train of signals $v = F(\xi)$ passing this point as $\xi = lx_0 + my_0 + nz_0 - ct$ varies with the time t.

A similar interpretation is possible for the solution $v = G(lx + my + nz + ct)$ which corresponds to a plane wave of arbitrary profile moving with speed c along the direction $-\mathbf{n}$. Note also that the direction $\mathbf{n}$ of propagation of these plane waves is arbitrary and that any superposition of plane waves also satisfies the wave equation.

Vibrations of Membranes

Many vibration problems for continuous media give rise to the wave equation (42). The simplest of these are the elastic string problems discussed in §7.2. The generalization to plate vibrations is straightforward. We refer to a thin plate with a zero bending stiffness as a membrane. The transverse vibrations of a membrane stretched over a plane frame under an all-round tension satisfy

$$\frac{\partial^2 v}{\partial x^2} + \frac{\partial^2 v}{\partial y^2} = \frac{1}{c^2}\frac{\partial^2 v}{\partial t^2} \tag{43}$$

where the plane of the frame is $z = 0$, and the displacement of the membrane normal to the plane $z = 0$ is $v(x, y, t)$. The wave speed c is given by $c^2 = T_0/\sigma$ where T_0 is the all-round tension and σ is the mass per unit area of the membrane. To illustrate the nature of the mathematical problems, we shall discuss the vibrations of both rectangular and circular membranes.

Rectangular Membrane

Consider a rectangular membrane $0 \leqslant x \leqslant a, 0 \leqslant y \leqslant b$ which is stretched over a rectangular frame under an all-round tension, and which is clamped around its edges so that the boundary conditions are

$$\begin{aligned} v(0, y, t) = 0, \quad v(a, y, t) = 0, \\ v(x, 0, t) = 0, \quad v(x, b, t) = 0. \end{aligned} \tag{44}$$

Following the methods of §7.2, let us look for separated solutions of the form $v = X(x)Y(y)T(t)$. Then the first two boundary conditions (44) become

$$X(0)Y(y)T(t) = 0, \quad X(a)Y(y)T(t) = 0$$

for all values of y in the range $0 \leqslant y \leqslant b$ and all $t \geqslant 0$. If $Y(y)T(t) = 0$ for all possible values of y and t, then the displacement v is always zero. Since this is not the case, the first two conditions of (44) imply that

$$X(0) = 0, \quad X(a) = 0.$$

Similarly the second two boundary conditions (44) separate into

$$Y(0) = 0, \quad Y(b) = 0.$$

On substituting the separated solution $v = X(x)Y(y)T(t)$ into the wave equation (43), we find that

$$\frac{X''(x)}{X(x)} + \frac{Y''(y)}{Y(y)} = \frac{1}{c^2}\frac{T''(t)}{T(t)}.$$

Since x, y and t are independent variables each of these terms is a constant. Thus

$$\frac{X''(x)}{X(x)} = \lambda, \quad \frac{Y''(y)}{Y(y)} = \mu, \quad \frac{T''(t)}{T(t)} = c^2(\lambda + \mu). \tag{45}$$

As in §7.2, the solution of equation (45) for $X(x)$ can satisfy the boundary conditions $X(0) = 0, X(a) = 0$ only if λ is a negative constant. Hence we set $\lambda = -p^2$. The boundary conditions then require, as in §7.2, that $\sin pa = 0$. Thus $pa = n\pi$, where n is an integer, and $X(x)$ is a constant multiple of $\sin(n\pi x/a)$. Similarly $Y(y)$ can satisfy the separated boundary conditions $Y(0) = 0$, $Y(b) = 0$ only when $\mu = -q^2$ and $qb = m\pi$, where m is an integer. Thus $Y(y)$ is a multiple of $\sin(m\pi y/b)$, and the shape function $X(x)Y(y)$ for a normal mode is proportional to $\sin(n\pi x/a)\sin(m\pi y/b)$ where m and n are integers. The corresponding time variation from equation (45) satisfies

$$T''(t) = -c^2(p^2 + q^2)T(t) \quad \text{where} \quad p = n\pi/a, \quad q = m\pi/b.$$

Consequently $T(t)$ consists of sines and cosines of $c\left(\dfrac{n^2}{a^2} + \dfrac{m^2}{b^2}\right)^{1/2} \pi t$. The normal modes (eigenfunctions) are therefore

$$v = \sin\frac{n\pi x}{a}\sin\frac{m\pi y}{b}\left\{A\sin c\left(\frac{n^2}{a^2} + \frac{m^2}{b^2}\right)^{1/2}\pi t + B\cos c\left(\frac{n^2}{a^2} + \frac{m^2}{b^2}\right)^{1/2}\pi t\right\}$$

for integer values of n and m. The natural frequency for the n, mth normal mode is $\dfrac{c}{2}\left(\dfrac{n^2}{a^2} + \dfrac{m^2}{b^2}\right)^{1/2}$. The fundamental frequency is $\dfrac{c}{2}\left(\dfrac{1}{a^2} + \dfrac{1}{b^2}\right)^{1/2}$ and corresponds to the $n = 1$, $m = 1$ normal mode.

It will be noticed that these frequencies are all higher than those for an elastic string of length a with the same wave speed c. The string frequencies $cn/2a$ are attained in the plate as the dimension $b \to \infty$, that is, when the plate resembles a long strip. Why are they not attained as $b \to 0$?

The nature of the vibration is determined completely only when the initial conditions are prescribed. As an example consider initial conditions similar to those given by equation (20), namely a given initial displacement $v(x, y, 0) = f(x, y)$ and zero initial velocity, $\partial v/\partial t = 0$. To match these initial conditions we assume the displacement can be expressed as a linear combination of all of the normal modes, thus

$$v = \sum_{n=1}^{\infty} \sum_{m=1}^{\infty} \sin\frac{n\pi x}{a}\sin\frac{m\pi y}{b}\left\{A_{mn}\cos c\left(\frac{n^2}{a^2} + \frac{m^2}{b^2}\right)^{1/2}\pi t\right.$$

$$\left. + B_{mn}\sin c\left(\frac{n^2}{a^2} + \frac{m^2}{b^2}\right)^{1/2}\pi t\right\}$$

where A_{mn}, B_{mn} are arbitrary constants for $m = 1, 2, 3, \ldots, n = 1, 2, 3, \ldots$. The initial conditions are satisfied if

$$\sum_{n=1}^{\infty} \sum_{m=1}^{\infty} A_{mn}\sin\frac{n\pi x}{a}\sin\frac{m\pi y}{b} = f(x, y), \quad 0 \leqslant x \leqslant a, \quad 0 \leqslant y \leqslant b, \tag{46}$$

and $B_{mn} = 0$. Hence the problem reduces to that of expanding the known function $f(x, y)$ in terms of the set of eigenfunctions for the problem, evaluated at $t = 0$. In this case equation (46) is simply a double Fourier series representation and by repeated application of the Euler formulae (equations (18) of §2.4) for Fourier series the solution is easily found to be

$$A_{mn} = \frac{4}{ab}\int_0^a\left\{\int_0^b f(x, y)\sin\frac{m\pi y}{b}\,dy\right\}\sin\frac{n\pi x}{a}\,dx.$$

Note that if the initial velocity is specified as $\partial v/\partial t = g(x, y)$ at $t = 0$ then the equation relating B_{mn} to $g(x, y)$ may be found by the same technique. For less regularly shaped regions both the eigenfunctions and the inversion formulae are difficult to find.

Circular Membrane

Consider a circular membrane $x^2 + y^2 \leqslant a^2$ stretched over a plane circular frame under an all-round tension. The solution of the two-dimensional wave equation (43) for a circular region is most easily obtained by expressing the problem in plane polar coordinates. On transforming the coordinates in equation (43) to ρ, ϕ where $x = \rho \cos \phi, y = \rho \sin \phi$, the equation becomes

$$\frac{\partial^2 v}{\partial \rho^2} + \frac{1}{\rho} \frac{\partial v}{\partial \rho} + \frac{1}{\rho^2} \frac{\partial^2 v}{\partial \phi^2} = \frac{1}{c^2} \frac{\partial^2 v}{\partial t^2} \tag{47}$$

[see §6.7]. For simplicity let us look for axially-symmetric vibrations of the form

$$v = R(\rho) T(t).$$

The boundary condition $v = 0$ on $\rho = a$ for all values of t implies that $R(a) = 0$. The wave equation (47) becomes

$$\frac{1}{R(\rho)} \left(R''(\rho) + \frac{1}{\rho} R'(\rho) \right) = \frac{1}{c^2} \frac{T''(t)}{T(t)}. \tag{48}$$

As the radial coordinate ρ and the time t are independent variables, each side of (48) must be a constant. For a periodic vibration this constant must be negative $(-p^2)$ so that equation (48) separates into

$$T''(t) = -c^2 p^2 T(t), \quad R''(\rho) + \frac{1}{\rho} R'(\rho) = -p^2 R(\rho). \tag{49}$$

Clearly $T(t) = A \cos pct + B \sin pct$. The equation for $R(\rho)$ is less simple as it is a second-order ordinary differential equation with coefficients which depend on the radial variable ρ. This equation cannot be solved by the methods of Chapter 1, but the approach described in Chapter 6 of Volume 2 soon yields a solution in terms of a (convergent) infinite series. This solution is denoted by $R(\rho) = J_0(p\rho)$ and is finite in $0 \leqslant \rho \leqslant a$. The function $J_0(x)$ is called a Bessel function of order zero and equation (49) is a particular case of Bessel's differential equation. There is a second solution of equation (49), denoted by $R(\rho) = Y_0(p\rho)$ but it cannot be used in this problem as it tends to infinity as $\rho \to 0$. Hence the axially-symmetric solution of equation (47) is

$$v = R(\rho) T(t) = J_0(p\rho)(A \cos pct + B \sin pct). \tag{50}$$

Since the edge of the membrane is held so that $v = 0$ on $\rho = a$ for all values of t, the arbitrary constant p must satisfy the eigenvalue equation

$$J_0(pa) = 0. \tag{51}$$

This equation has an infinite number of roots $pa = \alpha_1, \alpha_2, \alpha_3, \ldots,$. These roots are tabulated in several texts, in particular in Abramowitz and Stegun [3], p. 409. Hence

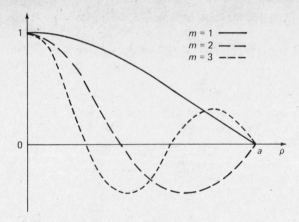

Fig. 7.10   Bessel functions $J_0(\alpha_m\rho/a)$ for $m = 1, 2, 3$

the mth axially-symmetric normal mode for a circular membrane has the shape function $J_0(\alpha_m\rho/a)$ and vibrates with frequency $\alpha_m c/2\pi a$. The functions $J_0(\alpha_m\rho/a)$ for $m = 1, 2, 3$, and $0 \leqslant \rho \leqslant a$, are illustrated in Fig. 7.10. The function $J_0(\alpha_m\rho/a)$ has $m - 1$ zeros in the range $0 < \rho < a$ so that the mth axially-symmetric normal mode has $m - 1$ circular nodal lines. A *nodal line* is a locus of points at which the transverse displacement of the membrane is always zero in a particular mode of vibration. Clearly any attempt to satisfy initial conditions on the membrane will require an examination of the properties of Bessel functions which is inappropriate in this text. The subject is fully covered in Churchill [5], Chapter 8.

A more general solution which allows for asymmetric vibrations of a circular membrane may be obtained by looking for a separated solution of equation (47) in the form $v = R(\rho)\Phi(\phi)T(t)$. As above, the vibrations are periodic in time and give $T''(t)/T(t) = -p^2 c^2$. Since v must remain unchanged when the angular variable is increased from ϕ to $\phi + 2\pi$, the function $\Phi(\phi)$ must have period 2π. It is easily shown that $\Phi(\phi)$ must satisfy $\Phi''(\phi) = -n^2\Phi(\phi)$, so that $\Phi(\phi) = A \cos n\phi + B \sin n\phi$. This function has period 2π only if n is an integer. Finally the equation for $R(\rho)$ becomes Bessel's equation

$$\rho^2 R''(\rho) + \rho R'(\rho) + (p^2\rho^2 - n^2)R(\rho) = 0.$$

This has the independent solutions $R(\rho) = J_n(p\rho)$ and $R(\rho) = Y_n(p\rho)$, where $J_n(x)$ and $Y_n(x)$ are *Bessel functions of order* n of the first and second kinds respectively. $J_n(p\rho)$ is finite for all values of ρ, but $Y_n(p\rho) \to \infty$ as $\rho \to 0$. Hence $R(\rho) = J_n(p\rho)$ is the required solution of Bessel's equation for this problem. Since the boundary condition on $\rho = a$ is $v = 0$, then

$$J_n(pa) = 0, \tag{52}$$

which gives an infinite set of eigenvalues for p for each integer value of n. The shape functions for the surface with n radial nodal lines are

$$J_n(p\rho)(A_n \cos n\phi + B_n \sin n\phi)$$

where p satisfies (52). The natural frequencies corresponding to these modes are then $pc/2\pi$.

Again the problem of satisfying initial conditions for the asymmetrical vibrations of a circular membrane is beyond the scope of this book. Bessel's equation and functions are of frequent occurrence in the solution of partial differential equations in circular and cylindrical regions. Further information on these topics may be found in Churchill [5], Chapter 8, and Morse and Feshbach [6], Chapter 11.

Exercises

1. The shape functions for the normal modes of a rectangular membrane are $\sin(n\pi x/a)\sin(m\pi y/b)$ where n and m are integers. Show that the nodal lines for the cases $n = 2, m = 2$ and $n = 2, m = 3$ are as indicated on Fig. 7.11. The $+$ and $-$ signs indicate deflections of opposite sign.

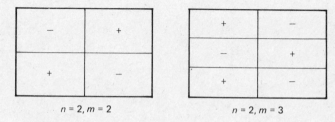

$$n = 2, m = 2 \qquad\qquad n = 2, m = 3$$

Fig. 7.11   Nodal lines for vibrations of a rectangular plate

2. A square membrane $0 \leqslant x \leqslant a, 0 \leqslant y \leqslant a$ is distorted into the shape $y = \sin(\pi x/a)\sin(2\pi y/a)$ and then released from rest. What is the frequency of the resulting motion?

3. In a square plate $(b = a)$ the $n = 1, m = 2$ and $n = 2, m = 1$ modes vibrate with the same frequency. Hence show that the combined displacement field is

$$\sin\frac{\pi x}{a}\sin\frac{\pi y}{a}\left(A\cos\frac{\pi x}{a} + B\cos\frac{\pi y}{a}\right)\cos\frac{c\sqrt{5}\pi t}{a}.$$

The nodal lines are given by the equation

$$A\cos\frac{\pi x}{a} + B\cos\frac{\pi y}{a} = 0, \qquad 0 \leqslant x \leqslant a, 0 \leqslant y \leqslant a$$

for a constant value of B/A. Find the nodal lines for each of the cases $A = 0, B = 0$, $B = \pm A$.

4. Show that when $b = 2a$ the modes $n = 2, m = 2$ and $n = 1, m = 4$ of the rectangular membrane of exercise 1 have the same frequency. Show that some nodal lines are

given by the equation

$$A \cos \frac{\pi x}{a} + B \cos \frac{\pi y}{a} = 0, \quad 0 \leqslant x \leqslant a, 0 \leqslant y \leqslant 2a,$$

for a constant value of B/A. Sketch the nodal lines for each of the cases $A = 0, B = 0$, $B = \pm A$.

7.5 THE HEAT CONDUCTION AND DIFFUSION EQUATION

Conduction of Heat

The heat conduction equation was formulated in §6.6. It is based on (a) Fourier's law of heat conduction, which states that

$$\mathbf{q} = -K \operatorname{grad} \theta, \tag{53}$$

where $\mathbf{q}$ is the heat conduction vector, θ the temperature and the coefficient K is the thermal conductivity of the material, and (b) the equation

$$c \frac{\partial \theta}{\partial t} = -\operatorname{div} \mathbf{q}$$

which, when multiplied by δV, equates the rate of accumulation of heat in an infinitesimal volume δV to the inflow of heat across the surface of the volume. The constant c is the heat capacity of the material per unit volume. Thus it follows on eliminating $\mathbf{q}$ that the temperature satisfies the *heat conduction equation*

$$\frac{\partial^2 \theta}{\partial x^2} + \frac{\partial^2 \theta}{\partial y^2} + \frac{\partial^2 \theta}{\partial z^2} = \frac{1}{\kappa} \frac{\partial \theta}{\partial t}, \tag{54}$$

at all interior points of the body. The constant $\kappa = K/c$ is called the thermal diffusivity of the body.

Diffusion

The simplest mathematical model of diffusion of a liquid through a porous solid is also governed by equation (54). In this case $\theta(x, y, z, t)$ represents the concentration of the liquid (mass per unit volume) at the point (x, y, z) at time t. The liquid is assumed to diffuse from a region of high concentration to a region of low concentration according to the equation $\mathbf{F} = -\kappa \operatorname{grad} \theta$ where $\mathbf{F}$ is the mass flow vector and κ is the constant diffusion coefficient. The rate of mass accumulation at a point is $\partial \theta / \partial t = -\operatorname{div} \mathbf{F}$. The diffusion equation is produced by combining these two equations and is identical with equation (54) when $\theta(x, y, z, t)$ is identified as the concentration. When discussing solutions of (54), we shall always refer to thermal problems but this second physical interpretation should be borne in mind.

One-dimensional Heat Conduction

When the temperature θ is independent of y and z, equation (54) becomes

$$\frac{\partial^2 \theta}{\partial x^2} = \frac{1}{\kappa} \frac{\partial \theta}{\partial t}. \tag{55}$$

There are two common physical situations which satisfy these conditions. The first is heat conduction in a thin bar $0 \leqslant x \leqslant a$ whose sides are insulated against heat loss. The second is heat conduction in a plate with plane faces $x = 0$ and $x = a$ which has a large cross-sectional area and is such that the boundary conditions on the plane faces are independent of y and z. In this section we refer only to the first case although the second is of equal interest and also corresponds to certain diffusion problems in chemical engineering.

Again, we look for separated solutions of the type $\theta = X(x)T(t)$. This leads to the equations

$$\frac{X''(x)}{X(x)} = \frac{1}{\kappa} \frac{T'(t)}{T(t)} = \text{constant}.$$

If this constant has the positive value p^2, the time dependence is $T(t) = \exp(p^2 \kappa t)$ which increases exponentially with time. This behaviour is unrealistic in most physical problems, and most boundary conditions encountered in practice will not allow such eigenfunctions to occur. When the constant has the negative value $-p^2$, the equations give

$$\theta = (A \cos px + B \sin px) \exp(-p^2 \kappa t). \tag{56}$$

When $p = 0$, the solution is

$$\theta = Ax + B \tag{57}$$

which is independent of time and represents a steady flow of heat down a uniform temperature gradient.

EXAMPLE 1

Consider a thin bar of length a with insulated sides. Let us suppose that the end $x = 0$ is held at the temperature $\theta = 100\,^{\circ}\text{C}$ and that the end $x = a$ is held at the temperature $\theta = 0\,^{\circ}\text{C}$ for all times $t > 0$. In addition, let us suppose that the temperature distribution in the bar at $t = 0$ is $\theta(x, 0) = f(x)$, $0 \leqslant x \leqslant a$. What is the temperature distribution in the bar at some subsequent time $t > 0$?

The boundary value problem is to solve the heat conduction equation

$$\frac{\partial^2 \theta}{\partial x^2} = \frac{1}{\kappa} \frac{\partial \theta}{\partial t},$$

subject to the inhomogeneous boundary conditions,

$$\theta(0, t) = 100, \quad \theta(a, t) = 0, \quad \text{for all } t > 0,$$

and the initial condition

$$\theta(x, 0) = f(x), \quad 0 \leqslant x \leqslant a.$$

Obviously, if we forget about the initial temperature distribution, we can satisfy the boundary conditions by the time-independent solution

$$\theta = 100(a - x)/a \tag{58}$$

which is a solution of the type (57). In fact this is the steady temperature distribution which will be attained in the bar after a long time.

Now let us look for a solution of the form

$$\theta = 100(a - x)/a + \Theta(x, t),$$

where Θ is also a solution of the heat conduction equation. On substituting this form for θ into the boundary conditions, we find that

$$\Theta(0, t) = 0, \quad \Theta(a, t) = 0,$$

and hence we have been able to use the particular solution (58) to produce homogeneous boundary conditions for Θ. These boundary conditions may be satisfied by a solution of the type (56) if

$$A = 0 \quad \text{and} \quad \sin pa = 0.$$

This equation has the eigenvalues $pa = n\pi$, where n is an integer. Thus each eigenfunction of the type

$$B_n \sin \frac{n\pi x}{a} \exp\left(-\frac{n^2 \pi^2 \kappa t}{a^2}\right)$$

where n is an integer and B_n is a constant, is a possible solution for $\Theta(x, t)$. By superposing the particular solution (58) and a linear combination of all possible solutions for $\Theta(x, t)$, the general solution satisfying the boundary conditions $\theta(0, t) = 100$, $\theta(a, t) = 0$ is found to be

$$\theta = 100 \left(\frac{a - x}{a}\right) + \sum_{n=1}^{\infty} B_n \sin \frac{n\pi x}{a} \exp\left(-\frac{n^2 \pi^2 \kappa t}{a^2}\right). \tag{59}$$

It remains to match this solution with the initial condition, which gives

$$100 \frac{(a - x)}{a} + \sum_{n=1}^{\infty} B_n \sin \frac{n\pi x}{a} = f(x), \quad 0 \leqslant x \leqslant a. \tag{60}$$

This is clearly a standard Fourier series problem from which the constants B_n, for $n = 1, 2, 3, \ldots$, may be determined.

In the particular case of a bar at zero initial temperature $f(x) = 0$, which is heated by a temperature $\theta = 100$ applied at the end $x = 0$ for all times $t > 0$, the other end being held at $\theta = 0$, the solution is given by equation (59), where the B_n are Fourier coefficients determined by the equation

$$\sum_{n=1}^{\infty} B_n \sin \frac{n\pi x}{a} = -100\left(\frac{a-x}{a}\right), \quad 0 < x \leqslant a. \tag{61}$$

On using the Euler formulae (18) of §2.4, we find $B_n = -200/n\pi$. The complete solution is

$$\theta = 100\left(\frac{a-x}{a}\right) - \frac{200}{\pi}\sum_{n=1}^{\infty}\frac{1}{n}\sin\frac{n\pi x}{a}\exp\left(-\frac{n^2\pi^2\kappa t}{a^2}\right). \tag{62}$$

The sum of the sine series is discontinuous at $x = 0$ when $t = 0$, which corresponds to the instantaneous temperature jump from 0 °C to 100 °C which is specified in the problem. It will be appreciated that the negative exponential function terms tend rapidly to zero as t increases, so that θ rises to the steady solution (58). In addition the series in equation (62) is increasingly dominated by its first term as t increases. These temperature distributions are illustrated in Fig. 7.12.

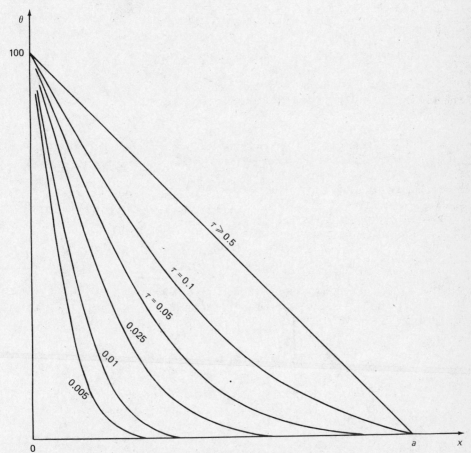

Fig. 7.12   Temperature distributions in a bar for constant values of $\tau = \kappa t/a^2$

The method of separation of variables can be used to solve any initial value problem for the heat conduction equation on $0 \leqslant x \leqslant a$ provided that the boundary conditions on $x = 0$ and $x = a$ are *constant*. If the boundary conditions depend on time, separated solutions of the form (56) are not suitable. For such a problem the solution may be found by using the Laplace transform and this is discussed in Chapter 5 of Volume 2. Thermal problems for infinite regions also may be tackled by Laplace or Fourier transform methods.

Methods of solution similar to those used in this section may be applied to the heat conduction equation (2) in more than one space variable.

Exercises

1. The solution (62) with $a = 1$ gives the temperature in a bar of unit length which is initially at a temperature of $0\,°C$ and is heated by the temperature $\theta = 100\,°C$ applied at the end $x = 0$ for $t > 0$, the end $x = 1$ being held at $\theta = 0\,°C$. What is the temperature at the mid-point of the bar as $t \to \infty$? Show that the temperature at the mid-point exceeds $25\,°C$ when $\kappa t > 0.095$, and $49\,°C$ when $\kappa t > 0.421$.

2. A plate of thickness a is at a uniform temperature $\theta = \theta_0$ for $t < 0$. If, at $t = 0$, its faces $x = 0$ and $x = a$ are suddenly cooled to $\theta = 0$ and kept at that temperature, find the temperature distribution in the plate. Sketch the heat flow across $x = 0$ as a function of time.

3. If a thin bar $0 \leqslant x \leqslant 1$ has the initial temperature distribution $\theta(x, 0) = 4x(1 - x)$ and its ends $x = 0, 1$ are held at the temperature $\theta = 0$ for all subsequent times, show that at time t

$$\theta(x, t) = \frac{32}{\pi^3} \sum_{k=0}^{\infty} \frac{\sin(2k + 1)\pi x}{(2k + 1)^3} \exp\{-(2k + 1)^2 \pi^2 \kappa t\}.$$

A numerical method of solution of this problem is given in §7.6 of Volume 2.

4. A plate of thickness a has the initial temperature distribution $\theta(x, 0) = f(x)$ at $t = 0$. If the faces $x = 0$ and $x = a$ are insulated so that the heat flow across each is zero, which requires

$$\frac{\partial \theta}{\partial x}(0, t) = 0, \quad \frac{\partial \theta}{\partial x}(a, t) = 0,$$

show that the solution is of the form

$$\theta = \tfrac{1}{2}A_0 + \sum_{n=1}^{\infty} A_n \cos\frac{n\pi x}{a} \exp\left(-\frac{n^2 \pi^2 \kappa t}{a^2}\right)$$

and find the values of the constants A_n. Confirm that as $t \to \infty$ the temperature tends to the mean value

$$\frac{1}{a}\int_0^a f(x)\,dx$$

of the initial temperature distribution.

5. A liquid diffuses through a porous membrane of thickness a. If the concentration $\theta(x, t)$ is maintained at c_0 on the $x = 0$ side of the membrane and c_1 on the $x = a$ side of the membrane, what is the concentration in the membrane after any transient terms have died away?

7.6 LAPLACE'S EQUATION

Laplace's equation for the field T in cartesian coordinates (x, y, z) is

$$\nabla^2 T \equiv \frac{\partial^2 T}{\partial x^2} + \frac{\partial^2 T}{\partial y^2} + \frac{\partial^2 T}{\partial z^2} = 0. \tag{63}$$

This is one of the fundamental equations of science since it governs a number of time-independent phenomena. If the temperature θ in the heat conduction equation (54) is independent of time, $\partial\theta/\partial t$ is zero and equation (54) reduces to Laplace's equation for the temperature field. We denote the steady temperature field which satisfies Laplace's equation (63) by T to distinguish it from the unsteady temperature field θ which satisfies the heat conduction equation (54). The heat conduction vector is $\mathbf{q} = -K$ grad T. Other physical quantities satisfying Laplace's equation are (a) the concentration of a liquid steadily diffusing through a uniform solid, (b) the velocity potential for steady irrotational flow of an incompressible inviscid fluid and (c) the electrostatic potential. This equation also occurs in other branches of electrical and magnetic field theory and in the mechanics of fluids and solids.

Laplace's equation occurs in many branches of physics because simultaneous equations of the form $\mathbf{q} = -K$ grad T, div $\mathbf{q} = 0$ arise frequently. They lead to Laplace's equation for the field T when $\mathbf{q}$ is eliminated. Several examples were given in §6.6. The fact that a number of different phenomena are governed by the same equation is important because it produces a great economy in mathematical effort and is the foundation for various analogue experimental methods.

The two-dimensional form of the equation occurs when T is independent of one variable (say z) and is

$$\nabla_1^2 T \equiv \frac{\partial^2 T}{\partial x^2} + \frac{\partial^2 T}{\partial y^2} = 0. \tag{64}$$

It was shown in §7.1 that the separated solutions of equation (64) of the form $T = X(x)Y(y)$ are given by

$$X(x) = Ae^{px} + Be^{-px}, \qquad Y(y) = C\cos py + D\sin py, \tag{65}$$

$$X(x) = A \cos px + B \sin px, \qquad Y(y) = Ce^{py} + De^{-py}, \tag{66}$$

$$X(x) = Ax + B, \qquad\qquad Y(y) = Cy + D, \tag{67}$$

where A, B, C, D and p are constants. We now consider some applications of these solutions.

Half-plane Problems

Consider the solution of Laplace's equation $\nabla_1^2 T = 0$ in the half-plane $y > 0$ subject to the boundary condition

$$T(x, 0) = a_n \cos \left(\frac{n\pi x}{l} \right) \tag{68}$$

on the boundary $y = 0$ and such that $T(x, y)$ is bounded for large values of y. Since the boundary condition is periodic of period $2l/n$ in x, a solution of type (66) would seem appropriate with $p = n\pi/l$. Since $T = X(x)Y(y)$ must be bounded for large values of y, $Y(y)$ cannot contain a term of the form e^{py} as this increases exponentially for large y when p is positive. Hence T has the form

$$T = (A \cos px + B \sin px)e^{-py}, \quad p > 0.$$

The solution which matches with the boundary conditions is given by $p = n\pi/l$, $A = a_n$, $B = 0$ so that

$$T = a_n \cos\left(\frac{n\pi x}{l}\right) \exp\left(-\frac{n\pi y}{l}\right).$$

A sketch of this solution is given in Fig. 7.13 for $n = 2$. Note that along each line $x = x_0$, the values of T decay rapidly as y increases.

Similarly, if the boundary condition (68) on $y = 0$ is replaced by $T(x, 0) = b_n \sin(n\pi x/l)$, the solution will be

$$T = b_n \sin(n\pi x/l) \exp(-n\pi y/l)$$

with the same rate of decay away from the boundary.

Suppose the boundary condition (68) on $y = 0$ is changed to $T(x, 0) = f(x)$, where $f(x) = f(x + 2l)$ is a periodic function of period $2l$. Then $f(x)$ has a Fourier series representation of the form

$$T(x, 0) = f(x) = \tfrac{1}{2}a_0 + \sum_{n=1}^{\infty} \left(a_n \cos \frac{n\pi x}{l} + b_n \sin \frac{n\pi x}{l} \right). \tag{69}$$

Hence the previous solutions may be superposed to show that the solution of Laplace's equation in $y \geqslant 0$ subject to (69) is

$$T = \tfrac{1}{2}a_0 + \sum_{n=1}^{\infty} \left(a_n \cos \frac{n\pi x}{l} + b_n \sin \frac{n\pi x}{l} \right) \exp\left(-\frac{n\pi y}{l}\right). \tag{70}$$

This solution is bounded as $y \to \infty$ and satisfies the periodic boundary condition on $y = 0$.

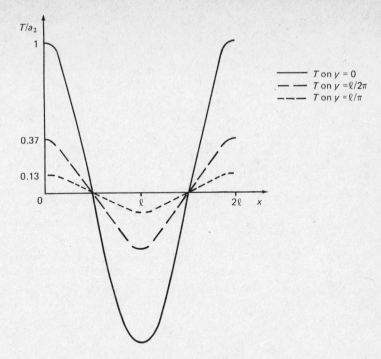

Fig. 7.13 Temperature distributions along the lines y = constant

It is much more difficult to find the solution of Laplace's equation in the half-plane $y > 0$, subject to the boundary condition $T(x, 0) = f(x)$ along $y = 0$, when $f(x)$ is not a periodic function. This problem is solved by the Fourier transform technique in §5.6 of Volume 2.

Semi-infinite Strip

Let us now consider solutions of Laplace's equation (64) in the strip $y > 0, 0 \leqslant x \leqslant a$. Suppose the boundary conditions are $T = 0$ on the edges $x = 0$ and $x = a$, $T(x, 0) = f(x)$ on $y = 0$ for $0 \leqslant x \leqslant a$ and $T(x, y) \to 0$ as $y \to \infty$ (see Fig. 7.14).

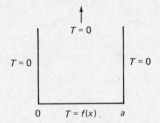

Fig. 7.14 Boundary conditions on a semi-infinite strip

If a separated solution $T = X(x)Y(y)$ is assumed, the boundary conditions on $x = 0$, $x = a$ imply that $X(0)Y(y) = 0$, $X(a)Y(y) = 0$ for all $y > 0$. Hence a non-zero value of T is possible if $X(0) = 0$ and $X(a) = 0$. If we test each of the solutions (65), (66), (67) against the boundary conditions, the only non-zero solutions are of the type (66) with $p = n\pi/a$ and have the form

$$X(x) = B \sin(n\pi x/a), \quad Y(y) = Ce^{n\pi y/a} + De^{-n\pi y/a}, \tag{71}$$

where n is an integer. Note that the nature of this solution is determined entirely by the boundary conditions on the opposite edges $x = 0$ and $x = a$.

Since $T = X(x)Y(y)$ tends to zero as $y \to \infty$ we must take $C = 0$. Thus the eigenfunctions of Laplace's equation in the strip which satisfy the boundary conditions on all edges except $y = 0$ are

$$T = B_n \sin\left(\frac{n\pi x}{a}\right) \exp\left(-\frac{n\pi y}{a}\right).$$

The general solution is obtained by superposing these solutions and is

$$T = \sum_{n=1}^{\infty} B_n \sin\left(\frac{n\pi x}{a}\right) \exp\left(-\frac{n\pi y}{a}\right). \tag{72}$$

The remaining boundary condition is $T(x, 0) = f(x)$ on $y = 0$ which gives

$$T(x, 0) = \sum_{n=1}^{\infty} B_n \sin\frac{n\pi x}{a} = f(x), \quad 0 \leqslant x \leqslant a. \tag{73}$$

Hence, the constants B_n for $n = 1, 2, 3, \ldots$, are simply the coefficients of the half-range Fourier sine series representation for $f(x)$. Exercise 2 at the end of this section gives the temperature field in a strip subject to zero temperatures along its sides and a known temperature on its end face.

Rectangular Region

The solution of a boundary value problem for Laplace's equation in a rectangular region is closely related to that for a strip. Consider the region $0 \leqslant x \leqslant a, 0 \leqslant y \leqslant b$ with the boundary values

$$T(0, y) = 0, \qquad T(a, y) = 0,$$
$$T(x, 0) = f(x), \quad T(x, b) = 0.$$

A particular case of these boundary conditions is illustrated on Fig. 7.15. The boundary conditions on the edges $x = 0$ and $x = a$ are identical to those for the strip and produce the same set of separated solutions (71), namely

$$X(x) = B \sin(n\pi x/a), \quad Y(y) = C \exp(n\pi y/a) + D \exp(-n\pi y/a)$$

for $n = 1, 2, 3, \ldots$. The boundary condition on $y = b$ is satisfied only if $Y(b) = 0$ which implies that

$$C \exp(n\pi b/a) + D \exp(-n\pi b/a) = 0.$$

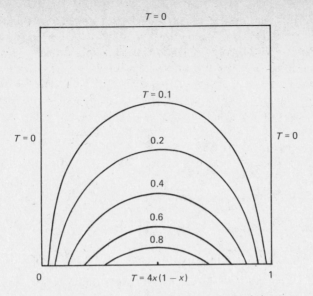

Fig. 7.15 Temperature contours for a square plate

Substitution for D gives

$$Y(y) = C \exp(n\pi b/a) \left[\exp\{n\pi(y-b)/a\} - \exp\{n\pi(b-y)/a\}\right],$$

from which $Y(y)$ may be expressed in the form of a constant multiple of $\sinh\{n\pi(b-y)/a\}$. Thus the eigenfunctions which satisfy the zero boundary conditions on the three edges $x = 0$, $x = a$ and $y = b$ are

$$B_n \sin\frac{n\pi x}{a} \sinh n\pi\frac{(b-y)}{a}.$$

The general solution is given by combining these to form

$$T = \sum_{n=1}^{\infty} B_n \sin\frac{n\pi x}{a} \sinh n\pi\frac{(b-y)}{a}. \tag{74}$$

The remaining boundary condition is on $y = 0$ and gives

$$T(x, 0) = \sum_{n=1}^{\infty} B_n \sinh\frac{n\pi b}{a} \sin\frac{n\pi x}{a} = f(x), \quad \text{for} \quad 0 \leqslant x \leqslant a.$$

Again the problem has been reduced to finding a half-range Fourier sine series representation for $f(x)$. The coefficients are simply

$$B_k = \frac{2}{a \sinh(k\pi b/a)} \int_0^a f(x) \sin\frac{k\pi x}{a}\, dx, \quad k = 1, 2, 3, \ldots \tag{75}$$

The contours of constant temperature T are sketched on Fig. 7.15 for a square plate

$(a = b = 1)$ with the temperature $T = f(x) = 4x(1 - x)$ applied to $y = 0$. Again note the rapid decay away from $y = 0$.

The boundary conditions in practical problems are likely to be more complicated than those considered here. If, for example, T is specified on all edges of a plate as $T(x, 0) = f_1(x)$, $T(a, y) = f_2(y)$, $T(x, b) = f_3(x)$, $T(0, y) = f_4(y)$, then the problem may be split into four sub-problems in each of which the temperature is zero on three edges and takes its specified value on the fourth. This is shown in Fig. 7.16. Obviously, by a rotation of axes, each of these sub-problems can be made to correspond to one solved by equations (74) and (75).

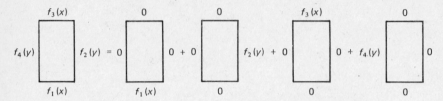

Fig. 7.16   Division of a boundary-value problem into sub-problems

So far the boundary conditions have been of the type in which the value of T is specified at all points of the boundary. Another natural condition for a thermal problem is $\partial T / \partial n \equiv \mathbf{n} \cdot \nabla T = 0$ which corresponds to zero heat flow across the boundary whose normal is $\mathbf{n}$, i.e. perfect insulation. A typical problem of this type is to determine the temperature in a rectangular region due to a specified temperature on a part of the boundary, the remainder of the boundary being insulated. If T is specified on both of the edges $y = 0$ and $y = b$, and both of the edges $x = 0$ and $x = a$ are insulated, the representative problem is that shown in Fig. 7.17. Since the boundary conditions on $x = 0$ and $x = a$ have changed from the previous example, the solution (71) no longer applies. The reader should confirm that the separation of variables method yields the distinct solutions

$$T = C + Dy, \quad T = \cos\frac{n\pi x}{a}\left\{A_n \exp\left(\frac{n\pi y}{a}\right) + B_n \exp\left(-\frac{n\pi y}{a}\right)\right\}, \quad n = 1, 2, 3, \ldots,$$

which satisfy the conditions on $x = 0$ and $x = a$. A linear combination of *all* these solutions should be used in boundary value problems of this type, e.g. in exercises 1

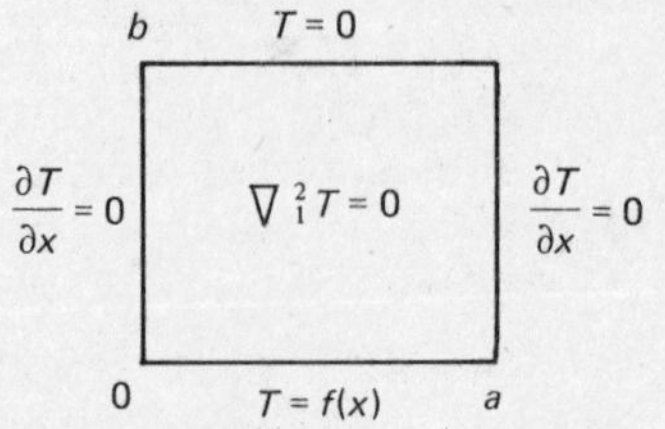

Fig. 7.17   A temperature problem for a plate with insulated sides

and 3. Note that the linear solution $C + Dy$ is easily forgotten and if omitted from the series will lead to incorrect results.

Circular Regions

As noted in §7.3, 7.4, the solution of a boundary value problem for a particular region is much simplified if a natural system of coordinates is used. Expressing Laplace's equation (64) in plane polar coordinates $\rho = (x^2 + y^2)^{1/2}$, $\phi = \tan^{-1}(y/x)$ gives

$$\frac{\partial^2 T}{\partial \rho^2} + \frac{1}{\rho} \frac{\partial T}{\partial \rho} + \frac{1}{\rho^2} \frac{\partial^2 T}{\partial \phi^2} = 0. \tag{76}$$

This result has been derived in §6.7.

Let us first look for solutions which are independent of the angle ϕ. These are referred to as *axially-symmetric solutions* since they are constant on each circle centred on the origin $\rho = 0$. If $T = R(\rho)$, then equation (76) reduces to

$$R''(\rho) + \frac{1}{\rho} R'(\rho) = 0.$$

This is a linear first-order equation for $R'(\rho)$ with the solution $\rho R'(\rho) = B$, and so

$$T = R(\rho) = A + B \log \rho \tag{77}$$

where A and B are constants. It will be recalled that $\log \rho$ becomes unbounded as $\rho \to 0$ and as $\rho \to \infty$.

Consider the solution of Laplace's equation in the circular region $0 \leqslant \rho \leqslant a$ subject to the boundary condition $T = T_a$ on $\rho = a$, where T_a is a constant. The constants in the solution (77) must satisfy

$$A + B \log a = T_a.$$

If B takes a non-zero value, then the temperature field (77) will become infinite at the centre of the disc. Since this is not physically reasonable, we put $B = 0$ and $A = T_a$. Hence the temperature field is a constant $T = T_a$ throughout the circular region $0 \leqslant \rho \leqslant a$.

The logarithmic term in equation (77) may be required in a region which does not contain the origin, such as an annular region $a \leqslant \rho \leqslant b$. If the temperature in the interior of a hollow cylindrical pipe $a \leqslant \rho \leqslant b$ is $T = T_a$ and the exterior temperature is $T = T_b$, then the constants in equation (77) satisfy

$$A + B \log a = T_a, \qquad A + B \log b = T_b.$$

Hence the temperature field within the pipe wall is

$$T = T_a \frac{\log(\rho/b)}{\log(a/b)} - T_b \frac{\log(\rho/a)}{\log(a/b)}.$$

This solution is illustrated in Fig. 7.18.

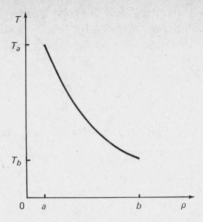

Fig. 7.18   Axially-symmetric temperature field as a function of the radius ρ

Note that the solution (77) is the only solution of Laplace's equation in plane polar coordinates which has axial symmetry. This solution is of importance in two-dimensional potential theory. Consider the temperature field $T = -(S/K)\log \rho$ where S is a constant. This field has a *two-dimensional point source* of heat at the origin. The heat conduction vector is

$$\mathbf{q} = -K \text{ grad } T = \frac{S}{\rho}(\mathbf{i} \cos \phi + \mathbf{j} \sin \phi)$$

and is a radial vector (see Fig. 7.19). The rate of heat outflow across the circle $\rho = \rho_0$ is $(S/\rho_0)2\pi\rho_0 = 2\pi S$ which is a constant on all circles centred on the origin. The strength of the source is defined to be S. Two-dimensional point sources also occur in

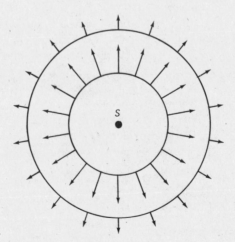

Fig. 7.19   Heat conduction vectors due to a point source

fluid mechanics and electrostatics. In three dimensions this two-dimensional point source corresponds to a *line source* of strength S per unit length along the z axis.

For more general problems for circular regions we must look for solutions which depend on ϕ also. Since $T(\rho, \phi)$ must not change after a complete circuit of the origin in which ϕ is replaced by $\phi + 2\pi$, it must satisfy

$$T(\rho, \phi + 2\pi) = T(\rho, \phi), \quad \text{for all } \phi, \tag{78}$$

and so $T(\rho, \phi)$ must have a period of 2π in the angular coordinate ϕ. For a separated solution of the type $T = R(\rho)\Phi(\phi)$, Laplace's equation (76) reduces to

$$\left(R''(\rho) + \frac{1}{\rho} R'(\rho) \right) \frac{\rho^2}{R(\rho)} = -\frac{\Phi''(\phi)}{\Phi(\phi)}. \tag{79}$$

Since ρ and ϕ are independent variables, each side of this equation must be a constant. If this constant is given the value p^2, then

$$\Phi(\phi) = A \cos p\phi + B \sin p\phi.$$

This has a period of 2π only if p is an integer n. The only other solution of equation (79) which has this property is that for $p = 0$ which generates the solution (77) again.

When the constant in equation (79) is n^2, the equation for $R(\rho)$ is

$$\rho^2 R''(\rho) + \rho R'(\rho) - n^2 R(\rho) = 0. \tag{80}$$

This is an example of Euler's ordinary differential equation with non-constant coefficients and has been discussed in §1.10. On looking for solutions of the form ρ^k, it is easily confirmed that equation (80) has the distinct solutions

$$R(\rho) = C\rho^n \quad \text{and} \quad R(\rho) = D\rho^{-n}.$$

Hence the separated solutions of equation (76) take the forms

$$T_n(\rho, \phi) = \rho^n (A_n \cos n\phi + B_n \sin n\phi) + \rho^{-n}(A_n' \cos n\phi + B_n' \sin n\phi), \tag{81}$$

where n is an integer and A_n, B_n, A_n', B_n' are constants. It should be noted that as $\rho \to 0$, $\rho^n \to 0$ but $\rho^{-n} \to \infty$ for $n = 1, 2, 3, \ldots$. Hence, for a circular region in which ρ can take the value $\rho = 0$, we must put $A_n' = B_n' = 0$ to remove the possibility of the temperature becoming infinite at the origin. For an annular region $a \leqslant \rho \leqslant b$ the complete expression (81) should be used as the point $\rho = 0$ lies outside the body and therefore does not give rise to a temperature singularity.

EXAMPLE 1
Consider Laplace's equation (76) in the circle $0 \leqslant \rho \leqslant a$ subject to the boundary condition $T(a, \phi) = f(\phi)$ on $\rho = a$ where $f(\phi)$ is a|known function. The sum of the bounded terms in the eigenfunctions (77) and (81) is

$$T(\rho, \phi) = \tfrac{1}{2}A_0 + \sum_{n=1}^{\infty} \rho^n (A_n \cos n\phi + B_n \sin n\phi), \tag{82}$$

where we denote the constant solution by $\tfrac{1}{2}A_0$ to fit the usual Fourier series formulae.

On $\rho = a$, the boundary condition becomes

$$\tfrac{1}{2}A_0 + \sum_{n=1}^{\infty} \{a^n A_n \cos n\phi + a^n B_n \sin n\phi\} = f(\phi), \quad \text{for } -\pi < \phi \leqslant \pi.$$

This is simply the general Fourier series representation for $f(\phi)$ and the constants may be evaluated using the Euler formulae (10) of §2.2. As a specific example suppose that $f(\phi) = 1$ for $0 < \phi < \pi$ and $f(\phi) = 0$ for $-\pi < \phi < 0$. Then from example 1 of §2.3 the coefficients are $A_0 = 1, A_n = 0, a^n B_n = \{1 - (-1)^n\}/n\pi$ and the temperature distribution throughout the region is

$$T(\rho, \phi) = \frac{1}{2} + \frac{2}{\pi}\left\{\frac{\rho}{a}\sin\phi + \frac{1}{3}\left(\frac{\rho}{a}\right)^3 \sin 3\phi + \frac{1}{5}\left(\frac{\rho}{a}\right)^5 \sin 5\phi + \ldots\right\}.$$

This solution is illustrated in Fig. 7.20.

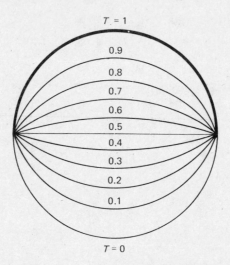

Fig. 7.20   Temperature contours in a circular disc

This method is easily extended to boundary value problems for annular regions.

The analytical solution of boundary value problems for Laplace's equation in finite regions of less regular shape in two dimensions cannot be easily accomplished. Since the real and imaginary parts of an analytic function of the complex variable $z = x + iy$ satisfies Laplace's equation (64), those methods of solution which are available are often closely linked with complex function theory and conformal transformations. Unless the regions are approximately rectangular, circular, annular or fit a small number of other simple shapes, the problems can only be handled by numerical means. These subjects are discussed in §§4.6 and 7.6 of Volume 2.

This section has dealt almost exclusively with Laplace's equation in two dimensions. The solutions of equation (63) in three cartesian coordinates x, y, z are closely related to those in plane cartesian coordinates. Separated solutions of the type

$$\frac{\cos}{\sin} px \ \frac{\cos}{\sin} qy \ \exp\{\pm z(p^2 + q^2)^{1/2}\}$$

where p and q are constants, may be used in boundary-value problems for Laplace's equation in rectangular box regions. Problem 6 of this chapter gives the solution of a typical problem. Solutions of Laplace's equation in other three-dimensional systems of coordinates are considered in the next section.

Exercises

1. Use the expressions (65), (66) and (67) to determine the solutions of Laplace's equation in the rectangular region $0 \leqslant x \leqslant a, 0 \leqslant y \leqslant b$, subject to the following sets of boundary conditions.

(a) $T(x, 0) = 100,$ $\quad\quad T(x, b) = -100$ $\quad$ for $0 \leqslant x \leqslant a$

$\quad\quad \dfrac{\partial T}{\partial x}(0, y) = 0,$ $\quad\quad \dfrac{\partial T}{\partial x}(a, y) = 0$ $\quad\quad$ for $0 \leqslant y \leqslant b$

(b) $\dfrac{\partial T}{\partial y}(x, 0) = 0,$ $\quad\quad \dfrac{\partial T}{\partial y}(x, b) = 0$ $\quad\quad$ for $0 \leqslant x \leqslant a$

$\quad\quad T(0, y) = 0,$ $\quad\quad\quad T(a, y) = 100$ $\quad\quad$ for $0 \leqslant y \leqslant b$

(c) $T(x, 0) = 0,$ $\quad\quad\quad T(x, b) = 0$ $\quad\quad$ for $0 \leqslant x \leqslant a$

$\quad\quad T(0, y) = 0$ $\quad\quad\quad\quad\quad\quad\quad\quad\quad$ for $0 \leqslant y \leqslant b$

$\quad\quad T(a, y) = 10 \sin\left(\dfrac{3\pi y}{b}\right),$ $\quad\quad\quad\quad$ for $0 \leqslant y \leqslant b$

(d) $T(x, 0) = 0,$ $\quad\quad\quad T(x, b) = 0$ $\quad\quad$ for $0 \leqslant x \leqslant a$

$\quad\quad T(0, y) = 0$ $\quad\quad\quad\quad\quad\quad\quad\quad\quad$ for $0 \leqslant y \leqslant b$

$\quad\quad T(a, y) = 10y$ $\quad\quad\quad\quad\quad\quad\quad\quad$ for $0 \leqslant y \leqslant b.$

2. Given that Laplace's equation $\nabla_1^2 T = 0$ has solutions of the form $e^{-px} \sin py$, show that the temperature $T(x, y)$ in the strip $x > 0, -l \leqslant y \leqslant l$ subject to the boundary conditions

$\quad\quad T \to 0 \quad$ as $\quad x \to \infty$

$\quad\quad T = 0 \quad$ on $\quad y = \pm l$

$\quad\quad T = 1 \quad$ on $\quad x = 0, \ 0 < y < l$

$\quad\quad T = -1 \quad$ on $\quad x = 0, -l < y < 0,$

is

$$T = \sum_{1}^{\infty} b_n \exp\left(-\frac{n\pi x}{l}\right) \sin\left(\frac{n\pi y}{l}\right), \quad \text{where } b_n = \frac{2}{n\pi}\{1 - (-1)^n\}.$$

3. Solve Laplace's equation $\nabla_1^2 T = 0$ in the rectangular region $0 \leqslant x \leqslant a, 0 \leqslant y \leqslant b$ subject to the boundary conditions

$$\frac{\partial T}{\partial x}(0, y) = 0, \qquad \frac{\partial T}{\partial x}(a, y) = 0,$$

$$T(x, 0) = x(a - x), \quad T(x, b) = 0.$$

Show that

$$T = \frac{1}{6} a^2 \left(1 - \frac{y}{b}\right) - \sum_{n=1}^{\infty} \frac{2a^2 \{1 + (-1)^n\}}{n^2 \pi^2 \sinh(n\pi b/a)} \cos \frac{n\pi x}{a} \sinh \frac{n\pi}{a}(b - y).$$

4. Use the solutions (77) and (81) of Laplace's equation in plane polar coordinates to solve the following problems:

(a)   The temperature T in a circular disc $0 \leqslant \rho \leqslant a$ satisfies Laplace's equation. If on the surface $\rho = a$ the temperature is $T_0 \cos 5\phi$, show that

$$T = T_0 \left(\frac{\rho}{a}\right)^5 \cos 5\phi$$

in the disc. In general, if on $\rho = a$, $T = f(\phi)$, show that the temperature in the disc can be found by using the Fourier series formulae.

(b)   The electrostatic potential V in the region $\rho > a$ outside a cylindrical conductor satisfies Laplace's equation. If $V = V_0 \cos 5\phi$ on the conductor $\rho = a$, and $V \to 0$ as $\rho \to \infty$, show that the potential in $\rho > a$ is

$$V = V_0 \left(\frac{a}{\rho}\right)^5 \cos 5\phi.$$

(c)   The velocity potential $V(\rho, \phi)$ for the two-dimensional irrotational flow of an ideal fluid satisfies Laplace's equation. The velocity of the fluid is $\mathbf{v} = \text{grad } V$, and the radial velocity is $\partial V/\partial \rho$. If the velocity of the fluid at infinity is parallel to $\phi = 0$ and is $\mathbf{v} = U\mathbf{i}$ and the flow passes around a circular cylinder $\rho = a$ on which the boundary condition is $\partial V/\partial \rho = 0$, confirm that the velocity potential is

$$V = U\rho \cos \phi + U \frac{a^2}{\rho} \cos \phi.$$

5. The velocity potential due to a two-dimensional point source (a line source normal to the x, y plane) of strength m at the point $x = 0, y = d$ in an infinite fluid is

$$V = m \log\{x^2 + (y - d)^2\}^{1/2}.$$

If a fixed boundary $y = 0$ is inserted into the flow giving rise to the boundary condition $\partial V/\partial y = 0$ on $y = 0$, show that the potential in $y > 0$ is

$$V = m \log\{x^2 + (y - d)^2\}^{1/2} + m \log\{x^2 + (y + d)^2\}^{1/2}.$$

Interpret the second term as an image source at $x = 0, y = -d$.

Determine the flow in the quandrant $x \geqslant 0$, $y \geqslant 0$ with the boundary conditions $\partial V/\partial x = 0$ on $x = 0$, $\partial V/\partial y = 0$ on $y = 0$, due to a fluid source of strength m at the point $x = a$, $y = b$ of the quadrant.

7.7 LAPLACE'S EQUATION IN CYLINDRICAL AND SPHERICAL POLAR COORDINATES

Cylindrical Polar Coordinates

Laplace's equation in cylindrical polar coordinates ρ, ϕ, z where $x = \rho \cos \phi$, $y = \rho \sin \phi$, $z = z$ is

$$\frac{\partial^2 T}{\partial \rho^2} + \frac{1}{\rho} \frac{\partial T}{\partial \rho} + \frac{1}{\rho^2} \frac{\partial^2 T}{\partial \phi^2} + \frac{\partial^2 T}{\partial z^2} = 0, \tag{83}$$

and has been derived in §6.7. A separated solution of the form $T = R(\rho)\Phi(\phi)Z(z)$ will be of use in the solution of Laplace's equation in a cylindrical region in which the z axis lies along the axis of the cylinder. Separated solutions of this type lead to the equations

$$\left(R''(\rho) + \frac{1}{\rho} R'(\rho) \right) \frac{1}{R(\rho)} + \frac{1}{\rho^2} \frac{\Phi''(\phi)}{\Phi(\phi)} = -\frac{Z''(z)}{Z(z)} = \text{constant}. \tag{84}$$

One type of cylindrical problem will produce exponential decay in the axial (z) direction, in which case the constant in equation (84) should be taken to be negative ($-p^2$). This gives

$$Z(z) = A e^{pz} + B e^{-pz}.$$

In addition we have seen in the last section that for circular or cylindrical problems $T(\rho, \phi, z)$ must have a period of 2π in ϕ. Moreover $\Phi''(\phi)/\Phi(\phi)$ must be constant so that $\Phi(\phi)$ takes the form

$$\Phi(\phi) = C \cos n\phi + D \sin n\phi \tag{85}$$

where n is an integer. Substituting these two forms into equation (84) shows that the radial dependence $R(\rho)$ satisfies

$$\rho^2 R''(\rho) + \rho R'(\rho) + (p^2 \rho^2 - n^2)R(\rho) = 0. \tag{86}$$

Again this is Bessel's equation, whose solutions $R(\rho) = J_n(p\rho)$ and $R(\rho) = Y_n(p\rho)$ were briefly discussed in §7.4 (for a fuller treatment see Churchill [5] or Morse and Feshbach [6]). Suitable bounded solutions of Laplace's equation for use in solid cylinders $0 \leqslant \rho \leqslant a$, $z \geqslant 0$ are

$$T = J_n(p\rho)(A_n \cos n\phi + B_n \sin n\phi)e^{-pz}, \quad p > 0, \tag{87}$$

where n is any integer. Linear combinations of these solutions can be used to satisfy the appropriate boundary conditions on the ends of cylinders and their lateral faces. In the case of axial symmetry, when T is independent of the angle ϕ, $n = 0$ and the solution is $T = J_0(p\rho)\exp(-pz)$. Details of the use of these solutions are given in Churchill [5], Ch. 8.

A second type of boundary value problem for a cylindrical region is produced when the boundary conditions on the lateral surface $\rho = a$ are periodic of period $2l$ in z. In this case we must consider solutions of the type

$$Z(z) = A \cos \frac{m\pi z}{l} + B \sin \frac{m\pi z}{l} \tag{88}$$

where m is an integer. Again the periodicity around the cylinder will restrict $\Phi(\phi)$ to be of the form (85). The resulting equation (84) for $R(\rho)$ is

$$\rho^2 R''(\rho) + \rho R'(\rho) - \left(\frac{m^2 \pi^2}{l^2} \rho^2 + n^2 \right) R(\rho) = 0. \tag{89}$$

This is a modification of Bessel's equation as it can be obtained from equation (86) by replacing ρ by $i\rho$. The corresponding solutions are denoted by

$$R(\rho) = I_n \left(\frac{m\pi\rho}{l} \right) \quad \text{and} \quad R(\rho) = K_n \left(\frac{m\pi\rho}{l} \right).$$

The function $I_n(x)$ is called a modified Bessel function of the first kind and is bounded for all values of x. The function $K_n(x)$ is a modified Bessel function of the second kind and like $Y_n(x)$ is divergent as $x \to 0$. The solutions of Laplace's equation which are bounded in a solid cylinder are of the type

$$T(\rho, \phi, z) = I_n \left(\frac{m\pi\rho}{l} \right) \cos n\phi \cos \left(\frac{m\pi z}{l} \right).$$

The axially-symmetric solutions occur when $n = 0$ and are

$$T(\rho, z) = I_0 \left(\frac{m\pi\rho}{l} \right) \cos \left(\frac{m\pi z}{l} \right),$$

where one or both of the cosines in the above expressions for $T(\rho, \phi, z)$ may be replaced by sine terms. Again linear combinations of these solutions are used in the solution of cylindrical problems with periodic boundary conditions in the axial direction. The manipulation of these series solutions will be aided by the various recurrence relations and orthogonality properties possessed by the Bessel functions (see, for example, Abramowitz and Stegun [3], Ch. 9).

It should be remarked that if the solution $T(\rho, \phi, z)$ is known to be independent of the axial coordinate z, equation (83) reduces to equation (76) and the (much simpler) two-dimensional solutions (77) and (81) derived in §7.6 may be used.

Spherical Polar Coordinates

The systems of spherical polar coordinates r, θ, ϕ and cartesian coordinates are related by

$$x = r \sin \theta \cos \phi, \quad y = r \sin \theta \sin \phi, \quad z = r \cos \theta$$

and

$$r = (x^2 + y^2 + z^2)^{1/2}, \quad \theta = \cos^{-1}(z/r) \quad \text{for } 0 \leqslant \theta \leqslant \pi, \quad \tan \phi = y/x,$$

(see Fig. 5.16). Here θ denotes the polar angle and ϕ the azimuthal angle.

Laplace's equation in spherical polar coordinates has the form (see §6.7)

$$\frac{\partial^2 T}{\partial r^2} + \frac{2}{r}\frac{\partial T}{\partial r} + \frac{1}{r^2}\frac{\partial^2 T}{\partial \theta^2} + \frac{\cot \theta}{r^2}\frac{\partial T}{\partial \theta} + \frac{1}{r^2 \sin^2 \theta}\frac{\partial^2 T}{\partial \phi^2} = 0. \tag{90}$$

In general T will depend on r, θ and ϕ. For problems in which the polar axis $\theta = 0$ is an axis of symmetry, the solutions are independent of the azimuthal angle ϕ. If every radius vector is an axis of symmetry, the problem is said to be radially symmetric and in this case T is a function of r only. For $T = R(r)$, Laplace's equation (90) becomes

$$R''(r) + \frac{2}{r}R'(r) = 0.$$

This is a first-order linear equation for $R'(r)$ with the integrating factor r^2. Hence it is easily shown that

$$T = R(r) = A + \frac{B}{r} \tag{91}$$

where A and B are arbitrary constants.

Let us find the solution of $\nabla^2 T = 0$ in the interior $0 \leqslant r < a$ of a sphere of radius a subject to $T = T_a$ on the surface $r = a$. This is a radially symmetric problem with the solution (91). If B is non-zero the value of T at the centre of the sphere is infinite. Since this is not physically reasonable, we take $B = 0$. Hence the solution is $T = T_a$ for $0 \leqslant r \leqslant a$; that is, the potential is a constant within the sphere. Example 4 of §6.4 shows that this solution is unique.

The solution of Laplace's equation for the region $r > a$ exterior to the sphere subject to $T = T_a$ on $r = a$ and the requirement that $T \to 0$ as $r \to \infty$ is clearly

$$T = T_a \, a/r, \quad \text{for } r \geqslant a.$$

If the radius a tends to zero and T_a increases so that $KT_a a \to m$ as $a \to 0$, then this solution tends to the basic three-dimensional *point source* solution of heat conduction $T = m/Kr$. The temperature due to a point source of strength m at the point (x_0, y_0, z_0) is

$$T = \frac{m}{K \, |\mathbf{r} - \mathbf{r}_0|} = \frac{m}{K\{(x - x_0)^2 + (y - y_0)^2 + (z - z_0)^2\}^{1/2}}.$$

The rate of outflow of heat from this source is $4\pi m$. There are corresponding point source solutions in electrostatics, gravitational theory and in fluid mechanics, see example 3 of §6.5.

For axially-symmetric problems it is natural to look for separated solutions of the form $T = R(r)\Theta(\theta)$ where the polar axis $\theta = 0$ is the axis of symmetry. Equation (90) becomes

$$\left(R''(r) + \frac{2}{r} R'(r) \right) \frac{r^2}{R(r)} = - \frac{\Theta''(\theta) - \cot \theta \Theta'(\theta)}{\Theta(\theta)} \tag{92}$$

where each side must be a constant as r and θ are independent variables. To solve this equation for $R(r)$ it is convenient to put the constant equal to $n(n+1)$ where n will be found to be an integer. Then the equation

$$r^2 R''(r) + 2rR'(r) - n(n+1)R(r) = 0$$

has the solution

$$R(r) = A_n r^n + B_n r^{-n-1}$$

where A_n and B_n are arbitrary constants. The corresponding equation for $\Theta(\theta)$ is

$$\Theta''(\theta) + \cot \theta \Theta'(\theta) + n(n+1)\Theta(\theta) = 0.$$

This equation may be written in a simpler form by expressing Θ in terms of $\cos \theta = \mu$. This gives

$$(1 - \mu^2) \frac{d^2\Theta}{d\mu^2} - 2\mu \frac{d\Theta}{d\mu} + n(n+1)\Theta = 0. \tag{93}$$

This is called *Legendre's equation* of order n. If n is an integer this has a solution which is finite in $-1 \leqslant \mu \leqslant 1$ and is given by

$$\Theta(\theta) = P_n(\mu) = P_n(\cos \theta),$$

where $P_n(\mu)$ is a *Legendre polynomial* of degree n in μ. The solutions of Legendre's equation are divergent at $|\cos \theta| = 1$ for non-integral values of n. The forms of the polynomials for $n = 0, 1, 2$ are detailed in exercise 6.

The solutions of Laplace's equation (90) with axial symmetry therefore take the form

$$T = \left(A_n r^n + \frac{B_n}{r^{n+1}} \right) P_n(\cos \theta) \tag{94}$$

where n is an integer. The solution for $n = 0$ is equation (91). Note that if A is non-zero then T is unbounded as r tends to infinity, which would be unacceptable for the region $r > b$. Similarly if B is non-zero, T is unbounded as r tends to zero, so that equation (94) can only apply for the spherical region $r \leqslant a$ if $B = 0$. Clearly, for the region $a \leqslant r \leqslant b$ between two spheres both constants A and B may be non-zero. Obviously it is possible to superpose solutions of the type (94) for $n = 0, 1, 2, 3, \ldots$.

As an example, consider the solution of Laplace's equation within the sphere $r \leqslant a$ subject to the axially-symmetric boundary conditions $T = f(\theta)$ on $r = a$. From equation (94) the sum of the appropriate solutions is

$$T = \sum_{n=0}^{\infty} A_n r^n P_n(\cos \theta). \tag{95}$$

On $r = a$ the boundary conditions give

$$\sum_{n=0}^{\infty} A_n a^n P_n(\cos \theta) = f(\theta), \qquad 0 \leqslant \theta \leqslant \pi. \tag{96}$$

This immediately raises a number of questions regarding the equation (96). Can any continuous function $f(\theta)$ be represented in the form (96)? Is the representation unique? Is the resulting series convergent and differentiable? It may be shown that there is an affirmative answer to each question. Further, as the Legendre polynomials satisfy the *orthogonality relations*

$$\int_{-1}^{1} P_n(\mu) P_k(\mu) \, d\mu = \begin{cases} 0, & n \neq k, \\ 2/(2k+1), & n = k, \end{cases} \tag{97}$$

the constants A_n are easily found by multiplying through equation (96) by $P_k(\cos \theta) \sin \theta$ and integrating from $\theta = 0$ to $\theta = \pi$ to give

$$a^k A_k = \frac{2k+1}{2} \int_{0}^{\pi} f(\theta) P_k(\cos \theta) \sin \theta \, d\theta, \qquad k = 0, 1, 2, 3, \ldots. \tag{98}$$

The derivation of these results is beyond the scope of this book but may be found in Churchill [5], Ch. 9. The method of separation of variables as described in §7.3 has led to Fourier series problems in the earlier sections of this chapter. This illustration has been included to indicate how the method may be applied to other sets of functions which arise naturally in the solution of partial differential equations.

Exercises

1. If the function T satisfies Laplace's equation in the cylindrical region $z \geqslant 0$, $0 \leqslant \rho \leqslant a$, subject to the boundary conditions

$$T = 1 \quad \text{on} \quad z = 0, \quad 0 \leqslant \rho \leqslant a,$$
$$T = 0 \quad \text{on} \quad \rho = a, \quad z \geqslant 0,$$
$$T \to 0 \quad \text{as} \quad z \to \infty,$$

show that

$$T = \sum_{n=1}^{\infty} A_n J_0(\alpha_n \rho/a) \exp(-\alpha_n z/a)$$

where the coefficients A_n must be chosen to satisfy

$$\sum_{n=1}^{\infty} A_n J_0(\alpha_n \rho/a) = 1, \quad 0 \leqslant \rho \leqslant a,$$

and α_n are the roots of the equation $J_0(\alpha_n) = 0, n = 1, 2, 3, \ldots.$

2. Confirm that the axially-symmetric solution $T(\rho, z)$ of Laplace's equation in the infinite cylinder $-\infty < z < \infty, 0 \leqslant \rho \leqslant a$ subject to the boundary condition $T = \cos \lambda z$

on $\rho = a$ is

$$T = \frac{I_0(\lambda\rho)}{I_0(\lambda a)} \cos \lambda z.$$

What is the solution which corresponds to the boundary condition $T = 1$ on $\rho = a$?

3. The electrostatic potential V satisfies Laplace's equation $\nabla^2 V = 0$. If V is the electrostatic potential for the region outside a sphere of radius a and if $V = V_0$ on $r = a$, $V \to 0$ as $r \to \infty$, find V.

4. Find the electrostatic potential in the region $a < r < b$ between two spheres when $V = V_a$ on $r = a$ and $V = V_b$ on $r = b$.

5. The electrostatic potential due to a point source of strength m (in the appropriate units) at (x_0, y_0, z_0) is

$$V = \frac{m}{|\mathbf{r} - \mathbf{r}_0|} = \frac{m}{\{(x - x_0)^2 + (y - y_0)^2 + (z - z_0)^2\}^{1/2}}.$$

Find the electrostatic potential in the half-space $z \geqslant 0$ due to a point source of strength m at $x_0 = 0$, $y_0 = 0$, $z_0 = d$, when the plane $z = 0$ is earthed so that $V = 0$ on $z = 0$. *Hint:* place an image source at $x = 0$, $y = 0$, $z = -d$, and find its strength.

6. The Legendre polynomials P_0, P_1, P_2 are $P_0(\cos \theta) = 1$, $P_1(\cos \theta) = \cos \theta$, $P_2(\cos \theta) = \frac{1}{2}(3 \cos^2 \theta - 1)$. Hence the simplest axially-symmetric solutions of Laplace's equation in spherical polar coordinates are

$$A_0 + \frac{B_0}{r}, \quad \left(A_1 r + \frac{B_1}{r^2}\right) \cos \theta, \quad \left(A_2 r^2 + \frac{B_2}{r^3}\right)(3 \cos^2 \theta - 1).$$

The irrotational flow of an ideal fluid has the velocity field $\mathbf{v} = \operatorname{grad} V$ where V is the velocity potential and satisfies $\nabla^2 V = 0$. Confirm that the uniform flow field $\mathbf{v} = U\mathbf{k}$ corresponds to $V = Ur \cos \theta$ where U is a constant. Similarly show that if a rigid sphere of radius $r = a$ is placed in this uniform flow field the potential becomes

$$V = U\left(r + \frac{a^3}{2r^2}\right) \cos \theta$$

where the boundary condition of zero normal flow on the sphere is $\partial V / \partial r = 0$ on $r = a$.

7.8 INHOMOGENEOUS EQUATIONS

So far attention has been concentrated on solving homogeneous partial differential equations subject to inhomogeneous boundary conditions.

As a typical problem for an inhomogeneous equation, let us investigate the solution of

$$\nabla_1^2 T = \frac{\partial^2 T}{\partial x^2} + \frac{\partial^2 T}{\partial y^2} = h(x, y) \tag{99}$$

in the rectangle $0 \leqslant x \leqslant a, 0 \leqslant y \leqslant b$, subject to the homogeneous boundary conditions

$$T(0, y) = 0, \quad T(a, y) = 0, \tag{100}$$
$$T(x, 0) = 0, \quad T(x, b) = 0,$$

where $h(x, y)$ is a known function. If T is interpreted as the temperature field, then equation (99) is the steady heat conduction equation in which $h(x, y)$ represents a distribution of heat sources and sinks in the rectangle. The problem is to determine the temperature in the rectangle subject to zero temperature around the boundary.

Alternatively, if we identify T as the transverse displacement (denoted by v in §7.4) of a membrane under all-round tension T_0, then equation (99) is the equation governing the static displacement of the membrane under a pressure distribution $T_0 h(x, y)$. The boundary conditions correspond to a rectangular membrane clamped to a plane frame. Equation (99) is known as *Poisson's equation*.

There are two methods of solving equation (99) subject to the conditions (100). The first method of solution reduces the problem to one of the type solved in §7.6. Suppose a particular integral $T = T_h(x, y)$ of equation (99) can be found so that

$$\nabla_1^2 T_h = h(x, y).$$

Now let us put $T = T_h + \hat{T}$. Then the unknown function $\hat{T}$ satisfies Laplace's equation (64) subject to inhomogeneous boundary conditions, which is the problem already considered in §7.6. On substituting into equation (99) we find

$$\nabla_1^2 \hat{T} = 0,$$

and the conditions (100) become

$$\hat{T}(0, y) = -T_h(0, y), \quad \hat{T}(a, y) = -T_h(a, y), \tag{101}$$
$$\hat{T}(x, 0) = -T_h(x, 0), \quad \hat{T}(x, b) = -T_h(x, b).$$

Hence it is possible to reduce the solution of an inhomogeneous equation with homogeneous boundary conditions to the solution of a homogeneous equation with inhomogeneous boundary conditions. This procedure requires a method for constructing a particular integral. Often these can be easily spotted. Suppose for example

$$\frac{\partial^2 T}{\partial x^2} + \frac{\partial^2 T}{\partial y^2} = H$$

where H is a constant. Then one particular integral is $T_h = -\tfrac{1}{2}Hx(a - x)$. On putting $T = -\tfrac{1}{2}Hx(a - x) + \hat{T}$, the boundary conditions (101) for $\hat{T}$ become

$$\hat{T}(0, y) = 0, \quad \hat{T}(a, y) = 0,$$
$$\hat{T}(x, 0) = \tfrac{1}{2}Hx(a - x), \quad \hat{T}(x, b) = \tfrac{1}{2}Hx(a - x).$$

Clearly several alternative particular integrals are possible, for example, $T_h = \frac{1}{2}Hy^2$, $T_h = \frac{1}{4}H(x^2 + y^2)$, but the one chosen above is quite convenient as it also satisfies the boundary conditions on $x = 0$ and $x = a$. The solution may now be completed by following the methods of §7.6 and is given in exercise 1. General methods of determining particular integrals are beyond the scope of this chapter, but they may often be found by extending the ideas of §1.7 to partial differential equations.

The second method of solution relies on the construction of eigenfunctions which satisfy the boundary conditions (100) exactly. However, instead of considering equation (99) immediately, we solve the related equation

$$\frac{\partial^2 T}{\partial x^2} + \frac{\partial^2 T}{\partial y^2} = \lambda T \tag{102}$$

where λ is an appropriate constant, subject to the boundary conditions (100). Separated solutions of (102) which also satisfy the boundary conditions (100) are

$$T = A_{mn} \sin \frac{n\pi x}{a} \sin \frac{m\pi y}{b}$$

where m and n are integers and A_{mn} are arbitrary constants. The arbitrary constant λ which occurs in (102) now takes the value $\lambda = -\pi^2\{(n/a)^2 + (m/b)^2\}$. Observe that these solutions are the shape functions which occur in a vibration problem for a rectangular membrane (see §7.4).

Consider the sum of these eigenfunctions

$$T = \sum_{m=1}^{\infty} \sum_{n=1}^{\infty} A_{mn} \sin\left(\frac{n\pi x}{a}\right) \sin\left(\frac{m\pi y}{b}\right).$$

This satisfies the boundary conditions (100). On substituting into equation (99) we find

$$\sum_{m=1}^{\infty} \sum_{n=1}^{\infty} -\pi^2 \left(\frac{n^2}{a^2} + \frac{m^2}{b^2}\right) A_{mn} \sin \frac{n\pi x}{a} \sin \frac{m\pi y}{b} = h(x, y). \tag{103}$$

This equation must hold at all points of the rectangle $0 \leqslant x \leqslant a, 0 \leqslant y \leqslant b$. The problem reduces to the question of whether it is possible to choose the arbitrary coefficients A_{mn} so that $h(x, y)$ may be represented by the double Fourier series in equation (103). An identical equation (46) occurs in the vibration problem for a rectangular membrane. As indicated in §7.4, a repeated application of the Euler formulae (equation (12) of §2.2) will determine the coefficients A_{mn}. Exercise 2 gives the solution in the particular case when $h(x, y)$ is a constant.

The technique of replacing the inhomogeneous term $h(x, y)$ in the basic equation (99) by the term λT, where λ is an arbitrary constant, is quite general and may be employed in other inhomogeneous equations.

The inhomogeneous term $h(x, t)$ in the one-dimensional wave equation

$$\frac{1}{c^2} \frac{\partial^2 v}{\partial t^2} = \frac{\partial^2 v}{\partial x^2} + h(x, t), \quad 0 \leqslant x \leqslant a,$$

corresponds to a time-dependent distribution of transverse loads on the elastic string. A similar term in the heat conduction equation

$$\frac{1}{\kappa}\frac{\partial\theta}{\partial t} = \frac{\partial^2\theta}{\partial x^2} + h(x, t), \quad 0 \leqslant x \leqslant a,$$

corresponds to a distribution of heat sources. These inhomogeneous equations, with suitable boundary and initial conditions, may be solved by using either the particular integral approach or the eigenfunction approach described in this section. Sometimes integral transform techniques are required to determine particular integrals.

Exercises

1. Solve the Poisson equation

$$\nabla_1^2 T = H$$

in the rectangle $0 \leqslant x \leqslant a, 0 \leqslant y \leqslant b$ subject to the condition $T = 0$ at all points of the boundary by using the particular integral $T_h = -\frac{1}{2}Hx(a - x)$. Show that the solution is

$$T = -\frac{1}{2}Hx(a - x) + \sum_{n=1}^{\infty} \frac{2Ha^2}{n^3\pi^3} \frac{\{1 - (-1)^n\}}{\sinh(n\pi b/a)} \sin\left(\frac{n\pi x}{a}\right) \left[\sinh\frac{n\pi(b - y)}{a} + \sinh\frac{n\pi y}{a}\right].$$

2. Solve exercise 1 by using the eigenfunction method. Show that the solution is

$$T = \sum_{m=1}^{\infty} \sum_{n=1}^{\infty} A_{mn} \sin\frac{n\pi x}{a} \sin\frac{m\pi y}{b}$$

where

$$A_{mn} = -\frac{4Ha^2 b^2\{1 - (-1^n)\}\{1 - (-1)^m\}}{\pi^4 nm(b^2 n^2 + a^2 m^2)}.$$

The solutions of exercises 1 and 2 are different representations of the same answer.

7.9 GENERAL SECOND-ORDER EQUATIONS

In this chapter, attention has been concentrated on the three special second-order partial differential equations, the wave equation (1), the heat conduction equation (2) and Laplace's equation (3), because of their practical importance. The general linear second-order equation in two variables x, y is

$$A\frac{\partial^2 v}{\partial x^2} + B\frac{\partial^2 v}{\partial x \partial y} + C\frac{\partial^2 v}{\partial y^2} + D\frac{\partial v}{\partial x} + E\frac{\partial v}{\partial y} + Fv = G \tag{104}$$

in which the coefficients $A, \ldots, G$ may depend on x and y. Laplace's equation (63) in two dimensions is the special case of equation (104) in which $A = C = 1$ and B, D, E, F, G are zero. The wave equation (13) and the heat conduction equation (55) in one space variable also become special cases of equation (104) when t is replaced by y. Equation (104) is inhomogeneous if $G \neq 0$ and homogeneous if $G = 0$.

It will have been observed that the three special equations have different properties and require different types of boundary conditions (or initial conditions) to specify a physically sensible problem. We say that equation (104) is of *elliptic* type if $B^2 - 4AC$ is negative, is of *parabolic* type if $B^2 - 4AC$ is zero, and is of *hyperbolic* type if $B^2 - 4AC$ is positive.

Laplace's equation is an elliptic equation. Another important elliptic equation is *Helmholtz's equation*

$$\frac{\partial^2 v}{\partial x^2} + \frac{\partial^2 v}{\partial y^2} + Fv = 0,$$

which reduces to Laplace's equation when $F = 0$. The heat conduction equation is a parabolic equation and the wave equation is a hyperbolic equation. The basic properties of parabolic and hyperbolic equations are often similar to those of the heat conduction equation and the wave equation respectively.

Another important case of equation (104) (with y replaced by t) is the *telegraph equation*

$$\frac{\partial^2 v}{\partial x^2} = KL\frac{\partial^2 v}{\partial t^2} + (KR + LS)\frac{\partial v}{\partial t} + RSv. \tag{105}$$

Here $v(x, t)$ represents the electric potential at time t at x units along a transmission line. The transmission line is assumed to have an electrostatic capacity K, a self-inductance L, a resistance R and a leakage conductance S, all per unit length. This equation is normally hyperbolic, since KL is positive, and the transmission phenomena are wave-like. The equation becomes parabolic if K or L is zero.

The natural initial conditions for a hyperbolic equation (for example, the wave equation) with respect to the time variable t are that *both v and $\partial v/\partial t$* are specified on $t = 0$. These are sometimes referred to as boundary conditions of the *Cauchy* type and have been used in §7.2 and §7.4. Such boundary conditions are too restrictive for parabolic equations. For a parabolic equation it is only possible to specify the value of *either* the field variable *or* its derivative on $t = 0$.

One set of natural boundary conditions for an elliptic equation (Laplace's equation) is that the value of the field variable T is specified at all points of the boundary. We call such boundary conditions *Dirichlet* conditions. In a thermal problem this corresponds to specifying the temperature at all points of the boundary. Another natural boundary condition occurs when the heat flow across the boundary is specified at each boundary point. This corresponds to specifying the normal derivative $\partial T/\partial n$ of the temperature at each boundary point and is called a *Neumann* condition. A third type of boundary condition in which $(\partial T/\partial n) + hT$ is specified on the boundary and h is a positive constant is sometimes called a thermal radiation condition or a *Robin* condition. Obviously Dirichlet, Neumann and Robin conditions may hold on different (non-overlapping) parts of the boundary for an elliptic equation. Such problems are referred to as *mixed* boundary value problems and are often much more difficult to solve analytically than the Dirichlet or Neumann boundary value problems. Several problems of this nature have been discussed by Sneddon [7] using integral transform techniques.

Exercises

1. Show that separated solutions of Helmholtz's equation

$$\frac{\partial^2 v}{\partial x^2} + \frac{\partial^2 v}{\partial y^2} + Fv = 0$$

in the rectangle $0 \leqslant x \leqslant a, 0 \leqslant y \leqslant b$ can satisfy the Dirichlet condition $v = 0$ at all boundary points, only if the constant F has the form

$$F = \left(\frac{m^2}{b^2} + \frac{n^2}{a^2}\right)\pi^2$$

where m and n are integers. What form should F take in order that the Neumann condition $\partial V/\partial n = 0$ is satisfied at all boundary points?

2. Confirm that the telegraph equation (105) has a solution of the form

$$e^{-kx} \cos \{\lambda(x - ct)\}.$$

Show that the wave speed c and the damping length k^{-1} depend on the wave length λ through the equations

$$c^2 = \frac{RS + \lambda^2}{\frac{1}{4}(KR + LS)^2 + KL\lambda^2}, \quad k = \frac{1}{2}(KR + LS)c.$$

PROBLEMS

1. Use the method of separation of variables to determine a solution of the one-dimensional wave equation

$$\frac{\partial^2 v}{\partial x^2} = \frac{1}{c^2}\frac{\partial^2 v}{\partial t^2} \quad \text{on } 0 \leqslant x \leqslant a, t \geqslant 0$$

subject to the boundary conditions

$$\frac{\partial v}{\partial x} = 0 \quad \text{on } x = 0, \quad \frac{\partial v}{\partial x} = 0 \quad \text{on } x = a$$

and the initial conditions

$$v(x, 0) = f(x), \quad \frac{\partial v}{\partial t}(x, 0) = 0.$$

Show that the solution has the form

$$v(x, t) = \frac{1}{2}A_0 + \sum_{n=1}^{\infty} A_n \cos\frac{n\pi x}{a}\cos\frac{n\pi ct}{a}$$

and find the coefficients A_n. If

$$f(x) = \begin{cases} \epsilon x, & 0 \leqslant x \leqslant \tfrac{1}{2}a, \\ \epsilon(a - x), & \tfrac{1}{2}a \leqslant x \leqslant a, \end{cases}$$

show that the string vibrates about the mean position $v = \tfrac{1}{4}\epsilon a$ and sketch the configurations of the string.

2. Confirm that the solution of the one-dimensional wave equation

$$\frac{\partial^2 v}{\partial x^2} = \frac{1}{c^2} \frac{\partial^2 v}{\partial t^2} \quad \text{on } 0 \leqslant x \leqslant a, \quad t \geqslant 0$$

subject to the boundary conditions

$$\frac{\partial v}{\partial x} = 0 \quad \text{on both } x = 0 \text{ and } x = a$$

and the initial conditions

$$v = f(x), \quad \frac{\partial v}{\partial t} = 0 \quad \text{on } 0 \leqslant x \leqslant a, \text{ when } t = 0,$$

is

$$v = \tfrac{1}{2}\{f_e(x - ct) + f_e(x + ct)\}.$$

Here $f_e(x)$ denotes the even periodic extension of $f(x)$ of period $2a$ (see §2.4).

3. A rectangular membrane $0 \leqslant x \leqslant a, 0 \leqslant y \leqslant b$ is set vibrating with the initial conditions $v = 0$, $\partial v/\partial t = V$ at $t = 0$ where V is a constant. If the boundary conditions are $v = 0$ and the transverse displacement satisfies the wave equation (43), show that

$$v = \sum_{m=1}^{\infty} \sum_{n=1}^{\infty} \frac{4V\{1 - (-1)^n\}\{1 - (-1)^m\}}{\pi^3 cmn \left(\dfrac{n^2}{a^2} + \dfrac{m^2}{b^2}\right)^{1/2}} \sin\frac{n\pi x}{a} \sin\frac{m\pi y}{b} \sin\left(\frac{n^2}{a^2} + \frac{m^2}{b^2}\right)^{1/2} \pi ct.$$

4. By determining a particular integral, solve the inhomogeneous heat conduction equation

$$\frac{1}{\kappa}\frac{\partial \theta}{\partial t} = \frac{\partial^2 \theta}{\partial x^2} + H$$

where H is a constant, in the region $0 \leqslant x \leqslant a$ subject to the boundary conditions $\theta(0, t) = 0$, $\theta(a, t) = 0$ and the initial condition $\theta(x, 0) = 0$. Show that the temperature tends to $\tfrac{1}{2}Hx(a - x)$ for large values of t.

5. Show that the eigenfunctions for the heat conduction equation

$$\frac{\partial^2 \theta}{\partial x^2} = \frac{1}{\kappa}\frac{\partial \theta}{\partial t}$$

in $0 \leqslant x \leqslant a$ subject to the boundary condition $\theta = 0$ on $x = 0$ and the radiation condition $\theta + h\, \partial\theta/\partial x = 0$ on $x = a$ are $\sin px \exp(-p^2 \kappa t)$, where the eigenvalues p satisfy the equation $\tan pa + hp = 0$.

6. Solve Laplace's equation $\nabla^2 T = 0$ in the rectangular box $0 \leqslant x \leqslant a, 0 \leqslant y \leqslant b,$ $0 \leqslant z \leqslant c$ subject to the boundary conditions $T = 0$ on the faces $x = 0, x = a, y = 0,$ $y = b$ and $z = c$. If $T = f(x, y)$ on $z = 0$, show that

$$T = \sum_{m=1}^{\infty} \sum_{n=1}^{\infty} A_{mn} \sin \frac{n\pi x}{a} \sin \frac{m\pi y}{b} \sinh\left(\frac{n^2}{a^2} + \frac{m^2}{b^2}\right)^{1/2} \pi(c - z)$$

where

$$A_{mn} = \frac{4}{ab \sinh\left(\dfrac{n^2}{a^2} + \dfrac{m^2}{b^2}\right)^{1/2} \pi c} \int_0^b \int_0^a f(x, y) \sin \frac{n\pi x}{a} \sin \frac{m\pi y}{b} \,dx\, dy.$$

7. The solution (82) of Laplace's equation in plane polar coordinates in the circle $\rho \leqslant a$ subject to the boundary condition $T(a, \phi) = f(\phi), 0 \leqslant \phi \leqslant 2\pi$ is

$$T(\rho, \phi) = \tfrac{1}{2} A_0 + \sum_{n=1}^{\infty} \rho^n (A_n \cos n\phi + B_n \sin n\phi),$$

where

$$a^n A_n = \frac{1}{\pi} \int_0^{2\pi} f(\tau) \cos n\tau \, d\tau, \qquad n = 0, 1, 2, 3, \ldots,$$

$$a^n B_n = \frac{1}{\pi} \int_0^{2\pi} f(\tau) \sin n\tau \, d\tau, \qquad n = 1, 2, 3, \ldots.$$

These formulae may be combined to give

$$T(\rho, \phi) = \frac{1}{2\pi} \int_0^{2\pi} f(\tau) d\tau + \frac{1}{\pi} \int_0^{2\pi} f(\tau) \sum_{n=1}^{\infty} \left(\frac{\rho}{a}\right)^n \cos n(\tau - \phi) \quad d\tau.$$

By expressing the cosine in terms of the exponential function, the sum can be expressed as a pair of geometric series. By summing these series show that

$$T(\rho, \phi) = \frac{a^2 - \rho^2}{2\pi} \int_0^{2\pi} \frac{f(\tau) d\tau}{a^2 - 2a\rho \cos(\tau - \phi) + \rho^2}.$$

This is *Poisson's formula* for the solution of Laplace's equation in the circle $\rho \leqslant a$ subject to $T(a, \phi) = f(\phi)$.

8. A three-dimensional thermal point source of strength m is placed at the point $(0, 0, z_0)$ in the region outside the sphere $x^2 + y^2 + z^2 \leqslant a^2$. If the sphere is cooled so that $T = 0$ on its surface, show that the temperature T outside the sphere can be written as

$$KT = \frac{m}{|\mathbf{r} - z_0 \mathbf{k}|} + \frac{m_1}{|\mathbf{r} - z_1 \mathbf{k}|}.$$

In this expression the image source has strength $m_1 = -am/z_0$ and is placed at the point $(0, 0, z_1)$ which is the image point of $(0, 0, z_0)$ in the sphere so that $z_0 z_1 = a^2$. Image sources of this type also occur in electrostatics, fluid mechanics and in gravitational theory.

9. The following expansion may be shown to be convergent in $|h| < 1$:

$$\frac{1}{\{1 - 2h \cos \theta + h^2\}^{1/2}} = \sum_{n=0}^{\infty} h^n P_n(\cos \theta)$$

where $P_n(\cos \theta)$ is the Legendre polynomial of degree n. The potential due to a thermal point source of strength m at the point $(0, 0, z_0)$ is

$$KT = \frac{m}{|\mathbf{r} - z_0 \mathbf{k}|}$$

where $\mathbf{r} = x\mathbf{i} + y\mathbf{j} + z\mathbf{k}$. In spherical polar coordinates, show that

$$KT = \frac{m}{\{z_0^2 - 2z_0 r \cos \theta + r^2\}^{1/2}} = \begin{cases} \dfrac{m}{z_0} \displaystyle\sum_{n=0}^{\infty} \left(\dfrac{r}{z_0}\right)^n P_n(\cos \theta), & r < z_0 \\[4mm] \dfrac{m}{z_0} \displaystyle\sum_{n=0}^{\infty} \left(\dfrac{z_0}{r}\right)^{n+1} P_n(\cos \theta), & r > z_0. \end{cases}$$

This result links the potential of a point source with the separated solutions (94).

BIBLIOGRAPHY

[1]   Ames, W. F., *Nonlinear Partial Differential Equations in Engineering*, Academic Press, New York (1965).

[2]   Coulson, C. A., *Waves*, Oliver and Boyd, Edinburgh (1958).

[3]   Abramowitz, M. and I. A. Stegun, *Handbook of Mathematical Functions*, Dover, New York (1965).

[4]   Stokey, W. F., Chapter 7 of *Shock and Vibration Handbook* (edited by C. M. Harris and C. E. Crede), McGraw-Hill, New York (1961).

[5]   Churchill, R. V., *Fourier Series and Boundary Value Problems*, McGraw-Hill, New York (1963).

[6]   Morse, P. M. and H. Feshbach, *Methods of Theoretical Physics*, McGraw-Hill, New York (1953).

[7]   Sneddon, I. N., *Mixed Boundary Value Problems in Potential Theory*, North-Holland, Amsterdam (1966).

CHAPTER 8

Linear Algebra — Theory

8.1 SYSTEMS OF LINEAR ALGEBRAIC EQUATIONS. MATRIX NOTATION

Many problems in engineering, science, economics and other subjects reduce to the solution of systems of linear algebraic equations. This chapter will be largely concerned with the theory of the manipulation and solution of such systems. Numerical methods of solution are dealt with in Chapter 10. To exemplify the manner in which systems of linear algebraic equations can arise in an engineering context we begin with some illustrations from electricity and mechanics.

Electrical Networks

Consider the simple electrical network shown in Fig. 8.1, with steady currents $I, I_1, \ldots, I_5$ in the various conducting wires with resistances $R_1, R_2, \ldots, R_5$ as shown. Kirchhoff's first law states that the net flow of current into any junction must be zero. Applying this to the junctions A, B, C, D in turn gives

$$
\begin{aligned}
I_1 + I_2 \quad\qquad &= I, \\
I_2 - I_3 - I_4 \quad &= 0, \\
I_1 \quad + I_3 \quad - I_5 &= 0, \\
I_4 + I_5 &= I.
\end{aligned}
\tag{1}
$$

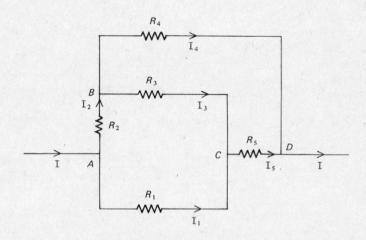

Fig. 8.1   Electrical network

Two points should be noted. (a) The four equations are not independent; the first is the sum of the other three. Thus only three of the equations give information about the system, and one equation could be discarded. (b) The equations are not sufficient to determine the currents $I_1, I_2, \ldots, I_5$ in terms of the given current I. To obtain a complete system of equations we might adopt Kirchhoff's second law, which states that the algebraic sum of the products of the current and resistance in any closed circuit without batteries, is zero. By applying this in turn to the circuits $ABCA$ and $BCDB$ there follows

$$
\begin{aligned}
-R_1 I_1 + R_2 I_2 + R_3 I_3 &= 0, \\
-R_3 I_3 + R_4 I_4 - R_5 I_5 &= 0.
\end{aligned}
\tag{2}
$$

A further equation could be obtained by considering the circuit $ABDCA$, but this would yield no new information. Equations (1) and (2) together determine $I_1, I_2, \ldots, I_5$, and are quite easily solved.

Frameworks

(a)   A simple pin-jointed plane framework is illustrated in Fig. 8.2(a). Let $T_1, T_2,$ T_3, T_4 denote the unknown tensions (a thrust is regarded as a negative tension) in the members, as illustrated, and let X_B, Y_B, X_C, Y_C be given loads applied as shown to the joints B and C. Since each joint is in equilibrium, the resultant horizontal and vertical components of force on B and C are zero, which gives

$$
\begin{aligned}
-T_2 &= -X_B, \\
T_1 &= -Y_B, \\
T_2 + \sqrt{\tfrac{1}{2}}T_3 &= -X_C, \\
\sqrt{\tfrac{1}{2}}T_3 + T_4 &= -Y_C.
\end{aligned}
\tag{3}
$$

There is no difficulty in solving these four equations for the four unknowns $T_1, T_2,$ T_3, T_4. The structure is determinate.

(b)   Suppose now that the framework is strengthened by the addition of the member CE shown in Fig. 8.2(b). The equations for equilibrium of the joints now give

$$
\begin{aligned}
-T_2 &= -X_B, \\
T_1 &= -Y_B, \\
T_2 + \sqrt{\tfrac{1}{2}}T_3 - \sqrt{\tfrac{1}{2}}T_5 &= -X_C, \\
\sqrt{\tfrac{1}{2}}T_3 + T_4 + \sqrt{\tfrac{1}{2}}T_5 &= -Y_C.
\end{aligned}
\tag{4}
$$

These are now four equations for five unknowns. There is not a unique solution, and the structure is indeterminate. To produce a system of equations with a unique solution, it is necessary to make further assumptions about the properties of the members. We suppose that they obey Hooke's Law so that, in any member $LT = EAe$ where T is the tension, e the extension, L the length, A the cross-sectional area and E is Young's modulus. For simplicity suppose that E and A are the same for each member, and that the members are fixed in position but free to rotate at A, D and E. Let the horizontal and vertical components of displacement of the joint B be U_B and V_B, and the corresponding components of displacement of C be U_C and V_C. Then the extensions of the members are easily calculated, and Hooke's Law applied to the five

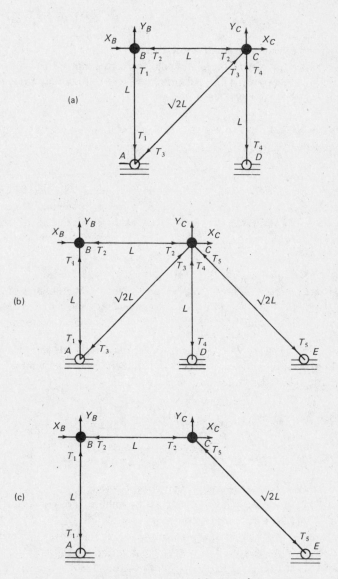

Fig. 8.2 Plane pin-jointed frameworks

members gives

$$LT_1 \qquad\qquad\qquad -EAV_B \qquad\qquad\qquad\qquad = 0,$$

$$LT_2 \qquad\qquad +EAU_B \qquad -EAU_C \qquad\qquad\qquad = 0,$$

$$\sqrt{2}LT_3 \qquad\qquad\qquad -\sqrt{\tfrac{1}{2}}EAU_C - \sqrt{\tfrac{1}{2}}EAV_C = 0, \quad (5)$$

$$LT_4 \qquad\qquad\qquad\qquad -EAV_C \qquad = 0,$$

$$\sqrt{2}LT_5 \qquad\qquad\qquad +\sqrt{\tfrac{1}{2}}EAU_C - \sqrt{\tfrac{1}{2}}EAV_C = 0.$$

Equations (4) and (5) are nine equations for nine unknowns $T_1, T_2, \ldots, T_5, U_B, V_B,$ U_C, V_C. In practice the easiest method of solution is to eliminate $T_1, T_2, \ldots, T_5$ by substituting from equations (5) into equations (4). Again the solution is not difficult (see example 4 of §8.2 and exercise 4 of §8.4).

(c)   Finally, suppose that the members AC and CD are removed, as in Fig. 8.2(c). The equations of equilibrium of the joints are now

$$T_2 \qquad\qquad = -X_B,$$

$$-T_2 \qquad\qquad = -Y_B,$$

$$T_2 - \sqrt{\tfrac{1}{2}}T_5 = -X_C, \qquad\qquad\qquad (6)$$

$$\sqrt{\tfrac{1}{2}}T_5 = -Y_C.$$

These are now four equations for three unknowns T_1, T_2, T_5. Unless $X_B + X_C + Y_C = 0$ the equations are self-contradictory, and have no solution. This absence of a solution reflects the physically obvious fact that the framework is a mechanism, which in general cannot stand in equilibrium under the given loads and will collapse.

Equations (1), (2) (or (1) and (2) together) (3), (4), (5) (or (4) and (5) together) and (6) are examples of *systems of linear algebraic equations*. A system of linear algebraic equations is a set of equations of the form

$$a_{11}x_1 + a_{12}x_2 + \ldots + a_{1n}x_n = b_1,$$

$$a_{21}x_1 + a_{22}x_2 + \ldots + a_{2n}x_n = b_2,$$

$$\ldots\ldots\ldots \qquad\qquad\qquad\qquad\qquad (7)$$

$$a_{m1}x_1 + a_{m2}x_2 + \ldots + a_{mn}x_n = b_m.$$

Equations (7) comprise m equations in the n unknowns $x_1, x_2, : \ldots, x_n$. The coefficients $a_{11}, a_{12}, \ldots, a_{mn}$ are given constant numbers, and so are $b_1, b_2, \ldots, b_m$. The commonest and most important case is that in which $m = n$, so that the number of equations is equal to the number of unknowns. However the above examples show that this is not necessarily the case, and m may be greater than, equal to, or less than n.

Systems of linear algebraic equations occur directly in many engineering problems. As well as in the problems of electrical networks and framed structures exemplified above, they arise in problems of surveying, in certain statistical problems, in all manner of vibration problems, in the economics of supply, demand and costing, and elsewhere. They also appear very frequently in problems of numerical analysis, especially as numerical approximations to differential equations. The problem in which some of equations (7) are replaced by inequalities is also of practical importance, and is considered in Chapter 1 of Volume 2.

In principle, equations such as equations (7) may be solved (provided that they have a solution) by the elementary methods of substitution or elimination. However for hand calculations these methods become prohibitively laborious if m and n exceed about five or six. It is easy to envisage electrical networks and framed structures which lead to much larger numbers (possibly hundreds) of equations and unknowns (consider, for example, the wiring of a motor car, or a large bridge) and then methods which can be easily adapted to computer solution are needed. A convenient tool for this is provided by matrix algebra. Throughout this chapter it is important to keep in mind that methods are required which will handle large systems of equations, although in the space available it is only possible to illustrate with quite small systems.

Matrices

An $m \times n$ *matrix* is an ordered array of numbers arranged in m rows and n columns. For example

$$\begin{pmatrix} 2 & -5 & \tfrac{1}{2} \\ \pi & 0 & 0.7 \end{pmatrix} \text{ is a 2 x 3 matrix,} \quad \begin{pmatrix} 1 \\ 3 \\ -1 \end{pmatrix} \text{ is a 3 x 1 matrix.}$$

There are many reasons why matrices are of interest to mathematicians, physicists, economists and others. However they are usually first encountered, especially as regards engineering applications, in connection with the study and solution of linear algebraic equations. Therefore in this chapter matrix properties will be developed in relation to this application. Accordingly, we first observe that a convenient abbreviation of equations (7) is

$$\mathbf{AX} = \mathbf{B}, \tag{8}$$

where $\mathbf{A}$, $\mathbf{X}$ and $\mathbf{B}$ represent the following arrays of numbers

$$\mathbf{A} = \begin{pmatrix} a_{11} & a_{12} \ldots a_{1n} \\ a_{21} & a_{22} \ldots a_{2n} \\ \ldots \ldots \\ a_{m1} & a_{m2} \ldots a_{mn} \end{pmatrix}, \quad \mathbf{X} = \begin{pmatrix} x_1 \\ x_2 \\ \vdots \\ x_n \end{pmatrix}, \quad \mathbf{B} = \begin{pmatrix} b_1 \\ b_2 \\ \vdots \\ b_m \end{pmatrix}. \tag{9}$$

Thus $\mathbf{A}$ is an $m \times n$ matrix, $\mathbf{X}$ an $n \times 1$ matrix and $\mathbf{B}$ an $m \times 1$ matrix. The numbers which form each array are called the *elements* of the matrix. The element in the ith row and jth column of $\mathbf{A}$ is denoted a_{ij} so that the first *index* (i) denotes the row and the second (j) denotes the column. Thus i takes the values 1 to m and j takes the values

1 to n and a_{ij} is the element at the intersection of the ith row and the jth column of **A**. We sometimes use the notation

$$\mathbf{A} = (a_{ij})$$

to denote the matrix **A** whose ijth element is a_{ij}. In this notation, unless it is otherwise clear from the context, it is necessary to specify the range of values which i and j take in order to know the size of **A**.

Symbols which represent matrices will be printed in bold face type, and symbols which represent ordinary numbers (also called scalars) will be printed in italic type.

Special Matrices

Matrices of various special forms are often encountered in applications. The most important are the following.

(a)   *Column vectors*   A matrix such as **X** or **B** in equation (9) which consists of a single column of numbers is a *column vector*.

(b)   *Row vectors*   A matrix consisting of a single row such as

$$\mathbf{C} = (c_1 \; c_2 \; \ldots \; c_n)$$

is called a *row vector*.

Row and column vectors, as special matrices, have some properties similar to those of the vectors described in Chapter 6, but are not identical to them. The vectors described in Chapter 6 usually represent physical quantities, whereas matrices do not necessarily do so. Although the terminology is ambiguous, it will usually be clear from the context which type of vector is involved in a given application.

(c)   *Square matrices*   If $m = n$, so that **A** is a square array of numbers with the number of columns equal to the number of rows, then **A** is a *square $n \times n$ matrix* or a *square matrix of order n*. If **A** is a square matrix, then in equation (7) the number of equations is equal to the number of unknowns.

The *leading diagonal* of a square matrix is the diagonal set of elements extending from its top left-hand corner to its bottom right-hand corner. Thus, if **A** is a square matrix the elements $a_{11}, a_{22}, a_{33}, \ldots, a_{nn}$ lie on its leading diagonal, which consists of the elements a_{ij} for which $i = j$.

(d)   *Symmetric matrices*   If, in a square matrix **A**, the element in the ith row and the jth column is equal to the element in the jth row and the ith column, that is if $a_{ij} = a_{ji}$ for all values of i and j, then **A** is *symmetric*. The symmetry is about the leading diagonal. An example of a fourth-order symmetric matrix is

$$\begin{pmatrix} 1 & 0 & -2 & 5 \\ 0 & 6 & 3 & 1 \\ -2 & 3 & 2 & 3 \\ 5 & 1 & 3 & 2 \end{pmatrix}.$$

(e)   *Anti-symmetric matrices*   If, in a square matrix $\mathbf{A}$, $a_{ij} = -a_{ji}$ for all values of i and j, then $\mathbf{A}$ is *anti-symmetric* (or *skew-symmetric*). Since in particular $a_{11} = -a_{11}$, $a_{22} = -a_{22}$, etc., all elements on the leading diagonal of an anti-symmetric matrix are zero. For example

$$\begin{pmatrix} 0 & 2 & -1 \\ -2 & 0 & 3 \\ 1 & -3 & 0 \end{pmatrix}$$ is a third-order anti-symmetric matrix.

(f)   *Upper and lower triangular matrices*   A square matrix $\mathbf{A}$ is *upper* (*lower*) *triangular* if all the elements below (above) its leading diagonal are zeros. Thus

$$\begin{pmatrix} 1 & -1 & 2 \\ 0 & 3 & 5 \\ 0 & 0 & 2 \end{pmatrix}$$ is upper triangular; $$\begin{pmatrix} 1 & 0 & 0 \\ 4 & 0 & 0 \\ 0 & 6 & 2 \end{pmatrix}$$ is lower triangular.

The elements on the leading diagonal may or may not be zeros.

(g)   *Diagonal matrices*   A *diagonal matrix* is a square matrix with zeros everywhere except on the leading diagonal. A diagonal matrix is of course symmetric. An example is

$$\begin{pmatrix} 4 & 0 & 0 & 0 \\ 0 & 3 & 0 & 0 \\ 0 & 0 & -5 & 0 \\ 0 & 0 & 0 & -1 \end{pmatrix} .$$

(h)   The *unit matrix* of order n has 1 at each position on the leading diagonal and zeros elsewhere. It is denoted by $\mathbf{I}_n$ or, if its order is clear from the context, simply by $\mathbf{I}$. Thus

$$\mathbf{I}_2 = \begin{pmatrix} 1 & 0 \\ 0 & 1 \end{pmatrix}, \quad \mathbf{I}_3 = \begin{pmatrix} 1 & 0 & 0 \\ 0 & 1 & 0 \\ 0 & 0 & 1 \end{pmatrix} .$$

$\mathbf{I}_n$ is a diagonal matrix of order n.

(i)   The *zero* or *null matrix*, of a given size, has zeros for all its elements. It is denoted by $\mathbf{0}$ and is not necessarily a square matrix.

Exercises

1. Which of the following matrices are (1) symmetric, or (2) anti-symmetric, or (3) upper triangular, or (4) none of these?

(a) $$\begin{pmatrix} 2 & 0 & 4 \\ 0 & 3 & -1 \\ 4 & -1 & 1 \end{pmatrix},$$ (b) $$\begin{pmatrix} 2 & 0 & 4 \\ 0 & 3 & 1 \\ -4 & -1 & 1 \end{pmatrix},$$

(c) $\begin{pmatrix} 0 & -5 & 3 & 2 \\ 5 & 0 & -1 & 6 \\ -3 & 1 & 0 & -4 \\ -2 & -6 & 4 & 0 \end{pmatrix}$,

(d) $\begin{pmatrix} 1 & 1 & -3 \\ 0 & 4 & -2 \\ 0 & 0 & -2 \end{pmatrix}$,

(e) $\begin{pmatrix} 0 & 1 & -3 \\ 0 & 0 & -2 \\ 0 & 0 & 0 \end{pmatrix}$,

(f) $\begin{pmatrix} 0 & 2 & 6 & 5 \\ 0 & 1 & 3 & 2 \\ 0 & 0 & 0 & 2 \end{pmatrix}$,

8.2 ELEMENTARY OPERATIONS OF MATRIX ALGEBRA

Equality of Matrices

Two matrices A and B are said to be equal if (a) they are of the same size, so that the number of rows of A equals the number of rows of B, and similarly for columns; and (b) all corresponding elements of A and B are equal. Thus, if $A = (a_{ij})$, $B = (b_{ij})$, and if $a_{ij} = b_{ij}$ for all values of i and j, we write $A = B$.

Transposition

Suppose A is an $m \times n$ matrix. Then from A a new matrix can be formed whose rows are the columns of A, taken in order, and whose columns are the rows of A, taken in order. This new matrix is called the *transpose* of A; it is an $n \times m$ matrix and is denoted by A^T. If a_{ij} is the ijth element of A, then a_{ji} is the ijth element of A^T. For example, if

$$A = \begin{pmatrix} 3 & 0 & 2 & 4 \\ 7 & -1 & -2 & 6 \\ 3 & 5 & -1 & -1 \end{pmatrix}, \quad \text{then} \quad A^T = \begin{pmatrix} 3 & 7 & 3 \\ 0 & -1 & 5 \\ 2 & -2 & -1 \\ 4 & 6 & -1 \end{pmatrix}.$$

The following results are immediate consequences of this definition and the definitions of §8.1.

(a)   The transpose of a row vector is a column vector, and vice versa.

(b)   The transpose of an nth-order square matrix is also an nth-order square matrix.

(c)   The transpose of a symmetric matrix is itself, so that A is a symmetric matrix if and only if $A^T = A$.

(d)   The transpose of an anti-symmetric matrix is the original matrix with each element multiplied by -1, and is itself anti-symmetric. B is an anti-symmetric matrix if and only if $B^T = -B$.

(e) The transpose of an upper triangular matrix is a lower triangular matrix, and vice versa.

(f) For any matrix $\mathbf{A}$, $(\mathbf{A}^T)^T = \mathbf{A}$.

So far we have only introduced a rather large number of definitions and made some immediate deductions from them. The next objective is to construct an algebra of matrices. This matrix algebra will be constructed so as to be as close as possible to our familiar ordinary algebra, but we shall find that it is necessary to introduce some important differences from ordinary algebra. The first step in formulating matrix algebra is to define the operations of matrix addition, subtraction and multiplication. The definitions to be adopted are ones which have been found in practice to be useful ones. In particular they facilitate the manipulation of systems such as equations (7).

Addition and Subtraction of Matrices

The sum $\mathbf{A} + \mathbf{C}$ of two $m \times n$ matrices $\mathbf{A}$ and $\mathbf{C}$ is defined in the natural way to be the $m \times n$ matrix whose ijth element is $a_{ij} + c_{ij}$. Similarly $\mathbf{A} - \mathbf{C}$ is the matrix whose ijth element is $a_{ij} - c_{ij}$. It is essential that $\mathbf{A}$ and $\mathbf{C}$ are the same size; it is impossible to add or subtract matrices of different sizes.

EXAMPLE 1

$$\text{Let} \quad \mathbf{A} = \begin{pmatrix} 2 & 4 & -1 & 6 \\ -7 & 1 & 8 & 3 \\ 5 & 2 & 0 & 1 \end{pmatrix}, \quad \mathbf{C} = \begin{pmatrix} 0 & 4 & 6 & 3 \\ 2 & 7 & -1 & 5 \\ 4 & 2 & -3 & 1 \end{pmatrix}.$$

Then

$$\mathbf{A} + \mathbf{C} = \begin{pmatrix} 2 & 8 & 5 & 9 \\ -5 & 8 & 7 & 8 \\ 9 & 4 & -3 & 2 \end{pmatrix}, \quad \mathbf{A} - \mathbf{C} = \begin{pmatrix} 2 & 0 & -7 & 3 \\ -9 & -6 & 9 & -2 \\ 1 & 0 & 3 & 0 \end{pmatrix}.$$

It follows immediately from the definition that if $\mathbf{A}$, $\mathbf{B}$ and $\mathbf{C}$ are all $m \times n$ matrices then

$$\mathbf{A} + \mathbf{B} = \mathbf{B} + \mathbf{A}, \quad (\mathbf{A} + \mathbf{B}) + \mathbf{C} = \mathbf{A} + (\mathbf{B} + \mathbf{C}), \quad (\mathbf{A} + \mathbf{B})^T = \mathbf{A}^T + \mathbf{B}^T. \tag{10}$$

Multiplication by a Scalar

If $\mathbf{A}$ is an $m \times n$ matrix whose ijth element is a_{ij}, and k is a scalar, then $k\mathbf{A}$ is defined to be the $m \times n$ matrix whose ijth element is ka_{ij}. As a special case k may be zero, and then

$$0\mathbf{A} = \mathbf{0}. \tag{11}$$

Matrix Multiplication

As well as multiplying a matrix by a scalar, it is possible to multiply one matrix by another matrix. Matrix multiplication arises as a generalization of a simple operation in elementary algebra. Suppose first that we have two relations

$$x = ay, \quad y = bz,$$

connecting the pairs of scalar variables x and y, and y and z respectively. By substituting for y from the second equation into the first, there follows

$$x = abz.$$

Now suppose we have two relations between three sets of variables $(x_1, x_2, \ldots, x_p)$, $(y_1, y_2, \ldots, y_n)$ and $(z_1, z_2, \ldots, z_q)$. In matrix notation these are written

$$\mathbf{X} = \mathbf{AY}, \quad \mathbf{Y} = \mathbf{BZ} \tag{12}$$

where $\mathbf{A}$ is a $p \times n$ matrix, $\mathbf{B}$ an $n \times q$ matrix and $\mathbf{X}, \mathbf{Y}, \mathbf{Z}$ are column vectors with p, n and q rows respectively. It is natural to 'substitute for $\mathbf{Y}$' from the second matrix equation into the first, and write

$$\mathbf{X} = \mathbf{ABZ} \tag{13}$$

and this can be done provided that the product $\mathbf{AB}$ is defined in a suitable way. For illustration, suppose $p = 2, n = 2, q = 3$, so that, written in full, equations (12) become

$$
\begin{aligned}
x_1 &= a_{11}y_1 + a_{12}y_2, \quad y_1 = b_{11}z_1 + b_{12}z_2 + b_{13}z_3, \\
x_2 &= a_{21}y_1 + a_{22}y_2, \quad y_2 = b_{21}z_1 + b_{22}z_2 + b_{23}z_3,
\end{aligned}
\tag{14}
$$

where now

$$
\mathbf{X} = \begin{pmatrix} x_1 \\ x_2 \end{pmatrix}, \quad
\mathbf{Y} = \begin{pmatrix} y_1 \\ y_2 \end{pmatrix}, \quad
\mathbf{Z} = \begin{pmatrix} z_1 \\ z_2 \\ z_3 \end{pmatrix},
$$

$$
\mathbf{A} = \begin{pmatrix} a_{11} & a_{12} \\ a_{21} & a_{22} \end{pmatrix}, \quad
\mathbf{B} = \begin{pmatrix} b_{11} & b_{12} & b_{13} \\ b_{21} & b_{22} & b_{23} \end{pmatrix}.
$$

By substituting for y_1, y_2 from the second set of equations (14) into the first set, we have

$$
\begin{aligned}
x_1 &= (a_{11}b_{11} + a_{12}b_{21})z_1 + (a_{11}b_{12} + a_{12}b_{22})z_2 + (a_{11}b_{13} + a_{12}b_{23})z_3, \\
x_2 &= (a_{21}b_{11} + a_{22}b_{21})z_1 + (a_{21}b_{12} + a_{22}b_{22})z_2 + (a_{21}b_{13} + a_{22}b_{23})z_3.
\end{aligned}
\tag{15}
$$

This is consistent with equation (13) and the notation previously employed provided that **AB** is interpreted to be the matrix

$$AB = \begin{pmatrix} a_{11} & a_{12} \\ a_{21} & a_{22} \end{pmatrix} \begin{pmatrix} b_{11} & b_{12} & b_{13} \\ b_{21} & b_{22} & b_{23} \end{pmatrix}$$

$$= \begin{pmatrix} a_{11}b_{11} + a_{12}b_{21} & a_{11}b_{12} + a_{12}b_{22} & a_{11}b_{13} + a_{12}b_{23} \\ a_{21}b_{11} + a_{22}b_{21} & a_{21}b_{12} + a_{22}b_{22} & a_{21}b_{13} + a_{22}b_{23} \end{pmatrix}. \quad (16)$$

This is an example of the operation which is called 'matrix multiplication'. Notice that the elimination of the y's from equations (14) can be done only when the number of columns of **A** is equal to the number of rows of **B**. Only then is the formation of the product **AB** (in that order) possible. If this condition is satisfied, the two matrices are said to be *conformable* for the product **AB**.

We may now extend equation (16) to define formally the process of matrix multiplication. Suppose a_{ij} is the ijth element of a $p \times n$ matrix **A** and b_{ij} is the ijth element of an $n \times q$ matrix **B**. Then the ijth element c_{ij} of the product **C** = **AB** is

$$c_{ij} = \sum_{r=1}^{n} a_{ir} b_{rj}$$

and **C** has p rows and q columns. Thus, to obtain the element in the ith row and jth column of **C** = **AB** select the ith row of **A**, and the jth column of **B**, multiply corresponding elements beginning at the left of the row of **B** and the top of the column of **A**, and sum all the resulting products.

EXAMPLE 2

Let $\quad A = \begin{pmatrix} 3 & 1 \\ 2 & 3 \\ 5 & 4 \end{pmatrix}, \quad B = \begin{pmatrix} 2 & 7 & 6 \\ 1 & 0 & 3 \end{pmatrix}.$

Then

$$AB = \begin{pmatrix} 3 & 1 \\ 2 & 3 \\ 5 & 4 \end{pmatrix} \begin{pmatrix} 2 & 7 & 6 \\ 1 & 0 & 3 \end{pmatrix} = \begin{pmatrix} 3 \times 2 + 1 \times 1 & 3 \times 7 + 1 \times 0 & 3 \times 6 + 1 \times 3 \\ 2 \times 2 + 3 \times 1 & 2 \times 7 + 3 \times 0 & 2 \times 6 + 3 \times 3 \\ 5 \times 2 + 4 \times 1 & 5 \times 7 + 4 \times 0 & 5 \times 6 + 4 \times 3 \end{pmatrix}$$

$$= \begin{pmatrix} 7 & 21 & 21 \\ 7 & 14 & 21 \\ 14 & 35 & 42 \end{pmatrix}.$$

Note that **A** is 3×2, **B** is 2×3, **AB** is 3×3.

$$\mathbf{BA} = \begin{pmatrix} 2 & 7 & 6 \\ 1 & 0 & 3 \end{pmatrix} \begin{pmatrix} 3 & 1 \\ 2 & 3 \\ 5 & 4 \end{pmatrix} = \begin{pmatrix} 2 \times 3 + 7 \times 2 + 6 \times 5 & 2 \times 1 + 7 \times 3 + 6 \times 4 \\ 1 \times 3 + 0 \times 2 + 3 \times 5 & 1 \times 1 + 0 \times 3 + 3 \times 4 \end{pmatrix}$$

$$= \begin{pmatrix} 50 & 47 \\ 18 & 13 \end{pmatrix}.$$

Note that **B** is 2 x 3, **A** is 3 x 2, **BA** is 2 x 2, and that $\mathbf{AB} \neq \mathbf{BA}$.

EXAMPLE 3

Let $\mathbf{A} = \begin{pmatrix} 1 & 2 & 3 \\ 4 & 5 & 6 \end{pmatrix}$, $\mathbf{X} = \begin{pmatrix} x_1 \\ x_2 \\ x_3 \end{pmatrix}$, $\mathbf{Y} = (y_1 \quad y_2)$.

Then

$$\mathbf{AX} = \begin{pmatrix} 1 & 2 & 3 \\ 4 & 5 & 6 \end{pmatrix} \begin{pmatrix} x_1 \\ x_2 \\ x_3 \end{pmatrix} = \begin{pmatrix} x_1 + 2x_2 + 3x_3 \\ 4x_1 + 5x_2 + 6x_3 \end{pmatrix},$$

$$\mathbf{YA} = (y_1 \quad y_2) \begin{pmatrix} 1 & 2 & 3 \\ 4 & 5 & 6 \end{pmatrix} = (y_1 + 4y_2 \quad 2y_1 + 5y_2 \quad 3y_1 + 6y_2).$$

However **A**, **X** and **Y** are not conformable for the products **XA** and **AY**, so these products do not exist.

EXAMPLE 4

In §8.1 equations (4) and (5) were derived for the tensions and displacements in the framework illustrated in Fig. 8.2(b). These equations can be expressed as follows

$$\begin{pmatrix} 0 & -1 & 0 & 0 & 0 \\ 1 & 0 & 0 & 0 & 0 \\ 0 & 1 & \sqrt{\frac{1}{2}} & 0 & -\sqrt{\frac{1}{2}} \\ 0 & 0 & \sqrt{\frac{1}{2}} & 1 & \sqrt{\frac{1}{2}} \end{pmatrix} \begin{pmatrix} T_1 \\ T_2 \\ T_3 \\ T_4 \\ T_5 \end{pmatrix} = \begin{pmatrix} -X_B \\ -Y_B \\ -X_C \\ -Y_C \end{pmatrix},$$

$$\frac{EA}{L} \begin{pmatrix} 0 & 1 & 0 & 0 \\ -1 & 0 & 1 & 0 \\ 0 & 0 & \frac{1}{2} & \frac{1}{2} \\ 0 & 0 & 0 & 1 \\ 0 & 0 & -\frac{1}{2} & \frac{1}{2} \end{pmatrix} \begin{pmatrix} U_B \\ V_B \\ U_C \\ V_C \end{pmatrix} = \begin{pmatrix} T_1 \\ T_2 \\ T_3 \\ T_4 \\ T_5 \end{pmatrix}.$$

Eliminating $T_1, T_2, \ldots, T_5$ from these gives

$$\frac{EA}{L}\begin{pmatrix} 0 & -1 & 0 & 0 & 0 \\ 1 & 0 & 0 & 0 & 0 \\ 0 & 1 & \sqrt{\tfrac{1}{2}} & 0 & -\sqrt{\tfrac{1}{2}} \\ 0 & 0 & \sqrt{\tfrac{1}{2}} & 1 & \sqrt{\tfrac{1}{2}} \end{pmatrix}\begin{pmatrix} 0 & 1 & 0 & 0 \\ -1 & 0 & 1 & 0 \\ 0 & 0 & \tfrac{1}{2} & \tfrac{1}{2} \\ 0 & 0 & 0 & 1 \\ 0 & 0 & -\tfrac{1}{2} & \tfrac{1}{2} \end{pmatrix}\begin{pmatrix} U_B \\ V_B \\ U_C \\ V_C \end{pmatrix}=\begin{pmatrix} -X_B \\ -Y_B \\ -X_C \\ -Y_C \end{pmatrix},$$

or

$$\frac{EA}{L}\begin{pmatrix} 1 & 0 & -1 & 0 \\ 0 & 1 & 0 & 0 \\ -1 & 0 & 1+\sqrt{\tfrac{1}{2}} & 0 \\ 0 & 0 & 0 & 1+\sqrt{\tfrac{1}{2}} \end{pmatrix}\begin{pmatrix} U_B \\ V_B \\ U_C \\ V_C \end{pmatrix}=\begin{pmatrix} -X_B \\ -Y_B \\ -X_C \\ -Y_C \end{pmatrix},$$

which relates the displacements of the joints B and C to the forces applied to these joints.

The definition of matrix multiplication has many consequences, some of which are the following.

(a) The product of a $p \times n$ matrix and an $n \times q$ matrix is a $p \times q$ matrix.

(b) If A and X are the matrices defined by equations (9), then AX is the column vector whose elements are the expressions on the left-hand side of equations (7). Hence the notation AX introduced in equation (8) is consistent with the definition of matrix multiplication.

(c) *In general* $AB \neq BA$, *even when both products exist* (see example 2 above). This is the main difference between matrix multiplication and ordinary algebraic multiplication. *In carrying out manipulations involving matrix multiplications it is essential to keep factors in their correct order*. It is of course possible for the product AB to exist but not BA (see example 3 above).

(d) *Distributive law*. It follows immediately from the definitions of matrix addition and multiplication that

$$(A + B)C = AC + BC, \quad A(C + D) = AC + AD,$$

provided that all the sums and products exist. These results may be extended. For example

$$(A + B)(C + D) = AC + AD + BC + BD.$$

Note that the order in which the factors occur in each product must not be changed, but that otherwise the matrices here follow the rules of ordinary algebra.

(e) *Continued products*. If A, B are conformable for the product AB, and B, C are conformable for the product BC, then $(AB)C$ and $A(BC)$ both exist, and are equal. They may be written unambiguously without brackets as **ABC**. This also may be extended so that, if the matrices are suitably conformable, products **ABCD**, and so on, can be formed.

(f)   *Powers of a square matrix*. When **A** is an $n \times n$ matrix, any positive integer power $\mathbf{A}^p$ is defined as

$$\mathbf{A}^p = \mathbf{AA} \ldots \ldots \mathbf{A} \quad \text{(to } p \text{ factors).}$$

(g)   *Multiplication by a unit matrix*. If **A** is a $p \times q$ matrix, then

$$\mathbf{AI}_q = \mathbf{I}_p \mathbf{A} = \mathbf{A}.$$

The unit matrices play a similar role in matrix algebra to that which the integer one plays in ordinary algebra.

EXAMPLE 5

Let $\mathbf{A} = \begin{pmatrix} 1 & 3 & 5 \\ 2 & 4 & 6 \end{pmatrix}$.

Then

$$\begin{pmatrix} 1 & 3 & 5 \\ 2 & 4 & 6 \end{pmatrix} \begin{pmatrix} 1 & 0 & 0 \\ 0 & 1 & 0 \\ 0 & 0 & 1 \end{pmatrix} = \begin{pmatrix} 1+0+0 & 0+3+0 & 0+0+5 \\ 2+0+0 & 0+4+0 & 0+0+6 \end{pmatrix} = \begin{pmatrix} 1 & 3 & 5 \\ 2 & 4 & 6 \end{pmatrix},$$

$$\begin{pmatrix} 1 & 0 \\ 0 & 1 \end{pmatrix} \begin{pmatrix} 1 & 3 & 5 \\ 2 & 4 & 6 \end{pmatrix} = \begin{pmatrix} 1+0 & 3+0 & 5+0 \\ 0+2 & 0+4 & 0+6 \end{pmatrix} = \begin{pmatrix} 1 & 3 & 5 \\ 2 & 4 & 6 \end{pmatrix}.$$

(h)   *Multiplication by a zero matrix*. If the products exist, then $\mathbf{0A} = \mathbf{0}$ and $\mathbf{A0} = \mathbf{0}$. A zero matrix corresponds to the zero in ordinary algebra.

(i)   *Transpose of a product*. If **A** and **B** are conformable for the product **AB**, then $\mathbf{B}^T$ and $\mathbf{A}^T$ are conformable for the product $\mathbf{B}^T \mathbf{A}^T$, and

$$(\mathbf{AB})^T = \mathbf{B}^T \mathbf{A}^T. \tag{17}$$

To prove the result (17), suppose that $\mathbf{A} = (a_{ij})$ is a $p \times n$ matrix and $\mathbf{B} = (b_{ij})$ is an $n \times q$ matrix. Then $\mathbf{A}^T$ is the $n \times p$ matrix whose ijth element is a_{ji}, and $\mathbf{B}^T$ is the $q \times n$ matrix whose ijth element is b_{ji}, so $\mathbf{B}^T \mathbf{A}^T$ exists, and its ijth element is

$$\sum_{r=1}^{n} b_{ri} a_{jr}.$$

The ijth element of $(\mathbf{B}^T \mathbf{A}^T)^T$ is obtained by interchanging i and j, so it is

$$\sum_{r=1}^{n} b_{rj} a_{ir} = \sum_{r=1}^{n} a_{ir} b_{rj}.$$

But the last expression is, by definition, the ijth element of $\mathbf{AB}$, so

$$(\mathbf{B}^T\mathbf{A}^T)^T = \mathbf{AB}. \tag{18}$$

Equation (17) follows by transposing both sides of equation (18). The result extends to any number of matrices so that, provided the matrices are suitably conformable

$$(\mathbf{ABC}\ldots\mathbf{FG})^T = \mathbf{G}^T\mathbf{F}^T\ldots\mathbf{C}^T\mathbf{B}^T\mathbf{A}^T.$$

Note the reversal of the order of the factors.

(j) If $\mathbf{A}$ is $p \times n$, $\mathbf{B}$ is $n \times q$, the calculation of $\mathbf{AB}$ requires pqn multiplications and $pq(n-1)$ additions. If p, q and n are large, the calculation is laborious. It is, however, one which is easily and rapidly performed on a digital computer.

Exercises

1. If

$$\mathbf{A} = \begin{pmatrix} 5 & 1 \\ -2 & 2 \end{pmatrix}, \quad \mathbf{B} = \begin{pmatrix} 2 & 3 \\ -4 & -1 \end{pmatrix},$$

evaluate $\mathbf{A} + \mathbf{B}$, $\mathbf{A} - 2\mathbf{B}$, $\mathbf{A} + 2\mathbf{A}^T - 3\mathbf{B} + 4\mathbf{B}^T$, $\mathbf{AB}$, $\mathbf{BA}$, $\mathbf{A}^2$, $\mathbf{ABA}^T$.

2. If

$$\mathbf{A} = \begin{pmatrix} 2 & 1 & 4 & -1 \\ 6 & 3 & -3 & -5 \\ 7 & -6 & 4 & 2 \end{pmatrix}, \quad \mathbf{B} = \begin{pmatrix} 1 & -1 & -1 & 0 \\ 2 & -4 & 5 & -3 \\ 2 & 1 & -1 & 1 \end{pmatrix},$$

evaluate $2\mathbf{A} + 3\mathbf{B}$, $\mathbf{A} - 2\mathbf{B}$, $\mathbf{AB}^T$ and $\mathbf{A}^T\mathbf{B}$.

3. If

$$\mathbf{A} = \begin{pmatrix} 2 & 1 & -4 \\ 0 & -2 & 3 \\ 0 & 0 & -1 \end{pmatrix}, \quad \mathbf{B} = \begin{pmatrix} 1 & 2 & 0 \\ 3 & 2 & 0 \\ 0 & 0 & -1 \end{pmatrix}, \quad \mathbf{C} = \begin{pmatrix} 1 & -2 & -3 \\ 0 & 2 & 3 \\ 0 & 0 & -1 \end{pmatrix}$$

find $\mathbf{AB}$, $\mathbf{BA}$, $\mathbf{AC}$, $\mathbf{A} + \mathbf{A}^T$ and $\mathbf{AA}^T$. Are any of these either (a) triangular or (b) symmetric? If so, could that property have been deduced before the calculation?

4. If

$$\mathbf{X} = (2 \ \ 4 \ \ 1)^T, \quad \mathbf{Y} = (3 \ \ 1 \ \ 2)^T,$$

evaluate $\mathbf{X}^T\mathbf{Y}$ and $\mathbf{XY}^T$.

5. Let

$$\begin{pmatrix} x_1 \\ x_2 \end{pmatrix} = \frac{1}{10} \begin{pmatrix} 2 & 1 & 2 \\ -4 & \frac{1}{2} & -2 \end{pmatrix} \begin{pmatrix} y_1 \\ y_2 \\ y_3 \end{pmatrix}, \quad \begin{pmatrix} y_1 \\ y_2 \\ y_3 \end{pmatrix} = \begin{pmatrix} 1 & 2 \\ 0 & 4 \\ 2 & 0 \end{pmatrix} \begin{pmatrix} z_1 \\ z_2 \end{pmatrix}.$$

By considering the product

$$(x_1 \quad x_2) \begin{pmatrix} x_1 \\ x_2 \end{pmatrix},$$

prove that $x_1^2 + x_2^2 = z_1^2 + z_2^2$.

6. If

$$\mathbf{A} = \begin{pmatrix} 1 & -1 & 2 \\ 0 & 3 & 1 \\ -2 & 1 & -2 \end{pmatrix},$$

find $\mathbf{A}^2$ and $\mathbf{A}^3$, and verify that $\mathbf{A}^3 - 2\mathbf{A}^2 - 2\mathbf{A} - 7\mathbf{I} = \mathbf{0}$.

7. Prove that any square matrix can be expressed as the sum of a symmetric matrix and an anti-symmetric matrix.

8.3 DETERMINANTS

It is assumed that the reader has some familiarity with the theory and manipulation of determinants. This section summarizes, largely without proof, their main properties.

An nth-order determinant is written

$$\begin{vmatrix} a_{11} & a_{12} & \cdots & a_{1n} \\ a_{21} & a_{22} & \cdots & a_{2n} \\ & \cdots \cdots & \\ a_{n1} & a_{n2} & \cdots & a_{nn} \end{vmatrix} \tag{19}$$

and is a certain homogeneous polynomial of degree n in the n^2 quantities $a_{11}, a_{12} \ldots a_{nn}$. In fact it is a sum of all the products of the type $\pm a_{1i}a_{2j}a_{3k} \ldots a_{nq}$ where $i, j, k \ldots q$ are the integers $1, 2, 3 \ldots n$, in some order. We shall not go into the rule for determining the sign of a given term. In particular, for a second-order determinant

$$\begin{vmatrix} a_{11} & a_{12} \\ a_{21} & a_{22} \end{vmatrix} = a_{11}a_{22} - a_{12}a_{21}, \tag{20}$$

and for a third-order determinant

$$\begin{vmatrix} a_{11} & a_{12} & a_{13} \\ a_{21} & a_{22} & a_{23} \\ a_{31} & a_{32} & a_{33} \end{vmatrix} = \begin{aligned} & a_{11}a_{22}a_{33} - a_{11}a_{23}a_{32} + a_{12}a_{23}a_{31} - a_{12}a_{21}a_{33} \\ & \qquad + a_{13}a_{21}a_{32} - a_{13}a_{22}a_{31}. \end{aligned} \tag{21}$$

It is essential at the outset to appreciate the distinction between a matrix and a determinant. A matrix is an *array* of numbers; it cannot be expressed as any single number. A determinant is *a single number* which is obtained by performing a certain sequence of multiplications, additions and subtractions on the members of a square array of numbers. With every square (but not with a non-square) matrix **A** there is *associated* a determinant, denoted det **A** or | **A** |, but **A** and its determinant are quite distinct.

Expansion of a Determinant

We first introduce two definitions.

(a)   *Minors*   If the ith row and jth column of the determinant (19) are deleted, there is left a determinant of order $n - 1$. This is called the *minor* of a_{ij} and is denoted M_{ij}.

(b)   *Cofactors*   The *cofactor* A_{ij} of a_{ij} is the signed minor given by

$$A_{ij} = (-1)^{i+j}M_{ij}.$$

EXAMPLE 1
In

$$\begin{vmatrix} a_{11} & a_{12} & a_{13} & a_{14} \\ a_{21} & a_{22} & a_{23} & a_{24} \\ a_{31} & a_{32} & a_{33} & a_{34} \\ a_{41} & a_{42} & a_{43} & a_{44} \end{vmatrix},$$

$$M_{23} = \begin{vmatrix} a_{11} & a_{12} & a_{14} \\ a_{31} & a_{32} & a_{34} \\ a_{41} & a_{42} & a_{44} \end{vmatrix}, \quad M_{42} = \begin{vmatrix} a_{11} & a_{13} & a_{14} \\ a_{21} & a_{23} & a_{24} \\ a_{31} & a_{33} & a_{34} \end{vmatrix}$$

and $A_{23} = (-1)^{2+3} M_{23} = -M_{23}, \qquad A_{42} = (-1)^{4+2} M_{42} = M_{42}.$

An nth-order determinant of a square matrix **A** is now defined in terms of $(n - 1)$th-order determinants (its cofactors) by the formula

$$\det \mathbf{A} = a_{11}A_{11} + a_{12}A_{12} + a_{13}A_{13} + \ldots + a_{1n}A_{1n}. \tag{22}$$

Since a second-order determinant is explicitly defined by equation (20), this formula defines determinants of orders 3, 4, 5, . . . , n successively in terms of their predecessors.

EXAMPLE 2

$$\begin{vmatrix} a_{11} & a_{12} & a_{13} \\ a_{21} & a_{22} & a_{23} \\ a_{31} & a_{32} & a_{33} \end{vmatrix} = a_{11}A_{11} + a_{12}A_{12} + a_{13}A_{13}$$

$$= a_{11}\begin{vmatrix} a_{22} & a_{23} \\ a_{32} & a_{33} \end{vmatrix} - a_{12}\begin{vmatrix} a_{21} & a_{23} \\ a_{31} & a_{33} \end{vmatrix} + a_{13}\begin{vmatrix} a_{21} & a_{22} \\ a_{31} & a_{32} \end{vmatrix}$$

$$= a_{11}(a_{22}a_{33} - a_{23}a_{32}) - a_{12}(a_{21}a_{33} - a_{23}a_{31}) + a_{13}(a_{21}a_{32} - a_{22}a_{31}),$$

which agrees with equation (21).

A very important property of a determinant, from which most of its other properties follow, is that det $\mathbf{A}$ may be evaluated by carrying out an expansion of the type given by equation (22), using any row or any column. Thus

$$\begin{aligned} \det \mathbf{A} &= a_{11}A_{11} + a_{12}A_{12} + a_{13}A_{13} + \ldots + a_{1n}A_{1n} \\ &= a_{21}A_{21} + a_{22}A_{22} + a_{23}A_{23} + \ldots + a_{2n}A_{2n} \\ &= \cdots \\ &= a_{n1}A_{n1} + a_{n2}A_{n2} + a_{n3}A_{n3} + \ldots + a_{nn}A_{nn} \\ &= a_{11}A_{11} + a_{21}A_{21} + a_{31}A_{31} + \ldots + a_{n1}A_{n1} \\ &= \cdots \\ &= a_{1n}A_{1n} + a_{2n}A_{2n} + a_{3n}A_{3n} + \ldots + a_{nn}A_{nn}. \end{aligned}$$

(23)

That is, the determinant may be evaluated by taking the elements of any of its rows, or any of its columns, multiplying each element by its corresponding cofactor, and adding. This process is called the *Laplacian expansion* of the determinant.

It is by no means obvious that the lines of equation (23) each yield the same result. For second and third-order determinants it is easy to verify directly that they do. For the general determinant of order n, the equivalence of the different expressions (23) can be proved by induction, by assuming them true for determinants up to order $n - 1$, and deducing their truth for determinants of order n.

Rules for Manipulation of Determinants

We can now list a number of results which follow more or less directly from the Laplacian expansion.

(a) *If all the elements in any row (column) of a determinant are zero, then the value of the determinant is zero.* This follows immediately on expanding by the row or column of zeros.

(b) *If only one element in a row (column) is non-zero, the determinant is the product of that element and its cofactor.* The proof is again to expand by this row or column.

(c)   *If the rows and columns of a determinant are transposed, the value of the determinant is unchanged*; that is

$$\det \mathbf{A} = \det \mathbf{A}^T.$$

The proof is by induction.

(d)   *If all the elements of one row (column) of a determinant are multiplied by a constant k, the value of the determinant is multiplied by k.* To prove, expand by the row or column whose elements are multiplied by k. Note that this multiplication rule is quite different from that for scalar multiplication of a matrix.

(e)   *Interchanging two rows (columns) of a determinant changes the sign of the determinant.* Again the proof is by induction.

(f)   *If two rows (columns) of a determinant are identical, the value of the determinant is zero.* This follows directly from (e).

(g)   *If the elements of one row (column) are proportional to corresponding elements of another row (column) the value of the determinant is zero.* This is an immediate consequence of (d) and (f).

(h)   *If each element in any row (column) is resolved into the sum of two quantities, the determinant can be expressed as the sum of two determinants.* For example

$$
\begin{vmatrix}
a_{11} + b_{11} & a_{12} & \cdots & a_{1n} \\
a_{21} + b_{21} & a_{22} & \cdots & a_{2n} \\
& & \cdots & \\
a_{n1} + b_{n1} & a_{n2} & \cdots & a_{nn}
\end{vmatrix}
$$

$$
=
\begin{vmatrix}
a_{11} & a_{12} & \cdots & a_{1n} \\
a_{21} & a_{22} & \cdots & a_{2n} \\
& & \cdots & \\
a_{n1} & a_{n2} & \cdots & a_{nn}
\end{vmatrix}
+
\begin{vmatrix}
b_{11} & a_{12} & \cdots & a_{1n} \\
b_{21} & a_{22} & \cdots & a_{2n} \\
& & \cdots & \\
b_{n1} & b_{n2} & \cdots & a_{nn}
\end{vmatrix}.
\tag{24}
$$

This can be verified by expanding each determinant by its first column. Note that the rule for addition of determinants is not the same as for addition of matrices.

(i)   *The value of a determinant is unchanged when to each element of any row (column) is added the corresponding element of any other row (column) multiplied by any constant factor.* This property follows from (g) and (h). It provides a very useful method of numerically evaluating determinants.

(j)   *If the elements of any one row (column) are multiplied by the cofactors of the corresponding elements of any other row (column) the sum of the resulting products is zero.* For example, if det $\mathbf{A}$ is a third-order determinant

$$a_{11}A_{21} + a_{12}A_{22} + a_{13}A_{23}$$

$$= -a_{11}\begin{vmatrix} a_{12} & a_{13} \\ a_{32} & a_{33} \end{vmatrix} + a_{12}\begin{vmatrix} a_{11} & a_{13} \\ a_{31} & a_{33} \end{vmatrix} - a_{13}\begin{vmatrix} a_{11} & a_{12} \\ a_{31} & a_{32} \end{vmatrix}$$

$$= -\begin{vmatrix} a_{11} & a_{12} & a_{13} \\ a_{11} & a_{12} & a_{13} \\ a_{31} & a_{32} & a_{33} \end{vmatrix}$$

= 0, since the first two rows are identical.

(k) *The determinant of an upper (lower) triangular matrix is the product of the elements on its leading diagonal.*

(l) *The determinant of a diagonal matrix is the product of the elements on the leading diagonal.*

A further result, which does not follow readily from equation (23), but is of importance is:

(m) *The determinant of the product of two square matrices of the same order is equal to the product of their determinants.* Thus if **A, B** are *square* matrices of the same order, then

$$\det(\mathbf{AB}) = \det(\mathbf{BA}) = \det \mathbf{A} \times \det \mathbf{B}. \tag{25}$$

The proof is quite involved and is omitted. A proof is given in Bell[1].

Exercises

1. Evaluate the following determinants:

$$\begin{vmatrix} 1 & 3 \\ -2 & 4 \end{vmatrix}, \quad \begin{vmatrix} 6 & 5 \\ 1 & -2 \end{vmatrix}, \quad \begin{vmatrix} 2 & -2 & 3 \\ 1 & 0 & 4 \\ 3 & 1 & 1 \end{vmatrix}, \quad \begin{vmatrix} 7 & -5 & -3 \\ 6 & 4 & 1 \\ -5 & 8 & 9 \end{vmatrix}, \quad \begin{vmatrix} 2 & -1 & 0 & 1 \\ 0 & 3 & 4 & 0 \\ 5 & 2 & -4 & -1 \\ 1 & 2 & -1 & 0 \end{vmatrix}.$$

2. Evaluate the following determinants:

$$\begin{vmatrix} 1 & 1 & 1 \\ b+c & c+a & a+b \\ b^2+c^2 & c^2+a^2 & a^2+b^2 \end{vmatrix}, \quad \begin{vmatrix} 1 & a^2 & a^4 \\ 1 & b^2 & b^4 \\ 1 & c^2 & c^4 \end{vmatrix}, \quad \begin{vmatrix} 1 & a & b+c+d & bcd \\ 1 & b & c+d+a & cda \\ 1 & c & d+a+b & dab \\ 1 & d & a+b+c & abc \end{vmatrix}.$$

3. If

$$\mathbf{A} = \begin{pmatrix} 2 & 1 & -1 \\ -2 & 3 & 1 \\ 4 & 5 & -3 \end{pmatrix}, \quad \mathbf{B} = \begin{pmatrix} 1 & 3 & 1 \\ 2 & -1 & -1 \\ 0 & 1 & 3 \end{pmatrix},$$

evaluate **AB**, **BA**, det **A**, det **B**, det **AB**, det **BA**, and verify that
det (**AB**) = det (**BA**) = det **A** × det **B**.

4. Solve the equations

(a)
$$\begin{vmatrix} 2 & x^2 & 3-x \\ 2 & 0 & 1 \\ 0 & 1 & 1 \end{vmatrix} = 0,$$

(b)
$$\begin{vmatrix} 2-x & 4 & -2 \\ 4 & 2-x & -2 \\ -2 & -2 & 4-x \end{vmatrix} = 0.$$

8.4 THE INVERSE OF A MATRIX

In the development of the algebra of matrices we so far have no operation analogous to that of division in ordinary algebra. Division by a number a is equivalent to multiplication by its reciprocal a^{-1}. In this section we construct a reciprocal or inverse matrix $\mathbf{A}^{-1}$ which in matrix algebra corresponds to the reciprocal a^{-1} in ordinary algebra.

Let there be given an nth-order square matrix $\mathbf{A} = (a_{ij})$ with cofactors A_{ij}. The *adjoint matrix* of **A** is defined to be

$$\text{adj } \mathbf{A} = (A_{ij})^T = (A_{ji}).$$

That is, the adjoint of **A** is obtained by replacing each element of **A** by its cofactor, and transposing. Now consider the ijth element of the product **A** × adj **A**. This is given by

$$(\mathbf{A} \times \text{adj } \mathbf{A})_{ij} = \sum_{r=1}^{n} a_{ir}(\text{adj } \mathbf{A})_{rj} = \sum_{r=1}^{n} a_{ir} A_{jr}. \tag{26}$$

The last expression in equation (26) is the sum of the products of the elements in the ith row of **A** with the cofactors of the corresponding elements in the jth row of **A**. If $i = j$, the last expression in equation (26) is just the expansion of det **A** by its ith row. Hence all the elements of **A** × adj **A** on the leading diagonal are equal to det **A**. If $i \neq j$, then the last expression in equation (26) is zero by (j) of §8.3. Hence

$$(\mathbf{A} \times \text{adj } \mathbf{A})_{ij} = \begin{cases} \det \mathbf{A} & \text{if } i=j, \\ 0 & \text{if } i \neq j. \end{cases}$$

Similarly, it can be shown that

$$(\text{adj } \mathbf{A} \times \mathbf{A})_{ij} = \begin{cases} \det \mathbf{A} & \text{if } i=j, \\ 0 & \text{if } i \neq j. \end{cases}$$

Hence

$$\mathbf{A} \times \text{adj } \mathbf{A} = \text{adj } \mathbf{A} \times \mathbf{A} = \begin{pmatrix} \det \mathbf{A} & 0 & \dots & 0 \\ 0 & \det \mathbf{A} & \dots & 0 \\ \multicolumn{4}{c}{\dots\dots\dots\dots\dots} \\ 0 & 0 & & \det \mathbf{A} \end{pmatrix} = \mathbf{I} \det \mathbf{A}. \tag{27}$$

Now suppose that det $\mathbf{A} \neq 0$. Since det $\mathbf{A}$ is simply a number (scalar), the matrix adj $\mathbf{A}$ can be divided by the scalar det $\mathbf{A}$ to form a new nth-order matrix. This matrix is denoted $\mathbf{A}^{-1}$, so that

$$\mathbf{A}^{-1} = \frac{1}{\det \mathbf{A}} \text{adj } \mathbf{A}. \tag{28}$$

Then it follows from equation (27) that

$$\mathbf{A}\mathbf{A}^{-1} = \mathbf{A}^{-1}\mathbf{A} = \mathbf{I}. \tag{29}$$

The matrix $\mathbf{A}^{-1}$ defined by equation (28) is called the *inverse* of $\mathbf{A}$. Its vital property is equation (29); multiplication on the left or right of a matrix by its inverse gives the unit matrix. Hence matrix multiplication by $\mathbf{A}^{-1}$ is a process analogous to multiplication by a number a^{-1} (or division by a) in ordinary algebra.

EXAMPLE 1

If $\mathbf{A} = \begin{pmatrix} 1 & 2 & 3 \\ 1 & 3 & 5 \\ 1 & 5 & 12 \end{pmatrix}$,   find $\mathbf{A}^{-1}$.

We have

$$A_{11} = \begin{vmatrix} 3 & 5 \\ 5 & 12 \end{vmatrix} = 11, \quad A_{12} = -\begin{vmatrix} 1 & 5 \\ 1 & 12 \end{vmatrix} = -7, \quad A_{13} = \begin{vmatrix} 1 & 3 \\ 1 & 5 \end{vmatrix} = 2,$$

$$A_{21} = -\begin{vmatrix} 2 & 3 \\ 5 & 12 \end{vmatrix} = -9, \quad A_{22} = \begin{vmatrix} 1 & 3 \\ 1 & 12 \end{vmatrix} = 9, \quad A_{23} = -\begin{vmatrix} 1 & 2 \\ 1 & 5 \end{vmatrix} = -3,$$

$$A_{31} = \begin{vmatrix} 2 & 3 \\ 3 & 5 \end{vmatrix} = 1, \quad A_{32} = -\begin{vmatrix} 1 & 3 \\ 1 & 5 \end{vmatrix} = -2, \quad A_{33} = \begin{vmatrix} 1 & 2 \\ 1 & 3 \end{vmatrix} = 1,$$

$$\det \mathbf{A} = 1 \times 11 + 2 \times (-7) + 3 \times 2 = 3,$$

$$\text{adj } \mathbf{A} = \begin{pmatrix} 11 & -7 & 2 \\ -9 & 9 & -3 \\ 1 & -2 & 1 \end{pmatrix}^T = \begin{pmatrix} 11 & -9 & 1 \\ -7 & 9 & -2 \\ 2 & -3 & 1 \end{pmatrix},$$

$$\mathbf{A}^{-1} = \frac{1}{\det \mathbf{A}} \text{adj } \mathbf{A} = \frac{1}{3}\begin{pmatrix} 11 & -9 & 1 \\ -7 & 9 & -2 \\ 2 & -3 & 1 \end{pmatrix}.$$

Check:

$$\mathbf{A}\mathbf{A}^{-1} = \frac{1}{3}\begin{pmatrix} 1 & 2 & 3 \\ 1 & 3 & 5 \\ 1 & 5 & 12 \end{pmatrix}\begin{pmatrix} 11 & -9 & 1 \\ -7 & 9 & -2 \\ 2 & -3 & 1 \end{pmatrix} = \mathbf{I},$$

$$\mathbf{A}^{-1}\mathbf{A} = \frac{1}{3}\begin{pmatrix} 11 & -9 & 1 \\ -7 & 9 & -2 \\ 2 & -3 & 1 \end{pmatrix}\begin{pmatrix} 1 & 2 & 3 \\ 1 & 3 & 5 \\ 1 & 5 & 12 \end{pmatrix} = \mathbf{I}.$$

Among the consequences of the definition (28) are the following.

(a) $\mathbf{A}^{-1}$ cannot be defined if det $\mathbf{A} = 0$. The inverse matrix $\mathbf{A}^{-1}$ exists only if (1) $\mathbf{A}$ is a square matrix, and (2) det $\mathbf{A} \neq 0$. If det $\mathbf{A} = 0$, $\mathbf{A}$ is said to be *singular*; if det $\mathbf{A} \neq 0$, $\mathbf{A}$ is said to be *non-singular*.

(b) The inverse of a symmetric matrix is symmetric.

(c) The inverse of a diagonal matrix with diagonal elements $a_{11}, a_{22}, \ldots, a_{nn}$ is a diagonal matrix with diagonal elements $a_{11}^{-1}, a_{22}^{-1}, \ldots, a_{nn}^{-1}$.

(d) The inverse of an upper (lower) triangular matrix is an upper (lower) triangular matrix.

(e) The inverse of the transpose of a matrix is equal to the transpose of its inverse, that is

$$(\mathbf{A}^T)^{-1} = (\mathbf{A}^{-1})^T.$$

This follows easily from the definition of adj $\mathbf{A}$ and equation (28).

Some further results follow from the fundamental property (29) of $\mathbf{A}^{-1}$.

(f) Taking the determinant of both sides of the equation (29) gives det $(\mathbf{A}\mathbf{A}^{-1}) =$ det $\mathbf{A} \times$ det $(\mathbf{A}^{-1}) = 1$, so that det $(\mathbf{A}^{-1}) = (\det \mathbf{A})^{-1}$.

(g) For any positive power p

$$\mathbf{A}^p(\mathbf{A}^{-1})^p = \mathbf{A}^{p-1}\mathbf{A}\mathbf{A}^{-1}(\mathbf{A}^{-1})^{p-1} = \mathbf{A}^{p-1}(\mathbf{A}^{-1})^{p-1} = \ldots = \mathbf{I}.$$

Hence $(\mathbf{A}^{-1})^p = (\mathbf{A}^p)^{-1}$. It follows that the rule $\mathbf{A}^p\mathbf{A}^q = \mathbf{A}^{p+q}$ applies to both positive and negative powers p and q.

(h) *Inverse of a product*   Let $\mathbf{C} = \mathbf{A}\mathbf{B}$, where $\mathbf{A}$ and $\mathbf{B}$ are both $n \times n$ square non-singular matrices (since det $\mathbf{A}\mathbf{B} =$ det $\mathbf{A} \times$ det $\mathbf{B}$, it follows that $\mathbf{C} = \mathbf{A}\mathbf{B}$ is non-singular). Multiplying both sides on the left by $\mathbf{A}^{-1}$ gives

$$\mathbf{A}^{-1}\mathbf{C} = \mathbf{A}^{-1}\mathbf{A}\mathbf{B} = \mathbf{I}\mathbf{B} = \mathbf{B}.$$

Now multiply both sides on the left by $\mathbf{B}^{-1}$, to obtain

$$\mathbf{B}^{-1}\mathbf{A}^{-1}\mathbf{C} = \mathbf{B}^{-1}\mathbf{B} = \mathbf{I}.$$

Finally, multiplying both sides on the right by C^{-1} gives

$$B^{-1}A^{-1} = IC^{-1} = C^{-1}.$$

Thus, since $C = AB$,

$$(AB)^{-1} = B^{-1}A^{-1}.$$

Note that, just as in the transposition of matrix products, the *order of the factors is reversed*. In general, if all the matrices are $n \times n$ square non-singular matrices, then

$$(ABC \dots G)^{-1} = G^{-1} \dots C^{-1}B^{-1}A^{-1}.$$

Solution of Linear Equations

If A is an $n \times n$ square matrix, and X and B are $n \times 1$ column vectors, the equation

$$AX = B \tag{30}$$

represents (see §8.1) a system of n linear algebraic equations in n unknowns. Provided that A is non-singular, each side of equation (30) may be multiplied on the left by A^{-1}, giving

$$A^{-1}AX = IX = X = A^{-1}B. \tag{31}$$

Hence $X = A^{-1}B$ is the solution of equation (30), and the unknowns $x_1, x_2, \dots, x_n$ are found by a matrix multiplication once A^{-1} is known.

EXAMPLE 2

Solve
$$x + 2y + 3z = 4,$$
$$x + 3y + 5z = 2,$$
$$x + 5y + 12z = 7.$$

Here, $A = \begin{pmatrix} 1 & 2 & 3 \\ 1 & 3 & 5 \\ 1 & 5 & 12 \end{pmatrix}$ and, from example 1, $A^{-1} = \dfrac{1}{3}\begin{pmatrix} 11 & -9 & 1 \\ -7 & 9 & -2 \\ 2 & -3 & 1 \end{pmatrix}.$

Hence

$$\begin{pmatrix} x \\ y \\ z \end{pmatrix} = \frac{1}{3}\begin{pmatrix} 11 & -9 & 1 \\ -7 & 9 & -2 \\ 2 & -3 & 1 \end{pmatrix}\begin{pmatrix} 4 \\ 2 \\ 7 \end{pmatrix} = \begin{pmatrix} 11 \\ -8 \\ 3 \end{pmatrix},$$

so $x = 11, y = -8, z = 3$. It is easily verified by substitution in the equations that this is the correct solution.

Written in full, using the definition (28) of A^{-1}, the solution $X = A^{-1}B$ of equation

(30) is

$$x_1 = (A_{11}b_1 + A_{21}b_2 + A_{31}b_3 + \ldots + A_{n1}b_n)/\det \mathbf{A},$$
$$x_2 = (A_{12}b_2 + A_{22}b_2 + A_{32}b_3 + \ldots + A_{n2}b_n)/\det \mathbf{A}, \tag{32}$$
$$\ldots\ldots\ldots\ldots$$
$$x_n = (A_{1n}b_1 + A_{2n}b_2 + \ldots\ldots\ldots + A_{nn}b_n)/\det \mathbf{A}.$$

The expression in brackets in the first equation above is just the expansion by its first column of the determinant which is obtained from det $\mathbf{A}$ by replacing the first column of $\mathbf{A}$ by a column $b_1, b_2, \ldots, b_n$.
Thus

$$x_1 = \begin{vmatrix} b_1 & a_{12} & a_{13} \ldots a_{1n} \\ b_2 & a_{22} & a_{23} \ldots a_{2n} \\ & \cdots\cdots \\ & \cdots\cdots \\ b_n & a_{n2} & a_{n3} \ldots a_{nn} \end{vmatrix} \Bigg/ \begin{vmatrix} a_{11} & a_{12} & a_{13} \ldots a_{1n} \\ a_{21} & a_{22} & a_{23} \ldots a_{2n} \\ & \cdots\cdots \\ & \cdots\cdots \\ a_{n1} & a_{n2} & a_{n3} \ldots a_{nn} \end{vmatrix},$$

and there are similar expressions for $x_2, x_3, \ldots, x_n$ (to obtain the numerator of the expression for x_r, replace the rth column of det $\mathbf{A}$ by $b_1, b_2, \ldots, b_n$). This is *Cramer's rule* for the solution of a system of linear algebraic equations. It is *not* an efficient method of solution for systems of more than three equations, and should not be used in practice. It does, however, highlight the fact that the solution encounters serious difficulties when det $\mathbf{A} = 0$ (i.e., $\mathbf{A}$ is singular), because each of equations (32) then involves the impossible operation of division by zero. In practical problems, difficulty can also arise when det $\mathbf{A}$ is non-zero but numerically small. This situation is discussed in §10.2.

Uniqueness of the Inverse

It will be shown that if $\mathbf{A}$ is non-singular then $\mathbf{A}^{-1}$, as defined by equation (28), is the only matrix with the properties $\mathbf{A}\mathbf{A}^{-1} = \mathbf{I}$ and $\mathbf{A}^{-1}\mathbf{A} = \mathbf{I}$. Suppose $\mathbf{A}$ possesses another 'right inverse' $\mathbf{R}$ such that $\mathbf{A}\mathbf{R} = \mathbf{I}$. Then

$$\mathbf{R} - \mathbf{A}^{-1} = \mathbf{I}(\mathbf{R} - \mathbf{A}^{-1}) = \mathbf{A}^{-1}\mathbf{A}(\mathbf{R} - \mathbf{A}^{-1}) = \mathbf{A}^{-1}(\mathbf{A}\mathbf{R} - \mathbf{A}\mathbf{A}^{-1})$$
$$= \mathbf{A}^{-1}(\mathbf{I} - \mathbf{I}) = \mathbf{A}^{-1}\mathbf{0} = \mathbf{0}.$$

Hence $\mathbf{R} = \mathbf{A}^{-1}$, and similarly the only 'left inverse' of $\mathbf{A}$, satisfying $\mathbf{L}\mathbf{A} = \mathbf{I}$, is $\mathbf{L} = \mathbf{A}^{-1}$.

The value of this result is that it shows that if by *any method* a matrix $\mathbf{L}$ or $\mathbf{R}$ can be found such that $\mathbf{L}\mathbf{A} = \mathbf{I}$ or $\mathbf{A}\mathbf{R} = \mathbf{I}$, then $\mathbf{L}$ or $\mathbf{R}$ is *the* inverse $\mathbf{A}^{-1}$. This is important, because although the definition (28) proves the existence of the inverse of a non-singular matrix and its properties (a)–(e), it does *not* provide, for $n > 3$, an efficient method of evaluating $\mathbf{A}^{-1}$. To illustrate the magnitude of the problem, the direct evaluation of adj $\mathbf{A}$ involves evaluating n^2 determinants of order $n - 1$. This means about $n(n!)$ multiplications. For $n = 20$ approximately 5×10^{19} multiplications would be required. There are about 3×10^7 seconds in one year, and a fast computer might perform 5×10^5 multiplications per second. Working non-stop, the calculation would be complete in about three million years. For $n = 100$, which is not large in contemporary applications, the number of multiplications is about 10^{160}, and the time required is about 6×10^{146} years. For comparison, the energy of the sun is expected to last about 3×10^{10} years. The direct method of inversion is clearly quite impracticable for large matrices. Fortunately, more efficient methods of matrix inversion are available, and the most useful of these are described in § 10.4.

Exercises

1. For each of the following matrices, find (1) all the minors, (2) all the cofactors, (3) the adjoint matrix. (4) the inverse matrix. In each case verify that the matrix pre- or post-multiplied by its inverse gives the unit matrix.

(a) $\begin{pmatrix} 1 & -1 \\ 2 & 3 \end{pmatrix}$,
(b) $\begin{pmatrix} 3 & -2 & 0 \\ -1 & 2 & 0 \\ 0 & 0 & -2 \end{pmatrix}$,
(c) $\begin{pmatrix} 5 & 1 & 4 \\ -1 & 3 & 0 \\ 3 & 1 & 1 \end{pmatrix}$,

(d) $\begin{pmatrix} 1 & 2 & 3 \\ 2 & 1 & 2 \\ 3 & 2 & 1 \end{pmatrix}$,
(e) $\begin{pmatrix} 0 & -1 & -3 \\ 1 & 0 & -2 \\ 3 & 2 & 0 \end{pmatrix}$,
(f) $\begin{pmatrix} 1 & -2 & 3 \\ 0 & -4 & 5 \\ 0 & 0 & 6 \end{pmatrix}$.

2. Use the results of exercise 1 to solve the following systems of equations.

(a) $5x_1 + x_2 + 4x_3 = 3,$
$-x_1 + 3x_2 \qquad = -2,$
$3x_1 + x_2 + x_3 = 1.$

(b) $x_1 + 2x_2 + 3x_3 = 4,$
$2x_1 + x_2 + 2x_3 = 1,$
$3x_1 + 2x_2 + x_3 = 7.$

3. For the matrix $\mathbf{A}$ of §8.2, exercise 6, find $\mathbf{A}^{-1}$ and verify that $7\mathbf{A}^{-1} = \mathbf{A}^2 - 2\mathbf{A} - 2\mathbf{I}$.

4. Find the inverse of the matrix

$$\begin{pmatrix} 1 & 0 & -1 & 0 \\ 0 & 1 & 0 & 0 \\ -1 & 0 & 1+\sqrt{\tfrac{1}{2}} & 0 \\ 0 & 0 & 0 & 1+\sqrt{\tfrac{1}{2}} \end{pmatrix},$$

which occurs in example 4 of §8.2. Hence, in the notation of that example, express U_B, V_B, U_C and V_C in terms of X_B, Y_B, X_C, Y_C. (This is a simple illustration of an important method in structural analysis).

8.5 ORTHOGONAL MATRICES

A square matrix $\mathbf{M}$ is said to be *orthogonal* if it has the properties

$$\mathbf{M}\mathbf{M}^T = \mathbf{I}, \quad \mathbf{M}^T\mathbf{M} = \mathbf{I}, \quad \mathbf{M}^T = \mathbf{M}^{-1}. \tag{33}$$

These three statements are equivalent; any one of them implies the other two. Also

$$\det \mathbf{M}\mathbf{M}^T = (\det \mathbf{M})^2 = \det \mathbf{I} = 1,$$

so $\det \mathbf{M} = \pm 1$. Note that $\det \mathbf{A} = \pm 1$ is a necessary but not a sufficient condition for $\mathbf{A}$ to be orthogonal. For example, if

$$\mathbf{A} = \begin{pmatrix} 5 & 6 \\ 4 & 5 \end{pmatrix},$$

then $\det \mathbf{A} = 1$, but $\mathbf{A}$ is not orthogonal.

Orthogonal matrices arise in a number of engineering applications, but are usually first encountered in connection with coordinate transformations. In the first instance consider a rotation of plane rectangular cartesian coordinates through an angle θ, as illustrated in Fig. 8.3. In the coordinate system Ox_1x_2 P has coordinates (x_1, x_2); in the system $O\bar{x}_1\bar{x}_2$ it has coordinates $(\bar{x}_1, \bar{x}_2)$. From elementary plane coordinate geometry these coordinates are related by

$$\bar{x}_1 = x_1 \cos \theta + x_2 \sin \theta, \qquad x_1 = \bar{x}_1 \cos \theta - \bar{x}_2 \sin \theta,$$
$$\bar{x}_2 = -x_1 \sin \theta + x_2 \cos \theta, \qquad x_2 = \bar{x}_1 \sin \theta + \bar{x}_2 \cos \theta.$$

In matrix notation these may be written

$$\bar{\mathbf{X}} = \mathbf{M}\mathbf{X}, \quad \mathbf{X} = \mathbf{M}^T\bar{\mathbf{X}}, \quad \text{where } \mathbf{M} = \begin{pmatrix} \cos \theta & \sin \theta \\ -\sin \theta & \cos \theta \end{pmatrix}. \tag{34}$$

$$\text{Then } \mathbf{M}\mathbf{M}^T = \begin{pmatrix} \cos \theta & \sin \theta \\ -\sin \theta & \cos \theta \end{pmatrix} \begin{pmatrix} \cos \theta & -\sin \theta \\ \sin \theta & \cos \theta \end{pmatrix}$$

$$= \begin{pmatrix} \cos^2 \theta + \sin^2 \theta & 0 \\ 0 & \cos^2 \theta + \sin^2 \theta \end{pmatrix} = \mathbf{I}.$$

Thus the matrix which describes the rotation from one plane rectangular cartesian coordinate system to another is orthogonal.

Analogous results hold in three (or more) dimensions. If a typical point P has coordinates (x_1, x_2, x_3) in a rectangular cartesian coordinate system $Ox_1x_2x_3$, and $(\bar{x}_1, \bar{x}_2, \bar{x}_3)$ in another rectangular system $O\bar{x}_1\bar{x}_2\bar{x}_3$, then $\mathbf{X} = (x_1 \ x_2 \ x_3)^T$ and $\bar{\mathbf{X}} = (\bar{x}_1 \ \bar{x}_2 \ \bar{x}_3)^T$ satisfy the relations

$$\bar{\mathbf{X}} = \mathbf{M}\mathbf{X}, \quad \mathbf{X} = \mathbf{M}^T\bar{\mathbf{X}}, \tag{35}$$

where $\mathbf{M}$ is an orthogonal matrix. Geometrically, the rows of $\mathbf{M}$ are the direction cosines of the axes $O\bar{x}_1$, $O\bar{x}_2$, $O\bar{x}_3$ with respect to the coordinates $Ox_1x_2x_3$, and the

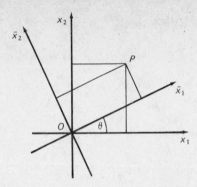

Fig. 8.3   Rotation of plane rectangular cartesian coordinates

columns of $\mathbf{M}$ are the direction cosines of the axes Ox_1, Ox_2, Ox_3 with respect to the coordinates $O\bar{x}_1\bar{x}_2\bar{x}_3$.

The same orthogonal matrix $\mathbf{M}$ describes the transformation of the components of a physical vector from the coordinate system $Ox_1x_2x_3$ to $O\bar{x}_1\bar{x}_2\bar{x}_3$. If the vector has components (F_1, F_2, F_3) in the first system and $(\bar{F}_1, \bar{F}_2, \bar{F}_3)$ in the second system, and we denote $\mathbf{F} = (F_1\ F_2\ F_3)^T$, $\bar{\mathbf{F}} = (\bar{F}_1\ \bar{F}_2\ \bar{F}_3)^T$, then

$$\bar{\mathbf{F}} = \mathbf{MF}, \quad \mathbf{F} = \mathbf{M}^T\bar{\mathbf{F}}. \tag{36}$$

Exercises

1. By calculating $\mathbf{MM}^T$, verify that the following matrices are orthogonal, and show directly that det $\mathbf{M} = 1$.

(a)
$$\mathbf{M} = \frac{1}{3}\begin{pmatrix} 1 & 2\sqrt{2} \\ -2\sqrt{2} & 1 \end{pmatrix}$$

(b)
$$\mathbf{M} = \frac{1}{3\sqrt{2}}\begin{pmatrix} \sqrt{2} & 2\sqrt{2} & -2\sqrt{2} \\ -4 & 1 & -1 \\ 0 & 3 & 3 \end{pmatrix}.$$

2. Two sets of rectangular cartesian coordinates are related by

$$\bar{x}_1 = \tfrac{1}{3}x_1 + \tfrac{2}{3}x_2 - \tfrac{2}{3}x_3,$$

$$\bar{x}_2 = -\frac{2\sqrt{2}}{3}x_1 + \frac{1}{3\sqrt{2}}x_2 - \frac{1}{3\sqrt{2}}x_3,$$

$$\bar{x}_3 = \frac{1}{\sqrt{2}}x_2 + \frac{1}{\sqrt{2}}x_3.$$

Use the result of exercise 1(b) to express x_1, x_2, x_3 in terms of $\bar{x}_1, \bar{x}_2, \bar{x}_3$. With respect to the (x_1, x_2, x_3) coordinates a physical vector has components $(2, -3, 5)$. What are its components with respect to the $(\bar{x}_1, \bar{x}_2, \bar{x}_3)$ system?

3. Prove that if $\mathbf{S}$ is any anti-symmetric matrix, then $(\mathbf{I} - \mathbf{S})(\mathbf{I} + \mathbf{S})^{-1}$ is orthogonal.

4. If $X = (x_1 \ x_2 \ldots x_n)^T$, $\bar{X} = (\bar{x}_1 \ \bar{x}_2 \ldots \bar{x}_n)^T$, and $\bar{X} = MX$, where M is orthogonal, prove that $x_1^2 + x_2^2 + \ldots + x_n^2 = \bar{x}_1^2 + \bar{x}_2^2 + \ldots + \bar{x}_n^2$.

8.6 PARTITIONED MATRICES

Some physical systems (for example many electrical networks and framed structures) are composed of subsystems which are connected by a relatively small number of links. Such systems often give rise to *sparse* matrices, which may be large, but contain a high proportion of zero elements. Also, the non-zero elements are often arranged in a definite pattern within the matrix, and frequently in comparatively small blocks. This makes it profitable on occasions to deal with groups of elements within a matrix, rather than with the matrix as a whole. For example, the matrix of the coefficients of equations (3),

$$A = \begin{pmatrix} 0 & -1 & 0 & 0 \\ 1 & 0 & 0 & 0 \\ \hline 0 & 1 & \sqrt{\tfrac{1}{2}} & 0 \\ 0 & 0 & \sqrt{\tfrac{1}{2}} & 1 \end{pmatrix} \tag{37}$$

is naturally divided up in the indicated manner.

Submatrices

Suppose that from an $m \times n$ matrix A we strike out $m - p$ rows and $n - q$ columns (the rows and columns need not be consecutive). This leaves a $p \times q$ array of the elements which is called a *submatrix* of A.

Partitioned matrices

If a matrix is divided into submatrices by vertical and horizontal lines between the columns and rows it is *partitioned*. For example

$$A = \begin{pmatrix} a_{11} & a_{12} \\ a_{21} & a_{22} \\ \hline a_{31} & a_{32} \end{pmatrix}, \quad B = \begin{pmatrix} b_{11} & b_{12} & b_{13} & b_{14} \\ b_{21} & b_{22} & b_{23} & b_{24} \end{pmatrix},$$

$$C = \begin{pmatrix} c_{11} & c_{12} & c_{13} & c_{14} \\ c_{21} & c_{22} & c_{23} & c_{24} \\ \hline c_{31} & c_{32} & c_{33} & c_{34} \end{pmatrix}. \tag{38}$$

We denote the first submatrix in A by A_1, the second by A_2, and so on, and write the matrices as

$$A = \begin{pmatrix} A_1 \\ A_2 \end{pmatrix}, \quad B = (B_1 \quad B_2 \quad B_3), \quad C = \begin{pmatrix} C_{11} & C_{12} & C_{13} \\ C_{21} & C_{22} & C_{23} \end{pmatrix}.$$

Multiplication of Partitioned Matrices

As an example, form the product AB of A and B in equations (38). By direct multiplication, this gives

$$AB = \left(\begin{array}{cc|cc|c} a_{11}b_{11}+a_{12}b_{21} & a_{11}b_{12}+a_{12}b_{22} & a_{11}b_{13}+a_{12}b_{23} & a_{11}b_{14}+a_{12}b_{24} \\ a_{21}b_{11}+a_{22}b_{21} & a_{21}b_{12}+a_{22}b_{22} & a_{21}b_{13}+a_{22}b_{23} & a_{21}b_{14}+a_{22}b_{24} \\ \hline a_{31}b_{11}+a_{32}b_{21} & a_{31}b_{12}+a_{32}b_{22} & a_{31}b_{13}+a_{32}b_{23} & a_{31}b_{14}+a_{32}b_{24} \end{array} \right).$$

(39)

On examination of equation (39) we find that

$$AB = \begin{pmatrix} A_1 \\ A_2 \end{pmatrix} (B_1 \quad B_2 \quad B_3) = \begin{pmatrix} A_1 B_1 & A_1 B_2 & A_1 B_3 \\ A_2 B_1 & A_2 B_2 & A_3 B_3 \end{pmatrix}.$$

(40)

Note that the multiplication is carried out just as though A and B were column and row vectors respectively. It is of course essential that the partitioning be made in such a way that the matrix products $A_1 B_1$, $A_1 B_2$ etc. all exist; matrices for which this is the case are said to be *conformably partitioned*.

The *general* rule for forming the product of two conformably partitioned matrices is exactly the same as the rule for matrix multiplication, with the submatrices acting as though they were matrix elements.

EXAMPLE 1

$$\left(\begin{array}{cc|cc} 2 & 1 & 1 & 0 \\ 1 & 2 & 0 & 1 \\ \hline 1 & 0 & 3 & 1 \\ 0 & 1 & 1 & 3 \end{array} \right) \left(\begin{array}{cc|cc} 1 & 2 & 1 & 0 \\ 2 & 1 & 0 & 1 \\ \hline 1 & 0 & 1 & 3 \\ 0 & 1 & 3 & 1 \end{array} \right)$$

$$= \left(\begin{array}{c|c} \begin{pmatrix} 2 & 1 \\ 1 & 2 \end{pmatrix}\begin{pmatrix} 1 & 2 \\ 2 & 1 \end{pmatrix} + \begin{pmatrix} 1 & 0 \\ 0 & 1 \end{pmatrix}\begin{pmatrix} 1 & 0 \\ 0 & 1 \end{pmatrix} & \begin{pmatrix} 2 & 1 \\ 1 & 2 \end{pmatrix}\begin{pmatrix} 1 & 0 \\ 0 & 1 \end{pmatrix} + \begin{pmatrix} 1 & 0 \\ 0 & 1 \end{pmatrix}\begin{pmatrix} 1 & 3 \\ 3 & 1 \end{pmatrix} \\ \hline \begin{pmatrix} 1 & 0 \\ 0 & 1 \end{pmatrix}\begin{pmatrix} 1 & 2 \\ 2 & 1 \end{pmatrix} + \begin{pmatrix} 3 & 1 \\ 1 & 3 \end{pmatrix}\begin{pmatrix} 1 & 0 \\ 0 & 1 \end{pmatrix} & \begin{pmatrix} 1 & 0 \\ 0 & 1 \end{pmatrix}\begin{pmatrix} 1 & 0 \\ 0 & 1 \end{pmatrix} + \begin{pmatrix} 3 & 1 \\ 1 & 3 \end{pmatrix}\begin{pmatrix} 1 & 3 \\ 3 & 1 \end{pmatrix} \end{array} \right)$$

$$= \left(\begin{array}{cc|cc} 5 & 5 & 3 & 4 \\ 5 & 5 & 4 & 3 \\ \hline 4 & 3 & 7 & 10 \\ 3 & 4 & 10 & 7 \end{array} \right).$$

Block diagonal matrices

A matrix which may be partitioned in to the form

$$
A = \begin{pmatrix}
A_{11} & 0 & & 0 \\
0 & A_{22} & & 0 \\
& & & \\
0 & 0 & & A_{nn}
\end{pmatrix}
\tag{41}
$$

where each submatrix A_{ii} is a square matrix, is said to be *block diagonal*. It is easily verified that its inverse is

$$
A^{-1} = \begin{pmatrix}
A_{11}^{-1} & 0 & & 0 \\
0 & A_{22}^{-1} & & 0 \\
& & & \\
0 & 0 & & A_{nn}^{-1}
\end{pmatrix}.
\tag{42}
$$

Inversion of Partitioned Matrices

Consider a square matrix A partitioned as follows

$$
A = \begin{pmatrix} A_{11} & A_{12} \\ A_{21} & A_{22} \end{pmatrix}
$$

in such a way that A_{11} and A_{22} are square, and A_{11} and A_{22} are non-singular. Let $B = A^{-1}$ be the inverse of A and partition B so that A and B are conformably partitioned for the product AB. Then

$$
I = AB = \begin{pmatrix} A_{11} & A_{12} \\ A_{21} & A_{22} \end{pmatrix} \begin{pmatrix} B_{11} & B_{12} \\ B_{21} & B_{22} \end{pmatrix} = \begin{pmatrix} A_{11}B_{11} + A_{12}B_{21} & A_{11}B_{12} + A_{12}B_{22} \\ A_{21}B_{11} + A_{22}B_{21} & A_{21}B_{12} + A_{22}B_{22} \end{pmatrix}.
$$

Hence

$$
A_{11}B_{11} + A_{12}B_{21} = I, \quad A_{11}B_{12} + A_{12}B_{22} = 0,
$$
$$
A_{21}B_{11} + A_{22}B_{21} = 0, \quad A_{21}B_{12} + A_{22}B_{22} = I.
\tag{43}
$$

Solving equations (43) for $B_{11}, B_{22}, B_{12}, B_{21}$ gives

$$
B = A^{-1} = \begin{pmatrix} (A_{11} - A_{12}A_{22}^{-1}A_{21})^{-1} & -A_{11}^{-1}A_{12}(A_{22} - A_{21}A_{11}^{-1}A_{12})^{-1} \\ -A_{22}^{-1}A_{21}(A_{11} - A_{12}A_{22}^{-1}A_{21})^{-1} & (A_{22} - A_{21}A_{11}^{-1}A_{12})^{-1} \end{pmatrix}.
\tag{44}
$$

This result is easily verified by direct multiplication. To evaluate A^{-1} in this way involves four matrix inversions, but the matrices may be chosen to have only one-half of the order of the original matrix, so this approach is useful when computer storage capacity is limited. It is also suitable for the inversion of sparse matrices, especially if the corresponding linear equations and unknowns are ordered so that the matrix is 'almost' block diagonal, with a small number of elements which do not fit the block diagonal form.

EXAMPLE 2
Invert the matrix A given by the equation (37).

In this case $A_{12} = 0$, so equation (44) becomes

$$A^{-1} = \begin{pmatrix} A_{11}^{-1} & 0 \\ -A_{22}^{-1}A_{21}A_{11}^{-1} & A_{22}^{-1} \end{pmatrix},$$

where

$$A_{11} = \begin{pmatrix} 0 & -1 \\ 1 & 0 \end{pmatrix}, \quad A_{22} = \begin{pmatrix} \sqrt{\tfrac{1}{2}} & 0 \\ \sqrt{\tfrac{1}{2}} & 1 \end{pmatrix}, \quad A_{21} = \begin{pmatrix} 0 & 1 \\ 0 & 0 \end{pmatrix}.$$

Now

$$A_{11}^{-1} = \begin{pmatrix} 0 & 1 \\ -1 & 0 \end{pmatrix}, \quad A_{22}^{-1} = \begin{pmatrix} \sqrt{2} & 0 \\ -1 & 1 \end{pmatrix}, \quad A_{22}^{-1}A_{21}A_{11}^{-1} = \begin{pmatrix} -\sqrt{2} & 0 \\ 1 & 0 \end{pmatrix}.$$

Hence

$$A^{-1} = \begin{pmatrix} 0 & 1 & 0 & 0 \\ -1 & 0 & 0 & 0 \\ \sqrt{2} & 0 & \sqrt{2} & 0 \\ -1 & 0 & -1 & 1 \end{pmatrix}.$$

This is easily verified by forming the product AA^{-1}.

Exercises

1. By introducing suitable partitioning, evaluate the following matrix products:

(a) $\begin{pmatrix} 2 & 1 & 0 & 0 \\ 1 & 2 & 0 & 0 \\ 0 & 0 & 2 & 1 \\ 0 & 0 & 1 & 2 \end{pmatrix} \begin{pmatrix} 1 & 0 \\ 0 & 1 \\ 1 & 0 \\ 0 & 1 \end{pmatrix},$

(b) $\begin{pmatrix} 1 & 1 & 0 & 0 & 1 \\ 1 & 1 & 0 & 0 & 0 \\ 0 & 0 & 1 & 2 & 0 \\ 0 & 0 & 2 & 1 & 2 \\ 2 & 0 & 0 & 2 & 1 \end{pmatrix} \begin{pmatrix} 1 & 1 & 1 \\ 1 & 1 & 1 \\ 0 & 2 & 0 \\ 2 & 0 & 2 \\ 0 & 2 & 0 \end{pmatrix}.$

2. By partitioning suitably, find the inverse of the following matrices:

(a) $\begin{pmatrix} 2 & 4 & 0 & 0 & 0 & 0 \\ 1 & 4 & 0 & 0 & 0 & 0 \\ 0 & 0 & 2 & 4 & 0 & 0 \\ 0 & 0 & 1 & 4 & 0 & 0 \\ 0 & 0 & 0 & 0 & 2 & 4 \\ 0 & 0 & 0 & 0 & 1 & 4 \end{pmatrix}$,   (b) $\begin{pmatrix} 4 & -1 & 1 & 0 \\ -1 & 4 & 0 & 1 \\ 1 & 0 & 4 & -1 \\ 0 & 1 & -1 & 4 \end{pmatrix}$.

8.7 INHOMOGENEOUS SYSTEMS OF LINEAR EQUATIONS

Before reading this section the reader is recommended to refer to the first part of §8.1. This described some physical problems which give rise to systems of linear algebraic equations.

In this section the solution of the system of linear equations (7) will be investigated systematically. In the matrix notation equations (7) have the form $AX = B$, where A is a given $m \times n$ matrix, B a given $m \times 1$ column vector and X an unknown $n \times 1$ column vector which, if possible, has to be determined. $AX = B$ represents a system of m equations in n unknowns; m and n are not necessarily equal, and we may have $m > n$, $m = n$ or $m < n$. If $B = 0$, so that the right-hand sides of equations (7) are all zero, the equations are said to be *homogeneous*; if $B \neq 0$, so that at least one of the equations (7) has a non-zero right-hand side, the equations are *inhomogeneous*. In this section they are considered to be inhomogeneous.

As already noted, a system of inhomogeneous equations may have either a unique solution, no solution, or an infinite number of solutions. These three possibilities are illustrated by the following simple numerical examples.

(a) $x_1 + x_2 + x_3 = 3,$ Precisely one solution $x_1 = 1, x_2 = 1, x_3 = 1$.

$x_1 + x_2 - x_3 = 1,$ (45)

$x_1 - x_2 + x_3 = 1.$

(b) $x_1 + x_2 + x_3 = 3,$ No solution; adding the first two equations gives

$x_1 + x_2 - x_3 = 1,$ $x_1 + x_2 = 2,$ but this contradicts the third. The equations are contradictory and there are no values of x_1, x_2 and x_3

$x_1 + x_2 \quad\quad = 5.$ which satisfy them all.

(c) $x_1 + x_2 + x_3 = 3,$ The first two equations imply the third, so the third gives

$x_1 + x_2 - x_3 = 1,$ no additional information and is redundant. There is an infinite number of solutions, say $x_1 = t, x_2 = 2 - t, x_3 = 1,$

$x_1 + x_2 \quad\quad = 2.$ where t may have any value.

A system of equations is said to be *consistent* (or *compatible*) if it has at least one solution, and *inconsistent* (*incompatible*) if it has none. An important requirement for the investigation of a system of linear equations is a test which will determine whether or not the system is consistent; if the equations can be shown to have no solutions then there is no point in proceeding further. One of the main purposes of this section is to devise such a test.

The Augmented Matrix

Given a system of equations $\mathbf{AX} = \mathbf{B}$, it is convenient to introduce the *augmented matrix* $(\mathbf{A} \mid \mathbf{B})$ which is the matrix of coefficients $\mathbf{A}$ augmented by $\mathbf{B}$ as an additional column. For example the augmented matrix for the system of equations (45) is

$$\begin{pmatrix} 1 & 1 & 1 & \vdots & 3 \\ 1 & 1 & -1 & \vdots & 1 \\ 1 & -1 & 1 & \vdots & 1 \end{pmatrix}.$$

The augmented matrix completely describes the system of equations.

Elementary Row Operations

The following operations can be performed on a system of equations without affecting their solution:

(a)   interchanging any two equations.

(b)   multiplying or dividing any equation by a finite non-zero constant.

(c)   adding to any equation any other equation multiplied by a finite constant.

For each of these operations there is a corresponding operation on the augmented matrix of the system, namely,

(a')   interchanging any two rows of the matrix.

(b')   multiplying any row of the matrix by a finite non-zero constant.

(c')   adding to any row of the matrix any other row multiplied by a finite constant.

These are called the *elementary row operations* on the augmented matrix.

Solution by Elimination (Pivotal Condensation)

In elementary algebra the reader will have learned to use the operations (a) (b) (c) to solve systems of linear equations by eliminating each variable in turn. When systematically applied, this method is an efficient numerical method of solution of linear equations, which is described in §10.2. In this section we are more concerned with theoretical considerations.

In the examples which follow, in order to make the process systematic the variables $x_1, x_2, x_3, \ldots$ are eliminated in turn. We also use operation (b) to arrange that, in the final system, each variable has the coefficient 1 in the equation in which it first occurs. The corresponding augmented matrix is shown to the right of each system of equations.

EXAMPLE 1

$$
\begin{aligned}
x_1 + 4x_2 - 2x_3 &= 3, \\
2x_1 - 2x_2 + x_3 &= 1, \\
3x_1 + x_2 + 2x_3 &= 11.
\end{aligned}
\qquad
\begin{pmatrix}
1 & 4 & -2 & \vdots & 3 \\
2 & -2 & 1 & \vdots & 1 \\
3 & 1 & 2 & \vdots & 11
\end{pmatrix}.
$$

Eliminate x_1 from the second and third equations, by subtracting twice the first equation from the second, and three times the first equation from the third.

$$
\begin{aligned}
x_1 + 4x_2 - 2x_3 &= 3, \\
- 10x_2 + 5x_3 &= -5, \\
- 11x_2 + 8x_3 &= 2.
\end{aligned}
\qquad
\begin{pmatrix}
1 & 4 & -2 & \vdots & 3 \\
0 & -10 & 5 & \vdots & -5 \\
0 & -11 & 8 & \vdots & 2
\end{pmatrix}.
$$

Divide the second equation by -10 and eliminate x_2 from the third equation.

$$
\begin{aligned}
x_1 + 4x_2 - 2x_3 &= 3, \\
x_2 - \tfrac{1}{2}x_3 &= \tfrac{1}{2}, \\
2\tfrac{1}{2}x_3 &= 7\tfrac{1}{2}.
\end{aligned}
\qquad
\begin{pmatrix}
1 & 4 & -2 & \vdots & 3 \\
0 & 1 & -\tfrac{1}{2} & \vdots & \tfrac{1}{2} \\
0 & 0 & 2\tfrac{1}{2} & \vdots & 7\tfrac{1}{2}
\end{pmatrix}.
$$

Divide the third equation by $2\tfrac{1}{2}$.

$$
\begin{aligned}
x_1 + 4x_2 - 2x_3 &= 3, \\
x_2 - \tfrac{1}{2}x_3 &= \tfrac{1}{2}, \\
x_3 &= 3.
\end{aligned}
\qquad
\begin{pmatrix}
1 & 4 & -2 & \vdots & 3 \\
0 & 1 & -\tfrac{1}{2} & \vdots & \tfrac{1}{2} \\
0 & 0 & 1 & \vdots & 3
\end{pmatrix}.
$$

The final set of equations can now be solved in turn for x_3, x_2 and x_1, giving $x_3 = 3, x_2 = 2, x_1 = 1$.

EXAMPLE 2

$$
\begin{aligned}
x_1 - 3x_2 - x_3 + 3x_4 &= 0, \\
-x_1 + 2x_2 + x_3 + 4x_4 &= 11, \\
3x_1 - 2x_2 - 2x_3 + x_4 &= 6.
\end{aligned}
\qquad
\begin{pmatrix}
1 & -3 & -1 & 3 & \vdots & 0 \\
-1 & 2 & 1 & 4 & \vdots & 11 \\
3 & -2 & -2 & 1 & \vdots & 6
\end{pmatrix}.
$$

Eliminate x_1 from the second and third equations.

$$
\begin{aligned}
x_1 - 3x_2 - x_3 + 3x_4 &= 0, \\
- x_2 + 7x_4 &= 11, \\
7x_2 + x_3 - 8x_4 &= 6.
\end{aligned}
\qquad
\begin{pmatrix}
1 & -3 & -1 & 3 & \vdots & 0 \\
0 & -1 & 0 & 7 & \vdots & 11 \\
0 & 7 & 1 & -8 & \vdots & 6
\end{pmatrix}.
$$

Multiply the second equation by -1 and eliminate x_2 from the third equation.

$$
\begin{aligned}
x_1 - 3x_2 - x_3 + 3x_4 &= 0, \\
x_2 - 7x_4 &= -11, \\
x_3 + 41x_4 &= 83.
\end{aligned}
\qquad
\begin{pmatrix}
1 & -3 & -1 & 3 & \vdots & 0 \\
0 & 1 & 0 & -7 & \vdots & -11 \\
0 & 0 & 1 & 41 & \vdots & 83
\end{pmatrix}.
$$

The equations do not have a unique solution; for example x_4 may be given any value, and then the equations can be solved in turn for x_3, x_2 and x_1. The solution can be expressed in the form

$$x_4 = t, \quad x_3 = 83 - 41t, \quad x_2 = -11 + 7t, \quad x_1 = 50 - 23t,$$

where t may be any number.

Redundant Equations

The process of elimination may lead to one or more equations of the form $0 = 0$. This indicates that one or more of the original equations can be derived from the remainder. The system then contains equations which are redundant in that they contain no information which is not present in the remaining equations.

EXAMPLE 3

$$
\begin{aligned}
x_1 + x_2 - x_3 &= 0, \\
x_1 + 2x_2 - x_3 &= 2, \\
x_1 + x_2 + x_3 &= 6, \\
2x_1 - 2x_2 + x_3 &= 1.
\end{aligned}
\qquad
\left(
\begin{array}{rrr|r}
1 & 1 & -1 & 0 \\
1 & 2 & -1 & 2 \\
1 & 1 & 1 & 6 \\
2 & -2 & 1 & 1
\end{array}
\right).
$$

Eliminate x_1 from the second, third and fourth equations.

$$
\begin{aligned}
x_1 + x_2 - x_3 &= 0, \\
x_2 &= 2, \\
2x_3 &= 6, \\
-4x_2 + 3x_3 &= 1.
\end{aligned}
\qquad
\left(
\begin{array}{rrr|r}
1 & 1 & -1 & 0 \\
0 & 1 & 0 & 2 \\
0 & 0 & 2 & 6 \\
0 & -4 & 3 & 1
\end{array}
\right).
$$

Eliminate x_2 from the fourth equation.

$$
\begin{aligned}
x_1 + x_2 - x_3 &= 0, \\
x_2 &= 2, \\
2x_3 &= 6, \\
3x_3 &= 9.
\end{aligned}
\qquad
\left(
\begin{array}{rrr|r}
1 & 1 & -1 & 0 \\
0 & 1 & 0 & 2 \\
0 & 0 & 2 & 6 \\
0 & 0 & 3 & 9
\end{array}
\right).
$$

Divide the third equation by 2 and eliminate x_3 from the fourth.

$$
\begin{aligned}
x_1 + x_2 - x_3 &= 0, \\
x_2 &= 2, \\
x_3 &= 3, \\
0 &= 0.
\end{aligned}
\qquad
\left(
\begin{array}{rrr|r}
1 & 1 & -1 & 0 \\
0 & 1 & 0 & 2 \\
0 & 0 & 1 & 3 \\
0 & 0 & 0 & 0
\end{array}
\right).
$$

Although there are initially more equations than unknowns the system has the unique solution $x_1 = 1, x_2 = 2, x_3 = 3$ because one of the equations is redundant.

Inconsistent Equations

The process of elimination may also lead to one or more equations of the form $0 = 1$. This indicates that the original equations contradict one another and have no solution; the system is inconsistent.

EXAMPLE 4

$$\begin{aligned}
x_1 + x_2 - x_3 &= 1, \\
x_1 + 2x_2 - x_3 &= 2, \\
x_1 + x_2 + x_3 &= 6, \\
2x_1 - 2x_2 + x_3 &= 1.
\end{aligned}
\qquad
\left(\begin{array}{ccc|c}
1 & 1 & -1 & 1 \\
1 & 2 & -1 & 2 \\
1 & 1 & 1 & 6 \\
2 & -2 & 1 & 1
\end{array}\right).$$

This differs from the system of example 3 only in the right-hand side of the first equation. Carrying out the same sequence of operations as in example 3 leads to the system.

$$\begin{aligned}
x_1 + x_2 - x_3 &= 1, \\
x_2 &= 1, \\
x_3 &= 2\tfrac{1}{2}, \\
0 &= 1.
\end{aligned}
\qquad
\left(\begin{array}{ccc|c}
1 & 1 & -1 & 1 \\
0 & 1 & 0 & 1 \\
0 & 0 & 1 & 2\tfrac{1}{2} \\
0 & 0 & 0 & 1
\end{array}\right).$$

The system is inconsistent and has no solution.

The Row Echelon Reduction of a Matrix

In practice the elimination process is most conveniently carried out by operating on the augmented matrix $(\mathbf{A} \mid \mathbf{B})$ rather than on the equations themselves. In each of examples 1–4 the final augmented matrix displayed has the properties

(1) The first non-zero element in any row is a '1'.

(2) This '1' lies to the right of the first non-zero element in the row above it,

and this form was achieved by performing elementary row operations $(a')\,(b')\,(c')$ on successive augmented matrices of the system. A matrix with the above properties (1) and (2) is said to be in *row echelon* form. Applying the elimination process to a system of equations is equivalent to reducing the augmented matrix of the system to row echelon form by sucessively applying elementary row operations.

The reduction of the augmented matrix to row echelon form is not unique; it may be done in many different ways but each will yield the same solution (or absence of solution) of the associated system of equations. It should be noted that the successive augmented matrices obtained during the reduction are in no sense *equal* to one another. They are merely connected by elementary row operations. It is also important to remember that the operations may only be carried out on the *rows* of the matrix, and not on its *columns*.

Test for Consistency

Suppose the augmented matrix $(\mathbf{A} \mid \mathbf{B})$ of the system of equations $\mathbf{AX} = \mathbf{B}$ is reduced to the row echelon form $(\mathbf{A}_R \mid \mathbf{B}_R)$. Then $(\mathbf{A}_R \mid \mathbf{B}_R)$ is called the *reduced augmented matrix*. If $(\mathbf{A}_R \mid \mathbf{B}_R)$ contains a row of the form

$$(0\ \ 0\ \ 0\ \ \ldots\ \ 0 \mid 1) \tag{46}$$

then this row corresponds to an equation $0 = 1$, and the equations are inconsistent.

Rank of a Matrix

The *rank* $r(\mathbf{A})$ (or simply r) of a matrix $\mathbf{A}$ is the largest integer r for which there exists a non-singular $r \times r$ submatrix of $\mathbf{A}$ (non-singular matrices were defined in §8.4 and submatrices in §8.6). For instance, the matrix

$$\begin{pmatrix} 4 & 2 & 2 & 3 \\ 1 & 1 & 0 & 1 \\ 2 & 0 & 2 & 1 \end{pmatrix}$$

is of rank 2, because, for example

$$\begin{vmatrix} 4 & 2 \\ 1 & 1 \end{vmatrix} \neq 0, \quad \text{or} \quad \begin{vmatrix} 4 & 2 \\ 2 & 2 \end{vmatrix} \neq 0,$$

but the determinants of all the 3×3 submatrices are zero. If $\mathbf{A}$ is a non-singular $n \times n$ matrix, so that $\det \mathbf{A} \neq 0$, then $r(\mathbf{A}) = n$. If $\mathbf{A}$ is an $m \times n$ matrix, no submatrix can have more than m rows or n columns, so $r \leqslant m, r \leqslant n$.

Row Echelon Reduction and Rank

By using elementary properties of determinants it can be verified that the elementary row operations (a′) (b′) (c′) do not change the rank of a matrix $\mathbf{A}$. Hence if $\mathbf{A}$ has rank r, so does any matrix derived from $\mathbf{A}$ by elementary row operations. In particular, if $\mathbf{A}$ is reduced by elementary row operations to a matrix $\mathbf{A}_R$ which has row echelon form, then $\mathbf{A}_R$ has rank r also. Moreover the rank r of a matrix which has row echelon form is easily seen to be the number of rows which do *not* consist entirely of zeros. Thus a method of finding the rank of any matrix is to reduce it to row echelon form, and count the number of rows which do not consist entirely of zeros.

Rank and Consistency

It has been shown that the equations $\mathbf{AX} = \mathbf{B}$ are inconsistent if the reduced augmented matrix $(\mathbf{A}_R \mid \mathbf{B}_R)$ contains a row of the form (46). The corresponding row of $\mathbf{A}_R$ then consists entirely of zeros. Hence $r(\mathbf{A}_R \mid \mathbf{B}_R) = r(\mathbf{A}_R) + 1$. But $r(\mathbf{A}_R \mid \mathbf{B}_R) = r(\mathbf{A} \mid \mathbf{B}), r(\mathbf{A}_R) = r(\mathbf{A})$, and so we have the following alternative form of the test for inconsistency: *the system* $\mathbf{AX} = \mathbf{B}$ *is inconsistent if* $r(\mathbf{A} \mid \mathbf{B}) > r(\mathbf{A})$.

Conversely, if $r(\mathbf{A} \mid \mathbf{B}) = r(\mathbf{A})$, the reduced augmented matrix does not contain a row of the form (46), there is no contradiction, and the equations are *consistent*.

All possibilities are now covered for, because $\mathbf{A}$ is a submatrix of $(\mathbf{A} \mid \mathbf{B})$, it is not possible to have $r(\mathbf{A} \mid \mathbf{B}) < r(\mathbf{A})$.

Summary of Cases

Now suppose that the equations are consistent, so that $r(\mathbf{A} \mid \mathbf{B}) = r(\mathbf{A}) = r$. Recall that $r \leqslant m, r \leqslant n$, where m is the number of equations and n the number of unknowns in the system $\mathbf{AX} = \mathbf{B}$.

The simplest case is $m = n = r$. $\mathbf{A}$ is then a non-singular square matrix (that is, det $\mathbf{A} \neq 0$, and $\mathbf{A}^{-1}$ exists) and the system has the unique solution $\mathbf{X} = \mathbf{A}^{-1}\mathbf{B}$.

If $m > r$, then $m - r$ of the equations are redundant.

If $n > r$, the equations are consistent but do not have a unique solution. Arbitrary values can be given to $n - r$ of the unknowns, and r equations solved for r unknowns in terms of the remaining $n - r$ unknowns.

Examples 1–4 above illustrate some of these possibilities. In each of these examples $r(\mathbf{A})$ and $r(\mathbf{A} \mid \mathbf{B})$ can be read off from the displayed reduced augmented matrices.

Exercises

1. For each of the following pairs of matrices $\mathbf{A}$, $\mathbf{B}$

(1) reduce the augmented matrix $(\mathbf{A} \mid \mathbf{B})$ to row echelon form
(2) hence find the rank of $\mathbf{A}$ and the rank of $(\mathbf{A} \mid \mathbf{B})$
(3) state whether or not the system $\mathbf{AX} = \mathbf{B}$ is consistent
(4) in the consistent cases, solve the system $\mathbf{AX} = \mathbf{B}$

(a) $\mathbf{A} = \begin{pmatrix} 1 & 1 & 0 \\ 2 & 0 & 1 \\ 3 & 0 & 1 \end{pmatrix}$, $\mathbf{B} = \begin{pmatrix} 1 \\ 1 \\ 1 \end{pmatrix}$, (b) $\mathbf{A} = \begin{pmatrix} 0 & 1 & 1 \\ 1 & -1 & -2 \\ 2 & -1 & -3 \end{pmatrix}$, $\mathbf{B} = \begin{pmatrix} 1 \\ 1 \\ 3 \end{pmatrix}$,

(c) $\mathbf{A} = \begin{pmatrix} 0 & 1 & 1 \\ 1 & -1 & -2 \\ 2 & -1 & -3 \end{pmatrix}$, $\mathbf{B} = \begin{pmatrix} 1 \\ 1 \\ 2 \end{pmatrix}$, (d) $\mathbf{A} = \begin{pmatrix} 2 & 3 & 4 \\ 3 & 4 & 5 \end{pmatrix}$, $\mathbf{B} = \begin{pmatrix} 5 \\ 6 \end{pmatrix}$,

(e) $\mathbf{A} = \begin{pmatrix} 0 & 1 & 1 \\ 1 & 0 & 1 \\ 1 & 1 & 0 \\ 1 & 1 & 1 \end{pmatrix}$, $\mathbf{B} = \begin{pmatrix} 2 \\ 2 \\ 2 \\ 3 \end{pmatrix}$, (f) $\mathbf{A} = \begin{pmatrix} 0 & 1 & 2 \\ 2 & 0 & 1 \\ 2 & 2 & 1 \\ 4 & 1 & 1 \end{pmatrix}$, $\mathbf{B} = \begin{pmatrix} 5 \\ 2 \\ 4 \\ 6 \end{pmatrix}$.

8.8 HOMOGENEOUS SYSTEMS OF LINEAR EQUATIONS

The system of equations (7) is *homogeneous* if all the constants $b_1, b_2, \ldots, b_m$ are zero. In matrix notation the system of homogeneous linear equations has the form $\mathbf{AX} = \mathbf{0}$.

A system of homogeneous equations always has the solution

$$x_1 = 0, \quad x_2 = 0, \quad x_3 = 0, \quad \ldots, \quad x_n = 0, \tag{47}$$

or, more concisely, $\mathbf{X} = \mathbf{0}$. Since the system always has this solution, it is *always consistent*. The zero solution (47) is called the *trivial solution*. Interest usually centres on whether or not there exist additional solutions besides the trivial solution; such solutions, if they exist, are called *non-trivial* solutions. It is clear that the most we may hope to determine in finding a non-trivial solution is the *ratios* of the variables

$x_1, x_2, \ldots, x_n$, because if $x_1, x_2, x_3, \ldots, x_n$ satisfy the equations, so do $\alpha x_1, \alpha x_2, \alpha x_3, \ldots, \alpha x_n$, where α is any constant.

Test for Non-trivial Solutions in the Case m = n

The most important case is that of n equations in n unknowns, so that $\mathbf{A}$ is a square matrix. Suppose that det $\mathbf{A} \neq 0$, so that $\mathbf{A}^{-1}$ exists. Then the solution of $\mathbf{AX} = \mathbf{0}$ is $\mathbf{X} = \mathbf{A}^{-1}\mathbf{0} = \mathbf{0}$ so that the only solution is the trivial solution. Hence a necessary condition for the existence of non-trivial solutions is that det $\mathbf{A} = 0$. It can be shown that this is also a sufficient condition. Thus *a necessary and sufficient condition for the system* $\mathbf{AX} = \mathbf{0}$ *of n equations in n unknowns to have non-trivial solutions is that* det $\mathbf{A} = 0$.

EXAMPLE 1
Find the non-trivial solutions of the system

$$
\begin{aligned}
x_1 + x_2 + x_3 + x_4 &= 0, \\
3x_1 + 2x_2 - 2x_3 &= 0, \\
2x_1 + 3x_2 \qquad - 2x_4 &= 0, \\
x_1 + 2x_2 + 3x_3 + x_4 &= 0.
\end{aligned}
$$

It is easily verified that the determinant of the coefficients is zero, so that non-trivial solutions exist. Consequently one of the original equations is redundant, and by elimination we find that the original system is equivalent to the new system

$$
\begin{aligned}
x_1 + x_2 + x_3 + x_4 &= 0, \\
x_2 + 5x_3 + 3x_4 &= 0, \\
x_3 + x_4 &= 0.
\end{aligned}
$$

Hence, solving in turn, $x_3 = -x_4, x_2 = -5x_3 - 3x_4 = 2x_4$, $x_1 = -x_2 - x_3 - x_4 = -2x_4$, so that $x_1:x_2:x_3:x_4 = -2:2:-1:1$, or $\mathbf{X}^T = c(-2 \quad 2 \quad -1 \quad 1)$, where c is any constant.

The Case m ≠ n

The general case in which $m \neq n$ can be dealt with by the row echelon reduction as for an inhomogeneous system. The main difference is that since now $\mathbf{B} = \mathbf{0}$, the augmented matrix $(\mathbf{A} \mid \mathbf{B})$ consists of $\mathbf{A}$ augmented by a column of zeros, so that any submatrix of $(\mathbf{A} \mid \mathbf{B})$ is either a submatrix of $\mathbf{A}$ or contains a column of zeros. Hence $r(\mathbf{A}) = r(\mathbf{A} \mid \mathbf{B})$; this confirms that the system is always compatible, having the trivial solution $\mathbf{X} = \mathbf{0}$.

The conditions for the system to have *non-trivial* solutions can be obtained by minor modifications of the arguments used in §8.7. *The necessary and sufficient conditions for the existence of non-trivial solutions is that* $r(\mathbf{A}) < n$. It is of course also necessary that $r(\mathbf{A}) \leqslant m$.

Systems of Homogeneous Linear Ordinary Differential Equations with Constant Coefficients

The solution of simultaneous linear ordinary differential equations with constant coefficients by the method of elimination was described in §1.9. For systems of *homogeneous* equations of this type it is usually preferable to proceed in a similar way to that which was used in the solution of a single homogeneous linear differential equation with constant coefficients; that is, by substituting into the equations a trial solution in which the unknowns are exponential functions of the independent variable. The differential equations are thereby reduced to a homogeneous system of linear algebraic equations. The following examples illustrate the method.

EXAMPLE 2
Solve the simultaneous differential equations

$$(3D + 7)y + (3D + 5)z = 0,$$
$$(4D + 11)y - (D + 5)z = 0,$$

where D denotes the operator d/dx.

This system was solved by elimination as example 2 of §1.9. Here we proceed by seeking solutions of the form

$$y = Ae^{mx}, \quad z = Ce^{mx}.$$

By substituting these into the equations and cancelling the factor e^{mx}, it follows that

$$(3m + 7)A + (3m + 5)C = 0,$$
$$(4m + 11)A - (m + 5)C = 0. \tag{48}$$

We require non-trivial solutions in which A and C are not both zero. These non-trivial solutions are possible only when m is chosen so that

$$\begin{vmatrix} 3m + 7 & 3m + 5 \\ 4m + 11 & -m - 5 \end{vmatrix} = 0.$$

Expanding the determinant and simplifying gives $m^2 + 5m + 6 = 0$, with solutions $m = -2$ and $m = -3$. When $m = -2$, equations (48) become

$$A - C = 0, \quad \text{and} \quad 3A - 3C = 0,$$

which have the non-trivial solution $A = C$. Hence one solution of the differential equation is

$$y = Ae^{-2x}, \quad z = Ae^{-2x}.$$

Similarly, taking $m = -3$, and replacing A and C by B and E respectively, equations (48) become

$$-2B - 4E = 0, \quad \text{and} \quad -B - 2E = 0,$$

which have the non-trivial solution $E = -\tfrac{1}{2}B$. Hence a second solution of the differential equations is

$$y = Be^{-3x}, \quad z = -\tfrac{1}{2}Be^{-3x}.$$

The general solution is the sum of the two solutions obtained above, namely,

$$y = Ae^{-2x} + Be^{-3x}, \quad z = Ae^{-2x} - \tfrac{1}{2}Be^{-3x},$$

which agrees with the result obtained in §1.9.

EXAMPLE 3
Solve the simultaneous differential equations

$$\frac{dx}{dt} = -y - z, \quad \frac{dy}{dt} = -x - z, \quad \frac{dz}{dt} = -x + y.$$

The trial solution is $x = Ae^{mt}, y = Be^{mt}, z = Ce^{mt}$, and this satisfies the differential equations if

$$\begin{aligned} mA + B + C &= 0, \\ A + mB + C &= 0, \\ A - B + mC &= 0. \end{aligned} \tag{49}$$

For non-trivial solutions, $\begin{vmatrix} m & 1 & 1 \\ 1 & m & 1 \\ 1 & -1 & m \end{vmatrix} = 0,$ which gives

$m = 0, m = -1, m = 1$. When $m = 0$, the solution of equations (49) is easily found to be $A:B:C = 1:1:-1$. Hence, since $e^0 = 1$, a solution of the differential equations is

$$x = A_1, \quad y = A_1, \quad z = -A_1 \tag{50}$$

Similarly, when $m = -1$, the solution of equations (49) is $A:B:C = 1:1:0$, so a second solution of the differential equations is

$$x = A_2 e^{-t}, \quad y = A_2 e^{-t}, \quad z = 0. \tag{51}$$

Finally, for $m = 1$, the solution of equations (49) is $A:B:C = 1:0:-1$, which gives as a third solution of the differential equations

$$x = A_3 e^t, \quad y = 0, \quad z = -A_3 e^t. \tag{52}$$

The general solution of the differential equations is obtained by adding the three solutions given above.

In examples 2 and 3 the roots of the equation for m turned out to be real numbers. In other cases, some or all of these roots will be complex. It is then usually preferable to express the solution in terms of sine, cosine and exponential functions in the manner described in §1.5.

Exercises

1. Determine whether or not the following systems of homogeneous equations have non-trivial solutions, and find these solutions when they exist:

(a)
$$x_1 + x_2 = 0,$$
$$2x_1 - x_3 = 0,$$
$$3x_1 + x_3 = 0.$$

(b)
$$x_2 + x_3 = 0,$$
$$x_1 - x_2 - 2x_3 = 0,$$
$$2x_1 - x_2 - 3x_3 = 0.$$

(c)
$$2x_1 - x_2 + 3x_3 = 0,$$
$$5x_1 - 4x_2 + 2x_3 = 0.$$

(d)
$$x_1 + 3x_2 = 0,$$
$$2x_1 + 2x_2 = 0,$$
$$-x_1 + 4x_2 = 0.$$

(e)
$$7x_1 + 3x_2 + 4x_3 + x_4 = 0,$$
$$x_1 + 5x_2 - x_3 + 2x_4 = 0,$$
$$-2x_1 - 7x_2 - 2x_3 - 2x_4 = 0,$$
$$2x_1 + 3x_2 + x_3 + x_4 = 0.$$

(f)
$$x_1 + 2x_2 + 3x_3 = 0,$$
$$-x_1 - 4x_2 + x_3 = 0,$$
$$-x_1 - 6x_2 + 5x_3 = 0,$$
$$x_1 - 2x_2 + 11x_3 = 0.$$

2. Solve the following systems of differential equations:

(a) $\dfrac{dy}{dt} + 3y - z = 0, \quad \dfrac{dz}{dt} + 2z - y = 0.$

(b) $(2D^2 - 6D + 4)y + (D^2 - D - 2)z = 0,$
$(D^2 + D - 2)y + (2D^2 + 6D + 4)z = 0,$ where D denotes d/dx.

(c) $\dfrac{dx}{dt} + 2x + y - z = 0, \quad \dfrac{dy}{dt} + x + 2y + z = 0, \quad \dfrac{dz}{dt} + x + y + 2z = 0.$

3. The equations governing the currents in the primary and secondary circuits of a transformer, when there is no applied e.m.f. and resistances are neglected, are

$$L_1 \frac{d^2 I_1}{dt^2} + M \frac{d^2 I_2}{dt^2} + \frac{I_1}{C_1} = 0, \quad L_2 \frac{d^2 I_2}{dt^2} + M \frac{d^2 I_1}{dt^2} + \frac{I_2}{C_2} = 0.$$

Find the general solution by adopting the trial solution

$$I_1 = A \cos(pt + \epsilon), \quad I_2 = B \cos(pt + \epsilon).$$

8.9 EIGENVALUES AND EIGENVECTORS

Algebraic eigenvalue problems involve systems of homogeneous linear equations in which the coefficients depend in a certain way on a parameter. In general such a system possesses only the trivial solution, but non-trivial solutions may exist for certain special values of the parameter. Many different physical and other problems can be formulated as algebraic eigenvalue problems; they arise particularly in the

study of vibrations and of stability, and in finding principal axes of inertia, stress and
strain.

A Vibration Problem

Consider the system of three springs (with moduli k_1, k_2 and k_3) and three masses
m_1, m_2 and m_3 shown in Fig. 8.4. The two masses m_1 and m_2 are connected by a
rigid rod of negligible mass, and the spring with modulus k_3 is connected to the mid-
point of this. The system might be interpreted as a very idealized model of a motor-
cycle suspension, with m_1 and m_2 representing the unsprung masses of the two wheels,
and m_3 the sprung mass of the cycle and rider. The vertical upward displacements of
the three masses from their equilibrium positions are y_1, y_2 and y_3, as illustrated.
Hence the extensions, from the equilibrium configuration, of the springs of moduli
k_1, k_2 and k_3 are, respectively, y_1, y_2 and $y_3 - \frac{1}{2}(y_1 + y_2)$. If there are no damping
forces present, the equations of motion of the three masses are

$$m_1\ddot{y}_1 = -k_1 y_1 + \frac{1}{2}k_3\{y_3 - \frac{1}{2}(y_1 + y_2)\},$$
$$m_2\ddot{y}_2 = -k_2 y_2 + \frac{1}{2}k_3\{y_3 - \frac{1}{2}(y_1 + y_2)\},$$
$$m_3\ddot{y}_3 = -k_3\{y_3 - \frac{1}{2}(y_1 + y_2)\}.$$

After rearrangement, these equations may be written

$$\begin{pmatrix} \ddot{y}_1 \\ \ddot{y}_2 \\ \ddot{y}_3 \end{pmatrix} = \begin{pmatrix} -(k_1 + \frac{1}{4}k_3)/m_1 & -\frac{1}{4}k_3/m_1 & \frac{1}{2}k_3/m_1 \\ -\frac{1}{4}k_3/m_2 & -(k_2 + \frac{1}{4}k_3)/m_2 & \frac{1}{2}k_3/m_2 \\ \frac{1}{2}k_3/m_3 & \frac{1}{2}k_3/m_3 & -k_3/m_3 \end{pmatrix} \begin{pmatrix} y_1 \\ y_2 \\ y_3 \end{pmatrix}. \tag{53}$$

These equations may be solved by the methods described in §1.9 or, more efficiently,
by the method given at the end of §8.8. However for a system such as this, in which

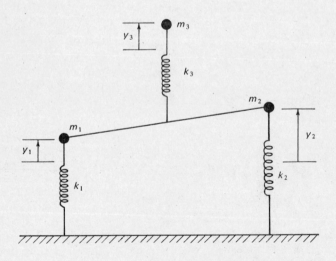

Fig. 8.4   Vibrations of three sprung masses

there is no damping, our experience indicates that the masses, once set in motion, may undergo undamped oscillations of a fixed frequency. This suggests seeking solutions in which the masses undergo simple harmonic oscillations with frequency $\omega/2\pi$ and amplitudes x_1, x_2 and x_3, so that the solution is of the form

$$y_1 = x_1 \cos(\omega t + \epsilon), \quad y_2 = x_2 \cos(\omega t + \epsilon), \quad y_3 = x_3 \cos(\omega t + \epsilon), \tag{54}$$

where ϵ is a constant. Substituting equations (54) into equations (53) and cancelling the factor $\cos(\omega t + \epsilon)$ gives

$$-\omega^2 \begin{pmatrix} x_1 \\ x_2 \\ x_3 \end{pmatrix} = \begin{pmatrix} -(k_1 + \tfrac14 k_3)/m_1 & -\tfrac14 k_3/m_1 & \tfrac12 k_3/m_1 \\ -\tfrac14 k_3/m_2 & -(k_2 + \tfrac14 k_3)/m_2 & \tfrac12 k_3/m_2 \\ \tfrac12 k_3/m_3 & \tfrac12 k_3/m_3 & -k_3/m_3 \end{pmatrix} \begin{pmatrix} x_1 \\ x_2 \\ x_3 \end{pmatrix}. \tag{55}$$

To be definite, suppose that in suitable units the masses and moduli have the values $m_1 = 1, m_2 = 1, m_3 = 4/3, k_1 = 1, k_2 = 1, k_3 = 4$. Then equations (55) become

$$-\omega^2 \begin{pmatrix} x_1 \\ x_2 \\ x_3 \end{pmatrix} = \begin{pmatrix} -2 & -1 & 2 \\ -1 & -2 & 2 \\ \tfrac32 & \tfrac32 & -3 \end{pmatrix} \begin{pmatrix} x_1 \\ x_2 \\ x_3 \end{pmatrix},$$

$$\text{or} \quad \begin{pmatrix} 2 - \omega^2 & 1 & -2 \\ 1 & 2 - \omega^2 & -2 \\ -\tfrac32 & -\tfrac32 & 3 - \omega^2 \end{pmatrix} \begin{pmatrix} x_1 \\ x_2 \\ x_3 \end{pmatrix} = \begin{pmatrix} 0 \\ 0 \\ 0 \end{pmatrix}. \tag{56}$$

These equations always have the solution $x_1 = 0, x_2 = 0, x_3 = 0$, but this solution involves no motion and is not of interest. Other solutions are possible only for special values of ω, namely those for which the determinant of the matrix of coefficients of the system of homogeneous equations (56) has the value zero, so that

$$\begin{vmatrix} 2 - \omega^2 & 1 & -2 \\ 1 & 2 - \omega^2 & -2 \\ -\tfrac32 & -\tfrac32 & 3 - \omega^2 \end{vmatrix} = 0.$$

By expansion, this gives

$$(1 - \omega^2)(\omega^4 - 6\omega^2 + 3) = 0,$$

which has the solutions $\omega^2 = 1$, $\omega^2 = 3 + \sqrt6$, and $\omega^2 = 3 - \sqrt6$. These values of ω give the *natural frequencies* of the system, and oscillations of the form (54) are possible only when ω has one of these values. If for example the value $\omega^2 = 1$ is taken, equations (56) become

$$x_1 + x_2 - 2x_3 = 0,$$
$$x_1 + x_2 - 2x_3 = 0,$$
$$-\tfrac32 x_1 - \tfrac32 x_2 + 2x_3 = 0.$$

Since the first two of these equations are identical, the equations are not now independent; in fact ω has been determined in such a way that they shall not be independent. The equations give immediately $x_3 = 0$ and $x_1 = -x_2$, so that $x_1 : x_2 : x_3 = 1 : -1 : 0$. This describes a *normal mode of vibration* in which *amplitude ratios* $x_1 : x_2 : x_3$ are $1 : -1 : 0$. Hence for this normal mode

$$\begin{pmatrix} y_1 \\ y_2 \\ y_3 \end{pmatrix} = a_1 \begin{pmatrix} 1 \\ -1 \\ 0 \end{pmatrix} \cos(t + \epsilon_1),$$

where a_1 and ϵ_1 are constants. In this normal mode, the mass m_3 is at rest, while m_1 and m_2 oscillate with equal amplitude but opposite phase.

Similarly the values $\omega^2 = 3 + \sqrt{6}$ and $\omega^2 = 3 - \sqrt{6}$ give two further non-trivial solutions of equations (56) in which the amplitude ratios $x_1 : x_2 : x_3$ are, respectively, $\sqrt{2} : \sqrt{2} : -\sqrt{3}$ and $\sqrt{2} : \sqrt{2} : \sqrt{3}$. Hence for these second and third normal modes

$$\begin{pmatrix} y_1 \\ y_2 \\ y_3 \end{pmatrix} = a_2 \begin{pmatrix} \sqrt{2} \\ \sqrt{2} \\ -\sqrt{3} \end{pmatrix} \cos(\omega_2 t + \epsilon_2), \quad \begin{pmatrix} y_1 \\ y_2 \\ y_3 \end{pmatrix} = a_3 \begin{pmatrix} \sqrt{2} \\ \sqrt{2} \\ \sqrt{3} \end{pmatrix} \cos(\omega_3 t + \epsilon_3),$$

where $\omega_2 = \sqrt{(3 + \sqrt{6})} \approx 2.334$ and $\omega_3 = \sqrt{(3 - \sqrt{6})} \approx 0.742$. In these second and third normal modes y_1 and y_2 have equal amplitudes and are in phase; in the second mode they are out of phase with y_3 and in the third mode they are in phase with y_3. It may be shown that the general solution of the original problem is the superposition of the solutions corresponding to the three normal modes, namely

$$\begin{pmatrix} y_1 \\ y_2 \\ y_3 \end{pmatrix} = a_1 \begin{pmatrix} 1 \\ -1 \\ 0 \end{pmatrix} \cos(t + \epsilon_1) + a_2 \begin{pmatrix} \sqrt{2} \\ \sqrt{2} \\ -\sqrt{3} \end{pmatrix} \cos(\omega_2 t + \epsilon_2)$$

$$+ a_3 \begin{pmatrix} \sqrt{2} \\ \sqrt{2} \\ \sqrt{3} \end{pmatrix} \cos(\omega_3 t + \epsilon_3),$$

where $a_1, a_2, a_3, \epsilon_1, \epsilon_2, \epsilon_3$ are arbitrary constants.

Eigenvalues and Eigenvectors

The problem discussed above reduced to the solution of a system of equations of the form

$$\mathbf{AX} = \lambda \mathbf{X} \tag{57}$$

where $\mathbf{A}$ is a given square matrix, $\mathbf{X}$ an unknown column vector, and $\lambda = \omega^2$ is a scalar. The problem is to find values of λ for which equation (57) has solutions other than the trivial solution $X = 0$, and the corresponding values of X. Only ratios of the elements of X can be found, not their absolute values.

In the problem discussed A was a 3 x 3 matrix. In general A may be a square matrix of any size; for example the vibrations of a mechanical system with four degrees of freedom would result in A being a 4 x 4 matrix. In studying vibrations of complicated systems A may well be a large matrix.

The values of λ for which equation (57) has non-trivial solutions are called *eigenvalues* of A (other terms in common use are *characteristic roots* and *latent roots*); the corresponding values of X are the *eigenvectors* of A. To find the eigenvalues and eigenvectors, first write equation (57) in the form

$$AX = \lambda IX,$$

and then as

$$(A - \lambda I)X = 0.$$

The condition for this homogeneous system of equations to have non-trivial solutions is (see §8.8)

$$\det(A - \lambda I) = 0. \tag{58}$$

Equation (58) gives the eigenvalues λ. When λ is an eigenvalue, at least one of equations (57) is redundant, and the system has a non-trivial solution. The procedure is best illustrated by an example.

EXAMPLE 1

Find the eigenvalues and eigenvectors of

$$A = \begin{pmatrix} 1 & -3 & \sqrt{2} \\ -3 & 1 & -\sqrt{2} \\ \sqrt{2} & -\sqrt{2} & 4 \end{pmatrix}.$$

The eigenvalue equation (58) is
$$\begin{vmatrix} 1-\lambda & -3 & \sqrt{2} \\ -3 & 1-\lambda & -\sqrt{2} \\ \sqrt{2} & -\sqrt{2} & 4-\lambda \end{vmatrix} = 0.$$

On expanding the determinant, this becomes

$$\lambda^3 - 6\lambda^2 - 4\lambda + 24 = 0,$$

or

$$(\lambda - 6)(\lambda - 2)(\lambda + 2) = 0,$$

so that the eigenvalues are $\lambda = 6, 2, -2$. To find the eigenvector corresponding to (say) $\lambda = 2$, substitute the value of A and $\lambda = 2$ in equations (57), which gives

$$- x_1 - 3x_2 + \sqrt{2}x_3 = 0,$$
$$-3x_1 - x_2 - \sqrt{2}x_3 = 0,$$
$$\sqrt{2}x_1 - \sqrt{2}x_2 + 2x_3 = 0.$$

Since $\lambda = 2$ is an eigenvalue, only two of these equations are independent (in fact the third equation is obtained by subtracting the second from the first and dividing by $\sqrt{2}$) so one equation, say the third, may now be discarded and the first two solved for the ratios $x_1 : x_2 : x_3$. This gives, for the eigenvector corresponding to the eigenvalue $\lambda = 2$

$$\mathbf{X} = \begin{pmatrix} x_1 \\ x_2 \\ x_3 \end{pmatrix} = \alpha \begin{pmatrix} 1 \\ -1 \\ -\sqrt{2} \end{pmatrix}, \text{ where } \alpha \text{ may be any constant.}$$

Since the eigenvectors are indeterminate to within a constant multiplier, any value of α except $\alpha = 0$ gives an equally good eigenvector. The eigenvectors corresponding to the eigenvalues $\lambda = 6$ and $\lambda = -2$ can be found in a similar way (see exercise 2).

Evidently, to find the eigenvalues of an $n \times n$ matrix $\mathbf{A}$ directly, it is necessary to (a) expand the determinant (58) as an nth degree polynomial in λ, and (b) solve the nth degree algebraic equation obtained by setting this polynomial equal to zero. If n is large, as it may well be in practice, both of these processes are formidable and indirect methods have to be used. Some numerical methods of finding eigenvalues and eigenvectors are described in §10.5.

Further Results

Eigenvalues and eigenvectors are of central importance in advanced linear algebra and its applications. Many of their properties are of practical as well as of theoretical interest. The following are some of the more important results.

(a) *If $\mathbf{A}$ is an $n \times n$ matrix with eigenvalues $\lambda_1, \lambda_2, \ldots, \lambda_n$, then $\det \mathbf{A} = \lambda_1 \lambda_2 \ldots \lambda_n$.* To prove this, note first that the coefficient of λ^n in the expansion of $\det(\mathbf{A} - \lambda\mathbf{I})$ is $(-1)^n$. Hence, since $\lambda_1, \lambda_2, \ldots, \lambda_n$ are the roots of $\det(\mathbf{A} - \lambda\mathbf{I}) = 0$, we have

$$\det(\mathbf{A} - \lambda\mathbf{I}) = (\lambda_1 - \lambda)(\lambda_2 - \lambda) \ldots (\lambda_n - \lambda),$$

which is an identity in λ. Therefore, setting $\lambda = 0$,

$$\det \mathbf{A} = \lambda_1 \lambda_2 \ldots \lambda_n.$$

An immediate consequence is that if one of the eigenvalues of $\mathbf{A}$ is equal to zero, then $\det \mathbf{A} = 0$, and conversely, if $\det \mathbf{A} = 0$, then at least one eigenvalue is equal to zero.

(b) In general, there is no necessity for the roots of equation (58) to be real numbers even if the elements of $\mathbf{A}$ are real. Hence the eigenvalues of $\mathbf{A}$ may be complex numbers. However, the following will be proved: *if $\mathbf{A}$ is a real symmetric matrix, its eigenvalues are all real numbers.*

Let λ_1 be an eigenvalue (possibly complex) of $\mathbf{A}$ and $\mathbf{X}_1$ (possibly complex) the corresponding eigenvector, so that

$$\mathbf{AX}_1 = \lambda_1 \mathbf{X}_1. \tag{59}$$

Since $\mathbf{A}$ is symmetric, $\mathbf{A} = \mathbf{A}^T$, and transposing equation (59) gives

$$\mathbf{X}_1^T \mathbf{A} = \lambda_1 \mathbf{X}_1^T. \tag{60}$$

Now let $\bar{\lambda}_1$ denote the complex conjugate of λ_1 and $\bar{\mathbf{X}}_1$ the complex conjugate of $\mathbf{X}_1$. Since $\mathbf{A}$ is real, taking the complex conjugate of equation (60) gives

$$\bar{\mathbf{X}}_1^T \mathbf{A} = \bar{\lambda}_1 \bar{\mathbf{X}}_1^T. \tag{61}$$

Now multiply equation (59) on the left by $\bar{\mathbf{X}}_1^T$ and equation (61) on the right by $\mathbf{X}_1$. This gives

$$\bar{\mathbf{X}}_1^T \mathbf{A} \mathbf{X}_1 = \lambda_1 \bar{\mathbf{X}}_1^T \bar{\mathbf{X}}_1, \quad \bar{\mathbf{X}}_1^T \mathbf{A} \mathbf{X}_1 = \bar{\lambda}_1 \bar{\mathbf{X}}_1^T \mathbf{X}_1,$$

from which it follows that

$$(\lambda_1 - \bar{\lambda}_1)\bar{\mathbf{X}}_1^T \mathbf{X}_1 = \mathbf{0}.$$

However $\bar{\mathbf{X}}_1^T \mathbf{X}_1 = (|x_1^2| + |x_2^2| + \ldots + |x_n^2|)$ and is not zero. Hence $\lambda_1 = \bar{\lambda}_1$, so the imaginary part of λ_1 is zero, and λ_1 is real. As an illustration of this result, note that the eigenvalues of the symmetric matrix in example 1 are real.

Many of the matrices which arise in practical problems are symmetric, and so the above result, and those which follow below, are of considerable importance and utility.

The following definition is now required. Suppose $\mathbf{A}$ is an $n \times n$ matrix, and $\mathbf{X}$ is an $n \times 1$ column vector. Then $\mathbf{X}^T \mathbf{A} \mathbf{X}$ is a 1×1 matrix with a single element. If this element (which is called a *quadratic form*) is *positive* for *all* choices of the vector $\mathbf{X}$ (except $\mathbf{X} = \mathbf{0}$), then $\mathbf{A}$ is said to be a *positive definite matrix*.

EXAMPLE 2
Suppose

$$\mathbf{A} = \begin{pmatrix} 1 & -1 \\ -1 & 2 \end{pmatrix}, \quad \mathbf{X} = \begin{pmatrix} x_1 \\ x_2 \end{pmatrix}.$$

Then $\mathbf{X}^T \mathbf{A} \mathbf{X} = (x_1^2 - 2x_1 x_2 + 2x_2^2)$. However $x_1^2 - 2x_1 x_2 + 2x_2^2 = (x_1 - x_2)^2 + x_2^2$, which is a sum of squares and therefore positive for all values of x_1 and x_2. Hence $\mathbf{A}$ is positive definite.

EXAMPLE 3
Suppose

$$\mathbf{A} = \begin{pmatrix} 1 & -2 \\ -2 & 2 \end{pmatrix}, \quad \mathbf{X} = \begin{pmatrix} x_1 \\ x_2 \end{pmatrix}.$$

Then $\mathbf{X}^T \mathbf{A} \mathbf{X} = (x_1^2 - 4x_1 x_2 + 2x_2^2)$. Now $x_1^2 - 4x_1 x_2 + 2x_2^2 = (x_1 - 2x_2)^2 - 2x_2^2$, and so is positive for some values of x_1 and x_2, and negative for other values of x_1 and x_2. Hence in this case $\mathbf{A}$ is not positive definite.

(c) *A symmetric matrix* $\mathbf{A}$ *is positive definite if and only if all of its eigenvalues are positive.* The proof of this result is not difficult, but is omitted.

Many physical systems can be reduced to equations of the form $AX = \lambda BX$, where
A is a symmetric matrix and B is a positive definite symmetric matrix. Then
$B^{-1}AX = \lambda X$, and so the equations have non-trivial solutions when λ is an eigenvalue
of $B^{-1}A$. The following extension of result (b) above is then useful.

(d) *If A and B are real symmetric $n \times n$ matrices, and B is positive definite, then the
eigenvalues of $B^{-1}A$ are all real numbers.*

The proof follows the lines of the proof of result (b), and details are omitted. To
illustrate the result we note that equations (55) are more naturally written in the form

$$
\begin{pmatrix} k_1 + \tfrac{1}{4}k_3 & \tfrac{1}{4}k_3 & -\tfrac{1}{2}k_3 \\ \tfrac{1}{4}k_3 & k_2 + \tfrac{1}{4}k_3 & -\tfrac{1}{2}k_3 \\ -\tfrac{1}{2}k_3 & -\tfrac{1}{2}k_3 & k_3 \end{pmatrix} \begin{pmatrix} x_1 \\ x_2 \\ x_3 \end{pmatrix} = \omega^2 \begin{pmatrix} m_1 & 0 & 0 \\ 0 & m_2 & 0 \\ 0 & 0 & m_3 \end{pmatrix} \begin{pmatrix} x_1 \\ x_2 \\ x_3 \end{pmatrix}.
$$

This is of the form $AX = \omega^2 BX$, where B is positive definite because the masses
m_1, m_2 and m_3 are positive. Hence the eigenvalues ω^2 are real.

(e) Two column vectors X, Y are said to be *orthogonal* if $X^T Y = 0$. (Here 0 represents
the 1×1 zero matrix (0)). It will be shown that *if A is symmetric, the eigenvectors
associated with two distinct eigenvalues of A are orthogonal.* Let λ_1, λ_2 be the
eigenvalues, X_1, X_2 the corresponding eigenvectors. Then

$$AX_1 = \lambda_1 X_1, \quad AX_2 = \lambda_2 X_2. \tag{62}$$

Transposing the first of these gives, since A is symmetric,

$$X_1^T A = \lambda_1 X_1^T. \tag{63}$$

Multiply the second of equations (62) on the left by X_1^T, and equation (63) on the
right by X_2, to obtain

$$X_1^T AX_2 = \lambda_2 X_1^T X_2, \quad X_1^T AX_2 = \lambda_1 X_1^T X_2.$$

Thus $(\lambda_1 - \lambda_2)X_1^T X_2 = 0$, and since $\lambda_1 \neq \lambda_2$ it follows that $X_1^T X_2 = 0$, so that X_1 and
X_2 are orthogonal. For an illustration of this result, see exercise 2.

Exercises

1. Find the eigenvalues and corresponding eigenvectors of the following matrices.

(a) $\begin{pmatrix} 5 & -2 \\ -2 & 3 \end{pmatrix}$

(b) $\begin{pmatrix} a & b \\ -b & a \end{pmatrix}$

(c) $\begin{pmatrix} 4 & 0 & 0 \\ 0 & 5 & 0 \\ 0 & 0 & 1 \end{pmatrix}$

(d) $\begin{pmatrix} 0 & 1 & 0 \\ 1 & 0 & 0 \\ 0 & 0 & 1 \end{pmatrix}$

(e) $\begin{pmatrix} 2 & -2 & 2 \\ 1 & 1 & 1 \\ 1 & 3 & -1 \end{pmatrix}$

(f) $\dfrac{1}{9}\begin{pmatrix} -11 & 2 & 8 \\ 2 & -2 & 10 \\ 8 & 10 & -5 \end{pmatrix}$

(g) $\begin{pmatrix} \cos\theta & \sin\theta & 0 \\ -\sin\theta & \cos\theta & 0 \\ 0 & 0 & 1 \end{pmatrix}$.

2. Find the remaining two eigenvectors of the matrix of example 1. Verify that the eigenvectors of this matrix are mutually orthogonal.

3. The equations of motion of the system of three springs and two masses shown in Fig. 8.5 are

$$m_1 \ddot{y}_1 = -k_1 y_1 - k_2(y_1 - y_2),$$
$$m_2 \ddot{y}_2 = k_2(y_1 - y_2) - k_3 y_2.$$

Find the natural frequencies and normal modes of vibration of the system if, in suitable units, $m_1 = 1, m_2 = 4, k_1 = 1, k_2 = 4, k_3 = 4$.

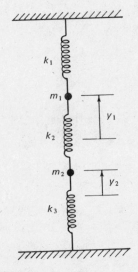

Fig. 8.5 Figure for exercise 3

4. Three identical simple pendula are connected by two identical elastic springs as shown in Fig. 8.6. For small oscillations the equations of motion are

$$ml\ddot{\theta}_1 = -mg\theta_1 - kl(\theta_1 - \theta_2),$$
$$ml\ddot{\theta}_2 = -mg\theta_2 + kl(\theta_1 - \theta_2) - kl(\theta_2 - \theta_3),$$
$$ml\ddot{\theta}_3 = -mg\theta_3 + kl(\theta_2 - \theta_3).$$

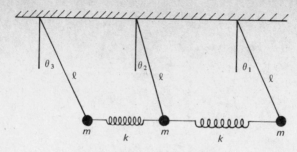

Fig. 8.6   Figure for exercise 4

Find the natural frequencies and normal modes of vibration, and describe the nature of the vibrations for each normal mode.

5. If the matrix $\mathbf{A}$ has eigenvalues $\lambda_1, \lambda_2, \ldots, \lambda_n$, prove that

(a) $k\mathbf{A}$ has eigenvalues $k\lambda_1, k\lambda_2, \ldots, k\lambda_n$,

(b) $\mathbf{A} - p\mathbf{I}$ has eigenvalues $\lambda_1 - p, \lambda_2 - p, \ldots, \lambda_n - p$,

(c) $\mathbf{A}^2$ has eigenvalues $\lambda_1^2, \lambda_2^2, \ldots, \lambda_n^2$,

(d) $\mathbf{A}^{-1}$ has eigenvalues $\lambda_1^{-1}, \lambda_2^{-1}, \ldots, \lambda_n^{-1}$.

PROBLEMS

1.   The matrices $\mathbf{A}$ and $\mathbf{B}$ are both non-singular $n \times n$ matrices, such that $\mathbf{A}$ is symmetric and $\mathbf{B}$ is anti-symmetric. State whether the following matrices are (1) symmetric, (2) anti-symmetric, or (3) neither symmetric nor anti-symmetric.

(a) $\mathbf{A}^T$ (b) $\mathbf{B}^T$ (c) $\mathbf{A}^{-1}$ (d) $\mathbf{B}^{-1}$

(e) $\mathbf{A} + \mathbf{B}$ (f) $\mathbf{A} - \mathbf{B}$ (g) $\mathbf{A} + \mathbf{A}^T$ (h) $\mathbf{B} + \mathbf{B}^T$

(i) $\mathbf{AB}$ (j) $\mathbf{AB}^T$ (k) $\mathbf{AA}^T$ (l) $\mathbf{B}^T\mathbf{B}$

(m) $\mathbf{ABA}$ (n) $\mathbf{B}^T\mathbf{AB}$ (o) $\mathbf{AB} + \mathbf{BA}$ (p) $\mathbf{AB} - \mathbf{BA}$

(q) $(\mathbf{A} + \mathbf{B})(\mathbf{A}^T + \mathbf{B}^T)$ (r) $(\mathbf{A} - \mathbf{B})(\mathbf{A}^T - \mathbf{B}^T)$.

2.   Show that the determinant of a matrix which may be partitioned into a triangular array of submatrices as

$$\begin{vmatrix} \mathbf{A}_{11} & 0 & \cdots & 0 \\ \mathbf{A}_{21} & \mathbf{A}_{22} & \cdots & 0 \\ \cdots & \cdots & \cdots & \cdots \\ \mathbf{A}_{m1} & \mathbf{A}_{m2} & \cdots & \mathbf{A}_{mm} \end{vmatrix}$$

is the product of the determinants of the diagonal submatrices, which are square.

3. Given that the quantities x_i, y_i, z_i $(i = 1, 2, 3)$ are related by the equations

$$x_1 = y_1 + 3y_2 - 2y_3, \quad y_1 = -2z_1 + z_2 + z_3,$$
$$x_2 = 4y_1 + 2y_2 + y_3, \quad y_2 = 2z_1 - z_2 \quad ,$$
$$x_3 = y_1 - 2y_2 + 3y_3, \quad y_3 = z_2 + 2z_3,$$

use matrix methods to express (a) the x_i in terms of the z_i and (b) the z_i in terms of the x_i.

4. A particle is moved from the point with coordinates (x_1, x_2, x_3) to the point with coordinates (y_1, y_2, y_3). These coordinates are related to the coordinates of a third point (z_1, z_2, z_3) by the two sets of equations

$$x_1 = 3z_1 - 2z_2 + 7z_3, \quad y_1 = \tfrac{1}{4}\sqrt{3}z_1 + \quad \tfrac{1}{4}z_2 - \tfrac{1}{2}\sqrt{3}z_3,$$
$$x_2 = -2z_1 + 4z_2 + z_3, \quad y_2 = -\tfrac{1}{2}z_1 + \tfrac{1}{2}\sqrt{3}z_2 \quad ,$$
$$x_3 = 7z_1 + z_2 - 2z_3, \quad y_3 = \tfrac{3}{4}z_1 + \tfrac{1}{4}\sqrt{3}z_2 + \quad \tfrac{1}{2}z_3.$$

Express each of these sets of equations in matrix form and verify that the matrix relating (y_1, y_2, y_3) to (z_1, z_2, z_3) is orthogonal. Hence obtain the relations for (x_1, x_2, x_3) in terms of (y_1, y_2, y_3).

5. By partitioning, determine the inverse of

$$\mathbf{A} = \begin{pmatrix} 2 & -5 & -2 & 0 \\ 1 & -1 & 0 & -2 \\ 1 & 0 & -1 & 2 \\ 0 & 1 & 1 & -3 \end{pmatrix}.$$

Hence obtain the solution $\mathbf{X}$ of the algebraic equations represented by $\mathbf{AX} = \mathbf{H}$ where $\mathbf{H}^T = |(1 \ -2 \ 2 \ -4)$.

6. Determine the rank of the matrix

$$\begin{pmatrix} 1 & 1 & -2 & 7 \\ 4 & -2 & 1 & -11 \\ 3 & 1 & -3 & 8 \end{pmatrix}$$

and find the most general solution of the system of equations

$$x + y - 2z = 7,$$
$$4x - 2y + z = -11,$$
$$3x + y - 3z = 8.$$

7. Determine the rank of the matrix

$$\begin{pmatrix} 4 & 2 & -2 \\ 3 & -1 & 3\tfrac{1}{2} \\ 2 & -2 & 5 \\ 4 & 1 & 0 \end{pmatrix}.$$

Hence state whether the system of equations

$$4x_1 + 2x_2 = -2,$$
$$3x_1 - x_2 = 3\frac{1}{2},$$
$$2x_1 - 2x_2 = 5,$$
$$4x_1 + x_2 = 0,$$

has (a) no solutions, (b) a unique solution, or (c) an infinity of solutions.

8. Prove that the equations

$$2x_1 + x_2 - 3x_3 + 2x_4 = 5,$$
$$-x_1 - 2x_2 + 2x_3 - x_4 = -2,$$
$$4x_1 - x_2 - 5x_3 + 4x_4 = 8,$$
$$x_1 - 4x_2 \qquad + x_4 = 4,$$

are not compatible. The above set contains a set of three equations which are compatible. Find this compatible set and obtain all their solutions.

9. Discuss the general solutions of

$$x_1 + 3x_2 - x_3 - 4x_4 = 2,$$
$$3x_1 - 3x_2 + 3x_3 - 2x_4 = -4,$$
$$-2x_1 \qquad - x_3 + 3x_4 = \beta,$$

for all values of β.

10. Show that one of the eigenvalues of the matrix

$$\begin{pmatrix} -1 & -3 & -6 \\ 2 & 4 & 2 \\ 2 & 2 & 7 \end{pmatrix}$$

has the value 5. Find the remaining two eigenvalues and the eigenvector corresponding to the smallest eigenvalue.

11. Determine the eigenvalues and eigenvectors of the matrix

$$A = \begin{pmatrix} 13 & -3 & 5 \\ 0 & 4 & 0 \\ -15 & 9 & -7 \end{pmatrix}.$$

Hence write down the eigenvalues and eigenvectors of the matrices A^3 and A^{-1}.

12. Prove that the eigenvalues of a real symmetric matrix are real. Find the eigenvalues of the matrix

$$\begin{pmatrix} 4 & -\sqrt{2/3} & 0 \\ -\sqrt{2/3} & 4 & -\sqrt{1/3} \\ 0 & -\sqrt{1/3} & 4 \end{pmatrix}$$

and an eigenvector corresponding to the smallest eigenvalue.

13. The equations

$$\frac{dV_1}{dt} = -2V_1 - 3V_2 - V_3,$$

$$\frac{dV_2}{dt} = V_1,$$

$$\frac{dV_3}{dt} = -V_1 - 3V_2 - 3V_3,$$

govern the behaviour of an electric circuit. Taking $V_1 = x_1 e^{\lambda t}$, $V_2 = x_2 e^{\lambda t}$, $V_3 = x_3 e^{\lambda t}$, determine the values of λ and the corresponding values of $x_1 : x_2 : x_3$ which satisfy these equations.

14. The oscillations of a mechanical system are governed by the equations

$$M_1 \ddot{y}_1 = -\lambda_1 y_1 + \lambda_2 (y_2 - y_1),$$
$$M_2 \ddot{y}_2 = -\lambda_2 (y_2 - y_1) + \lambda_3 (y_3 - y_2),$$
$$M_3 \ddot{y}_3 = -\lambda_3 (y_3 - y_2) - \lambda_4 y_3.$$

Assuming the displacements y_i may be expressed in the form $y_i = x_i \cos \omega t \, (i = 1, 2, 3)$, show that the equations may be written in the matrix form $(A - \omega^2 I)X = 0$. If $M_1 = 1$, $M_2 = 2, M_3 = 3, \lambda_1 = 1, \lambda_2 = 1, \lambda_3 = 2, \lambda_4 = 4$, determine the natural frequencies and amplitude ratios of the system.

15. Oscillations of a framework are known to be governed by the system of equations

$$\ddot{x}_1 = -\alpha x_1 + x_2,$$
$$\ddot{x}_2 = x_1 - 2x_2 + x_3,$$
$$\ddot{x}_3 = x_2 - 2x_3,$$

in which the coefficient α is not given. However, it is observed that the system has a normal mode of the form $X = D \cos t\sqrt{2}$. Deduce the value of α, find the frequencies of the remaining two normal modes of the system and find the eigenvector corresponding to the lowest frequency.

16. By using the method of Lagrange's multipliers, show that the greatest value of $X^T AX$, subject to $X^T X = |(R^2)$, where X is a column vector and A is a real symmetric matrix, occurs when X is an eigenvector of A.

17. If X and A are as in problem 16, and B is a symmetric positive definite matrix, show that the stationary values of $X^T AX$, subject to $X^T BX = (c^2)$, occur when X is a solution of the eigenvalue problem $AX = \lambda BX$.

BIBLIOGRAPHY

[1] Bell, W. W., *Matrices for Scientists and Engineers*, Van Nostrand Reinhold, Wokingham (1975).

[2]   Cohn, P. M., *Linear Equations*, Routledge and Kegan Paul, London (1958).
[3]   Edelen, D. G. B. and A. D. Kydoniefs, *An Introduction to Linear Algebra for Science and Engineering*, Elsevier, New York (1972).
[4]   Mirsky, L., *An Introduction to Linear Algebra*, Clarendon Press, Oxford (1955).
[5]   Noble, B., *Applied Linear Algebra*, Prentice-Hall, New Jersey (1969).

CHAPTER 9

Introduction to Numerical Analysis

9.1 NUMERICAL APPROXIMATION

In the preceding chapters, solutions of equations representing a large variety of engineering situations have been obtained in closed form or as converging series of standard functions. A mathematician would be satisfied with such solutions; an engineer would not, because ultimately he requires a numerical value or values. For example, the solutions of some beam vibration problems are shown in §7.2 to be explicitly expressed in terms of the roots of the equation

$$\cos x \cosh x = 1.$$

An engineer would need the numbers corresponding to those roots. The deflection curve of a uniformly loaded beam is in the form of a quartic; to find the positions of maximum deflection requires the solution of the cubic equation corresponding to points of zero slope. Again the numerical values of the roots are required. As a final example, the reader should recall that in the basic method of solution of ordinary differential equations with constant coefficients (see §1.5 and §1.7) it is necessary to solve for the roots of the auxiliary equation. This equation is a polynomial, and in practice it must be solved numerically.

Another important consideration is that often physical problems cannot be represented adequately by equations which can be solved analytically. In these cases the engineer *must* resort to numerical methods of solution.

Numerical analysis is the study of the numerical solution of problems. Apart from developing methods of solution, the theory is also concerned with the inaccuracy which is always introduced in any numerical computation. Without an estimate of this *error*, a numerical solution is worth little more than no solution at all.

In this chapter, we introduce the elements of numerical analysis, together with its elementary applications in evaluating formulae and finding the roots of single algebraic and transcendental equations. More advanced numerical analysis is treated in the subsequent chapters on the solution of systems of linear equations (Chapter 10), numerical interpolation, integration and differentiation (Chapter 11) and the numerical solution of differential equations (Volume 2, Chapter 7). For comprehensive treatments of the subject, the reader is referred to Fröberg [1], Noble [2], [3] and Williams [4].

Numbers, Decimals and Significant Figures

In mathematics, numbers are assumed to have an exact value, so that a mathematician knows precisely what is signified by the values of π, $\sqrt{2}$, sin 1 and any other irrational numbers. In practice, these values cannot be written exactly since the representation would require an infinite number of digits. It is customary to represent numbers in decimal form (though digital computers use binary form). Thus the number 1.4142 has four *decimals* or *decimal places* and represents the value of $\sqrt{2}$ accurately to four decimals, being correct to within five units in the fifth decimal place. It has five *significant figures*, which are defined as the number of correct digits starting with the first non-zero digit at the left.

Errors and Mistakes

An *error* ϵ is introduced whenever an exact number N is replaced by an approximation n; it is defined by

$$\epsilon = n - N. \tag{1}$$

The error introduced by replacing $\sqrt{2}$ by 1.4142 is of a particular type called *round-off error*. It is produced by rejecting all digits after a selected decimal place and arises as an inevitable consequence of the practical necessity of having to work with a finite number of significant figures. The standard procedure for rounding off is to leave the last digit unchanged if the discarded portion is less than half the last unit retained, increase the last digit by one if the discarded portion is more than half the last unit, and round off to the nearest even digit if the discarded portion is exactly half the last unit retained. Thus, on rounding off to four significant figures, we have

$$1.41421 \rightarrow 1.414, \quad 0.0618237 \rightarrow 0.06182, \quad 0.31625 \rightarrow 0.3162,$$
$$41.755 \rightarrow 41.76, \quad 1.75948 \rightarrow 1.759.$$

It is worth noting that successively reducing the number of significant figures can lead to a wrong answer, as can be seen from the values $1.75948 \rightarrow 1.7595 \rightarrow 1.760$.

Occasionally it is useful to retain some of the discarded information by placing the first discarded digit (rounded off) as a suffix after the number. If so, care must be taken to interpret the value correctly, since the notation can be confusing:

$$1.4142 \rightarrow 1.414_2, \quad 3.1416 \rightarrow 3.142_6.$$

Another type of error, called *truncation error*, is introduced whenever the computational method depends on 'cutting off' an infinite series representation. This truncation is implicit in many (if not most) numerical methods of solution (see Volume 2, Chapter 7, or Fröberg [1]).

Either or both of these errors may enter each stage of a computation, and can accumulate as the numerical procedure continues. This *accumulated error* is often difficult to control. Even when the magnitude of the round-off and truncation errors are controlled at each stage of the computation, the accumulated error can still grow and may swamp the true solution. Its presence can often be detected by comparing the two answers yielded when the computation is carried out by using two different procedures or by repeating the same procedure but with different step-lengths (see Volume 2, Chapter 7, or Noble [3]).

Errors should not be confused with *mistakes* (or *blunders*). These arise from human fallibility or from machine defects. The most common examples are the transposition of digits when writing down numbers (for example, writing 54235 in place of 54325), misreading repeated digits (5.42235 instead of 5.42335), faulty programming for automatic computers, and wrong experimental data. Great care must be taken to guard against numerical mistakes in calculations carried out on a hand-machine, though the most effective numerical methods have checks specifically built in as safeguards. Numerical mistakes occur very rarely on automatic computers.

Finally, it should be noted that there is such a thing as being 'too accurate'. In hand-machine work it is unnecessary and even counter-productive to include more figures than are significant. This only gives a greater opportunity for making mistakes. Similarly, it is useless and misleading to give an answer with more nominal accuracy than is justified by the accuracy of the given initial data.

Absolute and Relative Errors

It is convenient to distinguish between the error $\epsilon \, (= n - N)$, its absolute magnitude $|\epsilon|$ and its magnitude compared with the exact number N. The positive value $|\epsilon|$ is called the *absolute error*, and the ratio $|\epsilon/N|$ is the *relative error*. Since only n, and not N, is known, the relative error is more usefully given by $|\epsilon/n|$ provided ϵ is known to be small compared with n.

Let N_1 and N_2 be two numbers which are taken as positive, without any loss of generality. If n_1 and n_2 denote the approximations to N_1 and N_2 in any calculations, then the absolute errors for addition, subtraction, multiplication and division satisfy

$$|(n_1 + n_2) - (N_1 + N_2)| = |\epsilon_1 + \epsilon_2| < e_1 + e_2$$

$$|(n_1 - n_2) - (N_1 - N_2)| = |\epsilon_1 - \epsilon_2| < e_1 + e_2$$

$$|n_1 n_2 - N_1 N_2| \simeq |\epsilon_1 n_2 + \epsilon_2 n_1| < e_1 n_2 + e_2 n_1$$

$$\left| \frac{n_1}{n_2} - \frac{N_1}{N_2} \right| \simeq \left| \frac{\epsilon_1 n_2 - \epsilon_2 n_1}{n_2^2} \right| < \left(\frac{n_1}{n_2} \right) \left(\frac{e_1}{n_1} + \frac{e_2}{n_2} \right)$$

where the last two relations are based on the assumption that the errors are small compared with N_1 and N_2. Here e_1 and e_2 denote upper bounds on $|\epsilon_1|$ and $|\epsilon_2|$, so that $|\epsilon_1| < e_1$, $|\epsilon_2| < e_2$; they are sometimes called *maximum errors*.

The relative errors in

$$N_1 + N_2, \quad N_1 - N_2, \quad N_1 N_2, \quad N_1/N_2$$

are deduced in a similar manner; the approximate upper bounds are, respectively,

$$\frac{e_1 + e_2}{n_1 + n_2}, \quad \frac{e_1 + e_2}{n_1 - n_2}, \quad \frac{e_1}{n_1} + \frac{e_2}{n_2}, \quad \frac{e_1}{n_1} + \frac{e_2}{n_2}.$$

EXAMPLE

Compute the maximum possible relative errors in $N_1 + N_2$ and $N_1 - N_2$ if the numbers N_1 and N_2 have been rounded off to $n_1 = 49.84$ and $n_2 = 49.82$ respectively.

Rounding off implies that both numbers are accurate to within ± 0.005. Thus $|\epsilon_1|, |\epsilon_2| \leqslant 0.005$ and the maximum relative errors in $N_1 + N_2$ and $N_1 - N_2$ are respectively

$$\frac{0.005 + 0.005}{49.84 + 49.82} = 0.0001, \qquad \frac{0.005 + 0.005}{49.84 - 49.82} = 0.5.$$

The second part of this example illustrates the fact that the subtraction of almost equal numbers is a numerically bad procedure, leading to a loss of significant figures. It also shows how division by a small number magnifies any error in a computation. These two features are particularly important when the calculating machine has a display limited to very few significant figures, such as with a pocket calculator.

Order of Error

Normally the error in any numerical solution cannot be determined exactly (unless the exact solution can be found by another method, in which case the numerical solution is unnecessary). We can specify exact bounds on round off errors but not for truncation errors. However, a measure of the magnitude of a truncation error is provided by the (neglected) next term of the series. In fact, it is this *order* of error which is the useful quantity. If the error depends on the value of some small parameter h, then we say that the error is 'of order h', written $O(h)$, if the ratio ϵ/h tends to a finite limit as h approaches zero:

$$\epsilon = O(h) <\!=\!> \lim_{h \to 0}(\epsilon/h) = c$$

where c is some finite constant. If $c = 0$, we may write $\epsilon = o(h)$, but this notation is not important in numerical analysis. More generally,

$$\epsilon = O(h^p) <\!=\!> \lim_{h \to 0}(\epsilon/h^p) = c.$$

9.2 EVALUATION OF FORMULAE

All problems involving numerical computation eventually reduce to the evaluation of formulae. At this stage, considerable savings of time and reduction of error can be made by suitably arranging the numerical procedure. The choice of arrangement is largely a matter of experience, but there are a few basic rules which are obvious once they are pointed out.

The first rule is always to arrange formulae so that as few operations as possible are involved. This saves time, reduces accumulation of error and, on a hand machine, minimizes the chance of mistakes. Another rule with a similar advantage for hand computation is to choose the procedure which involves as little intermediate writing as possible. Furthermore, it should always be borne in mind that division takes longer than multiplication which in turn is far more time-consuming than addition. On a high-speed computer such as the ICL 1906, the respective ratios are roughly 12:6:1. As an illustration of the application of these rules, we consider the following example.

EXAMPLE 1

Rearrange the polynomial

$$P(x) \equiv a_n x^n + a_{n-1} x^{n-1} + \ldots + a_1 x + a_0$$

so as to give the most efficient procedure for its evaluation.

Inspection shows that in its given form the evaluation involves n additions and $\frac{1}{2}n(n+1)$ multiplications. Also, if no storage mechanism is available, the value of each term must be written down. By performing the calculation in reverse order and keeping a record of $x, x^2, \ldots$, the number of multiplications is reduced to $2n - 1$. The standard rearrangement is even more efficient, involving n additions but only $(n+1)$ multiplications and no storage facility:

$$P(x) \equiv ((\ldots((a_n x + a_{n-1})x + a_{n-2})x + \ldots + a_2)x + a_1)x + a_0.$$

The procedure is to first calculate the innermost bracket $(a_n x + a_{n-1})$; the result is then multiplied by the value of x and added to a_{n-2}, this result again being multiplied by x and then added to a_{n-3}, and so on.

Division is often avoided if possible. This is not only for reasons of time-saving, but also to avoid errors which may be introduced through round off at a fixed decimal place when dividing by very large numbers. The dangers associated with division by small numbers have already been noted in the previous section. Therefore one would compute

$$(a \times b \times c \times \ldots)/(u \times v \times w \times \ldots) \quad \text{not} \quad (a/u) \times (b/v) \times (c/w) \times \ldots.$$

The reader should always treat the above rules as guidelines and not as being inviolable. Sometimes two or more of the rules will be in conflict. This occurs particularly when the advantages of time-saving are weighed against loss of accuracy; circumstances must then determine what should be done. In the following example, division actually *increases* the accuracy.

EXAMPLE 2

Evaluate the roots of $x^2 - 48x + 2 = 0$ using five significant figures.

The two roots are given by

$$x = 24 \pm \sqrt{574} = 24 \pm 23.958$$

so that one root $x_1 = 47.958$ is accurate to five significant figures whereas the other root $x_2 = 0.042$ has only two significant figures. However, if the subtraction giving x_2 were replaced by a division using the property that $x_1 x_2 = 2$, one obtains $x_2 = 2/47.958 = 0.041703$, and retains five significant figure accuracy.

Exercises

1. The radii of two circular cylinders are measured to be 12.783 ± 0.002 and 0.531 ± 0.002. Calculate the area of cross-section of each cylinder, first using $\pi = 3.14 \pm 0.005$ and then using $\pi = 3.142 \pm 0.0005$. Give the absolute and relative errors in each case. Is there any gain in taking $\pi = 3.1416 \pm 0.00005$?

2. If $A = 7.13291, B = 7.13709, x = 0.142$ and $y = 0.315$, calculate the value of

$$C = (Ay - Bx)/(y - x)$$

both directly and by using the alternative form

$$C = A - x\,\frac{B - A}{y - x}.$$

Estimate the error in each case.

3. Evaluate the roots of the quadratic $x^2 - 15x + 1 = 0$ (a) directly, using the standard formula, and (b) using the formula for the larger root and the result that the product of the roots is unity to determine the smaller root. Estimate the error in each case and check your answers by adding the roots.

9.3 FLOW DIAGRAMS OR CHARTS

When an automatic computer is used to determine a numerical solution, it is obvious that the machine must be instructed on each individual operation it must make, and in an unambiguous manner. This series of instructions is termed a *computer program* and it must be written in a 'language' which can be interpreted by the machine.

Programming itself is not considered to be a part of the subject of numerical analysis. The logical ordering of the basic steps *is* a part, as it incorporates error estimates and safeguards against mistakes. In this context, the term 'step' means a set of related instructions, such as those required to evaluate a formula.

This sequential arrangement of steps is usually displayed in the form of a *flow diagram* or *flow chart*, and is relevant to both hand and automatic computation. Each step is represented, as in Fig. 9.1, by a box containing one of two types of command — *direct* and *alternative* (or '*if*') commands. Each box is linked to another by means of an arrow indicating the direction of the logical order. Direct commands include arithmetical operations, 'write' instructions and input of data; only one arrow leaves each such box, which is usually drawn in a rectangular shape. Alternative or '*if*' commands are always associated with a choice of direction in which to proceed; thus more than one arrow leaves each such box, which is often drawn as a diamond or some other non-rectangular shape. An alternative command usually occurs as a 'test' statement involving an inequality. There are three such statements in the flow chart shown in Fig. 9.1.

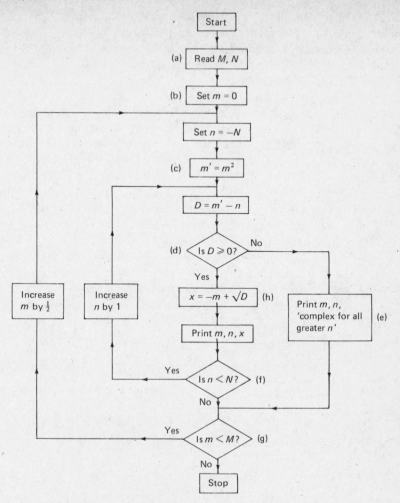

Fig. 9.1 Flow chart illustrating various types of statements

EXAMPLE

Write down a flow diagram for finding and printing all the real numbers x given by

$$x = -m + (m^2 - n)^{1/2}$$

for all pairs (m, n) where m changes in steps of ½ from 0 to M and n is an integer varying from $-N$ to N. M and N represent positive integers which are to be specified as input data.

A suitable flow diagram is shown in Fig. 9.1; the (a), (b), (c), . . . refer to the following comments. (a) is a read statement, allowing the user a freedom of choice in specifying M and N. At (b) a decision is made to select the pairs (m, n) in the sequence $(0, -N), (0, -N + 1), . . . , (0, N), (½, -N), (½, -N + 1), . . .$ rather than the order

$(0, -N), (\frac{1}{2}, -N), \ldots, (M, -N), \ldots$. Sometimes there is a gain in choosing a particular order, but the order is not important in this example. The step shown in (c) is not strictly necessary in a flow chart, but demonstrates how computer time can be saved. If (c) were excluded and the next step changed to read $D = m^2 - n$, the machine would have to compute the same m^2 for $2N + 1$ times. The first 'if' statement (at (d)) ensures that only real numbers are computed. If, at any stage, D is negative, implying complex x, the machine is told to bypass the next three steps by jumping to the step (g); the 'print' statement (e) on the way is optional. Note that the direction of the flow is unchanged. This is in contrast with the consequences of the other two 'if' statements at (f) and (g), which reverse the flow and are, therefore, drawn on the opposite side of the main flow path. These are sometimes termed *'loops'* or *'cycles'*, and occur whenever a series of steps is repeated. It is good practice never to have loops intersecting one another, since normally this indicates a fault in the logic and at best an inefficient program. As an example of this, the reader should consider the effect of interchanging steps (f) and (g).

Most computers (including hand machines) now have a built-in square-root facility, so that computing $\sqrt{D}$ in a procedure is, in effect, an arithmetical operation. If the facility is not available, then the instruction (h) implies that a sub-program (within the main program) must be used in order to evaluate $\sqrt{D}$. Such sub-programs are called *subroutines.*

Exercises

1. Write a flow diagram for evaluating the polynomial $P(x) = a_0 + a_1 x + \ldots + a_n x^n$ for arbitrary input of values of $a_0, a_1, \ldots, a_n$ and integer n, and for values of x increasing from $x = 0$ to $x = 1$ in steps of 0.1.

2. Construct a flow chart for evaluating $n!$ for $n = 0, 1, 2, \ldots, 10$.

3. Write down a flow chart for evaluating the continued fraction

$$f = N_0 + \cfrac{1}{N_1 + \cfrac{1}{N_2 + \cfrac{\vdots}{N_9 + \cfrac{1}{N_{10}}}}}$$

to a specified accuracy, and where the values $N_0, N_1, \ldots, N_{10}$ are to be inserted as input data.

9.4 SOLUTION OF SINGLE ALGEBRAIC AND TRANSCENDENTAL EQUATIONS

There are two types of method for solving problems numerically — *direct* and *iterative.* Direct methods are 'one-off' methods, designed to give the answer directly. The procedures are, therefore, usually lengthier and more complicated than iterative methods, which involve repeating the same simple procedure many times until the answer 'settles down'. However, the greater number of calculations required by iterative methods makes these less attractive for use on hand machines.

The simplest example of a direct method of solution is the use of the formula

$$x = \frac{-b + (b^2 - 4ac)^{1/2}}{2a} \tag{5}$$

for obtaining one of the roots of the quadratic equation $ax^2 + bx + c = 0$. The root is easily computed by using formula (5), provided square root tables are available to the required accuracy; if not, the direct solution is not straightforward. Checks must be incorporated in any direct solution in order to guard against mistakes; in this example, a check is provided by directly substituting the answer into the quadratic.

Although direct methods are important for solving systems of linear equations (see Chapter 10), they are of very little value in solving single equations. Formulae exist for solving cubic and quartic equations, but these formulae are so complicated that they are rarely used. It is not possible to produce formulae for the solution of higher order polynomial equations or for transcendental equations (which involve trigonometric or exponential functions). Hence the general equation

$$f(x) = 0 \tag{6}$$

must be solved numerically for its roots $x = X$ using iterative methods.

A function $g(x)$ is chosen in such a way that the sequence of values $x_0, x_1, x_2, \ldots$ generated by using an *iteration formula*

$$x_{n+1} = g(x_n), \quad n = 0, 1, 2, \ldots. \tag{7}$$

converges to the required root X of $f(x) = 0$:

$$\lim_{n \to \infty} x_n = X. \tag{8}$$

Hence $g(x)$ must be a function such that

$$X = g(X). \tag{9}$$

There are an infinite number of possible choices of $g(x)$ such that both equations (6) and (9) are satisfied when $x = X$. For example, this occurs for any choice of the coefficients $a_1, a_2, \ldots, a_m$ such that

$$g(x) = x + a_1 f(x) + a_2 \{f(x)\}^2 + \ldots + a_m \{f(x)\}^m. \tag{10}$$

Different forms of $g(x)$ lead to different iterative methods. The choice of $g(x)$ is governed by the form of the function $f(x)$ and by whether the number of iterations is important (as it would be if hand computation were necessary). In particular, $g(x)$ must be chosen such that the procedure converges.

In practice, the first approximation x_0 is determined graphically or by computing $y = f(x)$ for various x and finding when the value of y changes sign. The numerical procedure described by equations (7) and (8) is stopped when two successive values x_n, x_{n+1} differ by less than a specified amount or after a given number of iterations have taken place. The latter alternative is to safeguard against divergence of the sequence, or against prohibitively slow convergence.

Convergence of $x_{n+1} = g(x_n)$

If x_n is regarded as an approximation to X, so that

$$\epsilon_n = x_n - X \tag{11}$$

is the error in the approximation, then the basic iterative procedure (7) converges if $g(x)$ is such that

$$|\epsilon_{n+1}/\epsilon_n| < 1 \tag{12}$$

for sufficiently large n. From equations (7) and (11) it follows that

$$X + \epsilon_{n+1} = g(X + \epsilon_n)$$
$$= g(X) + \epsilon_n g'(\xi_n) \tag{13}$$

where ξ_n is a value in the range (x_n, X). Here we have used the first mean value theorem (see §4.2) for a continuous differentiable function:

$$g(x_n) - g(X) = (x_n - X)g'(\xi_n), \quad \xi_n \text{ in } (x_n, X)$$

where $g'(\xi_n)$ represents the value of the derivative of $g(x)$ at $x = \xi_n$. Using equations (9) and (13) then shows that

$$\epsilon_{n+1}/\epsilon_n = g'(\xi_n). \tag{14}$$

Hence the procedure converges provided $g(x)$ is a continuous differentiable function such that

$$|g'(\xi_n)| < 1. \tag{15}$$

This result is illustrated graphically in Fig. 9.2, where $y = x$ and $y = g(x)$ have been

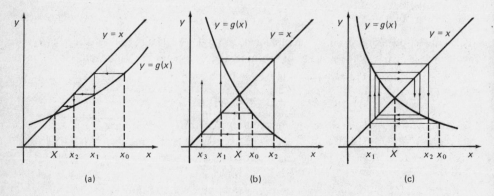

Fig. 9.2   Geometrical representation of $x_{n+1} = g(x_n)$ for various $g(x)$; (a) convergent procedure, (b) divergence, (c) slow convergence

drawn for several different functions $g(x)$. The iterative procedure (7) is given by following the arrowed paths. Starting from an arbitrary value x_0 of x on the curve $y = g(x)$, we move horizontally to the line $y = x$. This new value of x is equal to $g(x_0)$ and is therefore x_1 by the definition (7). Moving vertically to the curve $y = g(x)$ then gives $y_1 = g(x_1)$ so that the subsequent horizontal move to the line $y = x$ will give x_2. Repetition of this procedure gives $x_3, x_4, \ldots$, and shows whether or not the method converges (compare Figs. 9.2(a) and 9.2(b)).

Since X, and hence ξ_n, are not known *a priori*, it is convenient to express the condition for convergence in terms of known values such as x_n. Expanding $g'(\xi_n)$ in a Taylor series about x_n gives

$$g'(\xi_n) = g'(x_n) + (\xi_n - x_n)g''(x_n) + \ldots$$

so that, from equation (14),

$$\epsilon_{n+1}/\epsilon_n = g'(x_n) + 0(\epsilon_n). \tag{16}$$

Hence an alternative condition for convergence is that $g(x)$ should be such that at any stage of the computation

$$|g'(x_n)| < 1. \tag{17}$$

This is a sufficient, but not a necessary, condition for convergence, as can be seen from Fig. 9.2(c) where $|g'(x_1)| > 1$.

The Newton-Raphson Method

This very important procedure for solving $f(x) = 0$ is described by

$$x_{n+1} = x_n - \frac{f(x_n)}{f'(x_n)}, \tag{18}$$

the special choice of $g(x)$ now being

$$g(x) = x - \frac{f(x)}{f'(x)}. \tag{19}$$

The choice is suggested by the following analysis, in which all terms involving $\epsilon_n^2, \epsilon_n^3, \ldots$ are neglected in the Taylor series expansion:

$$0 = f(X) = f(x_n - \epsilon_n) \simeq f(x_n) - \epsilon_n f'(x_n).$$

Hence an approximate correction ϵ_n is $f(x_n)/f'(x_n)$, leading to the formula (18).

From equation (19) it is straightforward to show that in this case

$$g'(X) = \frac{f(X)f''(X)}{\{f'(X)\}^2}.$$

Therefore, since $f(X) = 0$,

$$g'(x_n) = g'(X + \epsilon_n) = g'(X) + \epsilon_n g''(X) + \ldots = 0(\epsilon_n).$$

This is a remarkable result, showing from equation (16) that not only is $|\epsilon_{n+1}|$ less

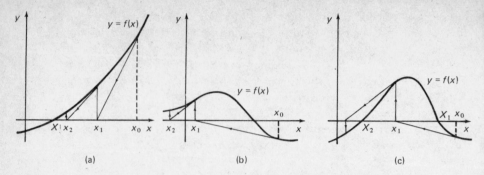

Fig. 9.3   Newton–Raphson method

than $| \epsilon_n |$ but is, in fact, of order ϵ_n^2, indicating very rapid convergence. The numerical implication of this is that the number of correct figures is effectively doubled by each iteration.

A graphical illustration of the method is shown in Fig. 9.3(a). The slope of the tangent at P_0 on the curve $y = f(x)$ is $f'(x_0)$. The slope is given also by $f(x_0)/(x_0 - x_1)$ so that x_1 is the same value as that given by equation (18) with $n = 0$. The figure shows how the procedure moves the values $x_0, x_1, \ldots$ progressively closer to the exact solution at $x = X$. It should be noted, however, that convergence to a required root X is not certain even if x_0 appears to be sufficiently close to it. Equation (18) indicates that difficulties must be expected whenever $f'(x)$ is zero near $x = X$, and particularly when the equation $f(x) = 0$ has two nearly equal roots in this region. A graphical illustration of each case is given in Figs. 9.3 (b), (c). The first approximation x_0 is much closer to the root X_1 than to X_2 in Fig. 9.3(c), but the procedure still converges to X_2. In each case the root can be located using the fixed secant method described later in this section.

EXAMPLE 1
Construct a flow diagram for the Newton-Raphson procedure.

The diagram is shown in Fig. 9.4, and illustrates how simply a flow diagram can be constructed for an iterative procedure. In the form shown, only the required number or the word 'divergent' is printed. If all the intermediate values of x_n are required, then the print statement should be moved into the loop. Note that by specifying δ and N the user is postulating his practical definitions of convergence and divergence, and these values must be decided *a priori* for automatic computation. Note also that the instruction to calculate $f(x_n)$ and $f'(x_n)$ would normally require a subroutine if the function $f(x)$ were at all complicated.

EXAMPLE 2
Compute the single real root of the cubic equation

$$3x^3 + x - 1 = 0$$

giving the answer to three decimal accuracy.

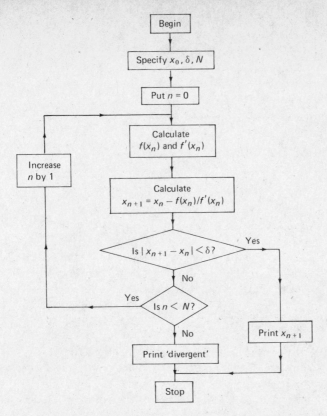

Fig. 9.4   Flow chart for the Newton–Raphson procedure

With $f(x) = 3x^3 + x - 1$, we note that $f(x)$ passes through a zero as x increases from 0 to 1; hence the iteration is started from $x_0 = 0$. Since $f'(x) = 9x^2 + 1$, the Newton-Raphson method gives

$$x_{n+1} = x_n - \frac{3x_n^3 + x_n - 1}{9x_n^2 + 1}.$$

Starting from $x_0 = 0$ and following the numerical procedure described in example 1 above, we obtain $x_1 = 1$ and the sequence

n	0	1	2	3	4	5	6
x_n	0	1	0.7	0.60	0.54	0.537	0.5366

showing that the root is at $X = 0.537$ to 3 decimal places. This may be verified by substitution into the original equation.

EXAMPLE 3

Obtain to four decimal accuracy the smallest non-zero root of $\cos x \cosh x = 1$.

This is an equation governing the solution of many vibration problems (see §7.2).

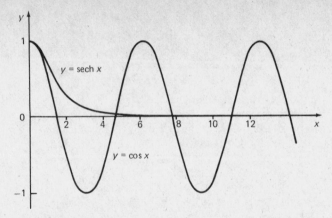

Fig. 9.5   Locating approximate roots of $\cos x \cosh x = 1$

An approximate value for the root is given by considering the intersection of the curves $y = \cos x$ and $y = \mathrm{sech}\, x$. Figure 9.5 suggests that $x_0 = 4.7$ is a suitable choice. Then, with $f(x) = \cos x \cosh x - 1$, we obtain the iteration formula

$$x_{n+1} = x_n - \frac{\cos x_n \cosh x_n - 1}{\cos x_n \sinh x_n - \sin x_n \cosh x_n} \tag{20}$$

leading to $x_1 = 4.731$, $x_2 = 4.7300 = x_3$, so that the solution is $X = 4.7300$.

Figure 9.5, in fact, shows that the roots are very nearly the roots of $\cos x = 0$ for $|x| > \pi/2$, i.e. $x \simeq \pm 3\pi/2, \pm 5\pi/2, \ldots$. If these values are used as first approximations, then equation (20) immediately gives the next approximation to be

$$x_1 = \pm \left[(2r + 1)\frac{\pi}{2} - (-1)^r \, \mathrm{sech}\, (2r + 1)\frac{\pi}{2} \right], \quad r = 1, 2, \ldots .$$

EXAMPLE 4

By considering $f(x) = x^2 - A$, derive an iterative formula for computing the *square root* $A^{1/2}$ of any positive number A.

$A^{1/2}$ is the root of $f(x) \equiv x^2 - A = 0$. Applying the Newton-Raphson formula (18) to this choice of $f(x)$ gives

$$x_{n+1} = x_n - \frac{x_n - A}{2x_n} = \tfrac{1}{2}\left(x_n + \frac{A}{x_n} \right). \tag{21}$$

This formula is almost universally used for automatic computation of square roots.

Nth Roots and Reciprocals

Formula (21) is a special case of the general formula derived from $f(x) = x^N - A$ to give $A^{1/N}$:

$$x_{n+1} = \frac{1}{N}\left[(N - 1)x_n + Ax_n^{1-N} \right]. \tag{22}$$

This formula is valid for positive and negative values of N. Thus an iterative method for determining $1/A$ is given by equation (22) with $N = -1$:

$$x_{n+1} = (2 - Ax_n)x_n,$$

and that for $A^{-1/2}$ is

$$x_{n+1} = \frac{1}{2}x_n(3 - Ax_n^2).$$

This is a remarkable formula in that it does not use division (apart from ½); it can also be used to compute $A^{1/2}$ as $AA^{-1/2}$.

Complex Roots

The Newton-Raphson formula can be used to obtain the roots of any equation. This is irrespective of whether those roots are real or complex and irrespective of any complex coefficients in the equation. The only restriction is that a complex starting value x_0 must be used if a complex root of an algebraic equation is sought. However, if the equation is algebraic and has *real* coefficients, *Bairstow's method* should be used. This makes use of the fact that all complex roots of such equations occur in conjugate pairs $a \pm ib$. The reader is referred to Fröberg [1] for details of the method which, like the Newton-Raphson method, converges rapidly with $\epsilon_{n+1} = O(\epsilon_n^2)$.

The Fixed Tangent Method

Although the Newton-Raphson method is a very good numerical method, the reader will soon find when using a desk calculator that the need to compute the derivative $f'(x_n)$ and to perform the division by $f'(x_n)$ at each iteration is a definite drawback, in some cases being extremely time-consuming. The same criticism also applies whenever an automatic computer is used, particularly with complicated functions requiring a subroutine.

This drawback is overcome in the *fixed tangent method* which replaces the variable gradient $f'(x_n)$ of the Newton-Raphson method by the fixed initial value $f'(x_0)$. The value of $f(x_n)/f'(x_0)$ is obtained by *multiplying* $f(x_n)$ by the constant $1/f'(x_0)$. The iterative procedure is then

$$x_{n+1} = x_n - f(x_n)/f'(x_0).$$

However, application of this method requires much greater care than does the Newton-Raphson method, particularly when choosing the initial value x_0, as is apparent from the following example.

EXAMPLE 5
Repeat example 2 using the fixed tangent method, and choosing (a) $x_0 = 1$, and (b) $x_0 = 0$.

(a) $x_0 = 1$ implies $f'(x_0) = 10$, so that $x_{n+1} = x_n - \frac{1}{10}f(x_n)$:

n	0	1	2	3	4	5	6	7	8	9	10
x_n	1	0.7	0.63	0.59	0.57	0.56	0.55	0.545	0.542	0.540	0.539.

The values converge to 0.537, albeit progressively more slowly.

(b) $x_0 = 0$ implies $f'(x_0) = 1$, so that $x_{n+1} = x_n - f(x_n)$

n	0	1	2	3	4
x_n	0	1	-2	25	-46874;

the process is now obviously divergent.

The contrasting behaviours resulting from the different choices of x_0 are explained by considering the condition (17) for convergence. In the fixed tangent method, $g(x)$ and $g'(x)$ take the forms

$$g(x) = x + cf(x), \quad g'(x) = 1 + cf'(x) \tag{23}$$

where $c = -1/f'(x_0)$. Condition (17) then shows that convergence is obtained if

$$-2 < cf'(x_n) < 0 \tag{24}$$

which in this case implies the condition

$$0 < f'(x_n)/f'(x_0) < 2. \tag{25}$$

In the solution (a) of example 5, $f'(x_n)/f'(x_0) = (9x_n^2 + 1)/10 \leqslant 1$, satisfying condition (25); on the other hand, for (b) the ratio is $9x_n^2 + 1$ with a value of 10 when $n = 1$ so that condition (25) is violated.

Methods not Requiring a Derivative

The simple analysis leading to condition (24) holds for *any* choice of c in equation (23) and need not depend on any derivative. Thus an $f'(x_0)$ leading to an 'awkward' value for c in a hand-computation should be replaced by a more convenient value. Alternatively, by choosing x_0 and x_1 on opposite sides of the root X, a more suitable c could be given by $c = -(x_1 - x_0)/\{f(x_1) - f(x_0)\}$, so that

$$x_{n+1} = x_n - \frac{x_1 - x_0}{f(x_1) - f(x_0)} f(x_n).$$

This is the *fixed secant method*, and is graphically illustrated in Fig. 9.6(a). The relevant criterion for convergence is still given by condition (24) which in this case implies that

$$0 < \frac{x_1 - x_0}{f(x_1) - f(x_0)} f'(x_n) < 2.$$

A similar method, using the most 'up to date' chord (that joining the points corresponding to x_{n-1} and x_n), is given by

$$x_{n+1} = x_n - \frac{x_n - x_{n-1}}{f(x_n) - f(x_{n-1})} f(x_n)$$

$$= \frac{x_{n-1}f(x_n) - x_n f(x_{n-1})}{f(x_n) - f(x_{n-1})}. \tag{26}$$

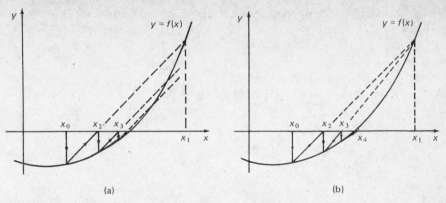

(a)   (b)

Fig. 9.6 Methods not requiring a derivative; (a) the fixed secant method, (b) the variable secant method

This method is called the *variable secant method* or the *method of regula falsi*, and is shown graphically in Fig. 9.6(b).

EXAMPLE 6

Repeat example 2 using the fixed and variable secant methods.

Since the sign of $f(x) = 3x^3 + x - 1$ changes between $x = 0$ and $x = 1$, we choose $x_0 = 0$ and $x_1 = 1$. Thus $f(x_0) = -1, f(x_1) = 3$ and the fixed secant method gives

$$x_{n+1} = x_n - \tfrac{1}{4}(3x_n^3 + x_n - 1).$$

n	0	1	2	3	4	5	6	7	8
x_n	0	1	0.25	0.43	0.51	0.53	0.536	0.5365	0.5366.

The variable secant method gives

$$x_{n+1} = \frac{x_{n-1}(3x_n^3 + x_n - 1) - x_n(3x_{n-1}^3 + x_{n-1} - 1)}{3x_n^3 + x_n - 3x_{n-1}^3 - x_{n-1}}.$$

n	0	1	2	3	4	5	6	7	8
x_n	0	1	0.25	0.39	0.61	0.52	0.535	0.537	0.5366.

Order of Convergence

The relatively slow rate of convergence of the fixed tangent and secant methods compared with the Newton-Raphson method has been explained by the order of the dependence of ϵ_{n+1} on ϵ_n. If, in an iterative method,

$$\epsilon_{n+1} = O(\epsilon_n^p),$$

the method is said to be of pth *order* and the power p would give the order of convergence. Thus the fixed tangent method is a first-order method and the Newton-Raphson a second-order method.

The variable secant method can be shown to be in between these methods, being of order $\frac{1}{2}(1 + \sqrt{5}) \simeq 1.62$. Its convergence is better than the first-order methods even though no derivative is required. It should be noted, however, that for some functions (polynomials, for example) evaluation of $(x_n - x_{n-1})f(x_n)/[f(x_n) - f(x_{n-1})]$ takes much longer than the computation of $f(x_n)/f'(x_n)$.

Methods with third-order (or higher order) convergence exist, but are rarely used in practice because usually the additional complexity of computation is not worth the reduction of number of steps.

Acceleration of Convergence

Since the simple first-order methods often result in comparatively slow convergence, the following method of accelerating their convergence is important, particularly for hand-computation. It is known as *Aitken's δ^2-process.*

For any first-order procedure, equation (14) shows that

$$\epsilon_{n+1}/\epsilon_n = g'(\xi_n) = g'(X) + O(\epsilon_n)$$

and similarly

$$\epsilon_n/\epsilon_{n-1} = g'(X) + O(\epsilon_{n-1}).$$

Hence, neglect of terms of $O(\epsilon)$ gives

$$\epsilon_{n+1}/\epsilon_n = \epsilon_n/\epsilon_{n-1}.$$

Substituting $x_n - X$ for ϵ_n, etc. and solving for X gives

$$X \simeq x_n - \frac{(x_n - x_{n-1})^2}{x_n - 2x_{n-1} + x_{n-2}}. \tag{27}$$

The value given by formula (27) is then used as the starting value for a new sequence of iterations.

Applying the method to the values in example 5(a) above, when convergence becomes obviously very slow at $n = 8$, would mean that a new sequence at $n = 9$ should start at

$$0.542 - \frac{(-0.003)^2}{0.002} = 0.5375.$$

The new sequence then gives x_n as $0.5375, 0.5372, 0.5370$ (working with four decimal places since accuracy is required to three) and a further use of the approximation (27) gives the required answer as 0.5366.

Exercises

1. Construct a flow diagram for the variable secant method.

2. Use (a) the fixed tangent method, (b) the variable secant method and (c) the

Newton-Raphson method, to find the real root near $x = 1$ of

$$x^3 + x - 3 = 0.$$

Make the answer accurate to four decimal places.

3. Use the fixed secant method, with accelerated convergence if necessary, to determine the real roots, accurate to three decimal places, of

$$f(x) = 4.17x^3 - 20.03x^2 - x + 5.21.$$

4. By applying the Newton-Raphson method with the function $f(x) = 1 - Ax^{-N}$, deduce an iterative formula for obtaining $A^{1/N}$. Show that it is *not* the same as formula (22). Use each formula to determine $\sqrt{3}$ accurate to five decimal places.

5. Use (a) the Newton-Raphson method, and (b) an iterative method not requiring a derivative, to solve $x = \exp(-x^2)$ to four significant figures.

PROBLEMS

1. An infinite continued fraction f is given by $\lim_{n \to \infty} f_n$ where

$$f_n = b_0 + \cfrac{a_1}{b_1 + \cfrac{a_2}{b_2 + \cfrac{a_3}{b_3 + \cfrac{\vdots}{\cfrac{b_{n-1} + a_n}{b_n}}}}}$$

and $a_1, a_2, \ldots, b_0, b_1, \ldots, b_n$ are specified numbers. The value of f_n is given by $f_n = A_n/B_n$ where A_n and B_n are determined from the recurrence relations

$$A_n = b_n A_{n-1} + a_n A_{n-2}, \qquad B_n = b_n B_{n-1} + a_n B_{n-2}$$

with $A_{-1} = 1, A_0 = b_0, B_{-1} = 0, B_0 = 1$.

Write a flow chart for determining f to a specified accuracy. Hence compute the value of $\tan^{-1} 0.35$ to four decimal places, given that

$$\tan^{-1} x = \cfrac{x}{1 + \cfrac{x^2}{3 + \cfrac{(2x)^2}{5 + \cfrac{(3x)^2}{7 + \ldots}}}}.$$

2. Graphically examine the convergence of each of the iterative procedures
(a) $x_{n+1} = \frac{1}{4}(x_n^2 - 1)$ and (b) $x_{n+1} = 4 + 1/x_n$. Hence compute the two roots of the

quadratic equation

$$x^2 - 4x - 1 = 0$$

giving your answer to three decimal accuracy.

3. Use Taylor's theorem to obtain an approximation for $f(x) = e^x \sin x$ near $x = 0$ in the form of a cubic in x and use the remainder term to determine the range of values of x over which the approximation is valid if the error is not to exceed ± 0.0005. Hence obtain approximate values of $f(0.2)$ and $f(-0.3)$, and compare your answers with those obtained using tables.

4. Use two different iterative methods, one involving the use of a derivative and the other not, to determine to five significant figures the smallest non-zero positive root of $x - 2 \sin 2x = 0$.

5. Let (X, Y) denote the exact solution of two simultaneous equations $f(x, y) = 0$, $g(x, y) = 0$. By expanding $f(X + h, Y + k)$ and $g(X + h, Y + k)$ about (X, Y), and neglecting terms involving h^2, hk, k^2 and higher powers of h and k, deduce Newton's iterative method of solution:

$$x_{n+1} = x_n + H(x_n, y_n), \quad y_{n+1} = y_n + K(x_n, y_n)$$

where

$$H(x, y) = \frac{g \dfrac{\partial f}{\partial y} - f \dfrac{\partial g}{\partial y}}{\dfrac{\partial f}{\partial x} \dfrac{\partial g}{\partial y} - \dfrac{\partial f}{\partial y} \dfrac{\partial g}{\partial x}}, \quad K(x, y) = \frac{-g \dfrac{\partial f}{\partial x} + f \dfrac{\partial g}{\partial x}}{\dfrac{\partial f}{\partial x} \dfrac{\partial g}{\partial y} - \dfrac{\partial f}{\partial y} \dfrac{\partial g}{\partial x}}.$$

Hence solve the simultaneous equations

$$x - \sin(y/x) = 0, \quad y = \cos y + \sin x,$$

giving your answer to three decimal accuracy.

6. By sketching the two curves $3x^2 + y^2 = 9$, $y + 2 \sin x = 2$, show that they have two points of intersection for one of which x is positive and for the other x is negative. Use iteration schemes of the form

$$x_{n+1} = F(x_n, y_n), \quad y_{n+1} = G(x_{n+1}, y_n)$$

to solve the equations to three decimal accuracy.

BIBLIOGRAPHY

[1]   Fröberg, C.-E., *Introduction to Numerical Analysis*, Addison-Wesley, Reading, Mass. (1965).
[2]   Noble, B., *Numerical Methods: 1*, Oliver and Boyd, Edinburgh (1964).
[3]   Noble, B., *Numerical Methods: 2*, Oliver and Boyd, Edinburgh (1964).
[4]   Williams, P. W., *Numerical Computation*, Nelson, London (1972).

CHAPTER 10

Linear Algebra — Numerical Methods

10.1 INTRODUCTION

In all branches of engineering there are practical problems which reduce to the solution of sets of linear algebraic equations. It is not uncommon for there to be hundreds or even thousands of such equations although often the coefficient matrices are sparse, that is, contain a large number of zeros. From a theoretical point of view the solution of a system of n equations in n unknowns may be written down using determinants (Cramer's rule, as described in §8.4). Though the use of determinants may be convenient for very small systems of, say, three or four equations, it was pointed out in Chapter 8 that this method proves quite impracticable for much higher order systems. This is because the number of arithmetic operations needed to evaluate an nth-order determinant directly is of the order of $n!$ and this increases very rapidly with n. Even evaluating the determinants in the best manner possible requires a number of operations proportional to n^4. The direct methods for the solution of linear equations described in this chapter reduce the computation to a number of operations proportional to n^3. Hence it is far more efficient numerically to use one of the *direct* or *iterative* methods described in §10.2 and §10.3. All the methods of this chapter are suitable for large systems although it is only practical here to illustrate them by small systems of orders 2, 3 and 4.

Direct methods are generally economical on computing time as the solution is obtained in a fixed number of arithmetic operations, but they require more programming time and more computer store than iterative methods. On the other hand, for the iterative methods which are much easier to program, the computing time is dependent upon the accuracy required of the solution and the method may be very time-consuming for a slowly convergent system. Most computer systems which are used for scientific work have readily available standard library subroutines. These libraries always include programs for solving linear algebraic equations which are based upon the direct methods of §10.2.

This chapter is concerned with the system of n equations in n unknowns

$$a_{11}x_1 + a_{12}x_2 + \ldots + a_{1n}x_n = b_1,$$
$$a_{21}x_1 + a_{22}x_2 + \ldots + a_{2n}x_n = b_2,$$
$$\cdot \qquad \cdot \qquad \ldots \qquad \cdot$$
$$a_{n1}x_1 + a_{n2}x_2 + \ldots + a_{nn}x_n = b_n,$$

where the coefficients a_{ij} and right-hand sides b_i are all constants. This system is written in matrix form as

$$AX = B, \tag{1}$$

where X is the column vector of unknowns and B is the column vector formed from the right-hand sides of the equations. It is assumed that B is not the zero vector and that $\det A \neq 0$. The difficult situation when $\det A$ is very small compared with the elements of A is considered in §10.2. The equations are then said to be *ill-conditioned*.

Formally the solution of equations (1) may be written as

$$X = A^{-1}B,$$

and sometimes it is useful actually to compute the inverse matrix A^{-1}. The inverse of a matrix is defined in terms of the adjoint matrix (see §8.4) which is formed from the cofactors of $\det A$. As with Cramer's rule this is not a practical method for numerical computation and the two methods of matrix inversion described in §10.4 are extensions of the direct methods of §10.2 for the solution of linear equations.

Closely associated with the problem of the solution of linear equations is that of finding the eigenvalues and eigenvectors of a matrix and in §10.5 a simple iterative method is described for finding the largest eigenvalue and corresponding eigenvector.

10.2 DIRECT METHODS FOR THE SOLUTION OF LINEAR EQUATIONS

Pivotal Condensation or Gaussian Elimination

This direct method for the solution of a system of linear equations is based on the straightforward elimination method of elementary algebra applied in a systematic fashion. The method is similar to the procedure of row echelon reduction discussed in detail in §8.7. The manner of the elimination is particularly important when only a limited number of decimal places can be used in the calculations. It was devised so as to minimize the computational error by ensuring that all the multiplying factors are less than unity.

The first step is to examine the system of equations (1) and select the largest coefficient of x_1 as the first *pivot*. The equation containing this coefficient is called the *pivotal equation* and multiples of this equation are added to each of the remaining equations to make the coefficients of x_1 zero. If the first pivot is a_{s1} then the multiplying factors are $-a_{11}/a_{s1}, -a_{21}/a_{s1}, \ldots$. This eliminates the variable x_1 from $(n-1)$ of the equations. The pivotal equation is then set aside leaving $(n-1)$ equations in the variables $x_2, x_3, \ldots, x_n$. The largest coefficient of x_2 is chosen as the second pivot and the elimination procedure is repeated. In this manner a set of *pivotal equations* is obtained having an upper triangular coefficient matrix of the form

$$
\begin{aligned}
a_{s1}x_1 + a_{s2}x_2 + \ldots \quad\quad &+ a_{sn}x_n = b_s, \\
\alpha_{22}x_2 + \alpha_{23}x_3 + \ldots \quad\quad &+ \alpha_{2n}x_n = d_2, \\
&\;\;\cdot \\
&\;\;\cdot \\
\alpha_{n-1,n-1}x_{n-1} + \alpha_{n-1,n}x_n &= d_{n-1}, \\
\alpha_{n,n}x_n &= d_n.
\end{aligned}
\tag{2}
$$

The value of x_n is found directly from the last equation. Then this value is substituted into the previous equation to yield the value of x_{n-1}, and so on. This is known as *back-substitution.*

When the calculations are performed by hand using a desk calculating machine a simple checking procedure can be included. This consists of carrying an extra column of numbers, the elements of which are the sums of the coefficients and the right-hand side element of each row. This extra sum column is operated on in the same manner as the equations themselves. At each stage the elements of this extra column should be the sum of all the coefficients of each new equation (apart from rounding errors). The procedure is illustrated in the following example.

EXAMPLE 1
Solve the system of equations

$$0.6x + 0.8y + 0.1z = 1,$$
$$1.1x + 0.4y + 0.3z = 0.2,$$
$$x + y + 2z = 0.5.$$

The coefficient 1.1 is the largest in the first column and is selected as the first pivot. Thus the second equation is the pivotal equation and is used to eliminate x from the other two equations. A new first equation is obtained by adding to the first equation $-0.6/1.1$ ($= -0.545455$) times the second equation. As a check this same operation is performed on the numbers 2.5 and 2.0 which are the sums of the coefficients and right-hand sides of the first and second equations respectively. This results in $2.5 - 0.545455 \times 2.0 = 1.409090$ which is exactly the sum of the coefficients and right-hand side of the new first equation. The new third equation is found by adding to it $-1/1.1$ ($= -0.909091$) times the second equation. The check is provided by $4.5 - 0.909091 \times 2.0 = 2.681818$, which only differs from the sum of the coefficients and right-hand side of the new third equation by 1 in the last figure. The whole scheme is set out in table 10.1, where the multipliers are in the column headed m, the pivots are underlined and the sum column is headed Σ.

The pivotal equations are

$$1.1x + 0.4y + 0.3z = 0.2,$$
$$0.636364y + 1.727273z = 0.318182,$$
$$-1.642857z = 0.6.$$

Back substitution gives the following results, to five decimal places,

$$z = -0.36522, \quad y = 1.49130 \quad \text{and} \quad x = -0.26087.$$

As a check on the final solution, these values can be substituted into the original set of equations or into the sum of the equations. For this example the sum is

$$(0.6 + 1.1 + 1)x + (0.8 + 0.4 + 1)y + (0.1 + 0.3 + 2)z = 1 + 0.2 + 0.5,$$

or $\qquad 2.7x + 2.2y + 2.4z = 1.7,$

and $\quad 2.7 \times (-0.26087) + 2.2 \times 1.49130 + 2.4 \times (-0.36522) = 1.69998.$

TABLE 10.1

m	x	y	z	b	Σ
−0.545455	0.6	0.8	0.1	1	2.5
	1.1	0.4	0.3	0.2	2.0
−0.909091	1	1	2	0.5	4.5
−0.914285		0.581818	−0.063637	0.890909	1.409090
		0.636364	1.727273	0.318182	2.681818
			−1.642857	0.600000	−1.042856

Ill-conditioned Equations

It is important to note that numerical methods may fail to yield the required accuracy when the solution is very sensitive to the values of the coefficients. Equations of this type are said to be *ill-conditioned*. The phenomenon is associated with the situation when the elements of A^{-1} are very much larger than the elements of A itself. A useful guide to this situation is given by the determinant of A which can be found as a by-product of pivotal condensation. Since the determinant of a matrix is unchanged by the elementary row operations of this method, and the determinant of a triangular matrix is the product of its diagonal elements, then

$$\det A = \pm a_{s1} \alpha_{22} \alpha_{33} \ldots \alpha_{nn}.$$

The sign depends upon the reordering necessary to obtain equations (2). When the modulus of det A is very small, the elements of A^{-1} tend to be very much larger than the elements of A and ill-conditioning occurs.

EXAMPLE 2
Solve the system of equations

$$0.6x + 0.8y + 0.1z = 1,$$
$$1.1x + 0.4y + 0.3z = 0.2,$$
$$1.71x + 1.2y + 0.41z = 1.2.$$

Using the method of pivotal condensation and working with four decimal places the results of table 10.2 are obtained giving

$$z = 0.5217, \quad y = 1.5883, \quad x = -0.5380.$$

The accuracy of this solution is suspect because there is a loss of significant figures in the coefficient of z in the second pivotal equation and also in the coefficients of the third pivotal equation. In fact the determinant of A is ± 0.0045 which is small compared with the individual elements of A. The solution found by using many more significant figures is

$$z = 0.54545, \quad y = 1.59091, \quad x = -0.54545.$$

TABLE 10.2

m	x	y	z	b	Σ
−0.3509	0.6	0.8	0.1	1	2.5
−0.6433	1.1	0.4	0.3	0.2	2.0
	1.71	1.2	0.41	1.2	4.52
		0.3789	−0.0439	0.5789	0.9139
0.9818		−0.3720	0.0362	−0.5720	−0.9077
			−0.0069	−0.0036	−0.0104

A comparison shows that on working with only four decimal places the answer obtained is accurate only to one decimal place. However, this solution does fit the equations very well. If the values

$$x = -0.5380, \quad y = 1.5883, \quad z = 0.5217$$

are substituted into the left-hand sides of the original equations they give

$$1.00001, 0.20003, 1.19988.$$

In this example the ill-conditioning is caused by the third equation being very close to the sum of the other two.

To improve the accuracy of the solution of an ill-conditioned system of equations, either the computations must be performed carrying more significant figures or corrections may be computed as follows. Let **X** be the exact solution, **X′** the computed solution, and $C = X - X'$ the required correction vector. Then, since

$$AX = B,$$

it follows that

$$A(X' + C) = B,$$

and **C** must be the solution of the system

$$AC = B - AX' = R.$$

The components of **R** are called the *residuals*. Further improvements can be made by calculating a new set of residuals and repeating the process.

EXAMPLE 3

Compute the corrections to the solution computed in example 2.

The residuals corresponding to the solution

$$x = -0.5380, \quad y = 1.5883, \quad z = 0.5217,$$

are

$$\mathbf{R} = \begin{pmatrix} 1 \\ 0.2 \\ 1.2 \end{pmatrix} - \begin{pmatrix} 0.6 & 0.8 & 0.1 \\ 1.1 & 0.4 & 0.3 \\ 1.71 & 1.2 & 0.41 \end{pmatrix} \begin{pmatrix} -0.5380 \\ 1.5883 \\ 0.5217 \end{pmatrix} = \begin{pmatrix} -0.00001 \\ -0.00003 \\ 0.00012 \end{pmatrix}.$$

Thus the required correction is the solution of the system

$$0.6c_1 + 0.8c_2 + 0.1c_3 = -0.00001,$$
$$1.1c_1 + 0.4c_2 + 0.3c_3 = -0.00003,$$
$$1.71c_1 + 1.2c_2 + 0.41c_3 = 0.00012,$$

where c_1, c_2 and c_3 are the three components of the correction vector $\mathbf{C}$. The pivotal condensation scheme of example 2 gives the pivotal equations

$$1.71c_1 + 1.2c_2 + 0.41c_3 = 0.00012,$$
$$0.3789c_2 - 0.0439c_3 = -0.00005211,$$
$$-0.0069c_3 = -0.0001584.$$

Back substitution gives

$$c_3 = 0.0230, \quad c_2 = 0.0025, \quad c_1 = -0.0072.$$

Adding these corrections on to the first solution gives the improved solution

$$x = -0.5452, \quad y = 1.5908, \quad z = 0.5447,$$

which is now accurate to three places of decimals.

The method of elimination works best when all the elements of $\mathbf{A}$ are of the same order of magnitude. When some elements are very much larger than others it is best either to scale one or more of the unknowns or combine the equations suitably to bring all the coefficients to the same order. Finally, it is a simple matter to use this direct elimination method for solving a set of equations with a number of different right-hand sides (see example 1 of §10.4). The row operations are applied to all the right-hand columns at the same time.

Triangular Decomposition or Choleski's Method

This method depends upon the result of matrix algebra which states that a square matrix $\mathbf{A}$ can be expressed in the form

$$\mathbf{A} = \mathbf{LU}, \tag{3}$$

where $\mathbf{L}$ is a lower triangular matrix and $\mathbf{U}$ is an upper triangular matrix. The only condition on $\mathbf{A}$ is that the determinants formed from the first r rows and r columns should be non-zero for $r = 1, 2, \ldots, n-1$. As $\mathbf{L}$ and $\mathbf{U}$ together have $n^2 + n$ non-zero elements and $\mathbf{A}$ has only n^2 elements, the diagonal elements of either $\mathbf{L}$ or $\mathbf{U}$ may be chosen arbitrarily, and the remaining elements are then determined uniquely. Given the decomposition (3) into triangular matrices the system of equations (1) is

$$\mathbf{LUX} = \mathbf{B}.$$

These equations are equivalent to the two systems of equations

$$\mathbf{UX} = \mathbf{Y}, \tag{4}$$

and

$$\mathbf{LY} = \mathbf{B}. \tag{5}$$

Equation (5) has the form

$$
\begin{aligned}
l_{11}y_1 &= b_1, \\
l_{21}y_1 + l_{22}y_2 &= b_2, \\
&\cdots \\
l_{n1}y_1 + l_{n2}y_2 + \ldots + l_{nn}y_n &= b_n,
\end{aligned}
$$

which may be solved for $\mathbf{Y}$ by forward-substitution, that is, y_1 is found from the first equation, this value is used in the second equation to give y_2 and so on until all the values of the elements of $\mathbf{Y}$ have been found. The computed value of $\mathbf{Y}$ is now used in equation (4), which has the form

$$
\begin{aligned}
u_{11}x_1 + u_{12}x_2 + \ldots &\quad+\quad u_{1n}x_n = y_1, \\
&\cdots \\
u_{n-1,n-1}x_{n-1} &+ u_{n-1,n}x_n = y_{n-1}, \\
u_{n,n}x_n &= y_n.
\end{aligned}
$$

This system of equations is solved by back-substitution, that is, x_n is found first from the last equation, then x_{n-1}, and so on back to x_1.

The core of the method is thus the decomposition (3) and this is now illustrated for a 3 x 3 matrix $\mathbf{A}$. For convenience the diagonal elements of $\mathbf{L}$ are chosen to be unity so that (3) becomes

$$
\begin{pmatrix} 1 & 0 & 0 \\ l_{21} & 1 & 0 \\ l_{31} & l_{32} & 1 \end{pmatrix}
\begin{pmatrix} u_{11} & u_{12} & u_{13} \\ 0 & u_{22} & u_{23} \\ 0 & 0 & u_{33} \end{pmatrix}
=
\begin{pmatrix} a_{11} & a_{12} & a_{13} \\ a_{21} & a_{22} & a_{23} \\ a_{31} & a_{32} & a_{33} \end{pmatrix}.
$$

Multiplying out the left-hand side gives

$$
\begin{pmatrix} u_{11} & u_{12} & u_{13} \\ l_{21}u_{11} & l_{21}u_{12} + u_{22} & l_{21}u_{13} + u_{23} \\ l_{31}u_{11} & l_{31}u_{12} + l_{32}u_{22} & l_{31}u_{13} + l_{32}u_{23} + u_{33} \end{pmatrix}
=
\begin{pmatrix} a_{11} & a_{12} & a_{13} \\ a_{21} & a_{22} & a_{23} \\ a_{31} & a_{32} & a_{33} \end{pmatrix}. \tag{6}
$$

This method proceeds by alternately finding a row of $\mathbf{U}$ and a column of $\mathbf{L}$. The first row of $\mathbf{U}$ is found directly by equating the corresponding elements of the first row of equation (6) giving

$$u_{11} = a_{11}, \quad u_{12} = a_{12}, \quad u_{13} = a_{13}.$$

Next the first column of **L** is completed by equating the second and third elements of the first columns of equation (6) to give

$$l_{21} = a_{21}/u_{11}, \quad l_{31} = a_{31}/u_{11}.$$

The second row elements of (6) are equated to complete the second row of **U** with

$$u_{22} = a_{22} - l_{21}u_{12}, \quad u_{23} = a_{23} - l_{21}u_{13}.$$

The second column of **L** is completed from the third elements of the second column of (6), namely

$$l_{32} = (a_{32} - l_{31}u_{12})/u_{22},$$

and finally equating the remaining element completes **U** with

$$u_{33} = a_{33} - l_{31}u_{13} - l_{32}u_{23}.$$

The general formulae for calculating the elements of **L** and **U** when **A** is an $n \times n$ matrix are

$$u_{1j} = a_{1j}, \quad l_{i1} = a_{i1}/u_{11},$$

$$u_{ij} = a_{ij} - \sum_{s=1}^{i-1} l_{is}u_{sj} \quad 1 < i \leqslant j,$$

and

$$l_{ij} = \left(a_{ij} - \sum_{s=1}^{j-1} l_{is}u_{sj} \right) \bigg/ u_{jj} \quad i \geqslant j > 1.$$

These equations are used alternately to complete **U** and **L**. This method is often used in computer programs as it is very economical on storage space. It is unnecessary to store the 0's in either **L** or **U** and the 1's on the diagonal of **L**. Furthermore the elements of **A** are used only once and the program can be arranged to replace the elements of **A** in the store by the elements of **L** and **U**.

EXAMPLE 4

Solve the system of equations

$$0.6x + 0.8y + 0.1z = 1,$$
$$1.1x + 0.4y + 0.3z = 0.2,$$
$$x + \quad y + \quad 2z = 0.5,$$

by triangular decomposition.

Replacing the elements a_{ij} by the numbers in this example, equation (6) may be written as

$$u_{11} = 0.6, \qquad u_{12} = 0.8, \qquad u_{13} = 0.1,$$
$$l_{21}u_{11} = 1.1, \quad l_{21}u_{12} + \quad u_{22} = 0.4, \qquad l_{21}u_{13} + u_{23} = 0.3,$$
$$l_{31}u_{11} = 1 \;, \quad l_{31}u_{12} + l_{32}u_{22} = 1 \;, \quad l_{31}u_{13} + l_{32}u_{23} + u_{33} = 2 \;,$$

and these equations give

$$L = \begin{pmatrix} 1 & 0 & 0 \\ 1.83\dot{3} & 1 & 0 \\ 1.66\dot{6} & 0.3125 & 1 \end{pmatrix}, \quad U = \begin{pmatrix} 0.6 & 0.8 & 0.1 \\ 0 & -1.06\dot{6} & 0.116\dot{6} \\ 0 & 0 & 1.796875 \end{pmatrix}.$$

Equation (5) takes the form

$$y_1 \qquad\qquad = 1 \;,$$
$$1.83\dot{3}y_1 + \qquad y_2 \qquad = 0.2,$$
$$1.66\dot{6}y_1 + 0.3125y_2 + y_3 = 0.5,$$

and by forward substitution

$$y_1 = 1, \quad y_2 = 0.2 - 1.83\dot{3} = -1.63\dot{3},$$
$$y_3 = 0.5 - 1.66\dot{6} + 0.3125 \times 1.63\dot{3} = -0.656250.$$

Using these values of **Y** the equation (4) becomes

$$0.6x + \quad 0.8y + \qquad 0.1z = \quad 1,$$
$$-1.06\dot{6}y + \quad 0.116\dot{6}z = -1.63\dot{3},$$
$$1.796875z = -0.656250,$$

and by back substitution

$$z = 0.656250/1.796875 = -0.36522$$
$$y = -(-1.63\dot{3} + 0.116\dot{6} \times 0.36522)/1.06\dot{6}$$
$$\quad = 1.49130,$$
$$x = (1 + 0.1 \times 0.36522 - 0.8 \times 1.49130)/0.6$$
$$\quad = -0.26086.$$

The amount of computation may be reduced for the special case in which **A** is *symmetric*. In this case it is possible to choose an **L** such that

$$LL^T = A. \tag{7}$$

Note that the matrix **L** does not have unit elements on the leading diagonal.

The general formulae for calculating the non-zero elements of **L** for an $n \times n$

matrix **A** are

$$l_{11}^2 = a_{11}, \quad l_{ii}^2 = a_{ii} - \sum_{s=1}^{i-1} l_{is}^2 \quad (i > 1),$$

$$(8)$$

$$l_{i1} = a_{1i}/l_{11}, \quad l_{ij} = \left(a_{ij} - \sum_{s=1}^{j-1} l_{js} l_{is} \right) \Big/ l_{jj} \quad (i > j).$$

EXAMPLE 5
Solve the system of equations

$$0.6x + 1.1y + 0.1z = 1.2,$$
$$1.1x + 0.4y + 0.3z = 0.2,$$
$$0.1x + 0.3y + 0.1z = 0.5,$$

by triangular decomposition.

With direct reference to the equations (8)

$$l_{11} = (0.6)^{1/2} = 0.774597,$$

$$l_{21} = 1.1/0.774597 = 1.420094,$$

$$l_{31} = 0.1/0.774597 = 0.129099,$$

$$l_{22} = [0.4 - (1.420094)^2]^{1/2} = 1.271482 \, i,$$

$$l_{32} = (0.3 - 1.420094 \times 0.129099)/1.271482 \, i$$

$$= -0.091757 \, i$$

$$l_{33} = [0.1 - (0.129099)^2 + (0.091757)^2]^{1/2}$$

$$= 0.302907.$$

The equations to determine y_1, y_2 and y_3 are

$$0.774597y_1 \qquad\qquad\qquad\qquad = 1.2,$$
$$1.420094y_1 + 1.271482 \, iy_2 \qquad\qquad = 0.2,$$
$$0.129099y_1 - 0.091757 \, iy_2 + 0.302907 \, y_3 = 0.5,$$

giving

$$y_1 = 1.549193, \quad y_2 = 1.572967 \, i, \quad y_3 = 0.513920.$$

The final solution is then given by

$$0.774597x + 1.420094y + 0.129099z = 1.549193,$$
$$1.271482y - 0.091757z = 1.572967,$$
$$0.302907z = 0.513920,$$

where a factor of i has been removed from the second equation, giving

$$z = 1.69663, \quad y = 1.35955, \quad x = -0.77528.$$

Exercises

1. Obtain the solution, correct to two decimal places, of the system of equations

$$4.2x + 2y + z = 11.2$$
$$x + 3y + z = 10$$
$$x + y + 5z = 18,$$

using (a) pivotal condensation and (b) triangular decomposition.

2. Use the method of triangular decomposition to solve each of the second-order systems

(a) $3x + 2y = 7$ (b) $10x + y = 15$
     $x + 5y = 11$ $x + 5y = 23,$

correct to three significant figures.

10.3 ITERATIVE METHODS FOR THE SOLUTION OF LINEAR EQUATIONS

When the coefficient matrix is sparse, that is, has many zeros, iterative methods for the solution of linear equations are normally used in preference to the direct methods of the last section unless the matrix has a very simple structure. In contrast to the direct methods which require a fixed number of arithmetic operations, the amount of computation for iterative methods is dependent upon the accuracy required.

All the iterative methods described in this section are based on the rewriting of the equations so that each unknown, in turn, is expressed in terms of the remainder of the unknowns. First, the original system of equations is rearranged, if necessary, so that no zeros lie on the leading diagonal of **A** and this rearrangement is always possible. Each equation is then divided by the corresponding diagonal element after which the coefficient matrix is split into three parts so that

$$(\mathbf{I} - \mathbf{L} - \mathbf{U})\mathbf{X} = \mathbf{D}, \tag{9}$$

where **L** and **U** are lower and upper triangular matrices respectively with zeros on the leading diagonals, **I** is the unit matrix and **D** is formed from the new right-hand sides after any rearrangement and division.

The equation (9) is written

$$\mathbf{X} = \mathbf{D} + \mathbf{LX} + \mathbf{UX}. \tag{10}$$

EXAMPLE 1
The system of equations considered in example 1 of §10.2 may be written as

$$x + 0.36364y + 0.27273z = 0.18182,$$
$$0.75x + y + 0.125z = 1.25, \tag{11}$$
$$0.5x + 0.5y + z = 0.25,$$

and then rearranged into the matrix form (10) as

$$
\begin{pmatrix} x \\ y \\ z \end{pmatrix} = \begin{pmatrix} 0.18182 \\ 1.25 \\ 0.25 \end{pmatrix} + \begin{pmatrix} 0 & 0 & 0 \\ -0.75 & 0 & 0 \\ -0.5 & -0.5 & 0 \end{pmatrix} \begin{pmatrix} x \\ y \\ z \end{pmatrix} + \begin{pmatrix} 0 & -0.036364 & -0.27273 \\ 0 & 0 & -0.125 \\ 0 & 0 & 0 \end{pmatrix} \begin{pmatrix} x \\ y \\ z \end{pmatrix}.
$$

Notice that the first and second equations have been interchanged in order that all elements of **L** and **U** be less than unity as this helps to ensure convergence.

Jacobi Iteration

This is an iterative scheme of the form

$$ X^{(n+1)} = D + LX^{(n)} + UX^{(n)}, \tag{12} $$

where $X^{(n)}$ is the nth approximation to the solution. In this method, a first approximation $X^{(0)}$ is substituted into the right-hand side of equation (12) to calculate $X^{(1)}$. This new approximation is then put into the right-hand side to calculate $X^{(2)}$, and so on. This *simple* or *Jacobi* iteration is also known as the *'method of simultaneous corrections'*.

TABLE 10.3

n	x	y	z
0	0.000000	0.000000	0.000000
1	0.181818	1.250000	0.250000
2	-0.340909	1.082386	-0.465909
3	-0.084710	1.563920	-0.120739
4	-0.353951	1.328625	-0.489605
5	-0.167789	1.576664	-0.237337
.	.	.	.
10	-0.287957	1.459618	-0.402080
.	.	.	.
20	-0.263547	1.488197	-0.368864
.	.	.	.
30	-0.261133	1.490998	-0.365577
.	.	.	.
40	-0.260895	1.491274	-0.365253
.	.	.	.
50	-0.260871	1.491301	-0.365221
51	-0.260867	1.491306	-0.365215
52	-0.260871	1.491302	-0.365220
53	-0.260868	1.491305	-0.365216
54	-0.260870	1.491303	-0.365219
55	-0.260868	1.491305	-0.365216

EXAMPLE 2
The Jacobi iteration scheme for example 1 is

$$x^{(n+1)} = 0.181818 \qquad\qquad - 0.36364y^{(n)} - 0.27273z^{(n)},$$
$$y^{(n+1)} = 1.25 \qquad - 0.75x^{(n)} \qquad\qquad\qquad - 0.125z^{(n)},$$
$$z^{(n+1)} = 0.25 \qquad - 0.5x^{(n)} - 0.5y^{(n)}.$$

Starting from a first approximation $(0, 0, 0)$ the results shown in table 10.3 are obtained. Note that it takes about 55 iterations to obtain the solution accurate to 5 decimal places.

Gauss-Seidel Iteration

In practice Jacobi iteration is not often used, because the rate of convergence may usually be improved by using the new values as soon as they become available. That is, the first equation determines $x_1^{(n+1)}$ and this value is used instead of $x_1^{(n)}$ in the second equation to give a new value $x_2^{(n+1)}$. Both $x_1^{(n+1)}$ and $x_2^{(n+1)}$ are used in the third equation, and so on. This is *Gauss-Seidel* iteration and may be written as

$$\mathbf{X}^{(n+1)} = \mathbf{D} + \mathbf{L}\mathbf{X}^{(n+1)} + \mathbf{U}\mathbf{X}^{(n)}. \tag{13}$$

EXAMPLE 3
The previous example becomes

$$x^{(n+1)} = 0.181818 \qquad\qquad - 0.36364y^{(n)} - 0.27273z^{(n)},$$
$$y^{(n+1)} = 1.25 \qquad - 0.75x^{(n+1)} \qquad\qquad - 0.125z^{(n)},$$
$$z^{(n+1)} = 0.25 \qquad - 0.5x^{(n+1)} - 0.5y^{(n+1)},$$

and starting with $(0, 0, 0)$ gives the results shown in table 10.4. Thus for this problem

TABLE 10.4

n	x	y	z
0	0.000000	0.000000	0.000000
1	0.181818	1.113636	−0.397727
2	−0.114669	1.385718	−0.385524
3	−0.216936	1.460892	−0.371978
4	−0.247966	1.482472	−0.367253
5	−0.257102	1.488733	−0.365816
6	−0.259771	1.490555	−0.365392
7	−0.260549	1.491086	−0.365268
8	−0.260776	1.491240	−0.365232
9	−0.260842	1.491285	−0.365222
10	−0.260861	1.491298	−0.365219
11	−0.260867	1.491302	−0.365218
12	−0.260868	1.491303	−0.365218

Gauss-Seidel iteration convergence is 5 times faster than the Jacobi iteration as the method gives the solution accurate to 5 decimal places in only 11 iterations.

However, iterative methods do not always converge. As a general rule it is essential to arrange the equations so that the largest coefficients lie on the leading diagonal. In fact, it can be shown that if $\mathbf{A}$ is *diagonally dominant,* that is, *in each row the absolute value of the diagonal element is greater than the sum of the absolute values of the other elements in that row*, then convergence is assured. Furthermore, the more dominant the diagonal elements, the faster the rate of convergence.

Successive Over-relaxation

A further improvement in the rate of convergence may often be obtained by a method known as *successive over-relaxation.* If the Gauss-Seidel iteration is written in the form

$$\mathbf{X}^{(n+1)} = \mathbf{X}^{(n)} + \{\mathbf{LX}^{(n+1)} + (\mathbf{U} - \mathbf{I})\mathbf{X}^{(n)} + \mathbf{D}\},$$

then the term $\{\mathbf{LX}^{(n+1)} + (\mathbf{U} - \mathbf{I})\mathbf{X}^{(n)} + \mathbf{D}\}$ is the correction or improvement made to the nth iterate to give the $(n + 1)$th iterate. A parameter ω is introduced to 'overcorrect' at each stage by the formula

$$\mathbf{X}^{(n+1)} = \mathbf{X}^{(n)} + \omega\{\mathbf{LX}^{(n+1)} + (\mathbf{U} - \mathbf{I})\mathbf{X}^{(n)} + \mathbf{D}\}. \tag{14}$$

This parameter ω is called the *relaxation factor.* The obvious difficulty of this method is how to choose the value of ω that gives the fastest rate of convergence. This optimum value of ω lies between 1 and 2 and is usually found by trial and error, although a formula is available for calculating it (see *Modern Computing Methods* [1] p. 39). It is particularly worth while trying to find a good value of ω when the system of equations is to be solved a number of times with different right-hand sides.

EXAMPLE 4
For the system (11) considered in this section the formulae are

$$x^{(n+1)} = x^{(n)} + \omega\{0.181818 - x^{(n)} - 0.36364y^{(n)} - 0.27273z^{(n)}\},$$
$$y^{(n+1)} = y^{(n)} + \omega\{1.25 - 0.75x^{(n+1)} - y^{(n)} - 0.125z^{(n)}\},$$
$$z^{(n+1)} = z^{(n)} + \omega\{0.25 - 0.5x^{(n+1)} - 0.5y^{(n+1)} - z^{(n)}\}.$$

When $\omega = 1.1$ an accuracy of 5 decimal places is obtained in 8 iterations, which is only a little faster than the Gauss-Seidel method. For some problems the improvement is very much greater than this.

Exercises

1. Use the Gauss-Seidel iteration method to obtain a solution correct to two decimal places of the system

$$10x + y = 15$$
$$x + 5y = 23.$$

2. Obtain a solution, correct to two decimal places, of the system

$$4.2x + 2y + z = 11.2$$
$$x + 3y + z = 10$$
$$x + y + 5z = 18$$

using the methods of (a) Jacobi and (b) Gauss-Seidel.

3. Use the method of successive over-relaxation to solve exercise 2. Compare the rates of convergence using two different choices for ω.

10.4 NUMERICAL METHODS OF MATRIX INVERSION

The inverse A^{-1} of a non-singular square matrix A is defined in §8.4 and has the property

$$AA^{-1} = I. \tag{15}$$

This section is concerned with the extension of the direct methods of §10.2 to the problem of finding A^{-1}.

Pivotal Condensation

If X_r is the rth column of the matrix A^{-1} and e_r is the rth column of the unit matrix I, then the matrices A^{-1} and I can be partitioned (see §8.6) as

$$A^{-1} = (X_1 \ X_2 \ \ldots X_n) \quad \text{and} \quad I = (e_1 \ e_2 \ \ldots e_n),$$

and equation (15) may be written

$$A(X_1 \ X_2 \ \ldots X_n) = (e_1 \ e_2 \ \ldots e_n).$$

By equating corresponding columns of this matrix equation, we obtain

$$AX_r = e_r \quad (r = 1, 2, \ldots n).$$

Thus the problem reduces to solving n linear systems of equations which all have the same left-hand sides and whose right-hand sides are the columns of I. To use the method of pivotal condensation to find the inverse A^{-1}, all the operations described in §10.2 are performed on all the columns of I at the same time. This gives equations of the form

$$A'X_r = f_r \quad (r = 1, 2, \ldots n),$$

where A' is upper diagonal and f_r are the new right-hand sides. Then a sequence of n back-substitutions with each right-hand side f_r in turn gives all the columns X_r of the inverse matrix.

EXAMPLE 1
Find the inverse of the matrix

$$\begin{pmatrix} 0.6 & 0.8 & 0.1 \\ 1.1 & 0.4 & 0.3 \\ 1 & 1 & 2 \end{pmatrix}.$$

The method follows the pattern of example 1 of § 10.2 and is shown in table 10.5.

TABLE 10.5

m	x_i	y_i	z_i	e_1	e_2	e_3	Σ
−0.545455	0.6	0.8	0.1	1	0	0	2.5
	1.1	0.4	0.3	0	1	0	2.8
−0.909091	1	1	2	0	0	1	5.0
−0.914285		0.581818	−0.063637	1	−0.545455	0	0.972726
		0.636364	1.727273	0	−0.909091	1	2.454545
			−1.642857	1	0.285713	−0.914285	−1.271428

Then a sequence of back-substitutions using the right-hand sides $(0, 1, 1)^T$, $(1, -0.909091, 0.285713)^T$ and $(0, 1, -0.914285)^T$ in turn generates the columns of A^{-1} and gives

$$A^{-1} = \begin{pmatrix} -0.43478 & 1.30435 & -0.17391 \\ 1.65217 & -0.95652 & 0.06087 \\ -0.60870 & -0.17391 & 0.55652 \end{pmatrix}.$$

Triangular Decomposition or Choleski's Method

This method is convenient for inverting matrices because the inverse of a triangular matrix is also a triangular matrix of the same type, and triangular matrices are easy to invert. We first decompose **A** into the product

$A = LU,$

where **L** is a lower triangular matrix and **U** an upper triangular matrix. The inverse of the matrix **A** is

$A^{-1} = U^{-1}L^{-1},$

remembering (§ 8.4) the result that the inverse of a product of matrices is the product of the inverse matrices but formed in the *reverse* order. The method of triangular decomposition is described in § 10.2 and thus the problem here is to invert the triangular matrices **L** and **U**. Since the inverse of a triangular matrix is itself a triangular matrix of the same type (§8.4(d)) the inverse of the matrix

$$\mathbf{L} = \begin{pmatrix} l_{11} & 0 & 0 \\ l_{21} & l_{22} & 0 \\ l_{31} & l_{32} & l_{33} \end{pmatrix},$$

is the solution of the matrix equation

$$\begin{pmatrix} l_{11} & 0 & 0 \\ l_{21} & l_{22} & 0 \\ l_{31} & l_{32} & l_{33} \end{pmatrix} \begin{pmatrix} x_{11} & 0 & 0 \\ x_{21} & x_{22} & 0 \\ x_{31} & x_{32} & x_{33} \end{pmatrix} = \begin{pmatrix} 1 & 0 & 0 \\ 0 & 1 & 0 \\ 0 & 0 & 1 \end{pmatrix},$$

where x_{ij} are the elements of the inverse matrix $\mathbf{L}^{-1}$. The left-hand side of this equation is evaluated to give

$$\begin{pmatrix} l_{11}x_{11} & 0 & 0 \\ l_{21}x_{11} + l_{22}x_{21} & l_{22}x_{22} & 0 \\ l_{31}x_{11} + l_{32}x_{21} + l_{33}x_{31} & l_{32}x_{22} + l_{33}x_{32} & l_{33}x_{33} \end{pmatrix} = \begin{pmatrix} 1 & 0 & 0 \\ 0 & 1 & 0 \\ 0 & 0 & 1 \end{pmatrix}.$$

Then equating corresponding elements from both sides the unknown values x_{ij} may be found in turn as follows

$$x_{11} = 1/l_{11}, \quad x_{21} = -l_{21}x_{11}/l_{22}, \quad x_{31} = -(l_{31}x_{11} + l_{32}x_{21})/l_{33},$$
$$x_{22} = 1/l_{22}, \quad x_{32} = -l_{32}x_{22}/l_{33}, \quad x_{33} = 1/l_{33}.$$

In a similar fashion the inverse of the upper triangular matrix $\mathbf{U}$ is given by

$$\mathbf{U}^{-1} = \begin{pmatrix} \dfrac{1}{u_{11}} & \dfrac{-u_{12}}{u_{11}u_{22}} & \dfrac{u_{12}u_{23}}{u_{11}u_{22}u_{33}} - \dfrac{u_{13}}{u_{11}u_{33}} \\[2ex] 0 & \dfrac{1}{u_{22}} & \dfrac{-u_{23}}{u_{22}u_{33}} \\[2ex] 0 & 0 & \dfrac{1}{u_{33}} \end{pmatrix}.$$

Having found $\mathbf{L}^{-1}$ and $\mathbf{U}^{-1}$ the product $\mathbf{U}^{-1}\mathbf{L}^{-1}$ is formed to give the required inverse $\mathbf{A}^{-1}$.

The general formulae for calculating the components x_{ij} of $\mathbf{L}^{-1}$ when $\mathbf{L}$ is a lower triangular $n \times n$ matrix are

$$x_{ii} = 1/l_{ii}, \quad x_{ij} = -\left(\sum_{s=j}^{i-1} l_{is}x_{sj} \right) \Big/ l_{ii} \qquad (j < i).$$

For the components y_{ij} of $\mathbf{U}^{-1}$ when $\mathbf{U}$ is an upper triangular $n \times n$ matrix the formulae are

$$y_{ii} = 1/u_{ii}, \quad y_{ij} = -\left(\sum_{s=i+1}^{j} u_{is}y_{sj} \right) \Big/ u_{ii} \qquad (i < j).$$

EXAMPLE 2

Invert the matrix

$$\begin{pmatrix} 0.6 & 0.8 & 0.1 \\ 1.1 & 0.4 & 0.3 \\ 1 & 1 & 2 \end{pmatrix}.$$

In example 4 of §10.2 this matrix was decomposed into the product

$$\mathbf{LU} = \begin{pmatrix} 1 & 0 & 0 \\ 1.833 & 1 & 0 \\ 1.666 & 0.3125 & 1 \end{pmatrix} \begin{pmatrix} 0.6 & 0.8 & 0.1 \\ 0 & -1.066 & 0.1166 \\ 0 & 0 & 1.796875 \end{pmatrix}.$$

The inverse $\mathbf{L}^{-1}$ of $\mathbf{L}$ is given as the solution of the matrix equation

$$\begin{pmatrix} x_{11} & 0 & 0 \\ 1.833x_{11} + x_{21} & x_{22} & 0 \\ 1.666x_{11} + 0.3125x_{21} + x_{31} & 0.3125x_{22} + x_{32} & x_{33} \end{pmatrix} = \begin{pmatrix} 1 & 0 & 0 \\ 0 & 1 & 0 \\ 0 & 0 & 1 \end{pmatrix}, \quad (16)$$

so that

$$\mathbf{L}^{-1} = \begin{pmatrix} 1 & 0 & 0 \\ -1.833 & 1 & 0 \\ -1.093750 & -0.3125 & 1 \end{pmatrix}.$$

Similarly

$$\mathbf{U}^{-1} = \begin{pmatrix} 1.666 & 1.25 & -0.173913 \\ 0 & -0.937500 & 0.060870 \\ 0 & 0 & 0.556522 \end{pmatrix},$$

and the inverse of $\mathbf{A}$ is the product

$$\mathbf{U}^{-1}\mathbf{L}^{-1} = \begin{pmatrix} -0.43478 & 1.30435 & -0.17391 \\ 1.65217 & -0.95652 & 0.06087 \\ -0.60870 & -0.17391 & 0.55652 \end{pmatrix}.$$

It was noted in §10.2 that for a real *symmetric* matrix the decomposition may have the form

$$\mathbf{A} = \mathbf{LL}^T.$$

In this case only one triangular matrix need be found and inverted since

$$\mathbf{A}^{-1} = (\mathbf{LL}^T)^{-1} = (\mathbf{L}^T)^{-1}\mathbf{L}^{-1} = (\mathbf{L}^{-1})^T\mathbf{L}^{-1}.$$

EXAMPLE 3
Invert the symmetric matrix

$$\begin{pmatrix} 0.6 & 1.1 & 0.1 \\ 1.1 & 0.4 & 0.3 \\ 0.1 & 0.3 & 0.1 \end{pmatrix}.$$

The decomposition of this symmetric matrix was presented in example 5 of §10.2. The matrix **L** is

$$\begin{pmatrix} 0.774597 & 0 & 0 \\ 1.420094 & 1.271482\,i & 0 \\ 0.129099 & -0.091757\,i & 0.302907 \end{pmatrix},$$

and the elements of the inverse $\mathbf{L}^{-1}$ are given by a matrix equation similar to equation (16). Hence

$$\mathbf{L}^{-1} = \begin{pmatrix} 1.290994 & 0 & 0 \\ 1.441886\,i & -0.786484\,i & 0 \\ -0.987000 & 0.238243 & 3.301343 \end{pmatrix},$$

and

$$\mathbf{A}^{-1} = (\mathbf{L}^{-1})^{T}\mathbf{L}^{-1} = \begin{pmatrix} 0.56180 & 0.89887 & -3.25843 \\ 0.89887 & -0.56180 & 0.78652 \\ -3.25843 & 0.78652 & 10.89887 \end{pmatrix}.$$

Exercises

1. Find by (a) pivotal condensation and (b) triangular decomposition the inverse of the matrix

$$\begin{pmatrix} 2 & 6 & 1 \\ 1 & 1 & 5 \\ 1 & 2 & 4 \end{pmatrix}.$$

2. Use Choleski's method to find the inverses of the matrices

(a) $\begin{pmatrix} 1 & 3 \\ 3 & 7 \end{pmatrix}$, (b) $\begin{pmatrix} 1 & 7 \\ 2 & 3 \end{pmatrix}$.

3. Invert the following symmetric matrix

$$\begin{pmatrix} 0.250 & -0.064 & 0.017 & -0.004 \\ -0.064 & 0.283 & -0.076 & 0.020 \\ 0.017 & -0.076 & 0.289 & -0.077 \\ -0.004 & 0.020 & -0.077 & 0.289 \end{pmatrix}.$$

10.5 EIGENVALUES AND EIGENVECTORS

The eigenvalues of a square matrix $\mathbf{A}$ are those values of λ for which the system

$$\mathbf{AX} = \lambda\mathbf{X},$$

has non-trivial solutions (see §8.9). The vectors $\mathbf{X}$ associated with each λ are the eigenvectors. The direct method given in §8.9 for finding the eigenvalues is impractical for large matrices as it involves finding the roots of a large order algebraic equation and so other methods must be used. The corresponding eigenvectors are the solution of a system of homogeneous equations and are determined only to within an arbitrary constant multiplier. In the iterative methods of this section the multiplier is chosen so that the largest element of each eigenvector is equal to unity.

Largest Eigenvalue

The following is an iterative method for finding the eigenvalue with the largest modulus and its associated eigenvector.

Suppose the matrix $\mathbf{A}$ has n real distinct eigenvalues $\lambda_1, \lambda_2, \ldots, \lambda_n$ where $|\lambda_1| > |\lambda_2| > \ldots > |\lambda_n|$ and corresponding eigenvectors $\mathbf{X}_1, \mathbf{X}_2, \ldots, \mathbf{X}_n$. Then starting with an arbitrary vector $\mathbf{Y}^{(0)}$ the scheme

$$\mathbf{Z}^{(i)} = \mathbf{AY}^{(i-1)},$$

$$\mathbf{Y}^{(i)} = \frac{1}{c_i}\mathbf{Z}^{(i)}, \tag{17}$$

where c_i is the numerically largest element of $\mathbf{Z}^{(i)}$, gives a sequence of vectors $\mathbf{Y}^{(i)}$ which in the limit $i \to \infty$ tends to the eigenvector $\mathbf{X}_1$. The eigenvalue λ_1 is given by the limit of the sequence of numbers c_i, as $i \to \infty$.

The above method follows from the result that an arbitrary vector $\mathbf{Y}^{(0)}$ may be expressed as a linear combination of all the eigenvectors $\mathbf{X}_s$ as follows

$$\mathbf{Y}^{(0)} = \sum_{r=1}^{n} \alpha_r \mathbf{X}_r,$$

where the α_r are constants. Then from equation (17)

$$\mathbf{Z}^{(1)} = \mathbf{AY}^{(0)}$$

$$= \sum_{r=1}^{n} \alpha_r(\mathbf{AX}_r)$$

$$= \sum_{r=1}^{n} \alpha_r \lambda_r \mathbf{X}_r$$

and

$$\mathbf{Y}^{(1)} = \frac{1}{c_1} \sum_{r=1}^{n} \alpha_r \lambda_r \mathbf{X}_r,$$

where c_1 is the numerically largest element of the vector $\mathbf{Z}^{(1)}$. Similarly

$$\mathbf{Z}^{(2)} = \frac{1}{c_1} \sum_{r=1}^{n} \alpha_r \lambda_r (\mathbf{A}\mathbf{X}_r)$$

$$= \frac{1}{c_1} \sum_{r=1}^{n} \alpha_r \lambda_r^2 \mathbf{X}_r,$$

and

$$\mathbf{Y}^{(2)} = \frac{1}{c_1 c_2} \sum_{r=1}^{n} \alpha_r \lambda_r^2 \mathbf{X}_r.$$

It follows after k iterations that

$$\mathbf{Y}^{(k)} = \frac{1}{c_1 c_2 \dots c_k} \sum_{r=1}^{n} \alpha_r \lambda_r^k \mathbf{X}_r$$

$$= \frac{\lambda_1^k}{c_1 c_2 \dots c_k} \left\{ \alpha_1 \mathbf{X}_1 + \sum_{r=2}^{n} \alpha_r \left(\frac{\lambda_r}{\lambda_1} \right)^k \mathbf{X}_r \right\}. \tag{18}$$

Since $|\lambda_r/\lambda_1| < 1$ for $r \neq 1$, then $|\lambda_r/\lambda_1|^k \to 0$ as $k \to \infty$. Furthermore the divisor c_k is chosen to ensure that the largest element of $\mathbf{Y}^{(k)}$ is always unity, and hence

$$\mathbf{Y}^{(k)} \to \mathbf{X}_1 \quad \text{as } k \to \infty.$$

Therefore

$$\mathbf{Z}^{(k)} = \mathbf{A}\mathbf{Y}^{(k-1)} \to \mathbf{A}\mathbf{X}_1 = \lambda_1 \mathbf{X}_1 \quad \text{as } k \to \infty,$$

so that the component of $\mathbf{Z}^{(k)}$ that corresponds to the unit component of $\mathbf{Y}^{(k-1)}$ must tend to the eigenvalue λ_1. A difficulty with the above method can occur should the starting vector $\mathbf{Y}_0$ be accidentally chosen such that α_1 is very small, in which case the convergence is very slow. An improvement in the rate of convergence can sometimes be made by a different choice of initial vector $\mathbf{Y}^{(0)}$.

EXAMPLE 1
Find the largest eigenvalue and corresponding eigenvector of the matrix

$$\begin{pmatrix} 17 & 9 & 5 \\ 0 & 8 & 10 \\ -5 & -5 & -3 \end{pmatrix}.$$

If the components of $\mathbf{Z}^{(i)}$ are $z_1^{(i)}, z_2^{(i)}, z_3^{(i)}$ and the components of $\mathbf{Y}^{(i)}$ are $y_1^{(i)}, y_2^{(i)}, y_3^{(i)}$, then for this matrix

$$z_1^{(i)} = 17 y_1^{(i-1)} + 9 y_2^{(i-1)} + 5 y_3^{(i-1)},$$
$$z_2^{(i)} = \qquad\quad 8 y_2^{(i-1)} + 10 y_3^{(i-1)},$$
$$z_3^{(i)} = -5 y_1^{(i-1)} - 5 y_2^{(i-1)} - 3 y_3^{(i-1)},$$

TABLE 10.6

i	$z_1^{(i)}$	$z_2^{(i)}$	$z_3^{(i)}$	$y_1^{(i)}$	$y_2^{(i)}$	$y_3^{(i)}$
0				1.0000	1.0000	1.0000
1	31.0000	18.0000	−13.0000	1.0000	0.5806	−0.4194
2	20.1290	0.4516	−6.6452	1.0000	0.0224	−0.3301
3	15.5513	−3.1218	−4.1218	1.0000	−0.2007	−0.2650
4	13.8681	−4.2564	−3.2012	1.0000	−0.3069	−0.2308
5	13.0836	−4.7636	−2.7729	1.0000	−0.3641	−0.2119
6	12.6635	−5.0321	−2.5437	1.0000	−0.3974	−0.2009
7	12.4193	−5.1877	−2.4105	1.0000	−0.4177	−0.1941
8	12.2701	−5.2827	−2.3292	1.0000	−0.4305	−0.1898
9	12.1761	−5.3425	−2.2779	1.0000	−0.4388	−0.1871
10	12.1157	−5.3809	−2.2449	1.0000	−0.4441	−0.1853
.	.	.	.	.	.	.
15	12.0149	−5.4451	−2.1899	1.0000	−0.4532	−0.1823
.	.	.	.	.	.	.
20	12.0020	−5.4533	−2.1829	1.0000	−0.4544	−0.1819
.	.	.	.	.	.	.
25	12.0003	−5.4544	−2.1820	1.0000	−0.4545	−0.1818

and if c_i is the numerically largest of $z_1^{(i)}, z_2^{(i)}$ and $z_3^{(i)}$ then

$$y_1^{(i)} = z_1^{(i)}/c_i, \quad y_2^{(i)} = z_2^{(i)}/c_i, \quad y_3^{(i)} = z_3^{(i)}/c_i.$$

Starting with the vector $\mathbf{Y}^{(0)} = (1, 1, 1)^T$ the results of this scheme are shown in table 10.6.

From the table it may be seen that the component of $\mathbf{Z}^{(i)}$ that corresponds to the unit component of $\mathbf{Y}^{(i-1)}$, to three decimal places, is 12 and the corresponding eigenvector has components $(1, -0.4545, -0.1818)^T$.

Referring back to equation (18) the rate at which $\mathbf{Y}^{(k)}$ tends to $\mathbf{X}_1$ is determined by the rate at which the terms

$$\sum_{r=2}^{n} \alpha_r \left(\frac{\lambda_r}{\lambda_1}\right)^k \mathbf{X}_r \to 0 \quad \text{as } k \to \infty.$$

However, the largest of the quotients λ_r/λ_1 is λ_2/λ_1 and so the rate of convergence will depend upon the rate at which $(\lambda_2/\lambda_1)^k \to 0$ as $k \to \infty$. For this reason the rate of convergence is often slow but it may sometimes be improved by a simple device. Since

$$(\mathbf{A} - p\mathbf{I})\mathbf{X}_i = (\lambda_i - p)\mathbf{X}_i, \tag{19}$$

for any p, the eigenvectors of the matrix $\mathbf{A} - p\mathbf{I}$ are the same as those of $\mathbf{A}$, but the eigenvalues differ by an amount p. Suppose for example $\lambda_1 = 6$, $\lambda_2 = 5$. Then the rate of convergence is determined by the rate at which $(5/6)^k \to 0$ as $k \to \infty$. But if instead of $\mathbf{A}$, $\mathbf{A} - 3\mathbf{I}$ is used, then the two largest eigenvalues are 3 and 2 and the rate of convergence is determined by the rate at which $(2/3)^k \to 0$. This is more than twice as fast since, for example,

$$\left(\frac{5}{6}\right)^{54} = 0.00005 \quad \text{and} \quad \left(\frac{2}{3}\right)^{24} = 0.00005.$$

EXAMPLE 2

Show that the rate of convergence in example 1 may be increased by using $A - 4I$ instead of A.

Now

$$A - 4I = \begin{pmatrix} 13 & 9 & 5 \\ 0 & 4 & 10 \\ -5 & -5 & -7 \end{pmatrix},$$

and following the same method as in example 1 and starting with the vector $Y^{(0)} = (1, 1, 1)^T$ the results of table 10.7 are obtained.

TABLE 10.7

i	$z_1^{(i)}$	$z_2^{(i)}$	$z_3^{(i)}$	$y_1^{(i)}$	$y_2^{(i)}$	$y_3^{(i)}$
0				1.0000	1.0000	1.0000
1	27.0000	14.0000	−17.0000	1.0000	0.5185	−0.6296
2	14.5185	−4.2222	−3.1852	1.0000	−0.2908	−0.2194
3	9.2857	−3.3571	−2.0102	1.0000	−0.3615	−0.2165
4	8.6637	−3.6110	−1.6769	1.0000	−0.4168	−0.1936
5	8.2811	−3.6027	−1.5611	1.0000	−0.4351	−0.1885
6	8.1419	−3.6254	−1.5051	1.0000	−0.4453	−0.1848
7	8.0682	−3.6297	−1.4796	1.0000	−0.4499	−0.1834
8	8.0342	−3.6334	−1.4669	1.0000	−0.4522	−0.1826
9	8.0169	−3.6348	−1.4607	1.0000	−0.4534	−0.1822
10	8.0085	−3.6356	−1.4576	1.0000	−0.4540	−0.1820
.	. . .	. . .	. . . . . .		. . .	. . .
15	8.0003	−3.6363	−1.4546	1.0000	−0.4545	−0.1818

From the table it may be seen that to an accuracy of three decimal places the largest eigenvalue of $A - 4I$ is 8, so that the largest eigenvalue of A is 12. The eigenvector corresponding to this eigenvalue is the same as before, namely $(1, -0.4545, -0.1818)$. The rate of convergence is appreciably increased as three decimal place accuracy is obtained in 15 iterations, as compared with 25 iterations in example 1.

Smallest Eigenvalue

The eigenvalues of the inverse matrix A^{-1} are $\lambda_1^{-1}, \lambda_2^{-1}$, etc. Therefore to find the numerically smallest eigenvalue of A the numerically largest eigenvalue of A^{-1} is sought by replacing $\mathbf{A}$ by $\mathbf{A}^{-1}$ in the formulae (17) giving

$$Z^{(i)} = \mathbf{A}^{-1} Y^{(i-1)}, \tag{20}$$

and

$$Y^{(i)} = \frac{1}{c_i} Z^{(i)}.$$

It is unnecessary to compute the inverse $\mathbf{A}^{-1}$ explicitly as (20) may be written

$$\mathbf{A} Z^{(i)} = Y^{(i-1)}. \tag{21}$$

Now at each iteration a system of equations with the same left-hand side must be solved to calculate the vector $Z^{(i)}$. Either of the direct methods of §10.2 would be suitable because the main calculation on the coefficient matrix $\mathbf{A}$ need only be done once and each system (21) can then be solved with a minimum of computation.

This method of finding the smallest eigenvalue may be used to find the eigenvalue nearest to a given value p. The eigenvalues of the matrix $\mathbf{A} - p\mathbf{I}$ are $\lambda_1 - p, \lambda_2 - p, \ldots, \lambda_n - p$ and if the numerically smallest eigenvalue of $\mathbf{A} - p\mathbf{I}$ is $\lambda_s - p$ then λ_s is the eigenvalue nearest to p.

EXAMPLE 3

Find the smallest eigenvalue of the matrix

$$\begin{pmatrix} 17 & 9 & 5 \\ 0 & 8 & 10 \\ -5 & -5 & -3 \end{pmatrix}.$$

To find the smallest eigenvalue the scheme is to solve the system

$$17 z_1^{(i)} + 9 z_2^{(i)} + 5 z_3^{(i)} = y_1^{(i-1)},$$
$$8 z_2^{(i)} + 10 z_3^{(i)} = y_2^{(i-1)},$$
$$-5 z_1^{(i)} - 5 z_2^{(i)} - 3 z_3^{(i)} = y_3^{(i-1)},$$

and then calculate

$$y_1^{(i)} = z_1^{(i)}/c_i, \quad y_2^{(i)} = z_2^{(i)}/c_i, \quad y_3^{(i)} = z_3^{(i)}/c_i,$$

where c_i is the numerically largest of $z_1^{(i)}, z_2^{(i)}$ and $z_3^{(i)}$. Starting with the vector $Y^{(0)} = (1, 1, 1)^T$ the first eight iterations for this scheme are shown in table 10.8.

The largest eigenvalue of $\mathbf{A}^{-1}$ is then 0.5 to four decimal places and therefore the smallest eigenvalue of $\mathbf{A}$ is $1/0.5 = 2.0$. The corresponding eigenvector to an accuracy of four decimal places is $(-0.41, 1, -0.6)^T$.

Finally, these iterative methods, which are simple to use, would not normally be used to find all the eigenvalues and eigenvectors of a matrix. Other methods, such as those due to Jacobi, Givens and Householder (see, for example, *Modern Computing Methods* [1] and Bell [4]), are based upon the use of orthogonal transformations

TABLE 10.8

i	$z_1^{(i)}$	$z_2^{(i)}$	$z_3^{(i)}$	$y_1^{(i)}$	$y_2^{(i)}$	$y_3^{(i)}$
0				1.0000	1.0000	1.0000
1	0.4063	−1.2813	1.1250	−0.3171	1.0000	−0.8780
2	−0.2612	0.7246	−0.4797	−0.3604	1.0000	−0.6620
3	−0.2108	0.5446	−0.3357	−0.3871	1.0000	−0.6164
4	−0.2025	0.5111	−0.3089	−0.3962	1.0000	−0.6044
5	−0.2006	0.5029	−0.3023	−0.3990	1.0000	−0.6011
6	−0.2002	0.5007	−0.3006	−0.3997	1.0000	−0.6003
7	−0.2000	0.5002	−0.3002	−0.3999	1.0000	−0.6001
8	−0.2000	0.5000	−0.3000	−0.4000	1.0000	−0.6000

which reduce the matrix to a simpler form and are used when all the eigenvalues are required.

Exercises

1. Find by iterative methods (a) the largest eigenvalue and corresponding eigenvector and (b) the smallest eigenvalue and corresponding eigenvector of the matrix

$$\begin{pmatrix} 1 & 2 \\ 3 & 4 \end{pmatrix}.$$

2. Find the eigenvalue of largest modulus of the matrix

$$\begin{pmatrix} 4 & 2 & -3 \\ 5 & 9 & 1 \\ 1 & -2 & 1 \end{pmatrix}.$$

PROBLEMS

1. Use the Gauss-Seidel iteration method to obtain the solution of the system of equations

$$
\begin{aligned}
x_1 + 10x_2 + x_3 &= 10, \\
3x_1 \qquad\quad + 10x_3 + x_4 &= 4, \\
2x_2 \qquad\quad + 10x_5 - x_6 &= 0, \\
20x_1 - 3x_2 \qquad\quad + 2x_5 &= 6, \\
2x_1 \qquad\quad + 20x_4 \qquad + 4x_6 &= 12, \\
x_2 - 3x_3 \qquad\qquad + 10x_6 &= 0,
\end{aligned}
$$

correct to two decimal places.

2. Write down a simple generalization of the Gauss-Seidel method for the solution of the non-linear system

$$x - 0.1y^2 + 0.5z^2 = 0.7,$$
$$y + 0.5x^2 - 0.1xz = 0.5,$$
$$z + 0.4y^2 + 0.1xy = 1.2.$$

Solve the system with an accuracy of two decimal places.

3. Devise a direct elimination procedure for the solution of the system of linear equations $AX = B$ when A has the tri-diagonal form

$$A = \begin{pmatrix} b_1 & c_1 & 0 & 0 & . & . & & . & & 0 \\ a_2 & b_2 & c_2 & 0 & . & . & & . & & 0 \\ 0 & a_3 & b_3 & c_3 & . & . & & . & & 0 \\ . & . & . & . & . & . & & . & & . \\ 0 & . & . & . & 0 & a_{n-1} & b_{n-1} & c_{n-1} \\ 0 & . & . & . & 0 & 0 & a_n & b_n \end{pmatrix}.$$

[This is one of the special forms of A for which a direct method is preferred to an iterative method even though A is sparse.] Use your method to find the solution correct to three decimal places of the system

$$4x - y \qquad\qquad = 3.2,$$
$$-x + 3y - z \qquad = 0.8,$$
$$-y + 3z - w = 1.3,$$
$$-z + 4w = 2.7.$$

4. The system of equations

$$2x_1 + 2x_2 - x_3 - 4x_4 = 8,$$
$$x_1 - x_2 + 3x_3 - x_4 = -3,$$
$$2x_1 + x_2 - x_3 = 2,$$
$$10x_1 + 3x_2 + 2.1x_3 - 6x_4 = 5,$$

is somewhat ill-conditioned. Use the method of pivotal condensation, working with *three* decimal places, to calculate an approximate solution. Improve this solution by computing corrections to this solution in the manner described in §10.2.

5. Find the inverse of each of the matrices

(a) $\begin{pmatrix} 1 & 3 & 1 & -1 \\ 2 & 0 & 1 & 1 \\ 0 & -1 & 4 & 1 \\ 0 & 1 & 1 & -5 \end{pmatrix}$,   (b) $\begin{pmatrix} 1 & 3 & 1 & -1 \\ 3 & 0 & 1 & 1 \\ 1 & 1 & 4 & 1 \\ -1 & 1 & 1 & -5 \end{pmatrix}.$

6. By modifying the method of §10.5 derive an iterative method of finding the largest eigenvalue and corresponding eigenvector for the more general eigenvalue problem

$$\mathbf{AX} = \lambda \mathbf{BX},$$

where $\mathbf{A}$ and $\mathbf{B}$ are both square matrices of the same size. Use this method to find the largest eigenvalue and corresponding eigenvector when

$$\mathbf{A} = \begin{pmatrix} 3 & 2 \\ 2 & 3 \end{pmatrix} \quad \text{and} \quad \mathbf{B} = \begin{pmatrix} 1 & -1 \\ 2 & 3 \end{pmatrix}.$$

BIBLIOGRAPHY

[1] *Modern Computing Methods*, H.M.S.O., London (1961).
[2] Williams, P. W., *Numerical Computation*, Nelson, London (1972).
[3] Fox, L., *An Introduction to Numerical Linear Algebra*, Clarendon Press, Oxford (1964).
[4] Bell, W. W., *Matrices for Scientists and Engineers*, Van Nostrand Reinhold, Wokingham (1975).

CHAPTER 11

Finite Differences

11.1 INTRODUCTION

In order to assess the behaviour and performance of a physical process or situation, an engineer often has to analyse data. The data may be accumulated and presented in a number of different ways and required for several types of operation. Typical examples are (a) when the data are in the form of discrete values $f_0, f_1, \ldots$ given at specified values $x_0, x_1, \ldots$ of the independent variable x, and the value $\bar{f}$ is required at some intermediate value $\bar{x}$; (b) when the data are given analytically by a function $f(x)$, and its integral is required in cases for which an analytical solution is impossible (for example, $\int_0^r \exp(-x^{3/2})\,\mathrm{d}x$); or (c) the data may be presented as a graph of f against x, and the derivative or rate of change of f is required at some particular value or values of x. Of all these examples of representing data, the graphical method might appear to be the most attractive, since the value of $\bar{f}$ could be read off 'by eye', the integral would be given by measuring the area under the curve, and even the derivative could be estimated by measuring the slope of the tangent at the required point. However, these would necessarily be approximate values and there would be no means of correctly estimating the error. To obtain more accurate values, numerical methods are required.

Graphs, being a *visual* representation of the behaviour of a function, are of no use for processing on a desk machine or automatic computer and must be replaced by an equivalent set of numbers. Similarly, many standard functions often exist, to all intents and purposes, only as tabulated values, and discrete data are by definition just that. So in describing numerical procedures to analyse data, we consider our raw material to be a *table of values* of the function specified at certain values of the independent variable. This table is obviously fundamentally important to the subsequent numerical work, and checking its accuracy is usually the first step when setting out to compute some values derived from the table.

Apart from accurate tabulation, the three operations most commonly performed on a set of data are interpolation, integration and differentiation. The latter two are operations of *calculus* involving limits and infinitesimals, so that they cannot be done directly numerically. If, however, the data are replaced by an approximating function such as a polynomial, then the calculus operations are easily carried out, as is interpolation also. Polynomials are not the only type of approximation for functions — alternative representations are Fourier series or eigenfunction expansions of various types, etc. — but they are the most convenient, and most numerical methods for dealing with interpolation, integration and differentiation are based on this approximation. The theoretical basis for these methods is *Weierstrass's Theorem* which says, in effect, that it is possible to approximate any continuous function, to any desired degree of accuracy in any finite interval, by a polynomial of sufficiently high degree.

Normally this polynomial is chosen to coincide with the data at suitably chosen points, in which case it is called a *collocation polynomial*. In practice it is usually convenient to specify these points to lie at equal intervals of x, i.e., at constant step-length.

Sometimes it is more useful to choose the approximating polynomial in such a way that a measure of the discrepancies between the data and the polynomial is minimized, though not actually required to be zero. An example of this is the 'method of least squares' described in Volume 2, Chapter 3. Such an approximation is often termed a Chebyshev approximation. This chapter will not, however, consider formulae developed from such procedures, although some can be obtained by using analysis similar to that used for collocation polynomials.

11.2 FINITE DIFFERENCES AND DIFFERENCE TABLES

We shall find that the numerical formulae are usually expressed not only in terms of the data values themselves but also in terms of differences between successive values. These differences are called *finite differences* and are most conveniently displayed in a *difference table*, such as that illustrated in table 11.1. The column of *first differences* consists of the differences of successive values of the function f itself. The next column is of *second differences*, which are the first differences of the column of first differences; higher order differences are defined in a similar manner. Note that the

TABLE 11.1

x	$f(x)$	First differences	Second differences	Third differences	Fourth differences
0.50	2.00000				
		−18182			
0.55	1.81818		3031		
		−15151		−701	
0.60	1.66667		2330		203
		−12821		−498	
0.65	1.53846		1832		131
		−10989		−367	
0.70	1.42857		1465		93
		−9524		−274	
0.75	1.33333		1191		63
		−8333		−211	
0.80	1.25000		980		48
		−7353		−163	
0.85	1.17647		817		
		−6536			
0.90	1.11111				

decimal point and unnecessary zeros are omitted, leaving only the significant digits in each difference. This is conventional in difference tables, and eliminates a possible source of mistakes. Also note that the entries in table 11.1 are the values of $1/x$, and will be used in some examples treated later in the chapter.

Notation

If x_0 is a given value of x, and h is a *constant* step-length, we denote $x_0 + rh$ by x_r and $f(x_r)$ by f_r where r is an integer. Thus

$$x_1 = x_0 + h, \quad x_2 = x_0 + 2h, \ldots, x_r = x_0 + rh, \quad x_{-r} = x_0 - rh, \ldots$$

$$f_0 = f(x_0), \quad f_1 = f(x_1), \ldots, f_r = f(x_r), \quad f_{-r} = f(x_{-r}), \ldots.$$

We use the notation $x = x_0(h)x_n$ to denote x varying over the range x_0 to x_n in steps of length h.

Forward Differences

The *first forward difference* of $f(x)$ at $x = x_r$ is denoted by Δf_r and defined by

$$\Delta f_r = f_{r+1} - f_r.$$

Thus in table 11.1 the value -0.12821 is the first forward difference at $x = 0.60$. Similarly, the *second forward difference* of $f(x)$ at $x = x_r$ is denoted by $\Delta^2 f_r$ and defined as the first forward difference of the first forward difference at $x = x_r$, so that

$$\Delta^2 f_r \equiv \Delta(\Delta f)_r = \Delta f_{r+1} - \Delta f_r.$$

Hence in table 11.1 the second forward difference at $x = 0.60$ is 0.01832 and at $x = 0.70$ is 0.01191. In general, the nth forward difference at $x = x_r$ is

$$\Delta^n f_r \equiv \Delta(\Delta^{n-1} f)_r = \Delta^{n-1} f_{r+1} - \Delta^{n-1} f_r.$$

Each difference, however high its order, can be expressed in terms of the function values. For example, the definition of $\Delta^2 f_r$ gives

$$\Delta^2 f_r = (f_{r+2} - f_{r+1}) - (f_{r+1} - f_r) = f_{r+2} - 2f_{r+1} + f_r.$$

The higher the order n, the further forward do we need tabular values; $\Delta^2 f_0$ needs values of f at x_0, x_1 and x_2, but $\Delta^3 f_0$ needs the value at x_3 also:

$$\Delta^3 f_0 = \Delta^2 f_1 - \Delta^2 f_0 = f_3 - 3f_2 + 3f_1 - f_0.$$

Backward Differences

Backward differences are defined in a manner analogous to forward differences and are denoted by ∇ instead of Δ. Thus the *first backward difference* of f at $x = x_r$ is

$$\nabla f_r = f_r - f_{r-1},$$

and higher order backward differences are similarly given by

$$\nabla^n f_r \equiv \nabla(\nabla^{n-1}f)_r = \nabla^{n-1}f_r - \nabla^{n-1}f_{r-1}.$$

It is easy to see that now we need to go *backward* for the necessary information and that the larger n is, the further backward do we need to go:

$$\nabla^2 f_0 = f_0 - 2f_{-1} + f_{-2}, \qquad \nabla^3 f_0 = f_0 - 3f_{-1} + 3f_{-2} - f_{-3}.$$

In table 11.1 we see that the value -0.12821 is the first backward difference at $x = 0.65$, *not* $x = 0.60$ as for the forward differences; 0.01191 is the second backward difference at $x = 0.80$, as well as being the second forward difference at $x = 0.70$.

Central Differences

These are again defined in a manner analogous to the forward and backward differences, but now draw on information both forward and backward from the relevant point. However, although even order central differences can be associated with a particular choice of x, odd order differences must now be associated with two adjacent values of x. The *first central difference* at x_r and x_{r+1} is defined by

$$\delta f_{r+\frac{1}{2}} = f_{r+1} - f_r.$$

We note that here the suffix $r + \frac{1}{2}$ is a notational convenience — it does not represent any quantity at $x = x_r + \frac{1}{2}h$. We also note that δf_r has no meaning. However, $\delta^2 f_r$ *does* have an unambiguous meaning denoting the second central difference at $x = x_r$:

$$\delta^2 f_r = \delta f_{r+1/2} - \delta f_{r-1/2},$$

and this can be expressed in terms of tabular values as

$$\delta^2 f_r = f_{r+1} - 2f_r + f_{r-1}.$$

Higher order central differences are again defined similarly:

$$\delta^{2n} f_r = \delta^{2n-1} f_{r+1/2} - \delta^{2n-1} f_{r-1/2}, \qquad \delta^{2n+1} f_{r+1/2} = \delta^{2n} f_{r+1} - \delta^{2n} f_r,$$

and these can also be expressed in terms of tabular values:

$$\delta^3 f_{r+1/2} = f_{r+2} - 3f_{r+1} + 3f_r - f_{r-1},$$
$$\delta^4 f_r = f_{r+2} - 4f_{r+1} + 6f_r - 4f_{r-1} + f_{r-2}.$$

In table 11.1, the second central difference at $x = 0.65$ is 0.01832, and the third central difference at $x = 0.65$ and 0.70 is -0.00367.

Finally we note that in table 11.1 the entry 0.01191 now describes the second central difference at $x = 0.75$ as well as being the second backward difference at $x = 0.80$ and the second forward difference at $x = 0.70$. This illustrates the fact that any *single* entry in a difference table corresponds to *each* of the three types of finite differences. The general result is, for integers r and n,

$$\Delta^n f_r = \nabla^n f_{r+n} = \delta^n f_{r+\frac{1}{2}n}.$$

EXAMPLE 1

Express ∇f_3, $\Delta^2 f_{-1}$, $\delta^3 f_{3/2}$ in terms of the function values $f_0, f_1, \ldots$, etc.

∇f_3 is the first backward difference at x_3 and $\Delta^2 f_{-1}$ is the second forward difference at x_{-1}. Hence, from the definitions,

$$\nabla f_3 = f_3 - f_2, \quad \Delta^2 f_{-1} = \Delta f_{-0} - \Delta f_{-1} = f_1 - 2f_0 + f_{-1}.$$

$\delta^3 f_{3/2}$ denotes the third central difference at x_1 and x_2; thus

$$\delta^3 f_{3/2} = \delta^2 f_2 - \delta^2 f_1 = f_3 - 2f_2 + f_1 - (f_2 - 2f_1 + f_0) = f_3 - 3f_2 + 3f_1 - f_0.$$

Finite Differences of a Function

Although the definitions given above are expressed in terms of tabular values, it is easy to extend the definitions to include finite differences of a continuous function $f(x)$. Thus the first differences of $f(x)$ with step-length h are

$$\Delta f(x) = f(x + h) - f(x), \quad \nabla f(x) = f(x) - f(x - h),$$
$$\delta f(x) = f(x + \tfrac{1}{2}h) - f(x - \tfrac{1}{2}h).$$

Higher order differences are defined in a similar manner.

The difference operators Δ, ∇ and δ behave very much like algebraic quantities, satisfying the associative law of addition, commutativity, etc. Thus, if f and g represent two continuous functions,

$$\Delta(f + g) = \Delta f + \Delta g,$$
$$\Delta^m(\Delta^n f) = \Delta^n(\Delta^m f) \equiv \Delta^{m+n} f,$$
$$\Delta(cf) = c\Delta f,$$

where c is a constant.

Finite Differences of a Polynomial

The ith differences of an nth degree polynomial are polynomials of degree $n - i$ if $0 < i \leqslant n$ and are zero if $i > n$. Bearing in mind the central role of polynomials in our theory, this is obviously an important result. It can be proved by considering a typical term $a_k x^k$, $0 \leqslant k \leqslant n$. Successive forward differences of x^k at a typical x are

$$\Delta x^k = (x + h)^k - x^k = khx^{k-1} + \tfrac{1}{2}k(k - 1)h^2 x^{k-2} + \ldots + kh^{k-1}x + h^k,$$
$$\Delta^2 x^k = k(k - 1)h^2 x^{k-2} + k(k - 1)(k - 2)h^3 x^{k-3} + \ldots + (2^k - 2)h^k,$$

$$\ldots\ldots$$

$$\Delta^i x^k = k(k - 1)\ldots(k - i + 1)h^i x^{k-i} + \ldots,$$

$$\ldots\ldots$$

$$\Delta^k x^k = k!h^k, \quad \Delta^{k+1}x^k = 0.$$

The required result follows immediately. In particular, the nth difference of a polynomial of degree n is

$$\Delta^n(a_0 + a_1 x + \ldots + a_n x^n) = 0 + 0 + \ldots + a_n n! h^n,$$

a constant proportional to h^n, and higher differences are zero. This shows that the higher differences of a polynomial become smaller, provided the step-length h is sufficiently small. Consequently, with Weierstrass's theorem, we can expect the higher differences of *any* data to decrease as the order of difference increases, for sufficiently small h.

Detecting and Correcting Mistakes in Tables

It is always wise to ensure that a table of values does not contain a mistake caused, for example, by misreading an experimental value or by transposing two digits when writing down the value. A convenient safeguard is provided by constructing a difference table. Whilst the differences of a correct table of values should decrease in magnitude as the order of differences increases, the effect of a mistake in one of the tabular values is to increase the differences and occurs in the following convenient way.

Suppose the value of f given at x_0 is written as $f_0 + \epsilon$ instead of the correct value f_0. Then the discrepancy ϵ is propagated in the difference table in the manner shown in table 11.2, in which only the discrepancies are shown in the second and higher differences. Table 11.2 indicates that not only is the effect of the mistake *magnified* as the order of differences increases, but also that the effect is *oscillatory* for any particular order. Hence isolated mistakes can not only be detected but also pinpointed. At the same time the *sum* of the effects for any order is zero; for example, in the column of second differences the sum of the faulty entries is

$$(\delta^2 f_{-1} + \epsilon) + (\delta^2 f_0 - 2\epsilon) + (\delta^2 f_1 + \epsilon) = \delta^2 f_{-1} + \delta^2 f_0 + \delta^2 f_1,$$

giving the same result as when the correct value f_0 is used. This result can be used to correct the pinpointed mistake.

Whilst this procedure will usually reveal random mistakes, it may well miss *systematic* mistakes. These are usually associated with experimental error, and could

TABLE 11.2

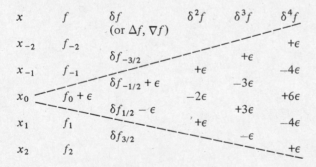

x	f	δf (or $\Delta f, \nabla f$)	$\delta^2 f$	$\delta^3 f$	$\delta^4 f$
x_{-2}	f_{-2}				$+\epsilon$
		$\delta f_{-3/2}$		$+\epsilon$	
x_{-1}	f_{-1}		$+\epsilon$		-4ϵ
		$\delta f_{-1/2} + \epsilon$		-3ϵ	
x_0	$f_0 + \epsilon$		-2ϵ		$+6\epsilon$
		$\delta f_{1/2} - \epsilon$		$+3\epsilon$	
x_1	f_1		$+\epsilon$		-4ϵ
		$\delta f_{3/2}$		$-\epsilon$	
x_2	f_2				$+\epsilon$

be caused by faulty measuring devices, for example, or by a persistent fault in the performance of the experiment.

EXAMPLE 2

Construct the difference table for the following data, and use it to detect and correct any mistakes in the given data:

0   1736   3420   5000   6248   7660   8660   9397   9848   10000.

The difference table is shown in table 11.3 and shows quite clearly (particularly in the fourth differences) that the incorrect entry is 6248. The $\delta^2 f$ column shows that the the average of the three relevant values of $\delta^2 f$ (which must be the same as the *correct* average) is:

$$\delta^2 f_0 \simeq \tfrac{1}{3}(-332 + 164 - 412) \simeq -197.$$

Since the tabulated, incorrect value is $\delta^2 f_0 - 2\epsilon$, we have

$$-197 - 2\epsilon \simeq 164, \quad \text{or} \quad \epsilon \simeq -180.$$

TABLE 11.3

f	δf	$\delta^2 f$	$\delta^3 f$	$\delta^4 f$
0000				
	1736			
1736		−52		
	1684		−52	
3420		−104		−176
	1580		−228	
5000		−332		724
	1248		496	
6248		164		−1072
	1412		−576	
7660		−412		725
	1000		149	
8660		−263		−172
	737		−23	
9397		−286		10
	451		−13	
9848		−299		
	152			
10000				

Hence the entry 6248 should, in fact, be about $f_0 + (-180)$ giving a corrected value of

$$f_0 = 6428.$$

The mistake is evidently a transposition mistake. To confirm that this is so, and to check against any other mistakes, one should re-difference using the corrected value.

Although in this example ϵ has been estimated by using the second differences, it should be noted that the same result could be obtained by using the third or fourth differences. However, it is usually better to use second differences once the mistake has been pinpointed.

Propagation of Errors

Table 11.2 also shows how an error (such as that due to round-off) is propagated. Furthermore it shows that apparently negligible errors introduced at any early stage could eventually dominate a higher order difference column.

Divided Differences

A more general type of finite difference is required if the data are tabulated at *non-constant* step-lengths. It is convenient to retain the notation $x_0, x_1, \ldots$, etc., with the values ordered as

$$\ldots < x_{-1} < x_0 < x_1 < x_2 < \ldots$$

though now $x_2 - x_1$ need not be equal to $x_1 - x_0$, for example. Then the *first divided difference* of f_0 and f_1 is defined by

$$f[x_0, x_1] = \frac{f_1 - f_0}{x_1 - x_0} = f[x_1, x_0]. \tag{1}$$

Analogously, the *second divided difference* of f_0, f_1 and f_2 is defined by

$$f[x_0, x_1, x_2] = \frac{f[x_2, x_1] - f[x_1, x_0]}{x_2 - x_0}, \tag{2}$$

and the *n*th *divided difference* is

$$f[x_0, x_1, \ldots, x_n] = \frac{f[x_{n+1}, \ldots, x_1] - f[x_n, \ldots, x_0]}{x_{n+1} - x_0}. \tag{3}$$

By induction it is easy to show that

$$f[x_0, x_1, \ldots, x_n] = \sum_{i=0}^{n} \frac{f_i}{(x_i - x_0)(x_i - x_1)\ldots(x_i - x_{i-1})(x_i - x_{i+1})\ldots(x_i - x_n)},$$

and hence that all divided differences are symmetric under interchange of any two of their arguments.

EXAMPLE 3

Determine the divided differences of (a) $f(x) = 2x^2$, (b) $f(x) = x^3$ at a typical value x_0 of x.

(a) $f[x_0, x_1] = \dfrac{2x_1^2 - 2x_0^2}{x_1 - x_0} = 2(x_1 + x_0),$

$f[x_0, x_1, x_2] = \dfrac{2(x_2 + x_1) - 2(x_1 + x_0)}{x_2 - x_0} = 2.$

The third and higher divided differences are obviously zero.

(b) $f[x_0, x_1] = \dfrac{x_1^3 - x_0^3}{x_1 - x_0} = x_1^2 + x_1 x_0 + x_0^2,$

$f[x_0, x_1, x_2] = \dfrac{(x_2^2 + x_2 x_1 + x_1^2) - (x_1^2 + x_1 x_0 + x_0^2)}{x_2 - x_0} = x_2 + x_1 + x_0,$

$f[x_0, x_1, x_2, x_3] = \dfrac{(x_3 + x_2 + x_1) - (x_2 + x_1 + x_0)}{x_3 - x_0} = 1,$

and again the higher divided differences are zero.

By induction and using the symmetry property of divided differences, it can be shown that, just as for nth differences, the nth divided differences of a polynomial of degree n are constant and higher differences zero. Taken in conjunction with Weierstrass's Theorem, this result again implies that a table of divided differences can be used to detect mistakes; however, it does not now give an easy method of correcting those mistakes.

Exercises

1. Derive difference tables, accurate to four decimal places, for the functions

    (a) $f(x) = 1/(1 + x),$ (b) $f(x) = 4x^3 - 3x + 1,$

for the two cases $x = 0(0.5)3$ and $x = 0(0.25)3$. (Keep these for use later in the chapter.)

2. Re-difference table 11.3 with the entry 6248 replaced with 6428 and confirm that there are no other mistakes in the data.

3. Construct a table of divided differences, accurate to three decimal places, for the cubic

$$f(x) = 4x^3 - 3x + 1$$

for the values $x = 0, 1.0, 1.8, 2.4, 2.8, 3.0$, and confirm that the fourth divided differences are zero.

4. Show that

$$\delta f_{r+3/2} + \delta f_{r-1/2} = 2\delta f_{r+1/2} + \delta^3 f_{r+1/2},$$

$$\delta^{2n-1} f_{3/2} + \delta^{2n-1} f_{-1/2} = 2\delta^{2n-1} f_{1/2} + \delta^{2n+1} f_{1/2}.$$

11.3 INTERPOLATION

Suppose the data for f are known at specific points $x_0, x_1, \ldots$. The problem of interpolation is to obtain a useful estimate of the value of f at any intermediate point. In general, this estimate is made on the basis of replacing $(n+1)$ data points by an nth degree polynomial function $P(x)$. Normally we should require that the formulae derived would at least predict the correct values for f at the given data points. Different choices of these points lead to different forms for the collocation polynomial and consequently to different interpolation formulae. The procedure is represented graphically in Fig. 11.1, which shows the data as discrete points; X is a typical intermediate point in (x_0, x_1). $P_1(x), P_2(x)$ and $P_3(x)$ are three examples of possible approximating polynomials and each gives a different prediction $(F_1, F_2$ and $F_3)$ for f at X. The graph of $P_1(x)$ is a straight line, that of $P_2(x)$ is the parabola passing through f_{-1}, f_0 and f_1, and that of $P_3(x)$ is the parabola passing through f_0, f_1 and f_2.

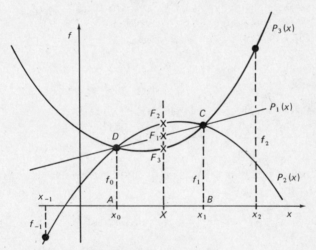

Fig. 11.1   Approximating polynomials passing through particular data points

Linear Interpolation

The simplest method of interpolating for the value of $f(x)$ at a typical point x in $x_0 < x < x_1$ is to approximate the behaviour of $f(x)$ against x by a straight line joining (x_0, f_0) to (x_1, f_1) so that between x_0 and x_1 $(= x_0 + h)$:

$$f(x) \simeq f_0 + (f_1 - f_0)(x - x_0)/h$$

$$= f_0 + u\delta f_{1/2} = f_0 + u\Delta f_0 = f_0 + u\nabla f_1, \tag{4}$$

where, for convenience here *and in subsequent formulae*, we introduce

$$u = (x - x_0)/h, \quad 0 \leqslant u \leqslant 1. \tag{5}$$

This formula (4) is often adequate if h is sufficiently small, but there is no indication here of the error in the approximation. The approximating polynomial is obviously of degree 1; the theory for higher degree polynomials provides the relevant error estimate.

Newton–Gregory Backward Difference Formula

This formula is obtained by constructing the interpolating polynomial $P(x)$ to coincide with f at the $(n+1)$ equally spaced points $x_0, x_{-1}, x_{-2}, \ldots, x_{-n}$. Thus we write

$$P(x) = a_0 + a_1(x - x_0) + a_2(x - x_0)(x - x_{-1})$$
$$+ a_3(x - x_0)(x - x_{-1})(x - x_{-2}) + \ldots$$
$$+ a_n(x - x_0)(x - x_{-1}) \ldots (x - x_{-n+1}), \tag{6}$$

and choose the coefficients $a_0, a_1, \ldots, a_n$ so that

$$P(x_0) = f_0, \quad P(x_{-1}) = f_{-1}, \ldots, P(x_{-n}) = f_{-n}.$$

The reason for choosing such an apparently cumbersome form for $P(x)$ is that it leads to a formula involving finite differences. Substituting $x = x_0, x_{-1}, \ldots, x_{-n}$ successively in equation (6) gives the simultaneous equations

$$f_0 = a_0, \quad f_{-1} = a_0 - a_1 h, \quad f_{-2} = a_0 - 2a_1 h + 2a_2 h^2,$$
$$\ldots, f_{-n} = a_0 - na_1 h + n(n-1)a_2 h^2 + \ldots + (-1)^n n! a_n h^n.$$

Solving in turn for $a_0, a_1, \ldots, a_n$ (a simple matter of forward substitution) then results in

$$a_0 = f_0, \quad a_1 h = a_0 - f_{-1} = f_0 - f_{-1} = \nabla f_0, \ldots, a_n h^n = \nabla^n f_0/n!.$$

Hence the interpolating polynomial (6) can be expressed very conveniently in terms of backward differences:

$$P(x) = P(x_0 + hu) = f_0 + u\nabla f_0 + \frac{1}{2}u(u+1)\nabla^2 f_0 + \frac{1}{3!}u(u+1)(u+2)\nabla^3 f_0 + \ldots$$

$$\ldots + \frac{1}{n!}u(u+1) \ldots (u+n-1)\nabla^n f_0. \tag{7}$$

In the same way we can construct the *Newton–Gregory forward difference formula* by using values for f at $x_0, x_1, x_2, \ldots, x_n$:

$$P(x) = P(x_0 + hu) = f_0 + u\Delta f_0 + \frac{1}{2}u(u-1)\Delta^2 f_0 + \frac{1}{3!}u(u-1)(u-2)\Delta^3 f_0 + \ldots$$

$$\ldots + \frac{1}{n!}u(u-1) \ldots (u-n+1)\Delta^n f_0. \tag{8}$$

EXAMPLE 1

Use the differences in table 11.1 to compute the value of f at $x = 0.57$ accurate to four decimal places.

For $x = 0.57$ we choose $x_0 = 0.55$ so that, with $h = 0.05$, we have $u = 0.4$. Then using formula (8) with the corresponding forward differences gives

$$f(0.57) = 1.81818 + (0.4)(-0.15151) + \tfrac{1}{2}(0.4)(-0.6)(0.02330)$$
$$+ \tfrac{1}{6}(0.4)(-0.6)(-1.6)(-0.00498)$$
$$+ \tfrac{1}{24}(0.4)(-0.6)(-1.6)(-2.6)(0.00131)$$
$$+ \tfrac{1}{120}(0.4)(-0.6)(-1.6)(-2.6)(-3.6)(0.00038)$$
$$= 1.81818 - 0.06060 - 0.00280 - 0.00032 - 0.00005 - 0.00001$$
$$= 1.7544.$$

In this calculation, accuracy is maintained by retaining an extra decimal place until the answer is obtained, and by confirming that the fifth and higher differences cannot affect the last decimal place.

Gauss's Interpolation Formula

This formula is the central difference equivalent to the Newton–Gregory formulae, and is based on the polynomial approximation:

$$P(x) = b_0 + b_1(x - x_0) + b_2(x - x_0)(x - x_1)$$
$$+ b_3(x - x_0)(x - x_1)(x - x_{-1}) + b_4(x - x_0)(x - x_1)(x - x_{-1})(x - x_2)$$
$$+ \ldots$$

to as many terms as required. Then choosing b_0, b_1, etc. so that $P(x)$ now agrees with the data at $x_0, x_1, x_{-1}, x_2, x_{-2}, \ldots$ we have

$$P(x) = f_0 + u\delta f_{1/2} + \frac{1}{2}u(u - 1)\delta^2 f_0 + \frac{1}{3!}u(u - 1)(u + 1)\delta^3 f_{1/2} + \ldots \qquad (9)$$

terminating after a finite number of terms. It should be emphasized here that the formulae (7), (8) and (9) are *not* infinite series.

Gauss's formula (9) is in fact not used in practice, but it is the basis of most of the useful formulae, such as Everett's, Bessel's and Stirling's formulae.

Everett's Formula

This formula involves only *even-order* central differences, which conveniently lie on tabular lines. It is obtained by substituting in equation (9) for the odd-order differences (for example, $\delta^3 f_{1/2} = \delta^2 f_1 - \delta^2 f_0$) to give

$$P(x) = E_0 f_0 + E_2 \delta^2 f_0 + E_4 \delta^4 f_0 + \ldots + F_0 f_1 + F_2 \delta^2 f_1 + F_4 \delta^4 f_1 + \ldots \qquad (10)$$

where

$$E_0 = 1 - u, \qquad\qquad\qquad\qquad F_0 = u,$$
$$E_2 = -u(1 - u)(2 - u)/3!, \qquad\qquad F_2 = u(u^2 - 1)/3!,$$
$$E_4 = -(-1 - u)u(1 - u)(2 - u)(3 - u)/5!, \quad F_4 = u(u^2 - 1)(u^2 - 4)/5!, \ldots .$$

Because of the importance of this formula, the values of these Everett coefficients $E_0, E_2, \ldots, F_0, F_2, \ldots$ may be found in convenient standard tables (see [4], for example) for $0 \leqslant u \leqslant 1$.

EXAMPLE 2
Use Everett's formula to determine from table 11.1 the value of f at $x = 0.61$, maintaining accuracy to four decimal places.

Taking $x_0 = 0.60$ and $h = 0.05$ gives $u = 0.2$, so that

$$E_0 = 0.8, \quad E_2 = -0.048, \quad E_4 = -0.008, \quad F_0 = 0.2, \quad F_2 = -0.032,$$
$$F_4 = 0.006; \quad f(0.61) = 1.6393.$$

In this case the fourth differences do not affect the accuracy, so no higher differences are required.

Bessel's Formula

This is a form which is symmetrical about the midpoint $u = \frac{1}{2}$. If in equation (9) we substitute the easily derived relations

$$\delta^2 f_0 = \tfrac{1}{2}(\delta^2 f_0 + \delta^2 f_1 - \delta^3 f_{1/2}), \quad \delta^4 f_0 = \tfrac{1}{2}(\delta^4 f_0 + \delta^4 f_1 - \delta^5 f_{1/2}), \text{ etc.}$$

and collect similar terms, we obtain Bessel's formula:

$$P(x) = f_0 + u\delta f_{1/2} + B_2(\delta^2 f_0 + \delta^2 f_1) + B_3 \delta^3 f_{1/2} + B_4(\delta^4 f_0 + \delta^4 f_1) + \ldots \qquad (11)$$

where $B_2 = \frac{1}{2} u(u - 1)/2!$, $B_3 = u(u - \frac{1}{2})(u - 1)/3!, \ldots$ are the Bessel coefficients. These coefficients, like Everett coefficients, may be found in standard tables (see [4]). It should be noted that B_3 has a maximum value of about 0.008 for $x_0 \leqslant x \leqslant x_1$, so that the third and higher difference terms in equation (11) can be neglected if $\delta^3 f$ is no more than 60 units in the last decimal (that is, 60×10^{-m} where m is the number of decimal places retained in f).

Stirling's Formula

This formula is symmetrical about x_0 (or equivalently $u = 0$) and is derived by substituting in equation (9) the relations

$$\delta f_{1/2} = \tfrac{1}{2}(\delta f_{1/2} + \delta f_{-1/2} + \delta^2 f_0), \quad \delta^3 f_{1/2} = \tfrac{1}{2}(\delta^3 f_{1/2} + \delta^3 f_{-1/2} + \delta^4 f_0), \text{ etc.}$$

giving

$$P(x) = f_0 + S_1(\delta f_{-1/2} + \delta f_{1/2}) + S_2 \delta^2 f_0 + S_3(\delta^3 f_{-1/2} + \delta^3 f_{1/2}) + S_4 \delta^4 f_0 + \ldots ,$$

$$\tag{12}$$

where $S_1 = \frac{1}{2}u$, $S_2 = \frac{1}{2}u^2$, $S_3 = \frac{1}{2}u(u^2 - 1)/3!$, $S_4 = u^2(u^2 - 1)/4!$,
$S_5 = \frac{1}{2}u(u^2 - 1)(u^2 - 2^2)/5!$, ... are the Stirling coefficients.

Use of the Interpolation Formulae; Order of Error

In general, the error in using any of these formulae is of the order of the first term to be omitted. Thus the Gauss formula (9) implies that linear interpolation carries an error of the order of $\frac{1}{2}u(u - 1)\delta^2 f$. In general it is easy to see from a difference table how many terms must be included in a particular formula to obtain a required accuracy.

Formulae which involve central differences give the best accuracy for a given amount of computation. They also have the philosophical merit of giving equal weight to the tabulated data on each side of the relevant data point! Hence the Newton–Gregory formulae are used only where central differences cannot be obtained, i.e., near the *ends* of the table as in example 1.

Stirling's formula is mainly used for deriving formulae for numerical integration and differentiation; the practical interpolation formulae are those of Everett and Bessel. If third differences are negligible for the accuracy required, then Bessel's formula is simpler and hence better. The criterion for neglecting the $\delta^3 f$ term has already been discussed. If $\delta^3 f > 60$ units in the last decimal, then Everett's formula is best.

Finally, we note that both E_4 and F_4 have maximum values of about 0.012, so that the error in using Everett's formula only up to second differences is of the order of $0.024\,\delta^4 f$. Thus we can neglect any fourth difference less than 20 units in the last decimal. If the fourth difference is greater than 20 but less than 400 units (1000 units if $\delta^4 f_0$ and $\delta^4 f_1$ are the same sign), then the same second difference formula can be used with negligible loss of accuracy provided the second differences are replaced by the *modified second differences*

$$\delta_m^2 f = \delta^2 f - 0.184\,\delta^4 f. \qquad (13)$$

This remarkable result is obtained by noting that E_4/E_2 varies very little over the range $0 \leqslant u \leqslant 1$, with $0.15 \leqslant -E_4/E_2 \leqslant 0.20$. The value 0.184 minimizes the error introduced in the special case of constant fourth differences. When the $\delta^4 f$ are not constant, a direct evaluation of the error introduced will show that it is almost invariably negligible.

EXAMPLE 3
Determine to four significant figures the value of f at $x = 0.815$ given that the difference table includes the following:

x	f	δf	$\delta^2 f$	$\delta^3 f$
0.80	1.2500		98	
		−735		−16
0.85	1.1765		82	

Since $\delta^3 f < 60$, Bessel's formula should be used, with $u = 0.3$. Thus

$$f(0.815) = 1.2500 + (0.3)(-0.0735) + \tfrac{1}{4}(0.3)(-0.7)(-0.0180)$$
$$= 1.2270.$$

EXAMPLE 4
Repeat example 2, using modified second differences.

The modified second differences are

$$\delta^2_m f_0 : 2330 - 0.184 \times 203 = 2293,$$
$$\delta^2_m f_1 : 1832 - 0.184 \times 131 = 1808.$$

Everett's modified formula to second difference table entries then gives

$$f(0.61) = (0.8)(1.66667) - (0.048)(0.02293) + (0.2)(1.53846) - (0.032)(0.01808)$$
$$= 1.6393_5.$$

The accuracy would be given to five decimal places if the data were given to six places instead of just five.

Extrapolation

Sometimes it may be necessary to estimate a value for f at a point *outside* the range of the given data. This operation is termed extrapolation, and should be treated with caution since it is easy to extrapolate functions into regions where they do not exist. The basic procedure is to use the Newton-Gregory interpolation formulae, the backward difference formula to move forward beyond the table and the forward difference formula to move backward.

EXAMPLE 5
Use table 11.1 to extrapolate f to $x = 0.45$ and $x = 0.95$, to four decimal places.

For $f(0.45)$ we have $u = -1$ and require the forward difference formula (8) for $x = 0.50$.

$$f(0.45) = 2.00000 - (-0.18182) + 0.03031 - (-0.00701) + 0.00203$$
$$- (-0.00072) + 0.00034$$
$$= 2.2222_2.$$

Here we have needed to compute the fifth and sixth differences in order to maintain accuracy. This is also necessary for $f(0.95)$ since again $|u| = 1$, resulting in non-decreasing coefficients. The result is $f(0.95) = 1.0526$.

Newton's Divided Difference Formula

For data given with non-constant step-length, the interpolation formula must be given in terms of divided differences. From their definitions (1), (2) and (3), divided differences satisfy the relations

$$f = f_0 + (x - x_0)f[x, x_0], \quad f[x, x_0] = f[x_0, x_1] + (x - x_1)f[x, x_0, x_1],$$
$$f[x, x_0, x_1] = f[x_0, x_1, x_2] + (x - x_2)f[x, x_0, x_1, x_2], \ldots .$$

Successive substitution then immediately gives *Newton's formula*:

$$f(x) = f_0 + (x - x_0)f[x_0, x_1] + (x - x_0)(x - x_1)f[x_0, x_1, x_2] + \ldots . \qquad (14)$$

For polynomial functions, equation (14) gives exact interpolation values (within round-off error, of course). For non-polynomial functions, the order of the error depends on the higher divided differences, just as in the case of ordinary differences.

Inverse Interpolation

Sometimes we need to determine the intermediate point x which corresponds to a given value $\bar{f}$, say, for $f(x)$. The usual procedure is to use an *iterative method* based on an interpolation formula. For example, the iterative solution for Bessel's formula (11) to second differences is given by

$$u^{(n+1)} = \frac{\bar{f} - f_0}{\delta f_{1/2}} - \frac{1}{4} u^{(n)}(u^{(n)} - 1)\left(\frac{\delta^2 f_0 + \delta^2 f_1}{\delta f_{1/2}}\right) \qquad (15)$$

where $u^{(n)}$ denotes the nth approximation to the exact solution u. It should be borne in mind here that the accuracy of the solution is already restricted by the fact that the third differences have been assumed negligible.

EXAMPLE 6
Use the values given in example 3 above to determine x accurate to three decimal places, when $f(x) = 1.2$.

Since the data are suitable for Bessel's interpolation formula, we use equation (15) with $u^{(0)} = 0$ to give

$$u^{(1)} = \frac{1.2 - 1.25}{-0.0735} = 0.680, \quad u^{(2)} = 0.68 - \frac{1}{4}(0.68)(-0.32)\frac{180}{-735} = 0.667,$$

$$u^{(3)} = 0.680 - \frac{1}{4}(0.667)(-0.333)\frac{180}{-735} = 0.666,$$

$$u^{(4)} = 0.680 - \frac{1}{4}(0.666)(-0.334)\frac{180}{-735} = 0.666.$$

Hence, from (5),

$$x = 0.8 + 0.666 \times 0.05 = 0.833.$$

Exercises

1. Using the data given in table 11.1, (a) compute $f(0.88)$ to four decimal accuracy and (b) determine the value of x for which f equals 1.28.

2. Working with the appropriate difference tables derived in exercise 1(a) of §11.2, determine $f(1.12)$ when the step-length is (i) $h = 0.5$ and (ii) $h = 0.25$. Give reasons for your choice of formula, and compare the results with the exact solution. Also determine the value of x for which f equals 0.35.

11.4 NUMERICAL INTEGRATION

In principle the numerical problem of computing a definite integral is similar to that of interpolation in that the data are replaced by a suitable approximating function $P(x)$ and the value of the integral determined by directly integrating $P(x)$:

$$\int_a^b f(x)\, dx \simeq \int_a^b P(x)\, dx.$$

Usually $P(x)$ is chosen to be a collocation polynomial, and again different choices of data points give different integration formulae. Normally the data points are equidistant, and this will be assumed in deriving the more commonly used integration formulae. The forms chosen for $P(x)$ then give error estimates in terms of finite differences. If the data points are not equidistant, the errors can be estimated in terms of divided differences.

Graphically the various approximations are equivalent to the areas $ABCD$ under the various curves, as represented in Fig. 11.1.

Trapezoidal Rule

This is the simplest integration formula, obtained by assuming CD to be a straight line; then the area $ABCD$ is simply $\frac{1}{2}h(f_0 + f_1)$. The error involved in this approximation may be deduced by integrating Bessel's formula (11) to second differences:

$$\int_{x_0}^{x_1} f(x)\, dx \simeq \int_{x_0}^{x_1} P(x)\, dx = h \int_0^1 P\{x(u)\}du$$

$$= h \int_0^1 [f_0 + u\delta f_{1/2} + \tfrac{1}{4}u(u-1)(\delta^2 f_0 + \delta^2 f_1)]\, du$$

$$= h[f_0 + \tfrac{1}{2}\delta f_{1/2} - \tfrac{1}{24}(\delta^2 f_0 + \delta^2 f_1)]$$

$$= \tfrac{1}{2}h(f_0 + f_1) - \tfrac{1}{24}h(\delta^2 f_0 + \delta^2 f_1). \tag{16}$$

Hence the error involved in using the trapezoidal rule over the single interval is approximately $\frac{1}{24}h(\delta^2 f_0 + \delta^2 f_1)$. By adding the integrals over successive ranges $(x_1, x_2), (x_2, x_3), \ldots$ of width h, we obtain

$$\int_{x_0}^{x_n} f(x)\, dx \simeq \tfrac{1}{2}h(f_0 + 2f_1 + 2f_2 + \ldots + 2f_{n-1} + f_n)$$

$$- \tfrac{1}{24}h(\delta^2 f_0 + 2\delta^2 f_1 + 2\delta^2 f_2 + \ldots + 2\delta^2 f_{n-1} + \delta^2 f_n). \tag{17}$$

The first group of terms corresponds to the *trapezoidal rule* over the entire range; the second group gives an approximation to the error involved in using this rule, and is of order

$$(\tfrac{1}{24}h)(2n)\delta^2 f = \tfrac{1}{12}(x_n - x_0)\,\delta^2 f,$$

where $\delta^2 f$ represents the average value of the relevant second differences.

EXAMPLE 1

Using the values given in table 11.1, determine $\displaystyle\int_{0.5}^{0.7} \frac{1}{x}\,dx$ using the trapezoidal rule.

With $h = 0.05$, table 11.4 shows $\delta^2 f \simeq 0.02$ so that the trapezoidal rule gives an error of order $(0.2)(0.02)/12 = 0.0003$. Hence the answer can be accurate only to *three* decimal places; because of the factor $\frac{1}{2}h$, this implies that only three decimal place accuracy is necessary for the data. Using equation (17) we obtain

$$\int_{0.5}^{0.7} \frac{1}{x}\,dx \simeq \frac{0.05}{2}\{2.000 + 2(1.818 + 1.667 + 1.538) + 1.429\} = 0.337_9,$$

where the suffix 9 implies rounding off of the four decimal result 0.3369.

Simpson's Rule

By integrating Stirling's formula (12) to fourth differences between x_{-1} and x_1 we obtain

$$\int_{x_{-1}}^{x_1} f(x)\,dx \simeq h \int_{-1}^{1} P\{x(u)\}\,du$$

$$= h \int_{-1}^{1} [f_0 + \tfrac{1}{2}u(\delta f_{-1/2} + \delta f_{1/2}) + \tfrac{1}{2}u^2 \delta^2 f_0$$

$$+ \tfrac{1}{12}u(u^2 - 1)(\delta^3 f_{-1/2} + \delta^3 f_{1/2}) + \tfrac{1}{24}u^2(u^2 - 1)\delta^4 f_0]\,du$$

$$= 2h(f_0 + \tfrac{1}{6}\delta^2 f - \tfrac{1}{180}\delta^4 f_0)$$

$$= \tfrac{1}{3}h(f_{-1} + 4f_0 + f_1) - \tfrac{1}{90}h\delta^4 f_0.$$

Similarly, for the typical interval (x_{2r}, x_{2r+2}),

$$\int_{x_{2r}}^{x_{2r+2}} f(x)\,dx \simeq \tfrac{1}{3}h(f_{2r} + 4f_{2r+1} + f_{2r+2}) - \tfrac{1}{90}h\delta^4 f_{2r+1}$$

so that the definite integral over the entire range (x_0, x_{2n}) is

$$\int_{x_0}^{x_{2n}} f(x)\,dx \simeq \tfrac{1}{3}h\{(f_0 + f_{2n}) + 4(f_1 + f_3 + \ldots + f_{2n-1}) + 2(f_2 + \ldots + f_{2n-2})\}$$

$$- \tfrac{1}{90}h(\delta^4 f_1 + \delta^4 f_3 + \ldots + \delta^4 f_{2n-1}). \tag{18}$$

The first three groups of terms give *Simpson's rule*, geometrically equivalent to representing $f(x)$ between x_0 and x_{2n} by parabolic segments joining points (x_{2r}, f_{2r})

and (x_{2r+2}, f_{2r+2}), for $r = 0, 1, \ldots, n-1$. The last group of terms estimates the error in Simpson's rule and, being of order $\frac{1}{180}(x_{2n} - x_0)\delta^4 f$, shows why this rule gives such an accurate numerical value for an integral.

EXAMPLE 2

Use Simpson's rule to determine $\displaystyle\int_{0.5}^{0.7} \frac{1}{x}\,dx$ with $h = 0.05$ and $h = 0.1$.

With $h = 0.05$, table 11.1 shows that $\delta^4 f \simeq 0.002$. Thus Simpson's rule (18) gives an error of order $\frac{1}{180}$ $(0.2)(0.002) \simeq 0.000002$, implying accuracy to *five* decimal places. So, compared with the trapezoidal rule used in example 1, we now get two extra decimal places for the additional work of only tabulating, or even *estimating*, the third and fourth differences. We thus find

$$\int_{0.5}^{0.7} \frac{1}{x}\,dx \simeq \tfrac{1}{3}(0.05)\{2.00000 + 1.42857 + 4(1.81818 + 1.53846) + 2(1.66667)\}$$

$$= 0.33649_1.$$

With $h = 0.1$, the new difference table 11.4 for $1/x$ shows that the error term is of order $(0.2)(0.02)/180 \simeq 0.00002$ implying accuracy still to four decimal places. Then

$$\int_{0.5}^{0.7} \frac{1}{x}\,dx \simeq \tfrac{1}{3}(0.1)\{2.00000 + 4(1.66667) + 1.42857\}$$

$$= 0.3365_1.$$

TABLE 11.4

x	f	δf	$\delta^2 f$	$\delta^3 f$	$\delta^4 f$
0.50	2.00000				
		−33333			
0.60	1.66667		9523		
		−23810		−3570	
0.70	1.42857		5953		1585
		−17857		−1985	
0.80	1.25000		3968		
		−13889			
0.90	1.11111				

Other Formulae Based on Finite Differences

Integrating Stirling's formula (12) to fourth differences over three intervals gives

$$\int_{x_0}^{x_3} f(x)\,dx \simeq \frac{3h}{8}\,(f_0 + 3f_1 + 3f_2 + f_3), \tag{19}$$

and shows that the error is of order $(3h/80)\delta^4 f_1$. This is therefore somewhat less accurate than Simpson's rule, but useful if we are *forced* to integrate over an *odd* number of intervals.

A higher order of accuracy, but more complicated computation, is given by integrating Stirling's formula to sixth differences over four intervals, when

$$\int_{x_{-2}}^{x_2} f(x)dx \simeq \frac{2h}{45}(7f_{-2} + 32f_{-1} + 12f_0 + 32f_1 + 7f_2) \tag{20}$$

with an error of order $(8h/945)\delta^6 f_0$; or, if we integrate over six intervals:

$$\int_{x_{-3}}^{x_3} f(x)dx \simeq h(6f_0 + 9\delta^2 f_0 + \tfrac{33}{10}\delta^4 f_0 + \tfrac{41}{140}\delta^6 f_0) + 0(\delta^8 f_0)$$

and replacing $41/140$ by $42/140 = 3/10$ gives *Weddle's rule*

$$\int_{x_{-3}}^{x_3} f(x)dx \simeq \frac{3h}{10}(f_{-3} + 5f_{-2} + f_{-1} + 6f_0 + f_1 + 5f_2 + f_3) \tag{21}$$

with an error of order $\tfrac{1}{140}h\,\delta^6 f_0$.

EXAMPLE 3

Use Weddle's rule to determine $\int_{0.5}^{0.8} \frac{1}{x}dx$.

Applying equation (21) gives

$$\int_{0.5}^{0.8} \frac{1}{x}dx \simeq \frac{3(.05)}{10}\{2.00000 + 5(1.81818) + 1.66667 + 6(1.53846) + 1.42857$$

$$+ 5(1.33333) + 1.25000\}$$

$$= 0.4700036.$$

The truncation error $\tfrac{1}{140}h\,\delta^6 f_0$ is of order 0.00000005, but this is now swamped by the round-off error implicit in the number of decimal places given in table 11.1.

Accuracy and Use of These Formulae

The trapezoidal and Simpson's rules and those given above are but a sample of the many formulae available for numerical integration (see Bibliography). Of these, the most important is undoubtedly Simpson's rule. Its accuracy and simple form suggest that it should be used in most cases. If we are not free to choose the step-length h (such as when the data are given at specific points) and if fourth-order differences are *not* negligible, then the more accurate formulae (20) and (21) should be used whenever possible.

For automatic computation, the simple form of the trapezoidal rule is often convenient, particularly when variable step-lengths are required. The step-lengths are successively reduced until an acceptable accuracy has been achieved or until no more intermediate data (for example, at mid-points) are available. Successive *halving* of the step-length is a particularly effective method of achieving accuracy with any of the integration formulae, since the difference between successive results for the integral can be used to control the error. Further details of such refinements may be found in Noble [3], Chapter 9.

For hand computation it is good practice to construct a difference table if only to safeguard against mistakes in the data. In these circumstances it is sensible to treat the error terms in the integration formulae as *corrections*, and add them to the relevant rule in order to improve the accuracy of the numerical result. Thus, in example 1, we can obtain a solution very close to four decimal accuracy by incorporating the error 0.0003 to give the improved result 0.3366. The accuracy could be even further improved by using modified differences (see equation (13)).

Gaussian Formulae

When an automatic computer is used, many of the advantages of integration formulae based on finite differences disappear. If the data are given in the form of a continuous function of x, then much more efficient formulae can be obtained by choosing suitable values for x which are *not* necessarily data points. Such formulae are called *Gaussian*.

Consider a very simple example:

$$\int_{x_{-1}}^{x_1} f(x)\mathrm{d}x \simeq Af(x_0 - \alpha h) + Bf(x_0) + Af(x_0 + \alpha h) \tag{22}$$

where A, B and α are constants. Simpson's rule (18) is the special case $\alpha = 1$, $A = h/3$, $B = 4h/3$. Now we choose A, B and α to give the smallest error possible.

By expanding both sides of equation (22) in Taylor series, it can be shown that both sides agree up to terms in h^6 if we set

$$2A + B = 2h, \quad A\alpha^2 h^2 = h^3/3, \quad A\alpha^4 h^4 = h^5/5.$$

Thus

$$\int_{x_{-1}}^{x_1} f(x)\mathrm{d}x = \frac{h}{9} \{5f(x_0 - \alpha h) + 8f_0 + 5f(x_0 + \alpha h)\} + O(h^7) \tag{23}$$

where $\alpha^2 = 3/5$, and the coefficient of the error term is very small $(f^{(vi)}/15750)$.

More general Gaussian formulae can be constructed, but these are outside the scope of this chapter. Normally the *coefficients* of the function values are *irrational*, not rational as in this simple case.

EXAMPLE 4

Use the Gaussian formula (23) to compute $\displaystyle\int_{0.5}^{0.8} \frac{1}{x}\,\mathrm{d}x$.

For $f(x) = 1/x$, equation (23) shows that for $h = 0.15$,

$$\int_{0.5}^{0.8} \frac{1}{x} dx \simeq \frac{0.15}{9} \left\{ 5 \frac{1}{0.65 - 0.15(0.7746)} + 8 \frac{1}{0.65} + 5 \frac{1}{0.65 + 0.15(0.7746)} \right\}$$

$$= 0.4700036.$$

Difficult Integrals

None of the integration formulae can be used directly in cases when (a) $f(x)$ is infinite at some point in the range of integration (although the integral itself need not be infinite) or (b) when the range itself is infinite.

In case (a) the difficulty often can be overcome analytically by either integrating by parts or subtracting out the singularity. Thus, for example

$$\int_0^1 e^x x^{-1/2} dx = [2x^{1/2} e^x]_0^1 - 2 \int_0^1 e^x x^{1/2} dx = 2e - 2 \int_0^1 e^x x^{1/2} dx$$

or alternatively

$$\int_0^1 e^x x^{-1/2} dx = \int_0^1 x^{-1/2} dx + \int_0^1 (e^x - 1)x^{-1/2} dx = 2 + \int_0^1 (e^x - 1)x^{-1/2} dx$$

where the new integral presents no difficulty, as

$$(e^x - 1)x^{-1/2} \to 0 \quad \text{as} \quad x \to 0.$$

In case (b) the way out is often by means of an appropriate substitution to render the limits finite, or by cutting off the range at a finite limit and analytically bounding the resulting truncation error. Hence, for example, substituting $x = \tan \theta$ gives

$$\int_1^\infty \frac{e^{-x} dx}{1 + x^2} = \int_{\pi/4}^{\pi/2} e^{-\tan \theta} d\theta,$$

which is easily computed. Truncation in another example gives

$$\int_0^\infty \exp(-x^2) dx = \int_0^X \exp(-x^2) dx + E(X), \quad X > 0,$$

where a bound for the error $E(X)$ can be found as

$$E(X) = \int_X^\infty \exp(-x^2) dx < \int_X^\infty \frac{x}{X} \exp(-x^2) dx = \frac{1}{2X} \exp(-X^2).$$

Obviously X can be chosen to give an acceptable order of accuracy.

Exercises

1. Working with the appropriate difference tables derived in exercise 1(b) of §11.2,

determine $\int_1^3 f(x)dx$ using Simpson's rule with (i) $h = 0.5$ and (ii) $h = 0.25$. Check your results against the exact analytical solution. Why do all three answers agree exactly in this case?

2. Prove the formulae (19), (20), (21) and (23).

3. Derive the integration formula relevant to tabulated divided differences:

$$\int_{x_0}^{x_1} f(x)dx = (x_1 - x_0)f_0 + \tfrac{1}{2}(x_1 - x_0)^2 f[x_0, x_1]$$
$$- \tfrac{1}{6}(x_1 - x_0)^3 f[x_0, x_1, x_2] + \ldots.$$

4. Take a set of values of a standard function (for example, sin x) tabulated in a book of tables, and use Simpson's rule and the various other formulae to integrate it numerically over some interval. Check your answers against the analytical solution.

11.5 NUMERICAL DIFFERENTIATION

Obtaining a reasonable estimate of the derivative of a function at a given point is numerically a much more 'difficult' problem than that of estimating its integral. This is because the process is inherently prone to inaccuracy, as is easily seen by considering the definition of the derivative of $f(x)$:

$$f' \equiv \frac{df}{dx} = \lim_{h \to 0} \frac{f(x+h) - f(x-h)}{2h}. \tag{24}$$

In principle we should get a progressively more accurate approximation for f' by taking successively smaller values of h. In practice this leads to computing the ratio of two very small quantities, which is numerically bad; this is demonstrated in table 11.5 where the single numbers on the right $(2.7, 2.72, \ldots)$ denote various approximations for $d(e^x)/dx$ at $x = 1$. The exact solution is, of course, $e = 2.71828 \ldots$ and the table shows that with e^x given accurately to four decimal places, the definition (24) gives an improving approximation as h decreases from 1 to 0.01, but then the values become more inaccurate again.

Just as practical integration formulae are obtained by integrating the approximating polynomials, practical formulae for differentiation are obtained by differentiating the interpolation formulae based on the approximating polynomials $P(x)$. Again, Stirling's formula is usually the best suited of these formulae. From Stirling's formula (12) to fourth differences we have

$$f' \equiv \frac{df}{dx} \approx \frac{dP}{dx} = \frac{1}{h}\frac{dP}{du} \quad \text{since} \quad u = \frac{x - x_0}{h},$$

$$= \frac{1}{h}\Big[\tfrac{1}{2}(\delta f_{-1/2} + \delta f_{1/2}) + u\delta^2 f_0 + \tfrac{1}{12}(3u^2 - 1)(\delta^3 f_{-1/2} + \delta^3 f_{1/2})$$
$$+ \tfrac{1}{12}u(2u^2 - 1)\delta^4 f_0\Big], \tag{25}$$

TABLE 11.5

x	e^x	approximate $\dfrac{d}{dx}(e^x)$				
0	1.0000					
0.5	1.6487					
0.9	2.4596					
0.99	2.6912					
0.999	2.7157					
		2.7	2.72	2.723	2.8430	3.1946
1.000	2.7183					
		$h = 0.001$	$h = 0.01$	$h = 0.1$	$h = 0.5$	$h = 1$
1.001	2.7210					
1.01	2.7456					
1.1	3.0042					
1.5	4.4817					
2.0	7.3891					

$$f'' \equiv \frac{d^2 f}{dx^2} \simeq \frac{1}{h^2}\frac{d^2 P}{du^2} = \frac{1}{h^2}\left[\delta^2 f_0 + \tfrac{1}{2}u(\delta^3 f_{-1/2} + \delta^3 f_{1/2}) + \tfrac{1}{12}(6u^2 - 1)\delta^4 f_0\right]. \quad (26)$$

Obviously, similar formulae may be obtained for higher derivatives by taking Stirling's formula to higher differences. These differences may also be incorporated to improve the accuracy. In effect, formulae such as equations (25) and (26) are a combination of derivatives and interpolates. Normally we require the values of derivatives at the data points. These are given by putting $u = 0$ in the formulae to give, for example,

$$f_0' = \frac{1}{2h}\left[\delta f_{-1/2} + \delta f_{1/2} - \tfrac{1}{6}(\delta^3 f_{-1/2} + \delta^3 f_{1/2}) + \tfrac{1}{30}(\delta^5 f_{-1/2} + \delta^5 f_{1/2}) - \ldots\right], \quad (27)$$

$$f_0'' = \frac{1}{h^2}\left[\delta^2 f_0 - \tfrac{1}{12}\delta^4 f_0 + \tfrac{1}{90}\delta^6 f_0 - \ldots\right]. \quad (28)$$

Again the formulae give not only a numerical approximation for the derivatives, but also an order of magnitude for the truncation errors involved. Thus equation (27) shows that the approximation for f_0' based on equation (24) carries with it an error of order $\tfrac{1}{6}h^{-1}\delta^3 f$. Similarly equation (28) suggests use of the approximation

$$f_0'' \simeq \frac{f_1 - 2f_0 + f_{-1}}{h^2},$$

which has an error of order $\tfrac{1}{12}h^{-2}\delta^4 f_0$.

The formulae also demonstrate the close relation between the derivatives and their first approximations in terms of differences. Thus the nth-order derivative involves dividing the nth-order difference by the nth power of h, and equivalently we deduce that

$$\delta f \equiv O(hf'), \quad \delta^2 f \equiv O(h^2 f''), \ldots, \delta^n f \equiv O(h^n f^{(n)}).$$

Since h must be small, these relations show that whereas numerical integration gives solutions of greater accuracy than that of the data, numerical differentiation invariably gives less.

EXAMPLE

Using the values of table 11.1, evaluate to three decimal places the derivative of $1/x$ at $x = 0.65$.

From equation (27) and table 11.1 we see that neglecting the $\delta^3 f$ term would introduce an unacceptable error of order $(0.005)/(0.3)$ affecting the second decimal place. However, the $\delta^5 f$ term is of order $(0.0005)/(1.5)$ and would not affect the required accuracy. Hence, keeping the *fifth* decimal place in the data in order to work to four decimal places with round-off to three, we calculate

$$f_0' \simeq \frac{1}{0.1} \, [-0.12821 - 0.10989 - \tfrac{1}{6}(-0.00498 - 0.00367)]$$

$$= -2.367,$$

which agrees with the exact value.

Exercises

1. Working with the appropriate difference tables derived in exercise 1(a) in §11.2, determine df/dx at $x = 1.12$ when the step-length is (i) $h = 0.5$ and (ii) $h = 0.25$. Compare your results with the exact values for $f(x) = 1/(1 + x)$.

2. Derive the mid-point formula

$$hf_{1/2}' \simeq \delta f_{1/2} - \tfrac{1}{24}\delta^3 f_{1/2} + \tfrac{3}{640}\delta^5 f_{1/2} - \ldots .$$

3. Write down the formula for f_1' equivalent to equation (27). Then use the relations of exercise 4 in §11.2 to deduce the formula

$$\tfrac{1}{2}h(f_0' + f_1') = \delta f_{1/2} + \tfrac{1}{12}\delta^3 f_{1/2} - \tfrac{1}{120}\delta^5 f_{1/2} + \ldots .$$

PROBLEMS

1. The following table contains a mistake in one of the values of $f(x)$. Locate this mistake and estimate the correct value. Using Bessel's interpolation formula to second differences, determine to six decimal places the value of x for which $f(x) = 0$.

x	1.010	1.015	1.020	1.025	1.030	1.035
$f(x)$	−1.08286	−0.87590	−0.66998	−0.46511	−0.26158	−0.05847

x	1.040	1.045	1.050
$f(x)$	+0.14333	+0.34413	+0.54393.

2. Neglecting fourth differences, evaluate the following numbers:

(a) $f(3.25)$, (b) $f(3.02)$, (c) $f'(3.2)$, (d) $\displaystyle\int_{3.0}^{3.4} f(x)\,dx$,

where $f(x)$ is given by the following table:

x	3.0	3.1	3.2	3.3	3.4	3.5
$f(x)$	20.086	22.198	24.533	27.113	29.964	33.115.

Estimate the accuracy of each of your results. Determine to three decimal places the value of x for which $f(x) = 25.0$.

3. Detect and correct the transposition mistake in the following table of values of $f(x)$:

x	0	6	12	18	24	30	36	42
$f(x)$	3.0716	3.2361	3.4203	3.6820	3.8637	4.1336	4.4454	4.8097.

Use Simpson's rule on the corrected values to determine $\displaystyle\int_{12}^{36} f(x)\,dx$, and show that the error involved is about 0.0002. Also determine $f(25)$, and find the value of x for which $f(x) = 4.0$.

4. Use the Newton-Gregory forward difference formula to third differences to derive the formula for interpolation to halves

$$f_{3/2} \simeq \tfrac{1}{16}(-f_0 + 9f_1 + 9f_2 - f_3).$$

The following is an extract from a table of a function $g(\alpha, \phi)$ of two variables α and ϕ. Use this to obtain by interpolation an approximate value of $g(25, 12\tfrac{1}{2}°)$. Give, with reasons, an estimate of the magnitude of the error in this calculation.

				ϕ		
	$0°$	$5°$	$10°$	$15°$	$20°$	$25°$
α						
0	0	873	1745	2618	3491	4363
10	0	873	1745	2617	3489	4359
20	0	873	1744	2615	3483	4348
30	0	872	1743	2611	3473	4330
40	0	872	1742	2606	3462	4308
50	0	872	1740	2601	3450	4284

BIBLIOGRAPHY

[1] Morton, B. R., *Numerical Approximation*, Routledge and Kegan Paul, London (1964).
[2] Fröberg, C.–E., *Introduction to Numerical Analysis*, Addison Wesley, Reading, Mass. (1965).
[3] Noble, B., *Numerical Methods: 2*, Oliver and Boyd, Edinburgh (1964).
[4] *Interpolation and Allied Tables*, H.M.S.O., London (1956).

CHAPTER 12

Elementary Statistics — Probability Theory

12.1 INTRODUCTION

The preceding chapters of this book deal with many different mathematical techniques but these techniques all have one feature in common, namely the problems to which they can be applied are *deterministic*. A deterministic problem is one which is stated in precise mathematical language and for which all the requisite information can be obtained so that explicit solutions may be sought. However, many real-life situations must be faced in which not all of the appropriate knowledge is available, so that the associated problems are *probabilistic*.

Suppose, for example, that it is proposed to build a dam. The calculation of the land area which will be inundated when the water behind the dam is of given height is deterministic, whereas the estimation of how often the rainfall will cause the dam to overflow is a probabilistic matter. Nevertheless, even though many such questions do not admit a 'specific' solution, they must be taken into account before any design can be finalized. This is true whenever manufacturing and production processes are involved, for matters of reliability, repeatability and so forth are all essentially probabilistic. To such statistical aspects the engineer must give attention if the most worthwhile result is to be achieved. The basic groundwork of probability theory is given in this chapter but the matter of statistical inference, which is concerned with decision-taking in the light of experimental evidence, will be deferred until Volume 2.

The very absence of 'certainty' in problems of a probabilistic nature has made many people view statistics with as much suspicion as some earlier scientists regarded the limiting processes of calculus. However, to state that an event is random is not to imply that its behaviour is without structure. Probability theory, like other branches of mathematics, has its own axioms, but the topic is especially capable of abuse in uneducated or mischievous hands. Certain words, used imprecisely in everyday language, assume specific meanings when applied in a statistical sense but because of the extensive use of statistical theory in economics, social sciences, medicine, the biological and physical sciences and technology, the terms employed and the methods of handling problems may vary. These are exemplified by the different approaches to probability which are found in the next three sections. Although each approach has its own use, they all essentially lead to the same results.

In this chapter are certain topics which may not be new to the reader. This is especially true of those parts of §12.2, §12.3 and §12.4 which deal with permutations and combinations, with data presentation and 'descriptive statistics', and with elementary set theory. Nevertheless, their inclusion is an attempt to make the probability theory reasonably self-contained, and the student may benefit from seeing these topics in what may be a slightly novel setting.

Exercise

1. Discuss the statements

    (a) 'Statistics can prove anything.'
    (b) 'Statistics can prove nothing.'

12.2 PROBABILITY AND EQUI-LIKELY EVENTS

Equi-likely Probability

Consider the tossing of a die, the faces of which are labelled 1, 2, 3, 4, 5 and 6. The possible outcomes are that the face numbered 1 or 2 or 3 or 4 or 5 or 6 is uppermost and if the cube is unbiased each of these results is equally likely. There is one chance in six of throwing a 1, one chance in six of throwing a 2 and so forth. If interest centres on whether the number is even, acceptable numbers would be 2, 4 and 6 so that there are three chances in six of the outcomes being even. If 'any number less than 10' were specified, each outcome would satisfy the criterion, the chances would be six out of six and the event would be a 'certainty'. Similarly, in a single withdrawal of a card from a well-shuffled pack of 52 the chance of selecting the eight of spades is one in fifty-two, and the chance of obtaining any card of the spade suit is thirteen in fifty-two.

The above ideas illustrate the *equi-likely definition of probability*, which is as follows:

> If an event E can occur in a total of r ways out of a total number s of equi-likely outcomes, then the probability of event E is defined as r divided by s.

The notation adopted is:

$$P(E) = \frac{r}{s} \quad \text{or, equivalently,} \quad \Pr\{E\} = \frac{r}{s}. \tag{1}$$

In this type of situation the problem is to determine the values of r and s and this often leads to the use of permutations and combinations.

Permutations and Combinations

A would-be entrant to university wishes to study engineering. Suppose that there are seven universities which offer the type of course he requires. There then arises the question of filling in the joint application form which requires not more than five entries to be made, in order of preference. This illustrates the idea of *permutations*.

DEFINITION   The number of ways in which r items may be selected from n distinct items, where the order of selection matters, is called *the number of permutations of n items taken r at a time.*

Customary notations are ^nP_r and $_nP_r$.

From n items the first selection can be made in n different ways, the second in $(n-1)$ different ways, and so on. There are $\{n-(r-1)\}$ items from which the rth withdrawal can be made and consequently

$$^nP_r = n(n-1)(n-2)\ldots\ldots(n-r+1) \quad \text{with} \quad 1 \leqslant r \leqslant n \tag{2}$$

$$= \frac{n!}{(n-r)!} \quad \text{where 0! is defined to be 1.}$$

The total number of ways open to the student is thus $7 \times 6 \times 5 \times 4 \times 3 = 2520$.

In many situations only the *content* of the selection and not the order is important. This would be the case for a university department which interviewed all candidates who had placed that department in any position on the form.

DEFINITION   The number of ways in which r items may be selected from n distinct items, where the order of selection is immaterial, is called *the number of combinations of n items taken r at a time.*

Customary notations are ^nC_r, $_nC_r$ and $\binom{n}{r}$. Of these the first will be adopted.

There are $^rP_1$ ways in which r items can be arranged among themselves. If no attention is paid to order then these $r!$ arrangements are all equivalent. Therefore

$$^nC_r = \frac{^nP_r}{r!} = \frac{n(n-1)\ldots(n-r+1)}{r!} = \frac{n!}{r!(n-r)!}. \tag{3}$$

The combination ^nC_r is immediately recognizable as the coefficient of t^r in the binomial expansion of $(1+t)^n$. Among the properties which may readily be deduced for $0 < r \leqslant n$ are:

$$^nC_r = {^nC_{n-r}}, \quad {^nC_r} + {^nC_{r-1}} = {^{n+1}C_r}, \quad {^nC_r} = \left(\frac{n}{r}\right)^{n-1}C_{r-1}. \tag{4a, b, c}$$

The definition may be extended by taking ^nC_r to be zero if $r < 0$ or $r > n$.

EXAMPLE 1

A bus service operates an 'exact fare' system. In how many ways can a fare of 9p be made exactly from a pocket containing five coins each of value 2p, three coins each of value 1p and three coins each of value ½p?

From this pocket the fare of 9p can be constructed with four different sets of coins, which will be labelled A, B, C and D. A consists of $\{2, 2, 2, 2, 1\}$, B of $\{2, 2, 2, 1, 1, 1\}$, C of $\{2, 2, 2, 1, 1, ½, ½\}$ and D of $\{2, 2, 2, 2, ½, ½\}$. Here the order of the coins is certainly immaterial. In case A, for example, any four of the five 2p coins will suffice, and these can be selected in $^5C_4$ different ways. *Each* of these arrangements can be chosen along with *any one* of the $^3C_1$ different ways of choosing a single 1p coin from the three available.

The total number of ways in which A can be constructed is therefore

$$^5C_4 \times {}^3C_1 = \frac{5 \times 4 \times 3 \times 2}{4 \times 3 \times 2} \times 3 = 15.$$

Similarly, the number of ways in which B, C and D can be formed are respectively

$$^5C_3 \times {}^3C_3 = 10, \quad {}^5C_3 \times {}^3C_2 \times {}^3C_2 = 90 \quad \text{and} \quad {}^5C_4 \times {}^3C_2 = 15.$$

The total number of ways is therefore $15 + 10 + 90 + 15 = 130$.

Now suppose that n objects are to be placed in k batches. The batches are of sizes $n_1, n_2, \ldots, n_k$ respectively, where $n_1 + n_2 + \ldots + n_k = n$ and within each batch no attention is paid to the order of the contained objects.

The first n_1 items may be selected in $^nC_{n_1}$ different ways. From the remaining $(n - n_1)$ objects the second batch of items may be selected in $^{n-n_1}C_{n_2}$ different ways, and so on. It follows that the total number of different ways N is

$$N = {}^nC_{n_1} \times {}^{n-n_1}C_{n_2} \times {}^{n-n_1-n_2}C_{n_3} \times \ldots \times {}^{n-(n_1+n_2+\ldots+n_{k-1})}C_{n_k}$$

$$= \frac{n!}{(n-n_1)!n_1!} \times \frac{(n-n_1)!}{(n-n_1-n_2)!n_2!} \times \ldots \times \frac{(n-n_1-n_2-\ldots-n_{k-1})!}{(n-n_1-n_2-\ldots-n_{k-1}-n_k)!n_k!},$$

so

$$N = \frac{n!}{n_1!n_2!\ldots n_k!}. \tag{5}$$

EXAMPLE 2

In how many ways can a *total* of 9 be obtained when a six-faced die is thrown five times?

A possible way of totalling 9 from five throws is the sequence $\{2, 2, 2, 2, 1\}$. The order in which these are thrown is immaterial. The total number of ways in which four 2's and a 1 can be thrown in five throws is $5!/(4!1!)$ so that there are 5 such ways. Similarly, the set of values $\{3, 2, 2, 1, 1\}$ can occur in $5!/(1!2!2!) = 30$ ways. The set $\{3, 3, 1, 1, 1\}$ can occur in $5!/(2!3!) = 10$ ways. The set $\{4, 2, 1, 1, 1\}$ can occur in $5!/(1!1!3!) = 20$ ways. Finally, $\{5, 1, 1, 1, 1\}$ can occur in $5!/(1!4!) = 5$ ways. Thus of the number of possible outcomes, $6^5 \equiv 7776$, a total of 70 result in a score of 9.

Consider now the situation when precisely m objects out of a total population of size n possess a certain property and a sample of size s is taken, the successive withdrawals being without replacement. In how many ways, without regard to order, may exactly r objects in the sample have the given property?

These r objects must have been taken from the total of m which possess the given property and, without regard to order, this selection can occur in ^mC_r different ways. Likewise the $(s - r)$ which do not have the property must have come from the remaining $(n - m)$ objects. Since any one arrangement of the r objects which possess the property may occur with each of the $^{n-m}C_{s-r}$ arrangements of the $(s - r)$ which do not, the total number of ways M of selecting precisely r objects with the property is given by

$$M = {}^mC_r \times {}^{n-m}C_{s-r}. \tag{6}$$

EXAMPLE 3

In how many ways can three engineering students be chosen in five selections from a list of nine students, four of whom are engineers?

Here $n = 9$, $s = 5$, $m = 4$ and $r = 3$. The number of ways is therefore ${}^4C_3 \times {}^5C_2 = 4 \times 10 = 40$.

Result (6) can readily be extended. Suppose that the population of size n consists of k batches of sizes $n_1, n_2, \ldots, n_k$ respectively where $\sum_{i=1}^{k} n_i = n$. The number of different ways M in which a sample of size s can contain s_1 objects from the first batch, s_2 objects from the second batch, ... and s_k objects from the kth batch, where

$$\sum_{i=1}^{k} s_i = s, \text{ is}$$

$$M = {}^{n_1}C_{s_1} \times {}^{n_2}C_{s_2} \times \ldots \times {}^{n_i}C_{s_i} \times \ldots \times {}^{n_k}C_{s_k}. \tag{7}$$

EXAMPLE 4

After completing a specified mileage the four shock-absorbers on each of three prototype road-vehicles were removed for inspection. Five of these twelve shock-absorbers were to be chosen for more detailed tests. How many of the possible selections include at least one front nearside shock-absorber and one rear offside one?

Let $\{s_1, s_2, s_3\}$ be an arrangement which consists of s_1 front nearside shock-absorbers, s_2 rear offside shock-absorbers and $s_3 = (5 - s_1 - s_2)$ other shock-absorbers. The arrangements of interest are therefore $\{3, 1, 1\}, \{3, 2, 0\}, \{2, 1, 2\}, \{2, 2, 1\}, \{1, 1, 3\}$ and $\{1, 3, 1\}, \{2, 3, 0\}, \{1, 2, 2\}$.

The arrangement $\{3, 1, 1\}$ may be obtained in ${}^3C_3 \times {}^3C_1 \times {}^6C_1 = 1 \times 3 \times 6 = 18$ ways,

$$\{3, 2, 0\} \qquad\qquad {}^3C_3 \times {}^3C_2 \times {}^6C_0 = 1 \times 3 \times 1 = 3,$$
$$\{2, 1, 2\} \qquad\qquad {}^3C_2 \times {}^3C_1 \times {}^6C_2 = 3 \times 3 \times 15 = 135,$$
$$\{2, 2, 1\} \qquad\qquad {}^3C_2 \times {}^3C_2 \times {}^6C_1 = 3 \times 3 \times 6 = 54,$$
$$\{1, 1, 3\} \qquad\qquad {}^3C_1 \times {}^3C_1 \times {}^6C_3 = 3 \times 3 \times 20 = 180.$$

By symmetry the values for $\{1, 3, 1\}, \{2, 3, 0\}$ and $\{1, 2, 2\}$ are respectively equal to the values calculated for $\{3, 1, 1\}, \{3, 2, 0\}$ and $\{2, 1, 2\}$.

The total number of arrangements having the given constraint is then $(18 \times 2) + (3 \times 2) + (135 \times 2) + 54 + 180 = 546$.

It is evident that questions of this type can become quite complicated. A major difficulty is often to decide, *within the meaning of the question*, which arrangements really do represent different situations and in particular whether permutations or combinations are involved.

Exercises

1. Establish the combination relationships (4).

2. Check the result of example 4 by evaluating the number of arrangements which *do not* satisfy the given conditions. (This number when added to 546 must give the total number of possible arrangements, namely $^{12}C_5$.)

12.3 PROBABILITY AND RELATIVE FREQUENCY

Relative Frequency

With the concept of equi-likelihood introduced in the previous section the probabilities are predetermined before any actual statistical investigation is carried out. In many situations, the probabilities cannot be hypothesized in advance but can only be estimated in the light of direct experimental evidence. Thus if an experiment is conducted n times and precisely m of these result in the particular outcome of interest, labelled E, then the proportion favourable to the event E is m/n, the *relative frequency*. The intuitive assertion is then made that the larger the value of the sample-size n the more accurately this experimental proportion would reflect the true value. On this basis the probability is the limiting value of m/n and thus is written

$$P(E) = \lim \frac{m}{n}. \tag{8}$$

This *empirical definition of probability* lacks the precision of the definition of limit used in mathematical analysis. It is not possible to *prove* that there is a specific value to which the ratio tends, and consequently the limit is said to *exist in a probabilistic sense*.

Most 'real-life' statistical problems require, at some stage, the gathering of data, and sampling is essential when estimates of probabilities are to be made using the relative frequency idea just described. The provision of sample data which may be regarded as truly representative of the situation at large is not always as straightforward as might appear and the matter of sampling is discussed further in Volume 2. Very often the statistician who is to analyse the data has not been responsible for their assembly and therefore must be prepared to handle them in whatever form and however incompletely they have been supplied. The examples provided in this chapter and in Chapter 3 of Volume 2 are typical in that they embrace a variety of measurement systems and units.

Graphical Presentation

Once the material has been gathered it is usually wise to plot the data in graphical or semi-graphical forms as these may show aspects which a scan of the raw figures has failed to reveal. It is the essence of good plotting neither to stress trivial variations nor to obscure important information.

It is usually possible to classify a random variable as either *continuous* or *discrete*. If the variable is continuous the data can take any value between certain limits. Typical examples are the heights of people and the number of hours of sunshine per day. Examples of variables essentially discrete in nature are the number of accidents in the working day of a factory and the number of digits to which a given numerical answer is accurate. A discrete variable usually, but not necessarily, takes the values $0, 1, 2, \ldots$.

To some extent the method of graphical presentation depends on the type of variable and on the information to be conveyed, and special graph paper may be employed (see §12.6). When the quantity is discretely-varying the most commonly used methods of graphical representation are *line graphs* and *frequency polygons*. The variable values x_i, say, are plotted as abscissae and the corresponding frequencies f_i (or the relative frequencies f_i/n where $\sum_i f_i = n$) are plotted as the y values. In frequency polygons the ends of the ordinates are joined by straight-line segments, as Fig. 12.1 shows.

EXAMPLE 1

An hour-long traffic census on a certain road recorded the number m of time intervals of one minute in which x vehicles passed a certain point. Illustrate the results, which are given in table 12.1.

TABLE 12.1

Number of vehicles x:	0	1	2	3	4	5	6 or more
Number of intervals m:	6	11	15	12	10	6	0

Two sensible ways of plotting these figures are shown in Fig. 12.1.

For a continuous variable the most usual graphical presentation is a *histogram*. The x axis again represents the variable value and the *areas* of the rectangles erected on the corresponding bases are proportional to the class frequencies.

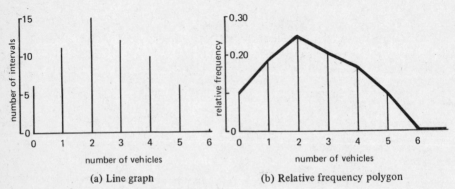

(a) Line graph   (b) Relative frequency polygon

Fig. 12.1   The traffic census data of table 12.1

For both discrete and continuous variables some further grouping may be desirable by increasing the size of the class intervals. When continuous data are plotted care must be taken concerning the end points of these intervals. For example, if ages with a class-interval of one year have been supplied were these quoted 'to the nearest year' or as 'age at last birthday'? By convention any measurement which appears to fall exactly on a class division is allocated one half to each of the adjacent intervals. Furthermore, if a histogram is to be constructed from results which include an 'open-ended' interval, e.g., 'over 70 mm' then it is customary to close such interval by choice of a reasonable upper limit.

EXAMPLE 2

Two hundred and fifty-six lengths of cable were chosen at random from the production run of a certain company and the load necessary to break each of these cables was determined. The results were grouped and then published as table 12.2. Draw a suitable histogram.

TABLE 12.2

Applied load (tons)	less than 9.0	9.0 – 9.2	9.2 – 9.4	9.4 – 9.6	9.6 – 9.8	9.8 – 10.0	10.0 – 10.2	10.2 – 10.4	10.4 – 10.6	10.6 – 10.8	10.8 – 11.0	more than 11.0
No. of cables	0	1	8	26	35	40	54	37	26	19	18	2

A histogram representation of the above data is shown in Fig. 12.2, where 'more than 11.0' has been chosen to mean belonging to the range 11.0–11.2 tons.

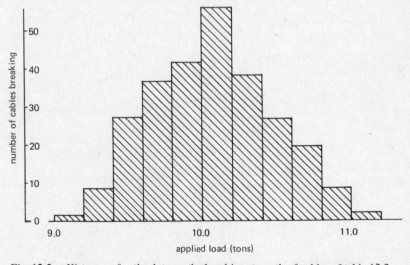

Fig. 12.2 Histogram for the data on the breaking strength of cables of table 12.2

Other schemes exist for the graphical illustration of data. Each tends to present a certain aspect particularly well; for example, the *bar chart* is especially useful in '*before and after*' types of situation. When, as is customarily the case, the bars are of equal width the quantities in question are proportional to the bar lengths.

EXAMPLE 3

Illustrate the coal output of four collieries which had the following tonnages for the indicated years.

	1972	1975
Hindle	998,074	1,213,070
South Riding	828,417	909,231
Farbridge	1,298,035	1,315,997
Bruddersford	1,078,112	1,320,562

A bar chart may be used, as shown in Fig. 12.3.

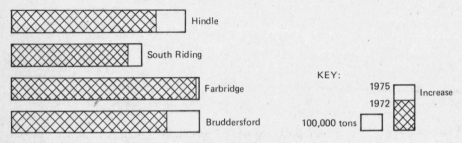

Fig. 12.3   Bar chart for the coal output data of example 3

Proportions are often best illustrated in a *pie-diagram*, using the appropriate sectors of a circle.

EXAMPLE 4

Figures for the percentage, by weight, of goods transported in a given region were as follows: Rail: 15%; Road: 80%; Air: 4%; Canal: 1%. Illustrate these.

A pie-diagram is suitable and is shown in Fig. 12.4.

Descriptive Statistics

The information provided by an observed frequency distribution can generally be conveniently summarized by certain parameters known as *descriptive statistics*. The most important of these refer to the *location* and the *spread* of the data. A statistic which specifies the location may be considered to be 'representative' of the data, and spread is a measure of how the distribution is clustered around this 'typical' value.

Inspection of the graph of the number of vehicles passing each minute in example 1 shows that the most commonly recorded value is 2. If a single observation only were taken, this would be the *most likely* value to ensue, and this is referred to as the

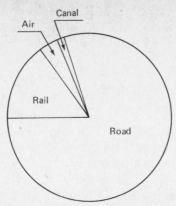

Fig. 12.4 Pie-diagram for the data in example 4 on the percentage, by weight, of goods transported by the various systems

modal value or *mode*. Clearly, discrete data of this nature need not contain a unique 'most popular' value and a small change in data may change the modal value considerably.

In the case of the histogram associated with example 2, the highest number of cables, 54, broke in the interval 10.0–10.2. Forty broke in the adjacent lower interval and 37 in the adjacent upper interval. A *specific* value for the mode is then obtained by simple proportion as shown in Fig. 12.5. The ordinate differences are respectively 14 and 17 so the mode is taken to occur at a value of $\left(10.0 + \dfrac{14}{14 + 17} \times 0.2\right)$ tons, which is 10.09 tons (accurate to two decimal places).

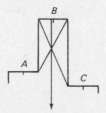

Fig. 12.5 Establishment of the mode for grouped measurements

Suppose that all the results are placed in ascending (or descending) numerical order, a procedure called *ranking*. A second measure of a 'typical' value occurs when the middle of the *ranked* results is taken and this is known as the *median value* or *median*. If there are an odd number of results, $(2m - 1)$ say, the median is the mth value, and when the number is even, $2m$ say, the median is defined to be a half of the sum of the mth and $(m + 1)$th values.

In example 1 (table 12.1), there were 60 readings of traffic flow, so that the values of the 30th and 31st (ranked) results must be found. As each has the value 2, the median is 2.

For the continuous data in example 2 (table 12.2), concern is with the 128th and 129th values, which are in fact the 18th and 19th of the 54 readings which fall in the range 10.0–10.2 tons. As the individual records of the values have not been given, the method is to assume these 54 readings to be equally spaced over that interval so that the median value is estimated as $\left(10.0 + \dfrac{18}{54} \times 0.2\right)$, that is 10.07 tons, if the accuracy is again to two decimal places.

The third measure of location, and in general the most useful, is the *arithmetic mean* of the sample and this is usually referred to simply as the *mean*. It is signified by a bar over the symbol which designates the values of the variable and is defined as the sum of the individual measurements divided by the total number of measurements. There is a clear analogy between this arithmetic mean and the centre of mass of a system of particles distributed along a line.

If n values of the variable X are observed, then the sample mean $\bar{x}$ is given by

$$\bar{x} = \frac{x_1 + x_2 + \ldots + x_n}{n} = \frac{1}{n} \sum_{j=1}^{n} x_j. \tag{9a}$$

The measurements are most often supplied in grouped form. In this case, if there are r classes and the ith class has f_i members, for $i = 1, 2, \ldots, r$,

$$\bar{x} = \frac{f_1 x_1 + f_2 x_2 + \ldots + f_r x_r}{f_1 + f_2 + \ldots + f_r} = \frac{1}{n} \sum_{i=1}^{r} f_i x_i, \tag{9b}$$

where $n = \sum_{i=1}^{r} f_i$ is the sample size.

In table 12.1 (example 1) the mean number of vehicles passing per minute is

$$\frac{6 \times 0 + 11 \times 1 + 15 \times 2 + 12 \times 3 + 10 \times 4 + 6 \times 5}{60} = \frac{147}{60} = 2.45.$$

In table 12.2 (example 2) the breaking loads are assumed to be concentrated at the mid-point of each interval in question. The mean breaking load in tons is then

$$\frac{1}{256} (1 \times 9.1 + 8 \times 9.3 + 26 \times 9.5 + 35 \times 9.7 + 40 \times 9.9 + 54 \times 10.1 + 37 \times 10.3$$

$$+ 26 \times 10.5 + 19 \times 10.7 + 18 \times 10.9 + 2 \times 11.1)$$

$$= 10.07. \text{ correct to two decimal places.}$$

In this particular example, therefore, the mode and arithmetic mean are in agreement to the accuracy considered. Devices to simplify the arithmetic exist, and these are employed in the calculations set out on pp. 446–447.

Several functions may be devised to measure the spread of the data. The first is the *range* which is defined as the difference between the largest and smallest recorded observations. As it depends only on the extreme values this measure may not be particularly useful.

Just as the median cuts a distribution into two equal parts, the *quartiles* quarter it, the *deciles* divide it into ten and the *percentiles* divide it into hundredths. The *inter-quartile range* is the value of $q_3 - q_1$ where q_3 is the *upper quartile*, that is a quarter of the measurements are numerically greater than q_3, and q_1 is the *lower quartile*, that is a quarter of the measurements are numerically less than q_1. Since the inter-quartile range contains one-half of the total number of measurements, it is also a measure of the spread. For the discrete data of example 1, $q_1 = 1, q_3 = 4$ and the inter-quartile range is therefore 3.

In statistical situations the most useful measure of the spread of data generally proves to be the *sample variance* s^2. If $\bar{x}$, the sample mean, has been computed from the measurements and n is the sample size, then the sample variance is defined by

$$s^2 = \frac{1}{n-1} \sum_{j=1}^{n} (x_j - \bar{x})^2 \tag{10a}$$

and the *sample standard deviation s* is the positive square root of this quantity. If the data have been grouped into r classes, then taking the frequency weighting into account

$$s^2 = \frac{1}{n-1} \sum_{i=1}^{r} f_i(x_i - \bar{x})^2. \tag{10b}$$

The choice of $(n-1)$ as normalizer in the denominator in preference to the more intuitive divisor n is due to concepts in estimation theory associated with degrees of freedom, and justification must be deferred until Chapter 3 of Volume 2. Here it is sufficient to note that when $n \geqslant 27$, the replacement of $(n-1)$ by n alters s^2 by less than 4% and s by less than 2%. It is therefore common practice to retain $(n-1)$ in equations (10) when the sample has fewer than about thirty members and is termed *small*, and to take n as the denominator when the sample is *large*, that is $n \geqslant 30$. Some authors use n as the divisor irrespective of sample size.

The actual calculation of means and variances from sets of data can be quite tedious but simplifying manipulations exist. Suppose that a set of n sample values $x_1, x_2, \ldots, x_r$ has been observed with frequencies $f_1, f_2, \ldots, f_r$ respectively. The linear transformation $y = ax + b$, where $a \neq 0$, represents a change of origin when $b \neq 0$ and a change of scale when $|a| \neq 1$.

Then

(i) $\quad \bar{y} = \frac{1}{n} \sum_j y_j = \frac{1}{n} \sum_j (ax_j + b) = \frac{1}{n}\left(a \sum_j x_j + bn \right) = \frac{1}{n}(an\bar{x} + bn),$

so

$$\bar{y} = a\bar{x} + b; \tag{11}$$

(ii) $\quad s_y^2 = \frac{1}{n-1} \sum_j (y_j - \bar{y})^2 = \frac{1}{n-1} \sum_j \{(ax_j + b) - (a\bar{x} + b)\}^2 \quad$ (using (11))

$$= \frac{1}{n-1} \sum_j (ax_j - a\bar{x})^2 = \frac{a^2}{n-1} \sum_j (x_j - \bar{x})^2 = a^2 s_x^2,$$

so

$$s_y^2 = a^2 s_x^2 \quad \text{and} \quad s_y = |a| s_x. \tag{12a, b}$$

The above results hold whether or not the data has been grouped. Further, for grouped data,

$$s^2 = \frac{1}{n-1} \sum_{i=1}^{r} f_i(x_i - \bar{x})^2 = \frac{1}{n-1} \left\{ \sum f_i x_i^2 - 2\bar{x} \sum f_i x_i + \bar{x}^2 \sum f_i \right\}$$

$$= \frac{1}{n-1} \left\{ \sum f_i x_i^2 - 2n\bar{x}^2 + n\bar{x}^2 \right\} = \frac{1}{n-1} \left\{ \sum f_i x_i^2 - n\bar{x}^2 \right\}.$$ (13a)

For computational purposes this is perhaps best written as

$$s^2 = \frac{1}{\sum_i f_i - 1} \left\{ \sum_i f_i x_i^2 - \frac{1}{\sum_i f_i} \left(\sum_i f_i x_i \right)^2 \right\}.$$ (13b)

With a given set of data the method is to choose a suitable 'working' scale and origin, do the necessary arithmetic using the new units and then convert back. Usually selection of the new scale presents no problem but choice of the new working origin requires care. If the new origin is less than the smallest value of the variable to occur, the resulting figures all have positive sign. On the other hand, choice of an origin somewhere near the arithmetic mean produces figures which are numerically smaller. The merits of these respective schemes can be compared in the following example.

EXAMPLE 5
Calculate the mean and standard deviation for the data on the breaking strength of cables, supplied in table 12.2,

(a)   using the transformation $y = (x - 9.1)/0.2$,
(b)   using the transformation $z = (x - 10.1)/0.2$.

The data and transformations yield the values shown in table 12.3.

TABLE 12.3

1	2	3a	4a	5a	3b	4b	5b
x_i (mid-range value)	f_i observed frequency	y_i	$f_i y_i$	$f_i y_i^2$	z_i	$f_i z_i$	$f_i z_i^2$
9.1	1	0	0	0	−5	−5	25
9.3	8	1	8	8	−4	−32	128
9.5	26	2	52	104	−3	−78	234
9.7	35	3	105	315	−2	−70	140
9.9	40	4	160	640	−1	−40	40
10.1	54	5	270	1350	0	0	0
10.3	37	6	222	1332	1	37	37
10.5	26	7	182	1274	2	52	104
10.7	19	8	152	1216	3	57	171
10.9	8	9	72	648	4	32	128
11.1	2	10	20	200	5	10	50
$\sum_i$	256		1243	7087		−37	1057

Notice that an entry in column 4 is the product of the corresponding entries in columns 2 and 3. Similarly, an entry in column 5 is the product of the corresponding entries in columns 3 and 4. Then

$$\bar{y} = \frac{\Sigma f_i y_i}{\Sigma f_i} = \frac{1243}{256} = 4.855, \qquad \bar{z} = \frac{\Sigma f_i z_i}{\Sigma f_i} = \frac{-37}{256} = -0.145,$$

so $\bar{x} = 0.2\bar{y} + 9.1 = (0.2 \times 4.855) + 9.1, \bar{x} = 0.2\bar{z} + 10.1 = (0.2 \times -0.145) + 10.1$, i.e. $\bar{x} = 10.07$ tons, verifying the result on p. 444.

$$s_y^2 = \frac{1}{n-1}\left\{\Sigma f_i y_i^2 - \frac{(\Sigma f_i y_i)^2}{n}\right\} \qquad s_z^2 = \frac{1}{n-1}\left\{\Sigma f_i z_i^2 - \frac{(\Sigma f_i z_i)^2}{n}\right\}$$

$$= \frac{1}{255}\left\{7087 - \frac{1545049}{256}\right\} \qquad = \frac{1}{255}\left\{1057 - \frac{1369}{256}\right\}$$

$$= \frac{7087 - 6035.3}{255} = \frac{1051.7}{255} \qquad = \frac{1057 - 5.3}{255} = \frac{1051.7}{255}$$

so $s_y^2 = s_z^2 = 4.124$ and $s_y = s_z = 2.03$.

In the original units, therefore, $s_x = 0.2 \times 2.03 = 0.406$ ton.

Further descriptive parameters exist. A quantity like $\Sigma f_i (x_i - \bar{x})^3$, suitably normalized, provides a measure of the lack of symmetry of the data and is associated with the *skewness* of the distribution. However, moments higher than the second are rarely used in an observed frequency distribution as their values tend to be grossly affected by any spurious outliers.

It is also evident that the grouping inherent in histograms may bring some bias into the calculation of sample moments. Theory suggests that no alteration is necessary for the mean when a common class interval c is chosen but that the sample variance should be reduced by $c^2/12$. Opinion is divided as to the utility of the adjustments, known as *Sheppard's Corrections*, and they will not be discussed further.

Exercises

1. Repeat the transportation pie diagram, example 4, for each of the following parameters: volume of the goods, value of the goods, number of vehicle journeys, and vehicle distance travelled. [Use available figures or plausible estimates.]

2. If A, B, C are the midpoints of the three *equal* lengths shown in Fig. 12.5, prove that the x value of the vertex of the parabola through these three points is equal to the mode.

3. If $d_i = x_i - \bar{x}$ prove that $\displaystyle\sum_{i=1}^{r} d_i = 0$.

4. Verify that the lower and upper quartiles for the continuous data of example 2 are given, to two decimal places, by $q_1 = 9.77$ tons and $q_3 = 10.35$ tons, respectively.

5. Verify that the sample variance is 2.18 for the traffic data of example 1.

12.4 PROBABILITY AND SET THEORY

Elementary Set Theory

A *set* is a collection of objects determined by some property which they possess in common, e.g.

> all living beings
> all the results of a certain experiment
> all the eigen-frequencies of a vibrating system.

The objects which constitute the set are known as its *elements*. The number of distinct elements in a set may or may not be finite. No significance is attached to the position in which an element appears in the set nor whether it is repeated.

If set S has three elements, e_1, e_2 and e_3, then we write $S = \{e_1, e_2, e_3\}$. The element e_i for $i = 1, 2, 3$ is a member of the set S, that is it 'belongs' to S, and is written $e_i \in S$ for $i = 1, 2, 3$. Also

$$\{e_1, e_2, e_3\} = \{e_1, e_3, e_2\} = \{e_1, e_1, e_3, e_2, e_3\}.$$

The elements may often conveniently be represented either by points or by regions of a plane and the set S itself by the interior of a simple curve in what is termed a *Venn diagram* (see Fig. 12.6(a)).

A set S_2 is a *subset* of S_1 if every element of S_2 belongs also to S_1 and is written $S_2 \subset S_1$. Equivalently, S_1 *contains* S_2, and this is written $S_1 \supset S_2$, (see Fig. 12.6(b)). It follows that any set is a subset of itself and that two sets are *equal* if and only if each is a subset of the other.

The *universal set U* has all mentioned sets as subsets.

The *null* or *empty set* ϕ is the set with no elements. This is not to be confused with the set which consists of the single element called zero.

Then for any set S we have $U \supset S \supset \phi$.

Set Operations

The *difference* of set S_2 with respect to S_1 is the set of all the elements in S_1 which are not members of S_2 (see Fig. 12.6(c)). This is written $S_1 - S_2$. Note that S_2 need not be a subset of S_1.

The *complement* of S is the set of elements which belong to U but do not belong to S (see Fig. 12.6(d)). The complement is written $Co(S)$, or S'.

$S' = U - S$ and $(S')' = S$.

The *intersection* of set S_1 and set S_2, written $S_1 \cap S_2$, is the set consisting of elements which belong both to S_1 and S_2 (see Fig. 12.6(e)). Note that $S_1 \cap S_2 = S_2 \cap S_1$. In particular, if $S_1 \cap S_2 = \phi$ the sets S_1 and S_2 are said to be *disjoint*.

The *union* of set S_1 and set S_2 is the set of elements belonging to at least one of the sets S_1 and S_2, and is written $S_1 \cup S_2$ (see Fig. 12.6(f)). Again the operation is commutative, i.e., $S_1 \cup S_2 = S_2 \cup S_1$.

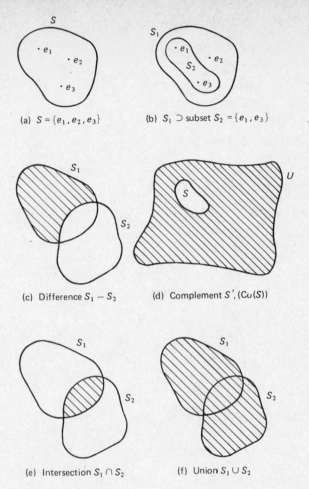

(a) $S = \{e_1, e_2, e_3\}$

(b) $S_1 \supset$ subset $S_2 = \{e_1, e_3\}$

(c) Difference $S_1 - S_2$

(d) Complement S', $(C_U(S))$

(e) Intersection $S_1 \cap S_2$

(f) Union $S_1 \cup S_2$

Fig. 12.6 Venn diagram illustrating sets and set operations

By way of illustration, let the universal set be the days of the week according to their English appellations, i.e., $U = \{$Sunday, Monday, Tuesday, Wednesday, Thursday, Friday, Saturday$\}$.

Let E_1 be those days uniquely determined by their initial letter,

$\quad E_2$ be those days uniquely determined by the number of letters in the name,

$\quad E_3$ be those days of the week which begin with a vowel,

$\quad E_4$ be those days on which May 1st may fall,

$\quad E_5$ be those days having initial letter in the first half of the alphabet,

$\quad E_6$ be those days with initial letter in the second half of the alphabet.

Therefore $E_1 = \{\text{Monday, Wednesday, Friday}\}$,

$\qquad E_2 = \{\text{Tuesday, Wednesday}\}$,

$\qquad E_3 = \phi$,

$\qquad E_4 = U$,

$\qquad E_5 = \{\text{Monday, Friday}\}$,

$\qquad E_6 = \{\text{Tuesday, Wednesday, Thursday, Saturday, Sunday}\}$,

Then for example, as may be seen from Fig 12.7,
$$E_5 = (E_6)'; \quad E_6 = (E_5)'; \quad E_5 \cup E_6 = U; \quad E_5 \cap E_6 = \phi; \quad E_1 \supset E_5;$$
$$E_1 \cup E_2 = \{\text{Monday, Tuesday, Wednesday, Friday}\}; \quad E_1 \cap E_2 = \{\text{Wednesday}\};$$
$$E_1 - E_2 = \{\text{Monday, Friday}\} = E_5.$$

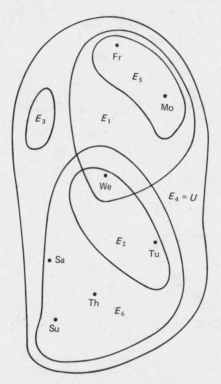

Fig. 12.7   Venn diagram for the 'days of the week' illustration

As the result of any of the given operations is to produce a further set, which may of course be empty, the ideas may be extended to more than two sets. A Venn diagram, Fig. 12.8, readily verifies the associative result $E \cap (F \cap G) = (E \cap F) \cap G$. This, together with the commutative result, means that brackets are unnecessary when $\cap$ is the only operator in the expression.

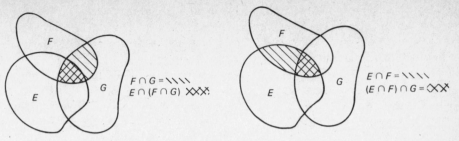

Fig. 12.8   The associative result for the intersection of three sets

Notation: $H_1 \cap H_2 \cap \ldots \cap H_n = \bigcap\limits_{i=1}^{n} H_i$.

When n is understood, alternative forms are $\bigcap\limits_{i} H_i$ and $\bigcap H_i$.

Similarly, $E \cup (F \cup G) = (E \cup F) \cup G$, so that commutativity again renders brackets unnecessary when only $\cup$ is involved.

Notation: $H_1 \cup H_2 \cup \ldots \cup H_n = \bigcup\limits_{i=1}^{n} H_i = \bigcup\limits_{i} H_i = \bigcup H_i$.

Some common set relationships are given in the exercises at the end of the section.

Sample Spaces and Probability

The preceding results make no assumptions concerning the nature of the sets involved. Set theory in general is capable of considerable development as many advanced mathematical texts show, and its use in statistics has proved to be particularly fruitful. When set theory is applied to probability it is customary to define the universal set as the collection of all possible outcomes of an experiment and then to refer to it as a *sample space*. The possible outcomes are called *sample points*. A subset which consists of all sample points possessing a stated property is an *event*. *Simple events* each correspond to a single sample point and *compound events* result from the union of two or more distinct simple events. A sample point is *favourable* to an event if the outcome entails the occurrence of the event. If in a trial at least one of a set of events is certain to occur then that set of events is said to be *exhaustive*. Two or more events are said to be *mutually exclusive* if an outcome favourable to one is necessarily unfavourable to the others. Any pair of mutually exclusive events cannot occur simultaneously and the corresponding sets are disjoint (see Fig. 12.9(a)).

Consider again the tossing of a six-sided die. The sample space in this case consists of the six sample points $\{1, 2, 3, 4, 5, 6\}$ where the digit indicates the number uppermost when the die comes to rest. Each of these six represents a simple event. One example of a compound event is 'the number exceeds 3' and another is 'the number is even'.

Suppose that a given sample space S consists of r simple events $E_1, E_2, \ldots, E_r$. To each of these simple events E_i a probability $P(E_i)$ is assigned, where $P(E_i) \geqslant 0$. It is natural to let the probability of an *impossible* event be 0 and the probability of a *certain* event be 1, and since by hypothesis in a trial one of $E_1, E_2, \ldots, E_r$ is *certain* to occur, $P(E_1 \text{ or } E_2 \text{ or } \ldots \text{ or } E_r) = P(S) = 1$. Furthermore, for any event E, $P(E)$ is defined to be the sum of the probabilities of the simple events which E contains.

. The student will recognize that $P(E \cup F)$ denotes the probability that *at least one* of events E and F occurs, and, similarly, $P(E \cap F)$ refers to the probability that *both* E and F occur. Now consider the Venn diagram when two events are mutually exclusive (see Fig. 12.9(a)). Their constituent simple events are all distinct and hence

$$P(E_1 \cup E_2) = P(E_1) + P(E_2) \quad \text{when} \quad E_1 \cap E_2 = \phi. \tag{14}$$

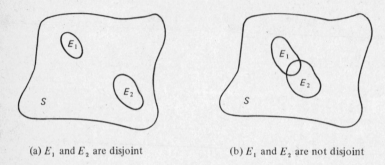

(a) E_1 and E_2 are disjoint   (b) E_1 and E_2 are not disjoint

Fig. 12.9   Venn diagram for the probability of two events E_1 and E_2

Using the associative property of the union of disjoint sets, this result immediately generalizes to:

$$P\left(\bigcup_{i=1}^{q} E_i\right) = \sum_{i=1}^{q} P(E_i) \tag{15}$$

for any q mutually exclusive events $E_1, \ldots, E_q$. This result, which is usually referred to as the *Addition Theorem of Probability*, may be stated as follows:

> The probability of one of a set of mutually exclusive events is the sum of their individual probabilities.

In the die-tossing illustration the probability of throwing an even number is the probability of any one of the three mutually exclusive outcomes '2' or '4' or '6'. With each of these events having a probability of $\frac{1}{6}$, the probability of an even number is $\frac{1}{6} + \frac{1}{6} + \frac{1}{6} = \frac{1}{2}$, as it is otherwise obvious.

That these properties (14) and (15) are in accord with those resulting from the 'relative frequency' approach may be demonstrated as follows. Suppose that of n outcomes, m_1 are favourable to event E_1 and m_2 favourable to E_2, where E_1 and E_2

are mutually exclusive. Then

$$P(E_1 \text{ or } E_2) = \lim \left\{ \frac{m_1 + m_2}{n} \right\}$$

$$= \lim \left\{ \frac{m_1}{n} + \frac{m_2}{n} \right\} = \lim \left\{ \frac{m_1}{n} \right\} + \lim \left\{ \frac{m_2}{n} \right\}$$

$$= P(E_1) + P(E_2). \tag{14}'$$

When E_1 and E_2 are not mutually exclusive, their intersection must contain one or more sample points. The probability associated with each common point contributes both to the probability of the occurrence of E_1 and to the probability of the occurrence of E_2 (see Fig. 12.9(b)). In this case the result is therefore

$$P(E_1 \cup E_2) = P(E_1) + P(E_2) - P(E_1 \cap E_2). \tag{16}$$

Clearly this result reduces to equation (14) when E_1 and E_2 are in fact disjoint, since $P(\phi) = 0$.

For three events E_1, E_2, E_3 the appropriate result is

$$P(E_1 \cup E_2 \cup E_3) = P(E_1) + P(E_2) + P(E_3) - P(E_1 \cap E_2) - P(E_2 \cap E_3)$$
$$- P(E_3 \cap E_1) + P(E_1 \cap E_2 \cap E_3). \tag{17}$$

This expression may readily be generalized to n events.

EXAMPLE 1
A manufacturing process produces components which may be defective in any one of the following ways with the stated probabilities:

too long (event A)	too wide (event C)
too short (event B)	too narrow (event D)

Events A and B are mutually exclusive and events C and D are mutually exclusive. The remaining probabilities are:

$$P(A) = 0.035, \quad P(B) = 0.020, \quad P(C) = 0.025, \quad P(D) = 0.030,$$
$$P(A \cap C) = 0.005, \quad P(A \cap D) = 0.004, \quad P(B \cap C) = 0.003, \quad P(B \cap D) = 0.002.$$

Draw the Venn diagram to illustrate the sample space, and find the probability that a component will have at least one of the faults listed.

The Venn diagram and associated probabilities are shown in Fig. 12.10. The probability of having at least one of these faults is therefore

$$0.005 + 0.026 + 0.004 + 0.017 + 0.024 + 0.003 + 0.015 + 0.002 = 0.096.$$

This probability may also be written down as

$$(0.035 + 0.020 + 0.025 + 0.030) - (0.005 + 0.004 + 0.003 + 0.002)$$
$$= 0.110 - 0.014 = 0.096.$$

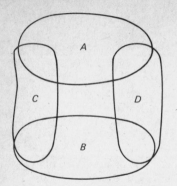 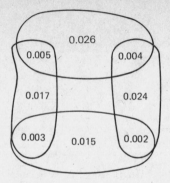

Fig. 12.10   Venn diagram and associated probabilities for defective items in example 1

Conditional Probability

The normalizing condition $P(S) = 1$ implies that the values of the probabilities are only established once the parent sample space S has been described, so that for an event E the probability $P(E)$ might more properly be written $P(E \mid S)$ to signify that it depends upon S. Suppose that E and T are each subsets of S with $P(T) > 0$, as illustrated in Fig. 12.11. The probability that event E occurs when T is known to have occurred is denoted by $P(E \mid T)$. This is called the *conditional probability of event E on event T* or, with T understood, the *conditional probability of E*. The effect is to reduce the sample space to T. If several machines are responsible for the total output of a certain component and $P(D)$ is the probability that a component is found to be defective, then $P(D \mid M_i)$ represents the probability that a defective item is made by the ith machine M_i.

Inspection of the Venn diagram shows that the sample points associated with $P(E \mid T)$ are precisely those contained in $E \cap T$, and hence $P(E \mid T)$ must be connected to $P(E \cap T)$ by a relationship of the form $P(E \mid T) = kP(E \cap T)$. Consider the special case $E = T$. As $P(T \mid T) = 1$ and $P(T \cap T) = P(T)$, it follows that k must have the value

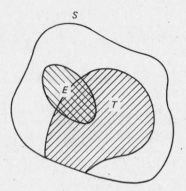

Fig. 12.11   Venn diagram illustrating conditional probability for event E with a reduced sample space T

$1/P(T)$ and hence

$$P(E \mid T) = \frac{P(E \cap T)}{P(T)}. \tag{18a}$$

This is the *Theorem of Conditional Probability.* It is trivially satisfied when $T = S$, the original sample space. Also, if $P(E) \neq 0$, then

$$P(T \mid E) = \frac{P(E \cap T)}{P(E)}. \tag{18b}$$

From example 1, the probability that a component is too wide, given that it is too long, is

$$P(C \mid A) = \frac{P(C \cap A)}{P(A)} = \frac{0.005}{0.035} = 0.1429.$$

To obtain the probability that a component is too long, given that it is not too wide, we use the result that for any pair of events E and F, $P(E \cap F') + P(E \cap F) = P(E)$, so that

$$P(A \mid C') = \frac{P(A \cap C')}{P(C')} = \frac{0.030}{0.975} = 0.03077.$$

The theorem may be extended by writing it in the form

$$P(E_4 \cap E_3) = P(E_4)P(E_3 \mid E_4)$$

and then letting $E_4 = E_1 \cap E_2$ so that

$$P\{(E_1 \cap E_2) \cap E_3\} = P(E_1 \cap E_2)P(E_3 \mid E_1 \cap E_2).$$

Therefore

$$P(E_1 \cap E_2 \cap E_3) = P(E_1)P(E_2 \mid E_1)P(E_3 \mid E_1 \cap E_2). \tag{19}$$

The general result is

$$P(E_1 \cap E_2, \ldots \cap E_n) = P(E_1)P(E_2 \mid E_1)P(E_3 \mid E_1 \cap E_2)P(E_4 \mid E_1 \cap E_2 \cap E_3)$$
$$\ldots P(E_n \mid E_1 \cap E_2, \ldots \cap E_{n-1}). \tag{20}$$

Dependent and Independent Events

The notion of conditional probability leads to the concept of *independence.*

DEFINITIONS   Two events are *statistically independent* if the occurrence of one is unaffected by the occurrence of the other. If the contrary is true they are said to be *dependent.*

If A and B are independent events, then symbolically

$$P(A \mid B) = P(A)$$

and the theorem of conditional probability $P(A \mid B) = P(A \cap B)/P(B)$ then reduces to

$$P(A \cap B) = P(A)P(B). \tag{21}$$

For r *independent* events $E_1, E_2, \ldots E_r$, the general form of the theorem of conditional probability becomes

$$P(E_1 \cap E_2, \ldots \cap E_r) = P(E_1)P(E_2) \ldots P(E_r). \tag{22}$$

This result is called the *Multiplication Theorem of Probability* and may be stated as follows.

The probability of the occurrence of independent events is the product of their individual probabilities.

The Multiplication Theorem should be carefully compared with the Addition Theorem given earlier as equation (15), because correct usage of these theorems is essential.

An example where the notion of conditional probability applies is the successive random withdrawals of a playing card from a well-shuffled pack. This is because the probability of, say, taking a card of a particular suit depends upon how many of that suit have already been removed. On the other hand, if the selected card is replaced in random position in the pack before the next withdrawal is made, the events are independent. When the number of possible outcomes is large any failure to replace has generally only minimal effect on probabilities.

EXAMPLE 2
Faced with exposure for embezzlement from the company they control, Alfonzano, Bertville and Cedricovitch decide to commit suicide by playing Russian roulette. With a single bullet in the revolver the chamber is to be spun and the revolver fired, and after each unsuccessful attempt the revolver will then be passed to the next criminal. If Alfonzano is to fire first, followed by Bertville and then Cedricovitch, find the respective probabilities that each will be the first to shoot himself.

Let p be the probability that on any one spin the bullet is in the firing chamber. Then the probability that it is not in the firing chamber is $(1 - p)$ and this will be denoted by q. From the data, the trials are independent and p is constant throughout the sequence.

The probability of the gun firing on the first attempt is p. The probability of firing for the *first* time on the second attempt is qp, since the first attempt must have been a failure, the probability of which was q, and the events are independent. The probability of firing for the first time on the rth attempt is similarly $q^{r-1}p$.

'A' will be the first victim if the gun fires for the first time on the 1st, 4th, 7th, ..., $(3s + 1)$th ... attempts and the probability of these mutually exclusive events is the sum of their individual probabilities, so

$$P(A) = p + q^3 p + q^6 p + \ldots + q^{3s} p + \ldots$$

$$= p(1 + q^3 + q^6 + \ldots + q^{3s} + \ldots) = \frac{p}{1 - q^3}.$$

As $\mid q^3 \mid < 1$ the summation of this geometric series is valid.

In similar manner the following results are obtained:

$$P(B) = qp + q^4 p + \ldots + q^{3s+1} p + \ldots = \frac{qp}{1 - q^3}$$

and

$$P(C) = q^2 p + q^5 p + \ldots + q^{3s+2} p + \ldots = \frac{q^2 p}{1 - q^3}.$$

Since $1 - q = p$, the respective probabilities can be written $1/(1 + q + q^2)$, $q/(1 + q + q^2)$, $q^2/(1 + q + q^2)$ with sum 1 as required for three mutually exclusive exhaustive events.

The Theorem of Inverse Probability

This theorem also bears the name of its discoverer, Rev. Thomas Bayes. Suppose that a sample space may be expressed as the union of n mutually exclusive events $E_1, \ldots, E_n$. If an event A is known to have occurred, what is the probability that this was due to the occurrence of the particular event E_k? *Bayes's Theorem* states that for $k = 1, 2, \ldots, n$ in turn,

$$P(E_k \mid A) = \frac{P(E_k) P(A \mid E_k)}{\sum\limits_{i=1}^{n} P(E_i) P(A \mid E_i)} \tag{23}$$

Proof

For each value of $j = 1, \ldots, n$,

$$P(A) P(E_j \mid A) = P(A \cap E_j) = P(E_j) P(A \mid E_j)$$

so that

$$P(E_j \mid A) = \frac{P(E_j) P(A \mid E_j)}{P(A)}. \tag{24}$$

Also, since events $E_1, E_2, \ldots, E_n$ are exhaustive,

$$P(E_1 \mid A) + P(E_2 \mid A) + \ldots + P(E_n \mid A) = 1,$$

and therefore

$$\frac{P(E_1) P(A \mid E_1)}{P(A)} + \frac{P(E_2) P(A \mid E_2)}{P(A)} + \ldots + \frac{P(E_n) P(A \mid E_n)}{P(A)} = 1$$

so

$$P(A) = \sum_{i=1}^{n} P(E_i) P(A \mid E_i).$$

Substitution into equation (24) gives

$$P(E_j \mid A) = \frac{P(E_j)P(A \mid E_j)}{\sum\limits_{i=1}^{n} P(E_i)P(A \mid E_i)}$$

and this result holds for $j = 1, 2, \ldots, n$ in turn.

The following terminology may be found when it is given that event A has occurred:

$P(E)$ is the *prior probability* of an event E,

$P(E \mid A)$ is the *posterior probability* of E,

$P(A \mid E)$ is the *likelihood* of E.

EXAMPLE 3

Three machines M_1, M_2 and M_3 produce nominally identical items. Past experience has shown that 4% of the output from machine M_1 is faulty, 3½% of the output from machine M_2 is faulty and 2½% of the output from machine M_3 is faulty. On a given day, M_1 has produced 20% of the total output, M_2 has produced 30% and M_3 the remainder. An item selected at random is found to be faulty. Find the probability that it was produced by the machine with the greatest output.

Let D denote a defective item. Then from the given information

$$P(D \mid M_1) = 0.040 \quad P(M_1) = 0.2 \quad P(M_1)P(D \mid M_1) = 0.0080$$
$$P(D \mid M_2) = 0.035 \quad P(M_2) = 0.3 \quad P(M_2)P(D \mid M_2) = 0.0105$$
$$P(D \mid M_3) = 0.025 \quad P(M_3) = 0.5 \quad P(M_3)P(D \mid M_3) = 0.0125$$

The machine with the greatest output on the day in question is M_3, and hence:

$$P(M_3 \mid D) = \frac{P(M_3)P(D \mid M_3)}{P(M_1)P(D \mid M_1) + P(M_2)P(D \mid M_2) + P(M_3)P(D \mid M_2)}$$

$$= \frac{0.0125}{0.0080 + 0.0105 + 0.0125} = \frac{0.0125}{0.0310} = 0.403.$$

Exercises

1. By drawing suitable Venn diagrams, one for each side of the relationship, verify the following results:

(a) $(A \cup B) \cap (A \cup C) = A \cup (B \cap C)$

(b) $(A \cap B) \cup (A \cap C) = A \cap (B \cup C)$

(c) $(A \cap B)' = A' \cup B'$

(d) $A \cup B = (A - B) \cup (A \cap B) \cup (B - A)$

(e) $A \subset (B - A)'$

(f) $(A \cup B) \cap C \neq A \cup (B \cap C)$ unless $A \subset C$

(g) $A \cap (B \triangle C) = (A \cap B) \triangle (A \cap C)$ where $\triangle$ is the *symmetric difference operator* defined by $D \triangle E = D \cup E - D \cap E$.

2. (a)   Verify result (17) by means of an appropriate Venn diagram.
   (b)   Extend result (17) by writing down the corresponding expression for $P(E_1 \cup E_2 \cup E_3 \cup E_4)$.

3. Prove the multiplication theorem $P(A \cap B) = P(A)P(B)$ for independent events A and B, using the relative frequency approach.

4. If $P(C|D) = P(C)$ prove that $P(D|C) = P(D)$.

5. Show that in example 1 no two of the defects A, B, C and D are statistically independent.

6. In example 3 find $P(M_1 | D)$ and $P(M_2 | D)$.

12.5 THE RANDOM VARIABLE

Probability Distributions

A random variable with which it is possible to associate a probability distribution is called a *variate*. This section and the next will be concerned with univariate theory, and §12.7 will consider functions of more than one random variable.

Suppose that a discrete variate is the outcome of some experiment. It is usual to employ a capital letter to signify the variate itself and to use small letters, where appropriate, to denote the values it may assume. Then if the probability that the variate X takes the ith value x_i is p_i,

$$P\{X = x_i\} = p_i \quad \text{for } i = 1, 2, \ldots, \tag{25}$$

where $p_i \geq 0$ and $\sum_i p_i = 1$.

The number of values assumed may be finite or infinite, according to the variate in question. These values $p_i, i = 1, 2, \ldots$ constitute the *probability distribution function* of this discrete variate, and some examples are shown in Fig. 12.16 on p. 475.

When the variate X is continuous it is customary to consider the probability that the variate falls in an element of width δx, so that

$$P\{x < X \leq x + \delta x\} = f(x)\delta x, \tag{26}$$

where $f(x) \geq 0$ and $\displaystyle\int_{-\infty}^{\infty} f(x)dx = 1$.

Note that the inequalities have been chosen in such a way that each value of x is included once. In many situations the value of $f(x)$ is zero outside a certain interval, $[a, b]$ say, so that the integral condition reduces to $\int_a^b f(x)dx = 1$. The function $f(x)$ is called the *probability density function* of the continuous variate. A well-known probability density function is illustrated in Fig. 12.17. Without ambiguity both the probability distribution function and probability density function can conveniently be abbreviated to their initial letters p.d.f.

In a similar manner the *cumulative distribution function $F(c)$* of a discrete variate is defined by

$$F(c) = \sum_{i=1}^{r} p_i \quad \text{where } x_r \leqslant c < x_{r+1} \tag{27}$$

and the *cumulative density function* of a continuous variate by

$$F(c) = \int_{-\infty}^{c} f(x)dx. \tag{28}$$

The letters c.d.f. may be used to denote these functions $F(c)$, both of which represent the probability that the variate does not exceed the particular value c. (Some texts refer to $F(x)$ as the *probability function* of the r.v. X.) Then for a continuous variate the p.d.f. $f(x) = dF(x)/dx$. Clearly $F(x)$ is a non-decreasing function, with $F(-\infty) = 0$ and $F(\infty) = 1$, and the probability that X lies in the range (x_1, x_2) is $F(x_2) - F(x_1)$.

EXAMPLE 1
Show that

$$f(x) = \begin{cases} e^{-x} & \text{if } x \geqslant 0 \\ 0 & \text{if } x < 0 \end{cases}$$

is a permissible p.d.f. Sketch the p.d.f. $f(x)$ and the c.d.f. $F(x)$ and determine the probability that the variate X lies in the range $(1, 3)$.

For all x the given function is defined and is non-negative, and

$$\int_{-\infty}^{\infty} f(x)dx = 0 + \int_{0}^{\infty} e^{-x} dx = \left[-e^{-x}\right]_0^{\infty} = 1 - 0 = 1,$$

so that $f(x)$ is a permissible p.d.f. The p.d.f. and c.d.f. are shown in Fig. 12.12, and

$$P\{1 < X \leqslant 3\} = \int_{1}^{3} f(x)dx = [-e^{-x}]_1^3 = e^{-1} - e^{-3}$$

$$= 0.368 - 0.050 = 0.318.$$

This probability that X lies in the range $(1, 3)$ is equal to the hatched area in Fig. 12.12(a) and to the difference in values of $F(3)$ and $F(1)$ in Fig. 12.12(b).

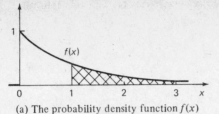

(a) The probability density function $f(x)$

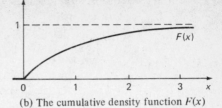

(b) The cumulative density function $F(x)$

Fig. 12.12   Figure for example 1

EXAMPLE 2

A large office block is under construction. All the girders running north–south have been placed in position, adjacent girders being a distance l apart. Above these the first of the east–west cross-girders, also of length l, is being swung when it slips and falls vertically with axis horizontal. If any orientation of this girder in the horizontal plane is equally likely, find the probability that it strikes one of the east–west girders.

Fig. 12.13   How the falling girder may miss or strike in example 2

Since the inclination θ of the girder to the east–west axis must lie in the range $(-\pi/2, \pi/2)$, the probability of lying in the range $(\theta, \theta + \delta\theta)$ is $\delta\theta/\pi$. For an inclination θ, the east–west projection of the girder is $l\cos\theta$, see Fig. 12.13. The associated probability of this overlapping a north–south girder is therefore $(l\cos\theta)/l$, and so the probability of the girders striking one another is

$$\int_{-\pi/2}^{\pi/2} \frac{\cos\theta\,d\theta}{\pi} = \frac{2}{\pi}\left[\sin\theta\right]_0^{\pi/2} = \frac{2}{\pi} = 0.637.$$

Because of the close analogy between the operations which are signified by the symbols Σ and $\int$ it is clear that discrete and continuous variates can generally be handled in similar fashions. Henceforth the corresponding definitions will be displayed alongside each other.

The rth *moment about zero* is denoted by μ_r' and is defined by

$$\mu_r' = \sum_i p_i x_i^r \quad \text{or} \quad \mu_r' = \int_{-\infty}^{\infty} x^r f(x)\,dx, \tag{29}$$

where r is any positive integer. For sufficiently high values of r the sum or integral may not converge and the corresponding moments fail to exist. When $r = 1$ we have

$$\mu_1' = \sum_i p_i x_i \quad \text{or} \quad \mu_1' = \int_{-\infty}^{\infty} x f(x) dx. \tag{30}$$

Thus μ_1' is the *arithmetic mean* of the distribution of the variate X. It is commonly denoted by μ.

The rth *moment about the mean* is denoted by μ_r and is defined by

$$\mu_r = \sum_i p_i (x_i - \mu)^r \quad \text{or} \quad \mu_r = \int_{-\infty}^{\infty} (x - \mu)^r f(x) dx. \tag{31}$$

provided that the sum or integral converges for the value of r in question.

In particular, $\mu_1 = 0$. A direct proof in the discrete case is

$$\mu_1 = \sum_i p_i (x_i - \mu) = \sum_i p_i x_i - \mu \sum_i p_i = \mu - \mu \times 1 = 0.$$

The sum of the deviations of a set of measurements from their sample mean is likewise zero (see the exercise on p. 447).

It is often easier to find the higher moments about the mean by evaluating appropriate moments about the origin. In particular the *variance*, which is the second moment μ_2, is given by

$$\mu_2 = \mu_2' - \mu^2, \tag{32}$$

a result which is analogous to the *theorem of parallel axes* associated with moments of inertia. (The corresponding result for *sample variances* has already been indicated in equation (13a).) Common notations for the variance of X are $\text{Var}(X)$, $V(X)$ and σ_X^2. The variance and its positive square root, the *standard deviation* σ_X, play most important roles in statistical theory.

Generally, if $\varphi(X)$ is any function of the variate X, then the *expectation* of $\varphi(X)$ is denoted by $E\{\varphi(X)\}$ and is defined by

$$E\{\varphi(X)\} = \sum_i p_i \varphi(x_i) \quad \text{or} \quad E\{\varphi(X)\} = \int_{-\infty}^{\infty} \varphi(x) f(x) dx. \tag{33}$$

Therefore

$$\mu_r' = E\{X^r\}, \qquad \text{the } expected \ value \text{ of } X^r, \tag{34}$$

and

$$\mu_r = E\{(X - \mu)^r\}, \qquad \text{the expected value of } (X - \mu)^r. \tag{35}$$

Note that

(a) $E\{c\} = c$ for any constant c, and so $E\{E\{\varphi(X)\}\} = E\{\varphi(X)\}$,

(b) $E\{\alpha_1\varphi_1(X_1) + \alpha_2\varphi_2(X_2)\} = \sum_i \{\alpha_1 p_{1i}\varphi_1(x_{1i}) + \alpha_2 p_{2i}\varphi_2(x_{2i})\}$

$$\text{for } \alpha_1, \alpha_2 \text{ any constants}$$

$$= \alpha_1 \sum_i p_{1i}\varphi_1(x_{1i}) + \alpha_2 \sum_i p_{2i}\varphi_2(x_{2i})$$

$$= \alpha_1 E\{\varphi_1(X_1)\} + \alpha_2 E\{\varphi_2(X_2)\}, \tag{36}$$

and hence E is a *linear operator*.

Interest is usually directed towards the lower moments, especially the first and second, since these serve to describe the most important properties of any p.d.f.

As the preliminary work on relative frequencies has indicated, the mean μ is a *measure of location* of the distribution, and Fig. 12.16, Fig. 12.17(a) and Fig. 12.18 each illustrate distributions possessing equal means. Fig. 12.17(b) shows the effect when the value of the mean is altered.

For a given distribution μ is, of course, fixed. It is *estimated* from a *sample* by the sample mean $\bar{x}$ defined by equation (9) but this value varies from sample to sample, an important point which is given greater consideration in Chapter 3 of Volume 2.

The variance μ_2 (or equivalently the standard deviation σ) is a *measure of the spread* of the distribution, and in each of Fig. 12.16, Fig. 12.17(b) and Fig. 12.18 curves with equal variances appear. In Fig. 12.17(a) the effect of alteration in variance is highlighted. An estimate of σ^2 is obtained from a sample by the quantity s^2 defined by equation (10). Although σ^2 is fixed, s^2 again depends upon the actual sample used.

The third moment about the mean, μ_3, is associated with *skewness*. All the curves in Fig. 12.17 are symmetric and have zero skewness but those in Fig. 12.16 are skewed positively.

Finally, the fourth moment, μ_4, is associated with the 'humpiness' of the distribution. Higher moments are increasingly difficult to interpret but it may be remarked that those of odd order are associated with skewness and those of even order with spread.

Observe that the mean bears the units in which the variate has been expressed, the variance possesses those units squared, and so forth. As it is useful to work in dimensionless quantities, the following are often employed:

the coefficient of variation, (c.v.), $= \dfrac{\sigma}{\mu} \times 100\%$ $\tag{37}$

for the skewness $\qquad\qquad \gamma_1 = \dfrac{\mu_3}{\sigma^3}$ $\tag{38}$

for the flatness $\qquad\qquad \beta_2 = \dfrac{\mu_4}{\mu_2^2}$ $\tag{39}$

and the coefficient of excess $\qquad \gamma_2 = \beta_2 - 3.$ $\tag{40}$

Of these only the coefficient of variation is dependent on choice of origin. With γ_1 given by equation (38), some texts define a coefficient of skewness β_1 to be $|\gamma_1|$ and others define β_1 to be γ_1^2. The quantity γ_2 is zero for the commonly-occurring normal variate (see §12.6). If $\gamma_2 < 0$ for a particular distribution the curve generally tends to be 'flattish' and is called *platykurtic*, whereas $\gamma_2 > 0$ suggests a curve more peaked and termed *leptokurtic*. Another name for flatness is *kurtosis* and β_2 is sometimes called the *coefficient of kurtosis*.

EXAMPLE 3

If $\lambda > 0$, verify that the discrete distribution given by $p_x = e^{-\lambda}(\lambda^x/x!)$ for $x = 0, 1, 2, \ldots$, is a proper p.d.f. and find its mean and variance.

Since $\lambda > 0$,

$$p_x = e^{-\lambda}\frac{\lambda^x}{x!} > 0 \quad \text{for } x = 0, 1, 2, \ldots.$$

Also

$$\sum_{x=0}^{\infty} p_x = \sum_{x=0}^{\infty} e^{-\lambda}\frac{\lambda^x}{x!} = e^{-\lambda}\sum_{x=0}^{\infty}\frac{\lambda^x}{x!} = e^{-\lambda}e^{\lambda} = 1.$$

The given distribution is therefore a proper p.d.f. The mean is

$$\mu = \sum_{x=0}^{\infty} p_x x = \sum_{x=0}^{\infty} e^{-\lambda}\frac{\lambda^x}{x!}x = e^{-\lambda}\sum_{x=1}^{\infty}\frac{\lambda^x x}{x!} = e^{-\lambda}\sum_{x=1}^{\infty}\frac{\lambda^x}{(x-1)!} = e^{-\lambda}\lambda\sum_{x=1}^{\infty}\frac{\lambda^{x-1}}{(x-1)!}$$

$$= e^{-\lambda}\lambda\sum_{x=0}^{\infty}\frac{\lambda^x}{x!} = e^{-\lambda}\lambda e^{\lambda} = \lambda.$$

Also

$$\mu_2' = \sum_{x=0}^{\infty} p_x x^2 = \sum_{x=0}^{\infty} e^{-\lambda}\frac{\lambda^x}{x!}x^2 = e^{-\lambda}\sum_{x=1}^{\infty}\frac{\lambda^x x^2}{x!} = e^{-\lambda}\sum_{x=1}^{\infty}\frac{\lambda^x x}{(x-1)!}$$

$$= e^{-\lambda}\sum_{x=1}^{\infty}\frac{(x-1)\lambda^x + \lambda^x}{(x-1)!} = e^{-\lambda}\left\{\sum_{x=2}^{\infty}\frac{\lambda^x}{(x-2)!} + \lambda\sum_{x=1}^{\infty}\frac{\lambda^{x-1}}{(x-1)!}\right\}$$

$$= e^{-\lambda}(\lambda^2 e^{-\lambda} + \lambda e^{\lambda}) = \lambda^2 + \lambda.$$

Therefore $\mu_2 = \mu_2' - \mu^2 = (\lambda^2 + \lambda) - (\lambda)^2 = \lambda.$

The mean and variance are therefore equal in this important distribution which is known as the *Poissonian distribution*. It is associated with 'rare events' as may be the case for the number of defective items encountered over given periods on a production line. A full account of this distribution will be given in §12.6.

EXAMPLE 4

Show that if $b > 0$, the continuous distribution defined by

$$f(x) = \frac{1}{(2\pi)^{1/2}b} e^{-\frac{1}{2}\left(\frac{x-a}{b}\right)^2} \qquad \text{for } -\infty < x < \infty$$

is a proper p.d.f. and find its mean and variance.

Since $b > 0$, it follows that $f(x) > 0$ for all x. Also the fact that $\displaystyle\int_{-\infty}^{\infty} f(x)dx = 1$

may be deduced by making the substitution $u = (x - a)/b$ and then using the standard

result $\displaystyle\int_{0}^{\infty} e^{-\frac{1}{2}t^2} dt = \left(\frac{\pi}{2}\right)^{1/2}$ which has been proved in §5.2. Therefore we are dealing

with a proper p.d.f.

The mean is given by

$$\mu = \int_{-\infty}^{\infty} xf(x)dx = \int_{-\infty}^{\infty} \frac{x \exp\left\{-\frac{1}{2}\left(\frac{x-a}{b}\right)^2\right\}}{(2\pi)^{1/2}b} dx$$

$$= \frac{1}{(2\pi)^{1/2}} \int_{-\infty}^{\infty} (bu + a)\exp(-\tfrac{1}{2}u^2)du = \frac{1}{(2\pi)^{1/2}} \left\{\left[-b \exp(-\tfrac{1}{2}u^2)\right]_{-\infty}^{\infty} + a(2\pi)^{1/2}\right\}$$

$$= 0 + a = a,$$

a result which could have been anticipated by observing that the distribution is
symmetric about $x = a$.

We have for the variance

$$\sigma^2 = \int_{-\infty}^{\infty} (x - \mu)^2 f(x)dx = \int_{-\infty}^{\infty} \frac{(x - a)^2 \exp\left\{-\frac{1}{2}\left(\frac{x-a}{b}\right)^2\right\}}{(2\pi)^{1/2}b} dx$$

$$= \frac{b}{(2\pi)^{1/2}} \int_{-\infty}^{\infty} u^2 \exp(-\tfrac{1}{2}u^2)b \, du = \frac{2b^2}{(2\pi)^{1/2}} \int_{0}^{\infty} u \times u \exp(-\tfrac{1}{2}u^2)du$$

$$= b^2 \left(\frac{2}{\pi}\right)^{1/2} \left\{\left[-u \exp(-\tfrac{1}{2}u^2)\right]_{0}^{\infty} + \int_{0}^{\infty} \exp(-\tfrac{1}{2}u^2)du\right\}$$

$$= b^2 \left(\frac{2}{\pi}\right)^{1/2} \left\{0 - 0 + \left(\frac{\pi}{2}\right)^{1/2}\right\} = b^2.$$

It follows that the p.d.f. which has just been considered can legitimately be written
in the form

$$f(x) = \frac{1}{(2\pi)^{1/2}\sigma} e^{-\frac{1}{2}\left(\frac{x-\mu}{\sigma}\right)^2}$$

where μ and σ respectively signify the mean and standard deviation. It is known as the normal distribution, to which reference has already been made, and it is dealt with in detail in the next section. Considerable use of its properties will be made in the discussion on inference in Chapter 3 of Volume 2.

Although the calculations in this pair of examples started from first principles, it is often possible to utilize simplifying procedures. These include suitable transformation of the variate and employment of *generating functions* which are so termed because they 'generate' useful quantities associated with the random variable.

Change of Origin and Scale

Suppose that the values taken by the variate X are transformed according to the equation $y = ax + b$, where necessarily $a \neq 0$. If $b \neq 0$, this clearly represents a change of origin and there is a change of scale if $|a| \neq 1$. Hence, using an obvious notation,

$$\mu_Y = a\mu_X + b, \tag{41}$$

$$\sigma_Y^2 = a^2 \sigma_X^2 \quad \text{and} \quad \sigma_Y = |a| \sigma_X. \tag{42a, b}$$

These results correspond exactly with results (11) and (12) obtained for relative frequencies and the proofs are identical with those given on p. 445. The generalization of equation (42a) is

$$\mu_{r,Y} = a^r \mu_{r,X} \quad \text{for } r = 2, 3, \ldots. \tag{43}$$

Consider the particular case $a = 1/\sigma_X, b = -\mu_X/\sigma_X$. Then

$$y = \frac{x - \mu_X}{\sigma_X} \tag{44}$$

and

$$\mu_Y = \frac{1}{\sigma_X}(\mu_X - \mu_X) = 0, \quad \sigma_Y^2 = \frac{\sigma_X^2}{\sigma_X^2} = 1.$$

A variate which has zero mean and unit standard deviation is called *standardized* and the relationship (44) shows how to standardize any variate of known mean and variance. For certain popular distributions, the values of the standardized variate, Z say, and the associated probabilities have been tabulated so that the corresponding value of the original variate X can immediately be found using the inverse transformation $x = \sigma_X z + \mu_X$. Examples of this useful procedure are included in §12.6.

Change of Variate

Suppose that X is a *discrete* variate and Y is a certain function of X. It is usually possible to find the corresponding p.d.f. of Y by straightforward evaluation.

EXAMPLE 5

The variate X takes the values $\quad -4 \quad -3 \quad -2 \quad -1 \quad 0 \quad 1 \quad 2 \quad 3 \quad 4 \quad 5$

with associated probabilities $\quad p_1 \quad p_2 \quad p_3 \quad p_4 \quad p_5 \quad p_6 \quad p_7 \quad p_8 \quad p_9 \quad p_{10}.$

Find the p.d.f. of Y where $Y = X^2$.

The only values which Y can take are $\quad 0 \qquad 1 \qquad 4 \qquad 9 \qquad 16 \qquad 25$

and occur when X is $\qquad\qquad\qquad 0 \quad -1, 1 \quad -2, 2 \quad -3, 3 \quad -4, 4 \quad 5$.

Hence the associated probabilities are $\quad p_5 \quad p_4 + p_6 \quad p_3 + p_7 \quad p_2 + p_8 \quad p_1 + p_9 \quad p_{10}.$

When X is *continuously* distributed the procedure is as follows. Suppose that the relationship $y = y(x)$ which connects the values taken by X and the values taken by Y has a graph of the form shown in Fig. 12.14(a).

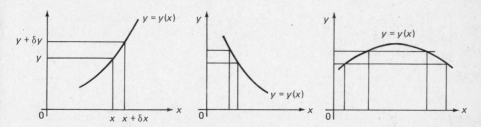

(a) $y = y(x)$ is an increasing function   (b) $y = y(x)$ is a decreasing function   (c) $y = y(x)$ is not 1:1

Fig. 12.14   Transforming a continuous variate

It is given that the p.d.f. of X is $f(x)$. Let $g(y)$ be the corresponding p.d.f. of Y. Since

$$P\{y < Y \leqslant y + \delta y\} = P\{x < X \leqslant x + \delta x\},$$

it follows that

$$g(y)\delta y = f(x)\delta x.$$

Therefore, taking the limit $\delta y \to 0$ gives

$$g(y) = f(x)\frac{dx}{dy}.$$

For any part of the range over which y decreases as x increases the graph must take the form shown in Fig. 12.14(b) where a positive increment δx gives rise to a negative increment δy. However, fundamental usage, as introduced by equation (26), demands that increments be positive. The result may therefore be written

$$g(y) = f(x)\left|\frac{dx}{dy}\right| \tag{45}$$

and it will be noted that this form also includes the earlier case.

Figure 12.14(c) shows a situation in which a particular y value arises from two x

values so that the contribution to y from each must be added. In the general case the summation is extended to include all the x values which correspond to the appropriate value of y, i.e.

$$g(y) = \sum \left\{ f(x) \left| \frac{dx}{dy} \right| \right\}. \tag{46}$$

EXAMPLE 6

The probability that unit dose of a proprietary weedkiller will destroy all weeds within a disc D of radius r about its point of application is $\exp(-2r)$. Find the p.d.f. for the radius and the p.d.f. for the area of the disc.

Let R be the random variable associated with the radius of effectiveness of the weedkiller. The problem supplies the c.d.f. of R, namely $P\{R \leqslant r\} \equiv F(r) = 1 - e^{-2r}$.

Therefore $f(r) = F'(r) = 2e^{-2r}$ where $0 \leqslant r < \infty$. The corresponding area affected is $a = \pi r^2$ so $r = (a/\pi)^{1/2}$ and $da/dr = 2\pi r$. The relation is $(1:1)$ over $(0, \infty)$, so that if the p.d.f. of the area is $g(a)$, then

$$g(a) = f(r) \left| \frac{dr}{da} \right| = 2e^{-2r} \times \frac{1}{2\pi r} = \frac{\exp\{-2(a/\pi)^{1/2}\}}{(\pi a)^{1/2}}$$

where $0 \leqslant a < \infty$.

Generating Functions

The three generating functions to be considered are:

> the probability generating function, (p.g.f.), $G(t)$
> the moment generating function, (m.g.f.), $M(\theta)$
> and the cumulant generating function, (c.g.f), $K(\theta)$.

Consider a discrete variate X for which $P\{X = x_i\} = p_i$ for $i = 1, 2, \ldots$. Then $G(t)$ is the *probability generating function* of X if p_i is the coefficient of t^{x_i} when $G(t)$ is expanded in powers of t. Therefore

$$G(t) = \sum_i p_i t^{x_i} = p_1 t^{x_1} + p_2 t^{x_2} + \ldots + p_r t^{x_r} + \ldots. \tag{47}$$

Note that t plays only a passive role. From equation (33) it follows that

$$G(t) = E\{t^X\}. \tag{48}$$

Do not confuse the p.g.f. with the p.d.f.! A simple illustration of a p.g.f. is that of an unbiased die, namely

$$G(t) = \tfrac{1}{6}t^1 + \tfrac{1}{6}t^2 + \tfrac{1}{6}t^3 + \tfrac{1}{6}t^4 + \tfrac{1}{6}t^5 + \tfrac{1}{6}t^6.$$

If the dummy variable t is now replaced by e^θ, the *moment generating function*

$M(\theta)$ is obtained, and

$$M(\theta) = E\{e^{\theta X}\}. \tag{49}$$

$$M(\theta) = \sum_i p_i \exp(\theta x_i) = \sum_i \left(p_i + p_i \theta x_i + p_i \frac{\theta^2 x_i^2}{2!} + \ldots + p_i \frac{\theta^r x_i^r}{r!} + \ldots \right)$$

$$= 1 + \theta \sum p_i x_i + \frac{\theta^2}{2!} \sum p_i x_i^2 + \ldots + \frac{\theta^r}{r!} \sum p_i x_i^r + \ldots$$

Thus

$$M(\theta) \equiv 1 + \theta \mu_1' + \frac{\theta^2}{2!} \mu_2' + \ldots + \frac{\theta^r}{r!} \mu_r' + \ldots . \tag{50}$$

Precisely this same relationship holds between $M(\theta)$ and the moments about the origin when the random variable X is continuous with p.d.f. $f(x)$, and $M(\theta)$ now given by

$$M(\theta) = \int_{-\infty}^{\infty} f(x)\, e^{\theta x}\, dx.$$

It follows that, once the m.g.f. is known, the value of μ_r' may be obtained either

(i)   by expanding the function and then taking the coefficients of $\theta^r/r!$ or, since $M(\theta)$ has been written as a Maclaurin expansion in θ,

(ii)   by evaluating $d^r M/d\theta^r$ at $\theta = 0$.

The *cumulant generating function* $K(\theta)$ is defined by

$$K(\theta) = \log\{M(\theta)\} \tag{51}$$

and it is suitable for use with both discrete and continuous variates. Substitution for $M(\theta)$ yields

$$K(\theta) = \log \left\{ 1 + \left(\theta \mu_1' + \frac{\theta^2}{2!} \mu_2' + \ldots + \frac{\theta^r}{r!} \mu_r' + \ldots \right) \right\}.$$

The terms on the right-hand side may be collected in ascending powers of θ after using the formal expansion

$$\log(1 + \alpha) = \alpha - \frac{\alpha^2}{2} + \frac{\alpha^3}{3} - \frac{\alpha^4}{4} + \ldots . \tag{52}$$

As the coefficient of $\theta^r/r!$ is called the rth *cumulant*, denoted by K_r, it follows that the first four cumulants are

$$K_1 = \mu_1' = \mu,$$
$$K_2 = \mu_2' - \mu_1'^2 = \mu_2,$$
$$K_3 = \mu_3' - 3\mu_1'\mu_2' + 2\mu_1'^3 = \mu_3, \tag{53a, b, c, d}$$
$$K_4 = \mu_4' - 4\mu_1'\mu_3' - 3\mu_2'^2 + 12\mu_1'^2\mu_2' - 6\mu_1'^4 = \mu_4 - 3\mu_2^2.$$

These results should be checked, see exercise 2. Using definitions (38), (39) and (40) for the skewness, flatness and coefficient of excess,

$$\gamma_1 = \mu_3/\sigma^3 = K_3/K_2^{3/2}, \quad \beta_2 = \mu_4/\mu_2^2 = K_4/K_2^2 + 3, \quad \gamma_2 = \beta_2 - 3 = K_4/K_2^2.$$

$$(54a, b, c)$$

It will be demonstrated that the commonly occurring distributions to be considered in the next section possess generating functions which are simple to handle. Quantities like the mean and variance are readily revealed and important properties associated with the distribution of sums of independent variates are easily established.

It may readily be shown that when X and Y are independent

$$E\{e^{\theta(X+Y)}\} = E\{e^{\theta X} \times e^{\theta Y}\} = E\{e^{\theta X}\}E\{e^{\theta Y}\}.$$

The left-hand side is the moment generating function of a random variable Z defined by $Z = X + Y$ and the right-hand side is the m.g.f. of X multiplied by the m.g.f. of Y.

Adopting the obvious notation, the above result generalizes to

$$M_Z(\theta) = \prod_{i=1}^{n} M_{X_i}(\theta) \tag{55}$$

where $Z = \sum_{i=1}^{n} X_i$ and the X_i are independent. A similar expression holds for $G_Z(t)$. The corresponding result for the c.g.f. may be found by taking the logarithm of each side of equation (55) and so

$$K_Z(\theta) = \sum_{i=1}^{n} K_{X_i}(\theta). \tag{56}$$

In particular, the rth cumulant of Z is given by

$$K_{r,Z} = \sum_{i=1}^{n} K_{r,X_i} \tag{57}$$

so that when $r = 1$

$$K_{1,Z} = \mu_Z = \mu_{X_1} + \mu_{X_2} + \ldots + \mu_{X_n} \tag{58}$$

and when $r = 2$

$$K_{2,Z} = \sigma_Z^2 = \sigma_{X_1}^2 + \sigma_{X_2}^2 + \ldots + \sigma_{X_n}^2. \tag{59}$$

It will be shown in §12.7 that when the variates are not independent result (58) continues to hold but equation (59) requires modification.

If as well as being independently distributed the $\{X_i\}$ are *identically* distributed, then

$$G_Z(t) = \{G_X(t)\}^n, \quad M_Z(\theta) = \{M_X(\theta)\}^n \quad \text{and} \quad K_Z(\theta) = nK_X(\theta). \tag{60a, b, c}$$

By way of illustration, the probability of throwing a total of 9 when five unbiased dice are tossed independently is the coefficient of t^9 in the expansion of

$(\frac{1}{6}t^1 + \frac{1}{6}t^2 + \frac{1}{6}t^3 + \frac{1}{6}t^4 + \frac{1}{6}t^5 + \frac{1}{6}t^6)^5$. This has been established as 70/7776 by the more elementary approach in §12.2 (example 2).

EXAMPLE 7
Evaluate the moment generating functions of the rectangular and triangular distributions shown in Fig. 12.15. The hardness in a square sheet of metal is assessed by impressing a diamond tool at a randomly selected point. If the corners of the sheet are at $(\pm\frac{1}{2}l, \pm\frac{1}{2}l)$ and the selected point is denoted by (x_1, x_2) and X_1 and X_2 are independent, determine the probability distribution of $X_1 + X_2$.

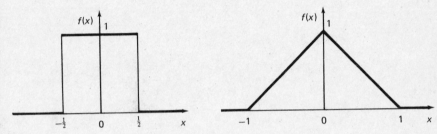

Fig. 12.15 The given rectangular and triangular distributions for example 7

For the rectangular distribution the p.d.f. is

$$f(x) = \begin{cases} 1 & \text{if } -\frac{1}{2} < x < \frac{1}{2} \\ 0 & \text{otherwise.} \end{cases}$$

Then

$$M(\theta) = \int_{-1/2}^{1/2} 1 \times e^{\theta x}\, dx = \frac{1}{\theta}\left[e^{\theta x}\right]_{-1/2}^{1/2} = \frac{1}{\theta}(e^{\theta/2} - e^{-\theta/2}).$$

For the triangular distribution the p.d.f. is

$$f(x) = \begin{cases} 1 + x & \text{if } -1 < x \le 0 \\ 1 - x & \text{if } 0 < x < 1 \\ 0 & \text{otherwise.} \end{cases}$$

Then

$$M(\theta) = \int_{-1}^{0} (1+x)e^{\theta x}\, dx + \int_{0}^{1} (1-x)e^{\theta x}\, dx$$

$$= \left[\frac{1}{\theta}e^{\theta x} + \frac{xe^{\theta x}}{\theta} - \frac{e^{\theta x}}{\theta^2}\right]_{-1}^{0} + \left[\frac{1}{\theta}e^{\theta x} - \frac{xe^{\theta x}}{\theta} + \frac{e^{\theta x}}{\theta^2}\right]_{0}^{1}$$

$$= \frac{e^{\theta} + e^{-\theta} - 2}{\theta^2} = \left\{\frac{1}{\theta}(e^{\theta/2} - e^{-\theta/2})\right\}^2.$$

Since this triangular distribution has as its m.f.g. the square of the m.f.g. of the given rectangular distribution, it follows that the *sum* of two independent variates, uniformly distributed over $(-\frac{1}{2}, \frac{1}{2})$ has the symmetric triangular distribution on $(-1, 1)$ as base.

In the particular case of the square metal sheet, X_1 and X_2 are each uniformly distributed over the range $(-\frac{1}{2}l, \frac{1}{2}l)$ so that $X_1 + X_2$ has the symetric triangular distribution on $(-l, l)$ as base.

The probability distributions discussed in the next section are those of the binomial, Poissonian and normal variates. The associated generating functions, where applicable, are readily derived and it is convenient to tabulate them here for reference purposes.

	p.g.f. $G(t)$	m.g.f. $M(\theta)$	c.g.f. $K(\theta)$
$Bi(n, p)$	$(q + pt)^n$	$(q + pe^\theta)^n$	$n \log(q + pe^\theta)$
$Po(\lambda)$	$e^{-\lambda(1-t)}$	$\exp\{-\lambda(1 - e^\theta)\}$	$-\lambda + \lambda e^\theta$
$N(\mu, \sigma^2)$		$\exp(\mu\theta + \frac{1}{2}\sigma^2\theta^2)$	$\mu\theta + \frac{1}{2}\sigma^2\theta^2$

Exercises

1. Show that, provided the appropriate sum or integral converges, any odd moment about the mean for any symmetric distribution is zero.

2. For both discrete and continuous variates prove the following three results

(a) $\mu_2 = \mu_2' - \mu_1'^2$

(b) $\mu_3 = \mu_3' - 3\mu_1'\mu_2' + 2\mu_1'^3$

(c) $\mu_4 = \mu_4' - 4\mu_1'\mu_3' + 6\mu_1'^2\mu_2' - 3\mu_1'^4$

and hence obtain equations (53) of the text.

3. Show that in any discrete probability distribution with mean μ and standard deviation σ,

$$\sigma^2 = \sum_i p_i(x_i - x_0)^2 - (x_0 - \mu)^2$$

where x_0 is any constant. What is the corresponding expression for a continuous variate?

4. In example 6, establish the area which is cleared of weeds, on average, in nine times out of every ten independent applications of the weedkiller.

12.6 BASIC VARIATES

The Binomial Distribution

Consider a sequence of *independent* trials each of which possesses precisely two possible outcomes. Examples are

> '0' or '1' in binary digits as used in computing,
> 'accept' or 'reject' in the inspection of production materials.

In the present context the two outcomes are commonly called 'success' and 'failure', and if the probability of 'success' remains constant for each trial, the sequence is referred to as a *Bernoulli sequence*. If the probability of success for such a trial is p then the corresponding probability of failure is $(1 - p)$ and this is commonly denoted by q.

Suppose that in n Bernoulli trials there are precisely r successes, where $0 \leqslant r \leqslant n$. The probability of getting a particular arrangement of the r successes and $(n - r)$ failures is $p^r q^{n-r}$. Since there are ${}^n C_r$ different ways in which these r successes can occur, each arrangement being equally likely,

$$\text{the probability of } r \text{ successes, without regard to order,} = {}^n C_r \, p^r q^{n-r} \tag{61}$$

and this is precisely the term in p^r in the binomial expansion of $(q + p)^n$. It immediately follows that the p.g.f. $G(t)$ is given by

$$G(t) = (q + pt)^n. \tag{62}$$

Replacement of t by e^θ gives the m.g.f. so that

$$M(\theta) = (q + pe^\theta)^n. \tag{63}$$

The c.g.f. is obtained by taking logarithms and

$$K(\theta) = n \log(q + pe^\theta). \tag{64}$$

Clearly the distribution is completely specified once the values of the *index n* and the *parameter p* of the distribution are known. The distribution is known as the *binomial* (or *Bernoulli*) *distribution* and is commonly denoted $Bi(n, p)$. Now

$$\frac{dK(\theta)}{d\theta} = \frac{npe^\theta}{q + pe^\theta} \quad \text{and} \quad \frac{d^2K(\theta)}{d\theta^2} = \frac{(q + pe^\theta)npe^\theta - np^2 e^{2\theta}}{(q + pe^\theta)^2} = \frac{npqe^\theta}{(q + pe^\theta)^2}.$$

Therefore, the mean is

$$\mu = \left. \frac{dK(\theta)}{d\theta} \right|_{\theta=0} = \frac{np}{q + p} = np \tag{65}$$

and the variance is

$$\mu_2 = \left. \frac{d^2K(\theta)}{d\theta^2} \right|_{\theta=0} = \frac{npq}{(q + p)^2} = npq. \tag{66}$$

That the mean is np can be directly argued from the fact that there are n independent trials each with a constant probability p of success. It can also be obtained by careful

manipulation of $\sum\limits_{r=0}^{n} p^r q^{n-r} r$.

By evaluating K_3 it may be shown that the skewness

$$\gamma_1 = \frac{q-p}{(npq)^{1/2}} \cdot \qquad\qquad (67)$$

EXAMPLE 1

Of twelve technicians, three are left-handed. If a certain adjustment has to be done once each day and amongst this workforce job-allocation is random, what is the probability that in 6 days the adjustment has been done on at least two occasions by left-handed technicians?

Let p be the probability that the adjustment on any one day was done by a left-handed technician. Then $p = \frac{3}{12} = \frac{1}{4}$ so $q = 1 - p = \frac{3}{4}$, and $n = 6$. The probability of having been done at least twice by a left-handed technician is the probability of having been done two or three or four or five or six times and this is

$$^6C_2 p^2 q^4 + {}^6C_3 p^3 q^3 + {}^6C_4 p^4 q^2 + {}^6C_5 p^5 q + {}^6C_6 p^6$$

$$= 15(\tfrac{1}{4})^2 (\tfrac{3}{4})^4 + 20(\tfrac{1}{4})^3 (\tfrac{3}{4})^3 + 15(\tfrac{1}{4})^4 (\tfrac{3}{4})^2 + 6(\tfrac{1}{4})^5 (\tfrac{3}{4}) + (\tfrac{1}{4})^6$$

$$= (\tfrac{1}{4})^6 (1215 + 540 + 135 + 18 + 1) = 1909/4096 = 0.466 \text{ to three d.p.}$$

This result is more easily obtained by observing that it must also be equal to one minus the probability that the adjustment was done no more than once by left-handed technicians, i.e.

$$1 - (\tfrac{3}{4})^6 - 6(\tfrac{3}{4})^5 (\tfrac{1}{4}) = 1 - \frac{3 \times 729}{4096} = 1 - \frac{2187}{4096} = \frac{1909}{4096} \cdot$$

In many 'real-life' situations interest centres on the number of faulty items likely to be emitted by a system, and in any calculation it then proves more convenient to designate these faulty items as the 'successes'.

Although comprehensive tables of the binomial coefficients exist, for larger values of n the binomial distribution involves a considerable amount of tedious calculation. It is, therefore, natural to ask whether the binomial distribution $Bi(n, p)$ tends to a limiting form as $n \to \infty$. In fact *two* limiting distributions exist, the reason for this being that the asymptotic form depends not only on n becoming large but also on the magnitude of p. More precisely, the limiting form depends on the size of np as the following argument indicates.

The skewness of the binomial distribution is given in equation (67) as $(q - p)/(npq)^{1/2}$. The $\sqrt{n}$ in the denominator will generally ensure that for large n the skewness tends to zero, suggesting a symmetric limiting distribution. However if, notwithstanding the large value of n, the probability p is so small that np has a 'moderate' value which may be denoted by λ, then $q = 1 - p \simeq 1$ and $\gamma_1 \simeq 1/\sqrt{\lambda} \neq 0$. Thus if λ is less than about 10, the skewness is not negligible and the limiting form of the distribution cannot be symmetric.

The symmetric limiting form is of common occurrence and is known as the *normal* or *Gaussian* distribution. This usage of 'normal' must not be confused with the alternative meanings of 'usual' and 'perpendicular'. The other limiting form is the *Poissonian* (or *Poisson*) distribution and it is to this asymmetric distribution that attention is first directed. Both of these distributions can be directly derived from appropriate physical situations without recourse to a discussion of the binomial distribution and its limiting forms (see for example §3.7(e)).

The Poissonian Distribution

A variate X is Poissonian if it can take the values $0, 1, 2, \ldots$, with p.d.f.

$$p_x = e^{-\lambda} \frac{\lambda^x}{x!} \quad \text{for } x = 0, 1, 2, \ldots, \tag{68}$$

where λ is a positive constant. This distribution has already been met in example 3 in §12.5, where it was shown that both the mean and the variance of the distribution are equal to λ, its *index* or *parameter*. The distribution is completely determined once the value of λ is known and may be unambiguously identified by the notation $Po(\lambda)$. The graph of $Po(4.0)$ is shown in Fig. 12.16, with the graph of $Bi(40, 0.1)$ superimposed for comparison purposes.

Note also the useful recurrence relation for the calculation of successive probabilities:

$$p_{x+1} = e^{-\lambda} \frac{\lambda^{x+1}}{(x+1)!} = \frac{\lambda}{(x+1)} \left\{ e^{-\lambda} \frac{\lambda^x}{x!} \right\} = \frac{\lambda}{x+1} p_x. \tag{69}$$

The p.g.f. $G(t)$ of the Poissonian distribution is given by

$$G(t) = \sum_{x=0}^{\infty} \left(e^{-\lambda} \frac{\lambda^x}{x!} \right) t^x = e^{-\lambda} \sum_{x=0}^{\infty} \frac{(\lambda t)^x}{x!} = e^{-\lambda} e^{\lambda t}. \tag{70}$$

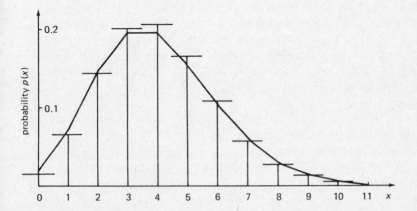

Fig. 12.16   Graphs of the binomial distribution $Bi(40, 0.1)$ and the Poissonian distribution $Po(4.0)$ with the same mean (segmented curve)

Therefore

$$M(\theta) = \exp\{-\lambda(1 - e^{\theta})\} \tag{71}$$

and

$$K(\theta) = -\lambda + \lambda e^{\theta}. \tag{72}$$

To show how the Poissonian distribution can arise as the limiting form of the binomial distribution, consider the $(r + 1)$th term of $Bi(n, p)$, namely $^{n}C_{r}p^{r}q^{n-r}$, which on using the substitution $p = \lambda/n$ becomes

$$\frac{n(n-1)\ldots(n-r+1)}{r!}\left(\frac{\lambda}{n}\right)^{r}\left(1-\frac{\lambda}{n}\right)^{n-r}$$

$$= \frac{n^{r}\left(1-\frac{1}{n}\right)\ldots\left(1-\frac{(r-1)}{n}\right)}{r!}\frac{\lambda^{r}}{n^{r}}\left(1-\frac{\lambda}{n}\right)^{n-r}$$

$$= \left\{\frac{\left(1-\frac{1}{n}\right)\ldots\left(1-\frac{r-1}{n}\right)}{\left(1-\frac{\lambda}{n}\right)^{r}}\right\}\frac{\lambda^{r}}{r!}\left(1-\frac{\lambda}{n}\right)^{n}.$$

Now let $n \to \infty$. The limit of the term within the brackets { } is 1, and the limit of $\left(1-\frac{\lambda}{n}\right)^{n}$ is $e^{-\lambda}$ which is a well-known result of elementary analysis. The right-hand side, therefore, has as limit $(\lambda^{r}/r!)e^{-\lambda}$ and this is precisely the $(r+1)$th term of the Poissonian distribution.

Because p must be so small, the Poissonian distribution is often known as the 'distribution of rare events in space and time'. Remember that, as in the binomial distribution, the outcomes must be independent. Situations considered to satisfy these conditions arise in the mass-production of components, and an example follows.

EXAMPLE 2
Certain mass-produced articles are known to have a failure rate of 1%. If they are packed in cartons of 120, what proportion of cartons can be expected to have defect-free contents and what proportion can be expected to contain two or more failures?

From the binomial distribution, the proportion of cartons expected to be defect-free, provided that the failures are independent, is

$$^{120}C_{0}(0.99)^{120}(0.01)^{0} = (0.99)^{120}.$$

Those cartons expected to contain 2 or more defects are a proportion

$$1 - \{(0.99)^{120} + 120(0.99)^{199}(0.01)^{1}\} = 1 - 2.19(0.99)^{119}.$$

Now consider the use of the Poissonian distribution as approximation. As the mean number of defects per carton is 120×0.01, the appropriate value of λ is 1.2. Thus,

the probability of having no failures is $e^{-1.2}$,
the probability of having one failure is $1.2e^{-1.2}$,

and therefore the probability of having two or more failures is

$$1 - (e^{-1.2} + 1.2e^{-1.2}) = 1 - 2.2e^{-1.2}.$$

It is usually far easier in these situations to evaluate the Poissonian values than the binomial ones. The following display of results for example 2 illustrates the accuracy of which the Poissonian approximation is capable.

		0 defects	2 or more
The answers correct to four decimal places		0.2993	0.3378
$Bi(120, 0.01)$ values ⎱ using only four-figure		0.2965	0.3442
$Po(1.2)$ values ⎰ tables		0.3012	0.3374

The Poissonian distribution also enjoys an additive property, as follows. Let X and Y be two independently distributed Poissonian variates with parameters λ_X and λ_Y respectively, and let $Z = X + Y$. The m.g.f. of Z is therefore given by

$$M_Z(\theta) = \exp\{-\lambda_X(1 - e^\theta)\} \times \exp\{-\lambda_Y(1 - e^\theta)\}$$
$$= \exp\{-(\lambda_X + \lambda_Y)(1 - e^\theta)\}$$

which is the m.g.f. of the Poissonian variate with parameter $(\lambda_X + \lambda_Y)$.

EXAMPLE 3
Experience has shown that on average four pairs of men's shoes and three pairs of ladies' shoes are left for repair at a cobbler's shop during a particular hour of the day. What is the probability that not more than a total of four pairs will be left during that period on any day?

Working to the hypothesis that the depositings of pairs of shoes for repair are independent events which follow Poissonian distributions, the additive property then implies that the total number of pairs deposited will follow a Poissonian distribution with mean $(4.0 + 3.0) = 7.0$.

If p_k is the probability that k pairs of shoes will be left then the probability that not more than four pairs of shoes will be deposited is

$$p_0 + p_1 + p_2 + p_3 + p_4 = e^{-7}\left(1 + \frac{7}{1} + \frac{7^2}{2} + \frac{7^3}{3!} + \frac{7^4}{4!}\right)$$

$$= 0.000912 \times 189.6 = 0.173.$$

A Poissonian distribution may be fitted to a suitable set of observations as follows. Calculate the sample mean $\bar{x}$ and use this as an estimate of λ, the population mean of the 'underlying' Poissonian distribution. The corresponding 'expected' frequencies are then obtained by multiplying the resulting probabilities by the sample size. Consider, for example, the traffic census data given in table 12.1. The general appearance of the distribution, coupled with the fact that the sample variance and mean do not differ greatly ($\bar{x} = 2.45$, p. 444 and $s^2 = 2.18$, p. 448) suggest that a Poissonian distribution may be appropriate.

EXAMPLE 4

Fit a Poissonian distribution to the data in table 12.1.

Since $\bar{x} = 2.45$ and $e^{-2.45} = 0.8629$, table 12.4 may be constructed by use of equation (68).

TABLE 12.4

Number of vehicles	x	0	1	2	3	4	5	6	Σ
Probability	p_x	0.0863	0.2114	0.2590	0.2115	0.1295	0.0626	0.0259	0.9862
Expected frequency	f_x	5.18	12.68	15.54	12.69	7.77	3.76	1.55	59.17

The final column provides a useful check on the calculation. When comparison is made between the observed frequencies and the values expected on this Poissonian hypothesis it is seen that the agreement is reasonable. Chapter 3 of Volume 2 shows how to make a formal 'goodness of fit' assessment.

The Normal Distribution

The second limiting form of the binomial distribution when n becomes large is the *normal* distribution, and, as has been remarked, ensues when p has a moderate value. The distribution is continuous and the p.d.f. has the form

$$f(x) = \frac{1}{(2\pi)^{1/2}\sigma} e^{-\frac{1}{2}\left(\frac{x-\mu}{\sigma}\right)^2} \qquad \text{for } -\infty < x < \infty, \tag{74}$$

where μ is the mean and σ is the standard deviation (see §12.5, example 4). The graphs of this function for a given value of μ and three values of σ are shown in Fig. 12.17(a) and the corresponding graphs for constant σ and three values of μ are shown in Fig. 12.17(b).

As the two parameters required to determine this distribution uniquely are μ and σ it is commonly denoted by $N(\mu, \sigma^2)$. In particular, $N(0, 1)$ signifies the standardized normal variate, (s.n.v.), Z, the p.d.f. of which is

$$f(z) = \frac{1}{(2\pi)^{1/2}} e^{-\frac{1}{2}z^2} \qquad \text{for } -\infty < z < \infty. \tag{75}$$

Here, perhaps unexpectedly, the derived variate is continuous. The result may be obtained by standardizing the binomial variate, converting the corresponding frequency polygon into a histogram and then allowing the class width δz to decrease whilst maintaining a histogram area of unity. Proceeding to the limit it is found that $df(z)/dz = -zf(z)$ and, after integrating, result (75) follows. Figure 12.18 shows the curve $N(16, 9.6)$ together with the graph of $Bi(40, 0.4)$, the binomial distribution with the same mean and variance.

Gauss was one of the earliest investigators of this probability density, his interest

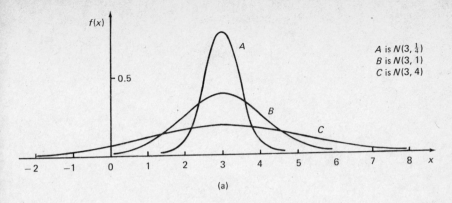

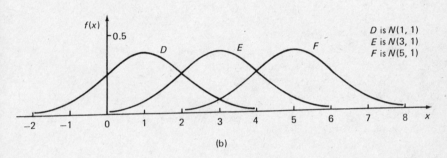

Fig. 12.17 The normal variate $N(\mu, \sigma^2)$; (a) showing the effect of altering σ^2 (b) showing the effect of altering μ

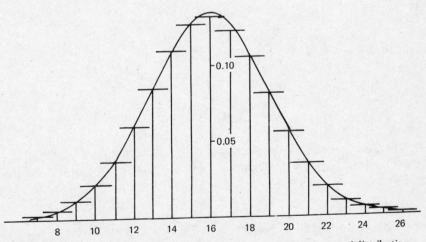

Fig. 12.18 Graphs of the binomial distribution $Bi(40, 0.4)$ and the normal distribution $N(16, 9.6)$ with the same mean and variance (smooth curve)

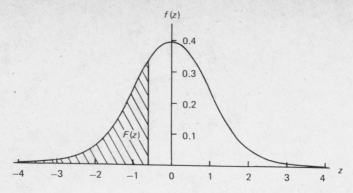

Fig. 12.19   The standardized normal distribution $N(0, 1)$; $f(z)$ is the p.d.f. and $F(z)$ is the c.d.f.

arising from the distribution of random errors in measurement. Because of this the function is often called the *Gaussian* distribution. In electronic engineering, in particular, random noise having a normal distribution is referred to as Gaussian.

As the transformation $z = (x - \mu_X)/\sigma_X$ converts a variate to standardized form (see equation (44)), the inverse transformation $x = \sigma_X z + \mu_X$ enables the values for the p.d.f. $f(x)$ and c.d.f. $F(x)$ to be computed for any normal variate X from the well-established values of the standardized variate Z. These are given in table A2 in the Appendix on p. 499 for $z \geqslant 0$ and the graph of Z is shown in Fig. 12.19.

From the symmetry of the distribution we have

$$f(-z) = f(z) \quad \text{and} \quad F(-z) = 1 - F(z). \tag{76a, b}$$

The *error function* is defined by

$$\text{erf } u = \frac{2}{\sqrt{\pi}} \int_0^u \exp(-t^2)dt. \tag{77}$$

It follows that if Z is $N(0, 1)$,

$$\text{erf}\left(\frac{z}{\sqrt{2}}\right) = P\{-z < Z < z\} \quad \text{and} \quad F(z) = \tfrac{1}{2} + \tfrac{1}{2}\text{erf}\left(\frac{z}{\sqrt{2}}\right). \tag{78a, b}$$

Inspection of the values of $F(z)$ in table A2 shows that in 95% of all cases the observed value will lie within about two standard deviations of the mean and on only 0.2% of the occasions will the observed value be more than about three standard deviations away from the mean. Facts such as these will be used in the discussion of inference in Chapter 3 of Volume 2.

EXAMPLE 5

Unadjusted clocks in a large batch gain on average 30 seconds a day, and the corresponding standard deviation is 75 seconds. If the gain is normally distributed in the batch and a clock is selected at random, find the probabilities that 24 hours after being set to the correct time:

(a)   the clock will be slow,
(b)   the clock will be more than 3 minutes fast,
(c)   the clock will be within 1 minute of the correct time.

Let X be the amount, in minutes, which the clock has gained after 24 hours. Then the three cases respectively require the evaluation of the probabilities $P\{X < 0\}$, $P\{X > 3\}$ and $P\{|X| < 1\}$. From the data, $\mu = \frac{1}{2}$ and $\sigma = 1\frac{1}{4}$ so that Z is a standardized normal variate if $z = (x - \frac{1}{2})/(1\frac{1}{4})$.

Using table A2,

(a) $P\{X < 0\} = P\left\{Z < \dfrac{0 - \frac{1}{2}}{5/4}\right\} = P\{Z < -0.4\} = P\{Z > 0.4\}$

$\qquad = 1 - F(0.4) = 1 - 0.655 = 0.345,$

(b) $P\{X > 3\} = P\left\{Z > \dfrac{3 - \frac{1}{2}}{5/4}\right\} = P\{Z > 2.0\} = 1 - F(2.0) = 1 - 0.977 = 0.023,$

(c) $P\{|X| < 1\} = P\left\{\dfrac{-1 - \frac{1}{2}}{5/4} < Z < \dfrac{1 - \frac{1}{2}}{5/4}\right\} = P\{-1.2 < Z < 0.4\}$

$\qquad = F(0.4) - F(-1.2) = 0.655 - (1.0 - 0.885) = 0.540.$

The derivations of the moment and cumulant generating functions are as follows:

$$M(\theta) = \frac{1}{\sqrt{(2\pi)}\sigma} \int_{-\infty}^{\infty} \exp\left\{-\frac{1}{2}\left(\frac{x - \mu}{\sigma}\right)^2\right\} \exp(\theta x)dx$$

$$= \exp(\mu\theta + \tfrac{1}{2}\sigma^2\theta^2)\left[\int_{-\infty}^{\infty} \frac{1}{\sqrt{(2\pi)}\sigma} \exp\left\{-\frac{1}{2}\left(\frac{x - (\mu + \sigma^2\theta)}{\sigma}\right)^2\right\}dx\right].$$

The function to be integrated will be recognized as $N(\mu + \sigma^2\theta, \sigma^2)$ and so the value of the integral is 1. Therefore

$$M(\theta) = \exp(\mu\theta + \tfrac{1}{2}\sigma^2\theta^2) \tag{79}$$

and

$$K(\theta) = \theta\mu + \tfrac{1}{2}\theta^2\sigma^2. \tag{80}$$

These results confirm the values of the mean and variance, and, since only the first two cumulants can be non-zero, the skewness and coefficient of excess are each 0.

Independent normal distributions also have the additive property, that is if X_1 and X_2 are independent normal variates, then $Y = X_1 + X_2$ also has a normal distribution. The proof is as follows.

Let X_1 be $N(\mu_1, \sigma_1^2)$, X_2 be $N(\mu_2, \sigma_2^2)$; then

$$M_Y(\theta) = M_{X_1}(\theta)M_{X_2}(\theta) = \exp(\mu_1\theta + \tfrac{1}{2}\sigma_1^2\theta^2) \times \exp(\mu_2\theta + \tfrac{1}{2}\sigma_2^2\theta^2)$$

$$= \exp\{(\mu_1 + \mu_2)\theta + \tfrac{1}{2}(\sigma_1^2 + \sigma_2^2)\theta^2\} \tag{81}$$

which is the m.g.f. of a normal variate with mean $(\mu_1 + \mu_2)$ and variance $(\sigma_1^2 + \sigma_2^2)$.

The above result may be generalized. If $\{X_i\}$, for $i = 1, 2, \ldots, n$ are n normal variates, independently distributed, and $Y = \sum\limits_{i=1}^{n} c_i X_i$ where the c_i are constants, then Y is normally distributed with mean $\sum\limits_{i=1}^{n} c_i \mu_i$ and variance $\sum\limits_{i=1}^{n} c_i^2 \sigma_i^2$.

In the particular case where $c_i = 1/n$ and the $\{X_i\}$ are *identically* distributed, $Y = (X_1 + \ldots + X_n)/n$ so that $\mu_Y = \mu_X$ and $\sigma_Y^2 = \sigma_X^2/n$.

EXAMPLE 6

On a housing estate under construction, doorways are to be fitted with doors which must be at least 2 mm narrower than the doorway for a possible fit. The mean width of the doorways is 755 mm, and that of the doors is 750 mm and the distribution of width of both doors and doorways may be assumed normal. What is the probability that at first trial a door will be too wide to fit, given that the standard deviation of the widths of doorways is 2.4 mm and that of the doors is 1.8 mm?

Let X be the r.v. associated with the width of the doorways. Then X is $N(755, 5.76)$.

Let Y be the r.v. associated with the width of the doors. Then Y is $N(750, 3.24)$.

If W is the r.v. associated with their difference, i.e., $w = x - y$, then by the additive property of normal distribution W is $N(755 - 750, 5.76 + 3.24) = N(5, 9.00)$.

It follows that if $z = \frac{1}{3}(w - 5)$ then Z is $N(0, 1)$.

A fit is not possible at first trial if $W < 2$, and the probability that this is so is therefore equal to the probability that the s.n.v. Z has a value less than -1.

From table A2, $P\{Z < -1\} = 0.159$, so on average about 16 doors in a hundred fail on first trial.

In order to fit a normal distribution to observed data it is necessary to standardize the variate using the estimations of μ and σ respectively provided by $\bar{x}$ and s. The method is illustrated by the following example.

EXAMPLE 7

Fit a normal distribution to the data on the breaking strength of cables given in table 12.2 (p. 441).

The solution of example 5 in §12.3 shows that, for this data, $\bar{x} = 10.07$ tons and $s = 0.406$ ton. These values, together with the data, can then be used to construct table 12.5.

TABLE 12.5

x	9.0	9.2	9.4	9.6	9.8	10.0	10.2	10.4	10.6	10.8	11.0	11.2
$x - \bar{x}$	−1.07	−0.87	−0.67	−0.47	−0.27	−0.07	0.13	0.33	0.53	0.73	0.93	1.13
$z = (x - \bar{x})/s$	−2.64	−2.14	−1.65	−1.16	−0.67	−0.17	0.32	0.81	1.31	1.80	2.29	2.78
$F(z)$	0.004	0.016	0.050	0.123	0.252	0.432	0.625	0.791	0.905	0.964	0.989	0.997
$F(z_{i+1}) - F(z_i)$	0.004	0.012	0.034	0.073	0.129	0.180	0.193	0.166	0.114	0.059	0.025	0.008	0.003
f_x	1.0	3.1	8.7	18.7	33.0	46.1	49.4	42.5	29.2	15.1	6.4	2.0	0.8

The values for the c.d.f. $F(z)$, where $z = (x - \bar{x})/s$, have been interpolated from table A2. To obtain the corresponding expected frequency f_x for a particular interval the difference in appropriate values of $F(z)$ has been multiplied by the total frequency. The agreement between the set of observed frequencies and those calculated in this manner is good, as shown by a comparison of table 12.2 and table 12.5, and also by Fig. 12.20 in which the curve $N(10.07, 0.165)$ is superimposed on the histogram.

Although care must be taken in calculations of this type, errors in computation often make themselves obvious. As with the Poissonian distribution, a knowledge of the physical situation to which the results refer together with a glance at (say) a histogram of the values are sufficient to indicate whether or not it might appear reasonable to 'fit' a normal distribution, at least as a first step. As an alternative preliminary investigation it is possible to use *normal probability paper* which is graph paper specially prepared so that the c.d.f. of a true normal distribution plotted against the variate value yields a straight line. The formal 'goodness of fit' test which provides an objective measure of the degree of agreement is discussed in Chapter 3 of Volume 2.

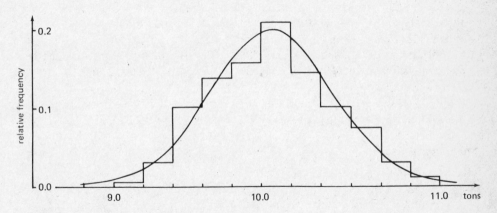

Fig. 12.20 Data for the breaking strength of cables (table 12.2) and corresponding normal variate $N(10.07, 0.165)$

Exercises

1. Suppose that a trial has three possible outcomes labelled A, B and C with associated probabilities p_A, p_B, p_C respectively and $p_A + p_B + p_C = 1$. Show that in n independent trials the probability of getting precisely r_A outcomes of type A, r_B of type B, and r_C of type C, where $r_A + r_B + r_C = n$, is

$$\frac{n!}{r_A! \, r_B! \, r_C!} \, p_A^{r_A} \, p_B^{r_B} \, p_C^{r_C}.$$

[Employ the ideas which lead to results (5) and (61).]

Generalize the above *trinomial* result to the *multinomial* situation.

2. Draw the graphs of $Po(2)$ for $x = 0(1)6$ and $Po(8)$ for $x = 0(1)15$ and compare with the graph of $Po(4)$. Note the tendency towards symmetry as λ is increased.

3. Verify example 3 directly by considering the probability that r pairs of men's shoes and s pairs of ladies' shoes are left for repair, where $r = 0, 1, 2, 3$ and 4 in turn and $r + s \leqslant 4$.

12.7 BIVARIATE AND MULTIVARIATE PROBABILITY DISTRIBUTIONS

The theory of probability distributions developed in the earlier sections has essentially been concerned with single variates, but it is evident that many quantities depend upon the values of more than one variable. For example, parameters which govern the weight of a person must include height and girth, and the output from a factory must depend upon machinery maintenance, workforce strength and availability of raw materials. The ideas employed in the preceding parts of this chapter can readily be extended to cope with these *multivariate* situations, though naturally some new concepts present themselves and the analysis can be heavier. The discussion will therefore be limited to *bivariate* distributions, and it will be further assumed that the variates are either both discrete or both continuous.

When the variates, X and Y say, are discrete, the probability that X takes the ith value x_i and Y takes the jth value y_j simultaneously is denoted by p_{ij}, that is

$$P\{X = x_i \text{ and } Y = y_j\} = p_{ij} \quad \text{for } i = 1, 2, \ldots \text{ and } j = 1, 2, \ldots .$$

Analogously to the conditions on p. 459 for a single discrete variate, the p_{ij} satisfy

$$p_{ij} \geqslant 0 \quad \text{and} \quad \sum_i \sum_j p_{ij} = 1. \tag{82}$$

The set of values $\{p_{ij}\}$ constitute the *joint probability distribution function.*

For the continuous-continuous case, it is usual to introduce the *joint probability density function* $f(x, y)$ such that

$$P\{x < X \leqslant x + \delta x, \ y < Y \leqslant y + \delta y\} = f(x, y)\delta x \, \delta y$$

where, again analogously to the conditions for a single continuous variate,

$$f(x, y) \geqslant 0 \quad \text{and} \quad \int_{-\infty}^{\infty} \int_{-\infty}^{\infty} f(x, y)\mathrm{d}x \, \mathrm{d}y = 1. \tag{83}$$

Geometrically, no part of $z = f(x, y)$ lies below the x, y plane, and between this surface and the plane $z = 0$ unit volume is enclosed.

Again, suppose that X and Y are discrete. Let $p_{i.}$ be the probability that X takes the value x_i, irrespective of the value taken by Y. Then

$$p_{i.} = \sum_j p_{ij}.$$

The set of values $p_{i.}$ are referred to as *marginal probabilities* and since $p_{i.} \geqslant 0$ and $\sum_i p_{i.} = 1$, it follows that these also constitute a probability distribution function,

namely the *marginal p.d.f.* of X. Similarly $p_{.j} = \sum_i p_{ij}$ is the probability that Y takes the

value y_j irrespective of the value of X. Analogous functions $p(x)$ and $q(y)$ exist when X and Y are continuous variates so that

$$p_{i.} = \sum_j p_{ij}, \qquad\qquad p(x) = \int_{-\infty}^{\infty} f(x,y)\,dy, \qquad\qquad (84a, b)$$

$$p_{.j} = \sum_i p_{ij}, \qquad\qquad q(y) = \int_{-\infty}^{\infty} f(x,y)\,dx. \qquad\qquad (84c, d)$$

Then, for example,

$$\mu_X = \sum_i \sum_j p_{ij} x_i \qquad \text{or} \qquad \mu_X = \int_{-\infty}^{\infty} \int_{-\infty}^{\infty} x f(x,y)\,dx\,dy$$

$$= \sum_i p_{i.} x_i \qquad\qquad\qquad = \int_{-\infty}^{\infty} x p(x)\,dx. \qquad\qquad (85a, b)$$

$$\sigma_Y^2 = \sum_i \sum_j p_{ij}(y_j - \mu_Y)^2 \quad \text{or} \quad \sigma_Y^2 = \int_{-\infty}^{\infty} \int_{-\infty}^{\infty} (y - \mu_Y)^2 f(x,y)\,dx\,dy$$

$$= \sum_j p_{.j}(y_j - \mu_Y)^2 \qquad\qquad = \int_{-\infty}^{\infty} (y - \mu_Y)^2 q(y)\,dy. \qquad (86a, b)$$

If in the discrete case the number of values assumed by i and j is not unduly large, it may be convenient to display the information in a (two-way) *probability contingency table*, as in table 12.6.

TABLE 12.6

		y_1	y_2	y_3	. .	y_s	
	x_1	p_{11}	p_{12}	p_{13}	. .	p_{1s}	$p_{1.}$
	x_2	p_{21}	p_{22} .	.	. . .	.	$p_{2.}$
X-value	x_3	p_{31}	.	. .	. .	.	.
	$\vdots$	$\vdots$				$\vdots$	$\vdots$
	x_r	p_{r1}	.	. .	. .	p_{rs}	$p_{r.}$
		$p_{.1}$	$p_{.2}$			$p_{.s}$	1

Y-value

The probability that X takes the value x_i, given that Y has taken the value y_j is the *conditional probability of X on Y*, and is denoted by $p_{i \mid j}$. The set of values $p_{i \mid j}$ constitute the *conditional p.d.f. of X on Y*. Similarly, $q_{j \mid i}$ is used to denote the probability that Y takes the jth value given that X has taken the value x_i. The corresponding functions in the continuous case are $g(x \mid y)$ and $h(y \mid x)$, so that

$$p_{i \mid j} = \frac{p_{ij}}{p_{.j}}, \quad g(x \mid y) = \frac{f(x, y)}{q(y)}. \tag{87a, b}$$

$$q_{j \mid i} = \frac{p_{ij}}{p_{i.}}, \quad h(y \mid x) = \frac{f(x, y)}{p(x)}. \tag{87c, d}$$

For independence of discretely-varying X and Y the requirement is clearly that $p_{i \mid j} = p_{i.}$ for each value of j or, equivalently, $q_{j \mid i} = p_{.j}$ for each value of i. We then recover the multiplicative theorem of probability that for independent events

$$p_{ij} = p_{i.} \times p_{.j}. \tag{as (21)}$$

When we have continuous variates which are independent,

$$g(x \mid y) = p(x), \quad h(y \mid x) = q(y) \quad \text{and} \quad f(x, y) = p(x)q(y).$$

The r, sth *moment about the origin*, μ'_{rs}, is the expected value of $X^r Y^s$ so

$$\mu'_{rs} = \sum_i \sum_j p_{ij} x_i^r y_j^s \quad \text{or} \quad \mu'_{rs} = \int_{-\infty}^{\infty} \int_{-\infty}^{\infty} x^r y^s f(x, y) \, dx \, dy. \tag{88a, b}$$

The r, sth *moment about the mean*, μ_{rs}, is the expected value of $(X - \mu_X)^r (Y - \mu_Y)^s$ so

$$\mu_{rs} = \sum_i \sum_j p_{ij}(x_i - \mu_X)^r (y_i - \mu_Y)^s$$

$$\text{or } \mu_{rs} = \int_{-\infty}^{\infty} \int_{-\infty}^{\infty} (x - \mu_X)^r (y - \mu_Y)^s f(x, y) \, dx \, dy.$$

$$\tag{89a, b}$$

In particular,

$$\mu_{11} = E\{(X - E\{X\})(Y - E\{Y\})\}$$
$$= E\{XY\} - E\{YE\{X\}\} - E\{XE\{Y\}\} + E\{E\{X\}E\{Y\}\}$$
$$= E\{XY\} - E\{X\}E\{Y\}. \tag{90}$$

μ_{11} is the *covariance* of X and Y. Alternative notations for the covariance are $Cov(X, Y)$ and $C(X, Y)$. If Y is replaced by X, the expression reduces to $E\{X^2\} - (E\{X\})^2$ which is recognized as the variance of X. Another special case occurs when X and Y are statistically independent so that $E\{XY\} = E\{X\}E\{Y\}$ and the covariance is therefore zero. However, a zero value for the covariance is not by itself *sufficient* to ensure that two quantities are statistically independent.

Division of the covariance by the product of the associated standard deviations produces a dimensionless quantity called the *correlation coefficient* denoted by ρ.

Then

$$\rho = \frac{\mu_{11}}{\sigma_X \sigma_Y}. \tag{91}$$

It follows that when $Y = X$ the value of the correlation coefficient is 1 and when X and Y are statistically independent $\rho = 0$ and the variates are then said to be *uncorrelated*. To show that $|\rho| \leqslant 1$ for *any* pair of variates X and Y consider

$$E\left\{ \left(\frac{Y - \mu_Y}{\sigma_Y} - \rho \frac{X - \mu_X}{\sigma_X} \right)^2 \right\} = E\left\{ \left(\frac{Y - \mu_Y}{\sigma_Y} \right)^2 - 2\rho \frac{(X - \mu_X)(Y - \mu_Y)}{\sigma_X \sigma_Y} \right.$$

$$\left. + \rho^2 \left(\frac{X - \mu_X}{\sigma_X} \right)^2 \right\}$$

$$= \frac{1}{\sigma_Y^2} E\{(Y - \mu_Y)^2\} - \frac{2\rho}{\sigma_X \sigma_Y} E\{(X - \mu_X)(Y - \mu_Y)\}$$

$$+ \frac{\rho^2}{\sigma_X^2} E\{(X - \mu_X)^2\}$$

$$= \frac{\sigma_Y^2}{\sigma_Y^2} - 2\rho \frac{\mu_{11}}{\sigma_X \sigma_Y} + \rho^2 \frac{\sigma_X^2}{\sigma_X^2} = 1 - 2\rho^2 + \rho^2 = 1 - \rho^2.$$

Since the expected value of a non-negative quantity must itself be non-negative it follows that $-1 \leqslant \rho \leqslant 1$.

A further important property is that $|\rho|$ is invariant when the variates undergo linear transformations. As it is clearly sufficient to prove the result when only one of the variates is so transformed, let $X' = aX + b$, where $a \neq 0$, so that $\mu_{X'} = a\mu_X + b$ and $\sigma_{X'}^2 = a^2 \sigma_X^2$. Then

$$\rho(X', Y) = \frac{E\{X'Y\} - E\{X'\}E\{Y\}}{\sigma_{X'}, \sigma_Y}$$

$$= \frac{E\{(aX + b)Y\} - E\{aX + b\}E\{Y\}}{|a| \sigma_X \sigma_Y}$$

$$= \frac{E\{aXY\} + E\{bY\} - E\{aX\}E\{Y\} - E\{b\}E\{Y\}}{|a| \sigma_X \sigma_Y}$$

$$= \frac{aE\{XY\} + bE\{Y\} - aE\{X\}E\{Y\} - bE\{Y\}}{|a| \sigma_X \sigma_Y} = \frac{a}{|a|} \left(\frac{E\{XY\} - E\{X\}E\{Y\}}{\sigma_X \sigma_Y} \right)$$

$$= \frac{a}{|a|} \rho(X, Y). \tag{92}$$

Thus $\rho(X', Y) = \rho(X, Y)$ if $a > 0$ and $\rho(X', Y) = -\rho(X, Y)$ if $a < 0$. The correlation coefficient ρ is a measure of the linear association between two random variables. When $\rho < 0$ the variables are said to be *negatively correlated* and when $\rho > 0$ the variates are *positively correlated*. It may be remarked that when more than two variates are involved the additional concept of *partial correlation* arises. Correlation plays an important role in the sampling of attributes, to be discussed in Chapter 3 of Volume 2.

It is now possible to generalize results (58) and (59) when $Z = X + Y$ and the variates X, Y are not necessarily independent. It must remain true that $\mu_Z = \mu_X + \mu_Y$ because the expectation E operates linearly on $(X + Y)$. For the variances we have

$$
\begin{aligned}
\sigma_Z^2 &= E\{Z^2\} - (E\{Z\})^2 = E\{(X + Y)^2\} - (E\{(X + Y)\})^2 \\
&= E\{X^2 + 2XY + Y^2\} - (E\{X\} + E\{Y\})^2 \\
&= E\{X^2\} + 2E\{XY\} + E\{Y^2\} - (E\{X\})^2 - 2E\{X\}E\{Y\} - (E\{Y\})^2 \\
&= E\{X^2\} - (E\{X\})^2 + 2(E\{XY\} - E\{X\}E\{Y\}) + E\{Y^2\} - (E\{Y\})^2 \\
&= \sigma_X^2 + 2\rho\,\sigma_X\sigma_Y + \sigma_Y^2 .
\end{aligned}
\tag{93}
$$

Of particular interest are the results

$$
\rho = 0 \Leftrightarrow \sigma_Z^2 = \sigma_X^2 + \sigma_Y^2, \qquad \rho = -1 \Leftrightarrow \sigma_Z^2 = (\sigma_X - \sigma_Y)^2 ,
$$

$$
\rho = +1 \Leftrightarrow \sigma_Z^2 = (\sigma_X + \sigma_Y)^2 .
\tag{94a, b, c}
$$

The correlation coefficient may also be indicated explicitly in joint probability distributions; for example, it can be shown that the bivariate normal distribution has as its p.d.f.

$$
f(x_1, x_2) = \frac{1}{2\pi\sigma_1\sigma_2(1 - \rho^2)^{1/2}} \times
$$

$$
\exp\left[-\frac{1}{2(1 - \rho^2)} \left\{ \frac{(x_1 - \mu_1)^2}{\sigma_1^2} - 2\rho\frac{(x_1 - \mu_1)(x_2 - \mu_2)}{\sigma_1\sigma_2} + \frac{(x_2 - \mu_2)^2}{\sigma_2^2} \right\} \right]
\tag{95}
$$

where $E\{X_i\} = \mu_i$, $\mathrm{Var}\{X_i\} = \sigma_i^2$ for $i = 1, 2$ and ρ is the correlation coefficient. These results may be verified by direct integration or by using the joint generating functions which it is possible to define. If, for example, the joint p.d.f. of a continuous bivariate distribution is $f(x, y)$ then the *joint moment generating function* $M(\theta_1, \theta_2)$ is given by

$$
M(\theta_1, \theta_2) = \int_{-\infty}^{\infty} \int_{-\infty}^{\infty} f(x, y) \exp(\theta_1 x) \exp(\theta_2 y) \mathrm{d}x\,\mathrm{d}y
\tag{96}
$$

where θ_1 and θ_2 are the pair of 'dummy' parameters.

The bivariate analogue of equation (46) is that if $u = u(x, y)$, $v = v(x, y)$, then the p.d.fs $g(u, v)$ and $f(x, y)$ are related by

$$
g(u, v) = \sum \left\{ f(x, y) \left| \frac{\partial(x, y)}{\partial(u, v)} \right| \right\},
\tag{97}
$$

where the Jacobian is defined in §5.2.

EXAMPLE 1

Find the joint p.d.f. for the number of front nearside shock-absorbers selected and the number of rear offside shock-absorbers under the stated conditions of example 4 of §12.2. Find the marginal p.d.fs and also find the conditional p.d.f. when one variate has the value 2. Evaluate the correlation coefficient.

Let X represent the number of front nearside shock-absorbers and Y be the number of rear offside shock-absorbers. Because of the calculations already carried out in that previous example and the exercise which followed, it is possible to write down immediately the joint p.d.f. in the form of a probability contingency table, as table 12.7.

TABLE 12.7

X \ Y	0	1	2	3
0	$\dfrac{6}{792}$	$\dfrac{45}{792}$	$\dfrac{60}{792}$	$\dfrac{15}{792}$
1	$\dfrac{45}{792}$	$\dfrac{180}{792}$	$\dfrac{135}{792}$	$\dfrac{18}{792}$
2	$\dfrac{60}{792}$	$\dfrac{135}{792}$	$\dfrac{54}{792}$	$\dfrac{3}{792}$
3	$\dfrac{15}{792}$	$\dfrac{18}{792}$	$\dfrac{3}{792}$	0

By summing the probabilities in rows, the four values which comprise the marginal p.d.f. of X are obtained as

$$p_{0.} = \frac{126}{792} \quad p_{1.} = \frac{378}{792} \quad p_{2.} = \frac{252}{792} \quad p_{3.} = \frac{36}{792}.$$

Also, given that Y has the value 2, the conditional p.d.f. of X is evaluated to be

$$p_{0|2} = \frac{60}{252} \quad p_{1|2} = \frac{135}{252} \quad p_{2|2} = \frac{54}{252} \quad p_{3|2} = \frac{3}{252}.$$

From the symmetry of table 12.7, the marginal p.d.fs of X and Y are identical and they also have identical conditional p.d.fs.

$$E\{Y\} = E\{X\} = \frac{1}{792}(126 \times 0 + 378 \times 1 + 252 \times 2 + 36 \times 3) = \frac{990}{792} = \frac{5}{4},$$

$$E\{Y^2\} = E\{X^2\} = \frac{1}{792}(378 \times 1 + 252 \times 4 + 36 \times 9) = \frac{1710}{792} = \frac{95}{45},$$

$$E\{XY\} = \frac{1}{792}(180 \times 1 + 270 \times 2 + 36 \times 3 + 54 \times 4 + 6 \times 6) = \frac{1080}{792} = \frac{15}{11}.$$

Therefore

$$\rho = \frac{E\{XY\} - E\{X\}E\{Y\}}{[E\{X^2\} - (E\{X\})^2]^{1/2}[E\{Y^2\} - (E\{Y\})^2]^{1/2}} = \frac{\dfrac{15}{11} - \left(\dfrac{5}{4}\right)^2}{\dfrac{95}{44} - \left(\dfrac{5}{4}\right)^2} = -\frac{1}{3}.$$

Exercises

1. Verify that the functions $g(x \mid y)$ and $h(y \mid x)$ are proper p.d.fs.

2. Prove results (58) and (93) for discrete bivariate distributions by respectively considering

$$\mu_{(X+Y)} \equiv \sum_i \sum_j p_{ij}(x_i + y_j); \quad \sigma^2_{(X+Y)} \equiv \sum_i \sum_j p_{ij}(x_i + y_j)^2 - \mu^2_{(X+Y)}.$$

12.8 SIMULATION AND MONTE CARLO METHODS

Random Numbers

Consider again example 2 of §12.5. An interpretation of the solution is that the random dropping of girders in the manner indicated could be used as an experimental means for the approximate determination of π. Rather less drastic would be the tossing of a pencil onto suitably ruled paper, but better still, the problem may be simulated by using *random numbers*.

A number consisting of n digits is *random* if each permissible digit is equally likely to appear in each of these n positions. (Random numbers for which the digits have non-uniform probability distributions may be obtained by suitable transformation of the variate.)

Suppose a number, three digits long, is required in the decimal scale. The probability of choosing any particular one of the digits $0, 1, \ldots, 9$ in the first position is $1/10$. Identical probabilities exist for each of the other positions so that the probability of any specified arrangement is $1/10^3$, a result which naturally agrees with the fact that there are exactly 10^3 integers which lie in the range 000 to 999 inclusive.

In computation it is often easier, at least initially, to work in the binary scale. In this scale, an example of a typical ten-digit number would be 1010011110, which corresponds in the decimal scale to

$$1 \times 2^9 + 0 \times 2^8 + 1 \times 2^7 + 0 \times 2^6 + 0 \times 2^5 + 1 \times 2^4 + 1 \times 2^3 + 1 \times 2^2 + 1 \times 2^1$$
$$+ 0 \times 2^0 = 512 + 128 + 16 + 8 + 4 + 2 = 670.$$

There are 2^{10} distinct ten-digit binary numbers. As 1024 exceeds 10^3 it follows that any three-digit decimal number can be constructed from a sequence of ten binary digits. An elementary technique of generating random numbers is therefore to toss an 'unbiased' coin an appropriate number of times, letting (say) a 'head' signify 0 and a 'tail' signify 1. After conversion to the decimal scale, any numbers which lie outside the desired range (which in the given example would be 1000 to 1023 inclusive) are ignored. The numbers generated by most computer library programs, although only 'pseudo-random', are in fact adequate for all but the most exacting of problems.

EXAMPLE

The following thirty decimal digits were randomly generated by a computer with the probability of $1/10$ that any particular digit was chosen in any position:

$$8\ 9\ 0\ 1\ 9\ 4\ 7\ 8\ 5\ 7\ 0\ 6\ 8\ 8\ 1\ 1\ 5\ 4\ 2\ 4\ 2\ 5\ 3\ 0\ 3\ 5\ 6\ 3\ 0\ 2.$$

Use them to obtain an approximate value for $\int_1^2 x^2\, dx$.

A suitable approximation to $\int_1^2 x^2\, dx$ is given by $\dfrac{1}{10} \sum_{i=1}^{10} x_i^2$ where the $\{x_i\}$

constitute a set of ten random numbers with rectangular distribution over the range $(1, 2)$. If therefore these supplied digits are split into ten successive groups of three, i.e., 890, 194, . . . , and then each group of three is preceded by a 1 and the resulting values are divided by 10^3, the following numbers ensue:

$$x_i : 1.890\ \ 1.194\ \ 1.785\ \ 1.706\ \ 1.881\ \ 1.154\ \ 1.242\ \ 1.530\ \ 1.356\ \ 1.302.$$

Then

$$\frac{1}{10} \sum_{i=1}^{10} x_i^2 = \frac{1}{10}(3.572 + 1.426 + 3.185 + 2.911 + 3.538 + 1.332 + 1.543 + 2.341$$

$$+ 1.839 + 1.695) = \frac{23.382}{10} = 2.34 \text{ to two d.p.}$$

The calculated value may be compared with the exact answer of $2\frac{1}{3}$. Different grouping would of course produce different approximations.

Simulation

The preceding examples have served to illustrate how random numbers could be employed to derive answers to certain problems soluble by other means. Experience in operations research and similar modern branches of mathematics has shown that many problems which may involve random variables prove easy or relatively easy to formulate but so far elude complete analysis. Suppose for example that road works require that a heavily used road in a city must be closed for some weeks. What will be the resulting changes in traffic pattern? Will they be sufficient to warrant extra controls on traffic usage of the remaining streets and if so, what should these controls be? Given a reasonable knowledge of the present traffic distribution, it may be possible to simulate possible situations by using random numbers; for example, each random generation of the digit 5 may correspond to a heavy lorry making the journey, with other types of event corresponding to other digits or groups of digits.

It must be emphasized that success in this approach, known for obvious reasons as a *Monte Carlo method*, depends upon an adequate knowledge of the probability distributions of the appropriate variates. Nevertheless, this method has made it possible to avoid what would otherwise have been expensive catastrophes.

Exercise

1. Devise an alternative scheme for grouping the set of 30 random digits given on p. 491, and so obtain a second approximate value for $\int_{1}^{2} x^2 \, dx$. Adopt a similar technique to approximately evaluate $\int_{0}^{1/2} x^{1/2} \, dx$ and compare your answer with the exact value.

PROBLEMS

1. From extensive data has been compiled the following ranking for the frequency of occurrence of letters in the English language, from E the most popular to J and Z the least used:

   E T A O N I S R H L D C U P F M W Y B G V K Q X J Z.

Using this information, try and break a code given the following example, in which there is a one-to-one relationship between each letter and its coded form; the letters have been grouped into fives and the punctuation has been removed.

WXOER XJYAH QFOWU YDYCQ ZOFVZ BOEVO MWXYM HZWWX
YVEUK YZWVO MLCOU HUBPB WQHFI VWHWB VWBZV LYCAY
HWYOE CPBDY VWXBV BVVXO JFUQO ECMCY SEYFW EVYOM
JOCIV JXBZX CYPHW YWOWX YVYVE UKYZW VMOCY THALP
YLCOU HUPQZ XHFZY PBGYP QEFZY CWHBF HFILY CXHLV

2. Prove, by induction or otherwise, that

(i) $\quad {}^nC_1 - \frac{1}{2}{}^nC_2 + \frac{1}{3}{}^nC_3 - \ldots + (-1)^{n-1}\frac{1}{n}{}^nC_n = 1 + \frac{1}{2} + \frac{1}{3} + \ldots + \frac{1}{n},$

(ii) $\quad {}^nC_0 + {}^nC_1 + {}^nC_2 + \ldots + {}^nC_n = 2^n.$

3. At a certain location, the following mean monthly temperatures have been established. Assuming the months to be of equal duration, calculate the average temperature for the year, μ, and also evaluate the population variance σ^2 and the coefficient of variation. *Write down* the corresponding three values when the units are degrees Fahrenheit.

   9.1 8.7 11.2 11.7 15.6 20.4 20.1 21.0 18.5 12.6 9.2 8.6 °C.

4.   Draw the sample space for selecting one domino from a standard set of 28 dominoes. (Any domino bears the pair of numbers (m, n), where $m, n = 0, 1, 2, \ldots, 6$ and the order in which m, n occur is immaterial.)

Now let C_r be the set of dominoes for which $|m - n| = r$ $r = 0, 1, \ldots, 6$

   D_s be the set of dominoes for which $m + n = s$ $s = 0, 1, \ldots, 12$

   E_t be the set of dominoes in which at least one of m, n is equal to t
   $t = 0, 1, \ldots, 6$.

Indicate the sets C_2, D_4 and E_3 on the sample space diagram. If a single domino is withdrawn from the set, evaluate the probabilities $P(C_r), P(D_s), P(E_t)$. Also evaluate

$$P(C_2 \cap D_4), \quad P(C_2 \cap E_3), \quad P(D_4 \cap E_3), \quad P(C_2 \cup D_4), \quad P(C_2 \cap D_4 \cap E_3),$$
$$P(C_2 \cup D_4 \cup E_3), \quad P(C_2 \mid E_3), \quad P(E_3 \mid C_2), \quad P(D_4 \mid C_2 \cap E_3).$$

If two dominoes are simultaneously withdrawn from the 28, what is the probability that this pair has a digit in common?

5.   A multiple-choice examination paper containing 100 questions is to be answered. There is a list of six suggested replies for each question and in each case one of these statements is correct and the remaining five are equally wrong. A candidate who correctly indicates the answer in 60 cases is awarded a percentage mark of 52. Justify this and evaluate the final mark of someone correct in 85 of the answers.

6.   If, on average, 5% of a certain item are faulty, what is the probability that in a sample of twenty more than one will not be perfect? What is the probability that the first faulty item will appear before the nth member of the sample is inspected?

7.   An inspector checks each carton at the end of a production line. If the article is satisfactory, it is then stacked in a rack made to contain n cartons. If the probability that a carton is faulty is p, where p is constant and the faulty items are randomly distributed throughout the production run, find the probability that the nth carton completes the rack.

8.   A 'knock-out' sports contest is arranged with 2^r teams, where r is a positive integer, entering the first round. A match between any two teams is played to a decision so that one half of the number of teams in any one round proceeds to the next. On the assumptions that the pairings for each round leading up to the final are completely random and that either team is equally likely to win in any encounter, show that the probability that two particular teams Northville and Southville meet in the second round is $\frac{1}{2}/(2^r - 1)$, and the probability that they meet in the course of the contest is $(\frac{1}{2})^{r-1}$.

9.   On an aircraft are n passengers, each with a single piece of baggage. At the arrival airport the passengers and their baggage are separated and pass one by one at unit time intervals through their respective checking systems to be subsequently reunited in the claim area. If the orders in which passengers and their baggage proceed are independent and both systems commence at the same time, prove that the expected period that the rth passenger waits for baggage in the claim area is $(n - r)(n - r + 1)/2n$ time units. Hence, show that the expected waiting time per passenger is $(n - 1)(n + 1)/6n$.

$$\left[\sum_{q=1}^{m} q = \frac{1}{2} m(m+1), \quad \sum_{q=1}^{m} q^2 = \frac{1}{6} m(m+1)(2m+1) \right].$$

10. An automatic method for sealing containers is found to have a 3% failure rate, the distribution of failures being random. To detect which containers have not been properly sealed, an acoustic screening test is devised to which 96% of the faulty containers react positively and to which only 5% of those satisfactory react positively. Determine the probability that a container which reacts positively is a faulty one.

11. The probability that at a certain bus stop the vehicle arrives on time is α and the probability that it arrives between t and $t + \delta t$ minutes late is $\alpha e^{-\beta t} \delta t$. If the bus is never early, show that $\beta = \alpha/(1 - \alpha)$. Given further that on average the bus is $2\frac{1}{4}$ minutes late, find α and β and deduce that only about three buses in eighty can be expected to be more than 9 minutes late in arrival.

[This in an example of a random variable held to be part discrete and part continuous.]

12. A process produces spherical grains of homogeneous material of density ρ. The probability that the radius of a grain lies in the range $(r, r + \delta r)$ is proportional to $r^2 e^{-r} \delta r$. Determine

(a)   the probability density function for their radii R,
(b)   the probability density function for their masses M.

Determine the mean diameter of a grain and the expected mass of a grain.

$$\left[I_n \equiv \int_0^\infty r^n e^{-r} \, dr = n! \quad \text{for } n \geqslant 0, n \text{ an integer.} \right]$$

13. If for all x the p.d.f. of X is $f(x) = \dfrac{1}{\sqrt{(2\pi)}} e^{-\frac{1}{2}x^2}$ find the p.d.fs of $U = |X|$ and of $V = X^2$.

14. What is the probability that in a sequence of Bernoulli trials there will be exactly k failures before the first success? Show that the corresponding p.g.f. for this variate is given by $G(t) = p/(1 - qt)$ where p is the probability of success in any one trial, $q = 1 - p$ and t is the dummy parameter. Deduce that the mean is q/p and the variance is q/p^2.

15. If X_1 is $Bi(n_1, p)$, X_2 is $Bi(n_2, p)$ and X_1 and X_2 are independent, show that $X_1 + X_2$ is $Bi(n_1 + n_2, p)$.

16. Let p_k be the probability that there will be 'k or more' occurrences in the Poissonian variates $Po(\lambda)$, for $\lambda = \frac{1}{2}, 1, 2, 4$. Plot your results as $\log p_k$ *vs* $\log \lambda$ for $k = 1, 2, 3$ and 5. Discuss ways in which this *Poisson summation chart* can be used.

17. In the first ten months of operation of a photo-copying machine, the following pattern of breakdowns was recorded:

number of breakdowns	0	1	2	3
number of months	3	5	1	1.

Assuming that the breakdowns are independent, that this data is typical and that a Poissonian distribution is appropriate for the probability of there being X breakdowns in any month, use this information to establish the proportion of months in which more than 2 breakdowns may be expected to occur.

18. In the manufacture of over-to-table kitchenware, faults liable to occur are that the items are cracked, discoloured, misshapen. The probabilities are

0.0020 that an item is cracked,
0.0019 that an item is discoloured,
0.0026 that an item is misshapen,
0.0004 that an item is both cracked and discoloured,
0.0005 that an item is both discoloured and misshapen,
0.0007 that an item is both misshapen and cracked,
0.0001 that an item has all three imperfections.

Determine the probability that an item selected at random
(a) will be perfect,
(b) will have exactly one imperfection,
(c) will have exactly two imperfections.

Write down the probability that a batch of 100 items, randomly selected,
(a) will all be perfect,
(b) will contain exactly one imperfect item,
(c) will contain exactly two imperfect items.

Approximately determine these three values by evaluating an appropriate expression based on the Poissonian distribution.

19. Electrical components were tested to destruction by reversing the direction of a large current through them a sufficient number of times. The number failing at each switching was recorded with the following results:

number of current reversals to failure
$\leqslant 6$ 7 8 9 10 11 12 13 14 15 16 17 18 19 20 21 22 23 24 25 $\geqslant 26$

number failing
0 5 3 7   5 15   8 24 28 28 29 28 21 16 12 13   8   3   8   4   0

Use this sample data to estimate the mean and variance of the parent population. Fit a normal distribution based on these estimates. Compare the observed proportion of components exceeding 20 switchings to failure with the proportion estimated from the fitted distribution.

20. 'Long-life' electric light bulbs manufactured by a certain firm are found to have mean lives of 1700 hours and the associated standard deviation is 320 hours. 'Standard' electric light bulbs also produced by the same firm have a mean life of 1400 hours and a standard deviation of 240 hours. If in each case the lifetime is assumed to follow a normal distribution and a bulb of each type is chosen at random, find

(a) the probability that the standard light bulb does not meet the manufacturer's claim of 'more than a thousand hours of light',

  (b)   the probability that the standard light bulb will survive the long-life bulb,

  (c)   the probability that the long-life bulb will outlast the standard bulb by more than 500 hours.

If random samples of four bulbs of each type are taken, what is the probability that the total life of the sample of standard bulbs exceeds the total life of the sample of 'long-life' bulbs?

21.   Evaluate the correlation coefficient $\rho(Y_1, Y_2)$ if $Y_1 = k_{11}X_1 + k_{12}X_2$, $Y_2 = k_{21}X_1 + k_{22}X_2$ where X_1 and X_2 are identically and independently distributed random variables and the ks are constants. Deduce that $X_1 - X_2$ and $X_1 + X_2$ are uncorrelated and illustrate this by drawing the corresponding sample space when X_1 and X_2 are the scores on the upper faces of two unbiased dice.

22.   Make an approximate determination of π by using a Monte Carlo method.

BIBLIOGRAPHY

Many books include aspects of statistics. Most introductory texts start with elementary ideas concerning probability, as discussed in this chapter and the majority continue to consider inference, to which Chapter 3 of Volume 2 is devoted. Some include sections on operations research and similar modern topics. Many merit attention for further reading. In the following list, the first is particularly rich in examples, both worked and unworked, and although the fourth book requires greater mathematical sophistication it deals with both theoretical aspects and situations which the practising engineer can expect to encounter.

[1]   Spiegel, M. R., *Theory and Problems of Statistics*, McGraw-Hill, New York (1961).
[2]   Neville, A. M., and J. B. Kennedy, *Basic Statistical Methods for Engineers and Scientists*, International Textbook Co., Scranton, Pa (1964).
[3]   Chatfield, C., *Statistics for Technology*, Associated Book Publishers.
[4]   Belz, M. H., *Statistical Methods in the Process Industries*, Macmillan, London (1973).

Appendix

TABLE A1: LAPLACE TRANSFORMS

$f(t)$ $\qquad\qquad\qquad\qquad\qquad\qquad \bar{f}(s) = \displaystyle\int_0^\infty e^{-st} f(t)\,dt$

Properties

$e^{at} f(t)$		$\bar{f}(s-a)$
$f(t-a)H(t-a)$	$(a>0)$	$e^{-as}\bar{f}(s)$
$f(at)$	$(a>0)$	$a^{-1}\bar{f}(a^{-1}s)$
$\displaystyle\int_0^t f(\tau)\,d\tau$		$s^{-1}\bar{f}(s)$
$t^n f(t)$	$(n=1,2,3,\ldots)$	$(-1)^n \bar{f}^{(n)}(s)$
$t^{-1} f(t)$		$\displaystyle\int_s^\infty \bar{f}(\sigma)\,d\sigma$
$f(t)*g(t) \equiv \displaystyle\int_0^t f(\tau)g(t-\tau)\,d\tau$		$\bar{f}(s)\bar{g}(s)$
$f^{(n)}(t)$		$s^n \bar{f}(s) - \displaystyle\sum_{r=1}^n s^{n-r} f^{(r-1)}(0)$
$\displaystyle\sum_{n=0}^{[t/a]} r^n f(t-na)$	$(a>0)$	$(1-re^{-as})^{-1}\bar{f}(s)$

Transform Pairs

$\delta(t-a)$	$(a>0)$	e^{-as}
$H(t-a)$	$(a>0)$	$s^{-1}e^{-as}$
$_r[t/a]$	$(a>0)$	$s^{-1}(1-re^{-as})^{-1}(1-e^{-as})$
$(-1)^{[t/a]}$	$(a>0)$ (square wave)	$s^{-1}\tanh(\tfrac{1}{2}as)$
t^n	$(n=0,1,2,3,\ldots)$	$n!\,s^{-n-1}$

t^{ν}	$(\nu > -1)$	$\Gamma(\nu + 1)s^{-\nu-1}$
$t^{-1}H(t - a)$	$(a > 0)$	$E_1(as)$
e^{kt}		$(s - k)^{-1}$
$\exp(-\tfrac{1}{4}a^{-1}t^2)$	$(a > 0)$	$\pi^{1/2}a^{1/2}\exp(as^2)\operatorname{erfc}(a^{1/2}s)$
$t^{-3/2}e^{-a/t}$	$(a > 0)$	$\pi^{1/2}a^{-1/2}\exp(-2a^{1/2}s^{1/2})$
$t^{-1}(e^{\alpha t} - e^{\beta t})$		$\log(s - \beta) - \log(s - \alpha)$
$\sinh kt$		$k(s^2 - k^2)^{-1}$
$\cosh kt$		$s(s^2 - k^2)^{-1}$
$\sin kt$		$k(s^2 + k^2)^{-1}$
$\cos kt$		$s(s^2 + k^2)^{-1}$
$t\sin kt$		$2ks(s^2 + k^2)^{-2}$
$t\cos kt$		$(s^2 - k^2)(s^2 + k^2)^{-2}$
$t^{-1}\sin kt$		$\tan^{-1}(ks^{-1})$
$t^{-1}(1 - \cos kt)$		$\tfrac{1}{2}\log(1 + k^2 s^{-2})$
$t^{-1/2}\cos kt^{1/2}$		$\pi^{1/2}s^{-1/2}\exp(-\tfrac{1}{4}k^2 s^{-1})$
$J_0(kt)$		$(s^2 + k^2)^{-1/2}$
$J_0(kt^{1/2})$		$s^{-1}\exp(-\tfrac{1}{4}k^2 s^{-1})$
$I_0(kt)$		$(s^2 - k^2)^{-1/2}$
$I_0(kt^{1/2})$		$s^{-1}\exp(\tfrac{1}{4}k^2 s^{-1})$
$\operatorname{erf}(kt^{1/2})$		$ks^{-1}(s + k^2)^{-1/2}$
$\operatorname{erfc}(kt^{-1/2})$	$(k > 0)$	$s^{-1}\exp(-2ks^{1/2})$
$E_1(t)$		$s^{-1}\log(s + 1)$
$\operatorname{Ci}(t)$		$-\tfrac{1}{2}s^{-1}\log(s^2 + 1)$
$\operatorname{Si}(t)$		$s^{-1}\cot^{-1}s$

TABLE A2   THE STANDARDIZED NORMAL VARIATE

Z is a standardized normal variate $N(0, 1)$

$f(z)$ is the probability density function $\dfrac{1}{\sqrt{(2\pi)}}\,e^{-\frac{1}{2}z^2}$.

$F(z)$ is the cumulative density function $\displaystyle\int_{-\infty}^{z}\dfrac{1}{\sqrt{(2\pi)}}\,e^{-\frac{1}{2}t^2}\,dt$.

$f(-z) = f(z)$
$F(-z) = 1 - F(z)$.

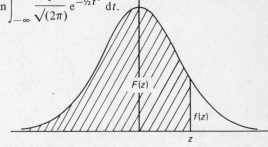

$f(z)$	z	0.00	0.01	0.02	0.03	0.04	0.05	0.06	0.07	0.08	0.09
0.399	0.0	0.5000	0.5040	0.5080	0.5120	0.5160	0.5199	0.5239	0.5279	0.5319	0.5359
0.397	0.1	0.5398	0.5438	0.5478	0.5517	0.5557	0.5596	0.5636	0.5675	0.5714	0.5753
0.391	0.2	0.5793	0.5832	0.5871	0.5910	0.5948	0.5987	0.6026	0.6064	0.6103	0.6141
0.381	0.3	0.6179	0.6217	0.6255	0.6293	0.6331	0.6368	0.6406	0.6443	0.6480	0.6517
0.368	0.4	0.6554	0.6591	0.6628	0.6664	0.6700	0.6736	0.6772	0.6808	0.6844	0.6879
0.352	0.5	0.6915	0.6950	0.6985	0.7019	0.7054	0.7088	0.7123	0.7157	0.7190	0.7224
0.333	0.6	0.7257	0.7291	0.7324	0.7357	0.7389	0.7422	0.7454	0.7486	0.7517	0.7549
0.312	0.7	0.7580	0.7611	0.7642	0.7673	0.7704	0.7734	0.7764	0.7794	0.7823	0.7852
0.290	0.8	0.7881	0.7910	0.7939	0.7967	0.7995	0.8023	0.8051	0.8078	0.8106	0.8133
0.266	0.9	0.8159	0.8186	0.8212	0.8238	0.8264	0.8289	0.8315	0.8340	0.8365	0.8389
0.242	1.0	0.8413	0.8438	0.8461	0.8485	0.8508	0.8531	0.8554	0.8577	0.8599	0.8621
0.218	1.1	0.8643	0.8665	0.8686	0.8708	0.8729	0.8749	0.8770	0.8790	0.8810	0.8830
0.194	1.2	0.8849	0.8869	0.8888	0.8907	0.8925	0.8944	0.8962	0.8980	0.8997	0.9015
0.171	1.3	0.9032	0.9049	0.9066	0.9082	0.9099	0.9115	0.9131	0.9147	0.9162	0.9177
0.150	1.4	0.9192	0.9207	0.9222	0.9236	0.9251	0.9265	0.9279	0.9292	0.9306	0.9319
0.130	1.5	0.9332	0.9345	0.9357	0.9370	0.9382	0.9394	0.9406	0.9418	0.9429	0.9441
0.111	1.6	0.9452	0.9463	0.9474	0.9484	0.9495	0.9505	0.9515	0.9525	0.9535	0.9545
0.094	1.7	0.9554	0.9564	0.9573	0.9582	0.9591	0.9599	0.9608	0.9616	0.9625	0.9633
0.079	1.8	0.9641	0.9649	0.9656	0.9664	0.9671	0.9678	0.9686	0.9693	0.9699	0.9706
0.066	1.9	0.9713	0.9719	0.9726	0.9732	0.9738	0.9744	0.9750	0.9756	0.9761	0.9767
0.054	2.0	0.9772	0.9778	0.9783	0.9788	0.9793	0.9798	0.9803	0.9808	0.9812	0.9817
0.044	2.1	0.9821	0.9826	0.9830	0.9834	0.9838	0.9842	0.9846	0.9850	0.9854	0.9857
0.035	2.2	0.9861	0.9864	0.9868	0.9871	0.9875	0.9878	0.9881	0.9884	0.9887	0.9890
0.028	2.3	0.9893	0.9896	0.9898	0.9901	0.9904	0.9906	0.9909	0.9911	0.9913	0.9916
0.022	2.4	0.9918	0.9920	0.9922	0.9925	0.9927	0.9929	0.9931	0.9932	0.9934	0.9936
0.018	2.5	0.9938	0.9940	0.9941	0.9943	0.9945	0.9946	0.9948	0.9949	0.9951	0.9952
0.014	2.6	0.9953	0.9955	0.9956	0.9957	0.9959	0.9960	0.9961	0.9962	0.9963	0.9964
0.010	2.7	0.9965	0.9966	0.9967	0.9968	0.9969	0.9970	0.9971	0.9972	0.9973	0.9974
0.008	2.8	0.9974	0.9975	0.9976	0.9977	0.9977	0.9978	0.9979	0.9979	0.9980	0.9981
0.006	2.9	0.9981	0.9982	0.9982	0.9983	0.9984	0.9984	0.9985	0.9985	0.9986	0.9986

z	0.675	1.282	1.645	1.960	2.326	2.576	3.090
$F(z)$	0.750	0.900	0.950	0.975	0.990	0.995	0.999

Answers to Exercises and Problems

CHAPTER 1

Exercises

§1.2

2.   (a) $2 \, dy/dx = y/x$,   (b) $dy/dx = 2xy$,

      (c) $dy/dx = x^{-1}(1 - y^2)^{1/2} \sin^{-1} y$

§1.3

1.   (a) $\sin x \cos y = C$,   (b) $Kt + C = \dfrac{1}{4T_0^3} \left(\log \dfrac{T_0 + T}{T_0 - T} + 2 \tan^{-1} \dfrac{T}{T_0} \right)$

2.   (a) $y = C \exp(-\tfrac{1}{3} x^3 / y^3)$,   (b) $x = C \sin(y/x)$

3.   (a) $\log(x^2 - xy + y^2 - x + y + \tfrac{1}{3}) - 2\sqrt{3} \tan^{-1} \left\{ \dfrac{2y - x + 1}{\sqrt{3}(x - \tfrac{1}{3})} \right\} = C$,

      (b) $x^2 - 2xy - y^2 + 6x + 2y = C$

4. $4(x - 2y) - \log(4x + 8y + 5) = C$

5.   (a) $y = \cos x + C \cos^2 x$,   (b) $y = -\tfrac{1}{3} \cos x + C \sec^2 x$

6.   (a) $x^3 + y^3 + 3xy = C$,   (b) $x + \sin xy = C$

7.   (a) $y = \tfrac{1}{2} x^2 e^x + C e^x$ (linear),

      (b) $x^2 + y^2 = C \exp\{2 \tan^{-1}(y/x)\}$ (homogeneous),

      (c) $y + 1 = C \exp\left(\dfrac{x - 1}{y + 1} \right)$ (reducible to homogeneous),

      (d) $e^y \log(1 + x) - x = C$ (exact)

8.   (a) $y = (Ce^x + x + 1)^{-1/2}$,   (b) $x + C = \tfrac{1}{2} \tan^{-1}(x + y) + \tfrac{1}{4} \log \dfrac{1 + x + y}{1 - x - y}$,

      (c) $y \sin x - x \sin y = C$

§1.5

1.   (a) $y = Ae^{3x} + Be^{-3x}$,   (b) $y = A\cos 3x + B\sin 3x$,

    (c) $y = Ae^{-3x} + Be^{-5x}$,   (d) $y = e^{-3x}(A\cos 2x + B\sin 2x)$,

    (e) $y = (Ax + B)e^{3x}$,   (f) $y = A + Be^{3x}$,

    (g) $y = Ae^{x} + B\cos 2x + C\sin 2x$,

    (h) $y = \exp(x/\sqrt{2})\{A\cos(x/\sqrt{2}) + B\sin(x/\sqrt{2})\}$
         $+ \exp(-x/\sqrt{2})\{C\cos(x/\sqrt{2}) + E\sin(x/\sqrt{2})\}$,

    (i) $y = (Ax + B)\cos x + (Cx + E)\sin x$,

    (j) $y = (A + Bx + Cx^{2} + Ex^{3})e^{-x}$

§1.7

1.   (a) $y = e^{x}(A\cos x + B\sin x) + 2e^{x}$,

    (b) $y = Ae^{x} + Be^{12x} + 2$,

    (c) $y = Ae^{x} + Be^{2x} + \frac{1}{2}x^{3} + \frac{7}{4}x^{2} + \frac{17}{4}x + \frac{33}{8}$,

    (d) $y = Ae^{x} + Be^{3x} - \frac{1}{2}\cos x - \sin x$,

    (e) $y = (A + 4x)e^{4x} + Be^{-4x}$,

    (f) $y = (A - \frac{1}{2}x + 2x^{2})e^{4x} + Be^{-4x}$,

    (g) $y = Ae^{px} + Be^{-px} + \dfrac{ax}{2p}\cosh px$,

    (h) $y = Ae^{2x} + Be^{-2x} + (C - 2x)e^{-x}$,

    (i) $y = e^{-x}(A\sin x + B\cos x) + \frac{1}{8}e^{x}(\sin x - \cos x)$,

    (j) $y = e^{-x}\{A\sin 2x + (B - \frac{1}{4}x)\cos 2x\}$

2.   (a) $s = \frac{1}{3}Ve^{-2t}\sin 3t$,

    (b) $y = \dfrac{(\pi^{2} - 1)\sinh t}{(\pi^{2} + 1)\sinh \frac{1}{2}} + \dfrac{2\sin \pi t}{\pi^{2} + 1}$,

    (c) $y = e^{-4t}$

3. $y = -\dfrac{g}{\Omega^{2}} + A\cos px + B\sin px + C\cosh px + E\sinh px$,

    (a) $y = \dfrac{g}{\Omega^{2}}\left[\dfrac{1}{2}\dfrac{\cos px}{\cos pl} + \dfrac{1}{2}\dfrac{\cosh px}{\cosh pl} - 1\right]$,

    (b) $y = \dfrac{g}{\Omega^{2}}\left[\dfrac{\cos px\sinh pl + \cosh px\sin pl}{\cos pl\sinh pl + \cosh pl\sin pl} - 1\right]$,

    where $p = (w\Omega^{2}/gEI)^{1/4}$

§1.9

1. (a) $y = A \exp\{\tfrac{1}{2}(-5 + \sqrt{5})t\} + B \exp\{\tfrac{1}{2}(-5 - \sqrt{5})t\} + 4e^t/11,$

   $z = \tfrac{1}{2}(1 + \sqrt{5})A \exp\{\tfrac{1}{2}(-5 + \sqrt{5})t\} + \tfrac{1}{2}(1 - \sqrt{5})B \exp\{\tfrac{1}{2}(-5 - \sqrt{5})t\}$
   $+ 5e^t/11,$

   (b) $y = 6Ae^{2x} - Be^{-2x} + Ce^x,$

   $z = -Ae^{2x} + 6Be^{-2x} + Ee^{-x}$

2. $x = \dfrac{MV}{H^2 e}\left(1 - \cos\dfrac{Het}{M}\right), \qquad y = \dfrac{MV}{H^2 e}\left(\dfrac{Het}{M} - \sin\dfrac{Het}{M}\right)$

§1.10

1. (a) $y = Ax^n + Bx^{-n},$

   (b) $y = Ax^{-1} + Bx^{-4} + \tfrac{1}{2}\log x - \tfrac{5}{8},$

   (c) $y = A(x - 2)^{-1} + B(x - 2)^{-2}$

Problems

1. (a) $x = C \exp\{\sin(y/x)\},$

   (b) $y = -2 + C \sec^2 x$

2. (a) $x + y = Cx^2 \exp\{-x/(x + y)\},$

   (b) $y = -\cot x + C \operatorname{cosec} x,$

   (c) $x^2 e^x \log y + xy = C$

3. (a) $(x^2 + y^2)e^x = C,$ (b)   Not exact

4. (a) $y = \exp(-\tfrac{1}{2}at)[A \exp\{\tfrac{1}{2}(a^2 - 25)^{1/2} t\} + B \exp\{-\tfrac{1}{2}(a^2 - 25)^{1/2} t\}] \; (a > 5),$

   $y = \exp(-\tfrac{1}{2}at)[A \sin\{\tfrac{1}{2}(25 - a^2)^{1/2} t\} + B \cos\{\tfrac{1}{2}(25 - a^2)^{1/2} t\}] \quad (a < 5),$

   $y = (A + Bt)\exp(-5t/2) \quad (a = 5),$

   (b) $y = \exp(-3t/2)(A \sin 2t + B \cos 2t) + \cos 2t + (8/3)\sin 2t$

5. $y = (A + Bx)e^x + (C + \tfrac{1}{3}x)e^{-2x},$

   $y = (1 + \tfrac{1}{3}x)e^{-2x}$

6. (a) $y = e^{2x}\{x - \sin x + \tfrac{2}{3}(1 - \cos x)\},$

   (b) $y = (x^2 + \tfrac{16}{5}x)e^{-x}$

7. (a) $y = x^{-2}(x - 1)e^x + Cx^{-2},$

   (b) $y = (A + Bx + \tfrac{1}{2}x^2)e^x$

8. (a) $y = \dfrac{x(x+C)}{x^2 + a^2}$,

    (b) $y = e^{-2x}(A \cos 3x + B \sin 3x) + 3 \cos x + \sin x$,

    (c) $y = (A + Bx + \frac{1}{2}x^2)e^{-x}$

9. (a) $y = \{\frac{1}{2} + C \exp(-x^2)\}/x$

    (b) $y = Ae^{-x} + Be^{-2x} + 3 \sin x + \cos x$,

    (c) $y = (A + x^2 - 2x)e^{-x} + Be^{-2x}$

10. $x = e^t$, $y = e^t$, $z = e^t$

11. $x = A \cos t + B \sin t - \frac{1}{2}(1 + t)e^{-t}$,

    $y = -(A + B)\cos t + (A - B)\sin t + \frac{1}{2}e^{-t} + e^t$

12. $x = Ae^{3t} + Be^{-3t} + C \sin t + E \cos t - e^{-t}$,

    $y = Ae^{3t} + 25Be^{-3t} + (3C + 4E)\sin t + (3E - 4C)\cos t - 9e^{-t}$,

    $x = \frac{1}{5}e^{-3t} - e^{-t}$, $y = 5e^{-3t} - 9e^{-t}$

13. $dx/dt = -e^{-t}(\cos t + \sin t)$, $dy/dt = e^{-t}(\cos t - \sin t)$

15. $y = t^{-4}\{\cos(3 \log t) + \exp(2\pi/3)\sin(3 \log t)\}$

16. $y = A \sin(2 \log x) + (B - \frac{1}{4} \log x)\cos(2 \log x) + \frac{1}{3} \sin(\log x)$

17. $x = t$, $y = -t$

CHAPTER 2
Exercises

§2.2

1. π, 2π, 10π, π/l, L, $2\pi/\omega$, $2\pi/\omega$, 2π, 6π, 2π

2. (a) $f(x) = \exp(x - 2\pi)$,

    (b) $f(x) = \exp\{x - (p + 1)\pi\}$ when p is odd,

    $$f(x) = \begin{cases} \exp(x - p\pi) & \text{for } p\pi \leqslant x < (p + 1)\pi \\ \exp\{x - (p + 2)\pi\} & \text{for } (p + 1)\pi \leqslant x < (p + 2)\pi \end{cases}$$ when p is even

3. (a) $a_0 = 0$, $a_n = 0$, $b_n = 2\{1 - (-1)^n\}(n\pi)^{-1}$ for $n = 1, 2, 3, \ldots$

    (b) $a_0 = \frac{1}{2}\pi$, $a_n = \{(-1)^n - 1\}(n^2\pi)^{-1}$, $b_n = (-1)^{n+1}n^{-1}$

    for $n = 1, 2, 3, \ldots$

4. $2\pi^{-1} \sum\limits_{n=1}^{\infty} n^{-1}\{1 + (-1)^{n+1}(1 + \pi)\}\sin nx$

5. $\frac{1}{6}L^2 + L^2 \sum\limits_{n=1}^{\infty} \left[\frac{2(-1)^n}{n^2\pi^2} \cos\left(\frac{n\pi x}{L}\right) + \left\{ \frac{(-1)^{n+1}}{n\pi} + \frac{2(-1)^n}{n^3\pi^3} - \frac{2}{n^3\pi^3} \right\} \sin\left(\frac{n\pi x}{L}\right) \right]$

§2.3

1. (a) None,   (b) $x = 0, \pm 2L, \pm 4L, \ldots$

2. (a) $f(\pi^+) = e^{-\pi}$, $f(\pi^-) = e^{\pi}$, $f'(\pi^+) = e^{-\pi}$,

    (b) $f(\pi^+) = \pi$, $f(\pi^-) = -\pi$, $f'(\pi^+) = 0$

4. Substitute $x = 0$

§2.4

1. (a) Odd,   (b) even,   (c) neither,   (d) neither,

    (e) even,   (f) odd

2. $\frac{1}{3}\pi^2 + \sum\limits_{n=1}^{\infty} [4n^{-2}(-1)^n \cos nx + 2n^{-1}\pi^{-1}\{1 - (-1)^n\}\sin nx]$

3. $\sum\limits_{r=0}^{\infty} 8r(4r^2 + 1)^{-1}\pi^{-1} \sin 2rx$

4. (a) $\sum\limits_{n=1}^{\infty} 2Ln^{-1}\pi^{-1}\{2 - 3(-1)^n\}\sin(n\pi t/L)$

    (b) $\frac{5}{2}L + \sum\limits_{n=1}^{\infty} 2Ln^{-2}\pi^{-2}\{(-1)^n - 1\}\cos(n\pi x/L)$

5. $g(x) = \frac{1}{2}\{f(x) + f(-x)\}$, $h(x) = \frac{1}{2}\{f(x) - f(-x)\}$

§2.5

1. $\sum\limits_{r=0}^{\infty} 4(2r + 1)^{-1}\pi^{-1} \sin\{(2r + 1)\pi t/L\}$

    Integrate between $t = \frac{1}{2}L$ and $t = x$ when x is positive and $t = -\frac{1}{2}L$ and $t = x$ when x is negative to obtain

    $|x| = \frac{1}{2}L - 4L\pi^{-2} \sum\limits_{r=0}^{\infty} (2r + 1)^{-2} \cos\{(2r + 1)\pi x/L\}$

2. $\quad 1 - \tfrac{1}{2}\cos x + 2 \sum_{n=2}^{\infty} (-1)^{n+1}(n^2 - 1)^{-1}\cos nx, \quad g(x) = f'(x) - \sin x,$

therefore Fourier series is $-\tfrac{1}{2}\sin x + 2\sum_{n=2}^{\infty} n(-1)^n(n^2 - 1)^{-1}\sin nx$

Problems

3. $\quad \tfrac{1}{2}\pi + 4\pi^{-1}\sum_{r=0}^{\infty}(2r + 1)^{-2}\cos\{(2r + 1)x\}$

4. $\quad \pi + \tfrac{1}{4}L + L\pi^{-2}\sum_{n=1}^{\infty}[\{(-1)^n - 1\}n^{-2}\cos(n\pi x/L) + \pi n^{-1}(-1)^{n+1}\sin(n\pi x/L)]$

5. $\quad 1 + \tfrac{1}{32}\pi^3 + \sum_{n=1}^{\infty}[\tfrac{3}{2}\pi n^{-2}(-1)^n + \tfrac{3}{2}\pi^{-1}n^{-4}\{1 - (-1)^n\}]\cos 2nx$

6. $\quad \pi^{-1}\sinh\pi + \dfrac{2\sinh\pi}{\pi}\sum_{n=1}^{\infty}\left\{\dfrac{(-1)^n}{n^2 + 1}\cos nx + \dfrac{n(-1)^{n+1}}{n^2 + 1}\sin nx\right\}$

7. $\quad \tfrac{1}{2}\pi + \pi^{-1}\sinh\pi + 2\pi^{-1}\sum_{n=1}^{\infty}\left\{\left[\dfrac{\{(-1)^n - 1\}}{n^2} + \dfrac{(-1)^n\sinh\pi}{1 + n^2}\right]\cos nx\right.$

$$\left. + \dfrac{n(-1)^{n+1}\sinh\pi}{1 + n^2}\sin nx\right\}$$

8. $\quad$ Substitute $x = \tfrac{1}{2}\pi$

9. $\quad$ (a) $\sum_{n=1}^{\infty} 3 ln^{-2}\pi^{-2}\sin(\tfrac{1}{3}n\pi)\sin(n\pi x/l),$

$\qquad$ (b) $\tfrac{1}{6}l + \sum_{n=1}^{\infty} ln^{-2}\pi^{-2}\{3\cos(\tfrac{1}{3}n\pi) - 2 - (-1)^n\}\cos(n\pi x/l)$

10. $\quad \sum_{n=1}^{\infty} 2n\pi(n^2\pi^2 + L^2)^{-1}\{1 - (-1)^n e^L\}\sin(n\pi x/L),$

$\qquad \sum_{n=1}^{\infty} 2L(n^2\pi^2 + L^2)^{-1}\{e^L(-1)^n - 1\}\cos(n\pi x/L)$

11. $\quad 12L^3\pi^{-3}\sum_{n=1}^{\infty}(-1)^n n^{-3}\sin(n\pi x/L)$, integrate between $x = -L$ and $x = y$ to obtain

$\frac{1}{2}A_0 + 48L^4\pi^{-4}\sum_{n=1}^{\infty}(-1)^{n+1}n^{-4}\cos(n\pi y/L)$ where $A_0 = 24L^4\pi^{-4}\sum_{n=1}^{\infty}n^{-4} = \frac{16}{15}L^4$

12. $\sum_{n=1}^{\infty}[\pi(-1)^{n+1}n^{-1} + 2\pi^{-1}n^{-3}\{(-1)^n - 1\}]\sin nx$, $f(x)$ is discontinuous at $x = \pm\pi$

13. 2π, even

14. $\sum_{n=1}^{\infty}a_n\{(25 - n^2\omega^2)\cos n\omega t + 0.03n\omega\sin n\omega t\}\{(25 - n^2\omega^2)^2 + (0.03n\omega)^2\}^{-1}$

where $a_n = 0$ for n even and $a_n = 4\pi^{-1}n^{-2}\omega^{-1}$ for n odd. $\frac{16}{15}\pi^{-1}\sin 5t$

15. $y(t) = e^{-kt/2}\{A\cos\omega t + B\sin\omega t\}$

$+\sum_{n=1}^{\infty}(-1)^n\{(n^2 - c^2)^2 + k^2n^2\}^{-1}\{kn^{-2}\cos nt + n^{-3}(n^2 - c^2)\sin nt\}$

where $\omega = (c^2 - \frac{1}{4}k^2)^{1/2}$. c approximately equal to a small integer

CHAPTER 3

Exercises

§3.1

1. (a) $2s^{-3}$,   (b) $n!s^{-n-1}$

2. $s(s^2 - k^2)^{-1}$

3. (a) $s(s^2 + \omega^2)^{-1}$,   (b) $\omega(s^2 + \omega^2)^{-1}$

4. (a) $t^3/6$,   (b) e^{3t},   (c) $\frac{1}{2}\sinh 2t$,   (d) $e^{2t} - 1$,

   (e) $e^{-t} + \cos t$

§3.2

1. $(s - 1)^{-2}$

2. $2(s - 1)^{-3}$

3. (a) $3(s^2 + s - 2)^{-1}$, $3s(s^2 + s - 2)^{-1}$, $(6 - 3s)(s^2 + s - 2)^{-1}$;

   (b) $(s + 1)(s^2 + 2s - 3)^{-1}$, $(3 - s)(s^2 + 2s - 3)^{-1}$, $(5s - 3)(s^2 + 2s - 3)^{-1}$;

   (c) $2s(s^2 + 1)^{-2}$, $2s^2(s^2 + 1)^{-2}$, $2s^3(s^2 + 1)^{-2}$

5. $\frac{4}{3}\cosh\sqrt{2}t - \frac{1}{3}\cos t$

§3.3

1. $\displaystyle\sum_{n=0}^{\infty} (t/a - n)\{H(t/a - n) - H(t/a - n - 1)\}$

2. $\epsilon^{-2}\{(t - t_0 + \epsilon)H(t - t_0 + \epsilon) - 2(t - t_0)H(t - t_0) + (t - t_0 - \epsilon)H(t - t_0 - \epsilon)\}$

§3.4

1. (a) $\tan^{-1}(s + 2)^{-1}$,   (b) $e^{-\pi s/2} \tan^{-1} s^{-1}$

2. (a) $\frac{1}{2}e^{-t}(\sin t - t \cos t)$,   (b) $\frac{1}{2}[(t - \pi)\cos t - \sin t]H(t - \pi)$

4. $(s^2 - 4)(s^2 + 4)^{-2}$, $2s(s^2 - 12)(s^2 + 4)^{-3}$

5. $\frac{1}{2}\log(s + 1) - \frac{1}{2}\log(s - 1)$

6. $s^{-2} - s^{-1}(e^s - 1)^{-1}$

7. $\frac{1}{3}(\cos t - \cos 2t)$

8. (a) $\tan^{-1} 3s^{-1}$,   (b) $\frac{1}{8}e^{-t/4}(\sin \frac{1}{4}t - \frac{1}{4}t \cos \frac{1}{4}t)$

§3.5

1. (a) $b^{-1}e^{at} \sin bt$,   (b) $\sin t - 2 \cos t + e^{-t}(\sin t + 2 \cos t)$,

    (c) $t \cosh 2t$,   (d) $\frac{3}{2}(e - 1)^{-1}(e^{-t} - e^{-2t}) - (t + \frac{1}{2}t^2)e^{-2t}$,

    (e) $\frac{1}{3}[\cos t\{1 - H(t - \frac{1}{2}\pi)\} \cos 2t + \frac{1}{2} \sin 2t \, H(t - \frac{1}{2}\pi)]$

2. $x = (96 \cos 3t - 110 \cos 4t + 14 \cos 2t)/35$,

    $y = (48 \cos 3t - 20 \cos 4t - 28 \cos 2t)/35$

3. $x = -2t \sin t$, $y = \cos t + t \sin t$

4. See answer to exercise 2 of §1.7

§3.6

1. (a) $\displaystyle\frac{1}{2} \sum_{n=0}^{[t]} (1 - 3^{-n-1})(t - n)$,   (b) $\displaystyle\sum_{n=0}^{[t]} \{2^{n+1} - (-\frac{3}{2})^{n+1}\}\sin(t - n)$,

    (c) $\displaystyle\frac{1}{9} \sum_{n=0}^{[t]} \{1 - (-2)^{n+1}(3n + 4)\}$,   (d) $\displaystyle\sum_{n=0}^{[t]} (-1)^n 2^{(n+1)/2} \cos\{(n - 1)\frac{1}{4}\pi\}$

2. (a) $\frac{1}{4}\{1 - (-3)^n\}$,   (b) $2^{1-n} + (-3)^n$

3. $\displaystyle H(t) + 2 \sum_{n=1}^{\infty} (-2)^n H(t - n) + \frac{1}{3} \sum_{n=2}^{\infty} \{1 - (-2)^{n-1}\}\cosh(t - n) \, H(t - n)$

4. $\displaystyle\sum_{n=0}^{[t]} 3^n(t-n)^{n+2}/(n+2)!$

5. $\frac{1}{3}(t + 3^{-1/2}2 \sin \sqrt{3}t)$

6. $\frac{1}{4}(1 + 3 \cosh 2t)$

7. $\pm 6^{1/2}t$

§3.7

1.   (a) $\frac{1}{8}m^{-1}(e^{-t} - e^{-9t})$;

     (b) $m^{-1}te^{-2t}$, $\frac{1}{4}m^{-1}\{1 - e^{-2t}(1 + 2t)\}$, $\frac{1}{8}m^{-1}\{e^{-2t}(1 + 2t) - \cos 2t\}$

2.   See answer to exercise 3 of §1.7.

3. $(EI)^{-1}\{Mx^4/24 - (M+P)x^3/6 + (\frac{1}{4}M + \frac{1}{3}P)x^2 + \frac{1}{6}P(x - \frac{2}{3})^3 H(x - \frac{2}{3})\}$

4. $\displaystyle -\frac{\gamma\alpha_1(\alpha_1 \cos \lambda t + \lambda \sin \lambda t - \alpha_1 e^{-\alpha_1 t})}{(\alpha_1 - \alpha_2)(\alpha_1^2 + \lambda^2)} + \frac{\gamma\alpha_2(\alpha_2 \cos \lambda t + \lambda \sin \lambda t - \alpha_2 e^{-\alpha_2 t})}{(\alpha_1 - \alpha_2)(\alpha_2^2 + \lambda^2)}$

5.   (1) $\sigma_0\phi_0[t + \frac{1}{2}\alpha t^2 - 2\{t - T + \frac{1}{2}\alpha(t - T)^2\}H(t - T)$

     $+ \{t - 2T + \frac{1}{2}\alpha(t - 2T)^2\}H(t - 2T)]$,

     (2) $\sigma_0\phi_\infty[t - \gamma^{-1}(1 - e^{-\gamma t}) - 2\{t - T - \gamma^{-1}(1 - e^{-\gamma(t-T)})\}H(t - T)$

     $+ \{t - 2T - \gamma^{-1}(1 - e^{-\gamma(t-2T)})\}H(t - 2T)]$

Problems

4.   (a) $k^{-2}(kt - \sin kt)$,   (b) $k^{-3}(\frac{1}{2}k^2 t^2 + \cos kt - 1)$

5. $\frac{1}{6}(5 \sin t + \cos t - e^{-t})$

7. $\frac{1}{4}\displaystyle\sum_{n=0}^{[t]} \{1 - \cos 2(t - n)\}$

8. $-\displaystyle\sum_{n=0}^{[t]} \cos(t - n - \frac{1}{2}n\pi)$

9. $\frac{1}{2}(1 + e^{-2t})$

10. $y(0) + (EI)^{-1}\{x^4/24 + \frac{1}{2}x^3 - \frac{3}{4}x^2 - \frac{2}{3}(x - \frac{1}{2})^3 H(x - \frac{1}{2})\}$,

     $47(384EI)^{-1}$

11. $\frac{1}{2}t^{-1} \sin 2t$

CHAPTER 4

Exercises

§4.1

1. (a) $f_x = 2x + 5y$, $\quad f_y = 5x + 4y - 1$, $\qquad$ (b) $f_x = ye^{xy}$, $\quad f_y = xe^{xy}$

$\quad$ (c) $f_x = \dfrac{1}{(1+x^2)(1+y^2)}$, $\quad f_y = -\dfrac{2y\,\tan^{-1}x}{(1+y^2)^2}$

2. $y = (r^2 - x^2)^{1/2}$, $\quad y_x = -x/y$, $\quad y_r = r/y$, $\quad r_y = y/r$

3. $2u$, $\quad 2v$, $\quad -2v$, $\quad 2u$

§4.2

1. $xy(x^2+y^2)^{-1/2}$, $\quad (x^2+2y^2)(x^2+y^2)^{-1/2}$, $\quad (1+3\cos\theta)\{\frac{1}{2}(1-\cos\theta)\}^{1/2}$

3. $G_u = -2x\cosh u$, $\quad G_x = y + x = 2x - 2\sinh u$

4. $f_x = \log(x+y) + \dfrac{x}{x+y}$, $\quad f_y = \dfrac{x}{x+y}$, $\quad f_{xx} = \dfrac{x-y}{(x+y)^3}$, $\quad f_{xy} = \dfrac{y}{(x+y)^2}$,

$f_{yy} = \dfrac{-x}{(x+y)^2}$, $\quad f_{xxx} = \dfrac{-x-3y}{(x+y)^3}$, $\quad f_{xxy} = \dfrac{-2y}{(x+y)^3}$, $\quad f_{xyy} = \dfrac{x-y}{(x+y)^3}$,

$f_{yyy} = \dfrac{2x}{(x+y)^3}$

$f(1+h, k) \simeq h + k + \frac{1}{2}(h^2 - k^2) + \frac{1}{6}(-h^3 + 3hk^2 + 2k^3)$, $\quad f(1.1, 0.1) \simeq 0.201$

§4.3

1. $4\cos\psi + (\pi+1)\sin\psi$

2. $\dfrac{2F_x F_z F_{xz} - F_x^2 F_{zz} - F_z^2 F_{xx}}{F_z^3}$, $\quad \dfrac{F_y F_z F_{xz} + F_x F_z F_{yz} - F_{xy}F_{zz} - F_z^2 F_{xy}}{F_z^3}$

$-\frac{1}{4}(y+z)^{-3}\cos^2 x - \frac{1}{2}(y+z)^{-1}\sin x$, $\quad 0$

3. $u_x = \dfrac{-ku(2k-u)}{k - u(2u-k)(2k-u)t}$, $\quad u_t = \dfrac{u^2(u-k)(2k-u)}{k - u(2u-k)(2k-u)t}$

4. $\dfrac{V-\beta}{R}$, $\quad \dfrac{-RT}{(V-\beta)^2} + \dfrac{2\alpha}{V^3}$, $\quad \dfrac{-R}{V-\beta}\left\{\dfrac{-RT}{(V-\beta)^2} + \dfrac{2\alpha}{V^3}\right\}^{-1}$

§4.4

1. $(0, 0)$ is a relative maximum, $(\frac{1}{3}, \frac{1}{3})$ is a saddle point.

2. $x = y = \frac{1}{3}$m, $\quad z = \frac{2}{3}$m.

4.   1, at $x = -\frac{2}{3}$, $y = -\frac{1}{3}$, $z = \frac{2}{3}$.

      Minimum distance from origin to the region $2x + y - 2z + 3 \leqslant 0$.

5. $(0, 2k\pi)$ are relative maxima, $(0, 2k\pi + \pi)$ are saddle points, k integer.

7. $A = a + \lambda/W_a$, $\quad B = b + \lambda/W_b$, $\quad C = c + \lambda/W_b$,

      where $\lambda = \{180 - (a + b + c)\}/(W_a^{-1} + W_b^{-1} + W_c^{-1})$.

      $A = 80°$, $\quad B = 45\frac{1}{2}°$, $\quad C = 54\frac{1}{2}°$.

§4.5

1. $f = 0.225$, $\quad \Delta f = 1/320 \approx 0.003$.

6. $x^{2/3} + y^{2/3} = 1$.

Problems

1. $f_{rr} = n(n-1)r^{n-2}\cos n\theta$, $\quad f_{r\theta} = -n^2 r^{n-1}\sin\theta$, $\quad f_{\theta\theta} = -n^2 r^n \cos n\theta$.

2. $\partial(x, y)/\partial(r, \theta) = r$, $\quad \partial(r, \theta)/\partial(x, y) = r^{-1}$

4.   (a) $2h - 3k + 2h^2 - 3hk$, $\quad$ where $h = x - 1$, $\quad k = y - 1$

      (b) $3 + \frac{1}{2}h + k - \frac{1}{8}h^2$, $\quad$ where $h = x - 1$, $\quad k = y - 1$

      (c) $1 + x + y - z + \frac{1}{2}(x^2 + 2xy + y^2 - 2yz - 2zx + z^2)$

      (d) $-1 + \frac{1}{2}(\pi^2 h^2 + 2\pi hk + k^2)$ $\quad$ where $h = x - 1$, $\quad k = y - \pi$

5. 13 ± 0.03

6.   Maximum value 4 at $(0, 0)$, minimum value 0 at $(2, 0)$ for $k > \frac{1}{2}$.

7. $x_i = a_i^{-2} \Big/ \sum_{p=1}^{n} a_p^{-2}$.

11. $f_x = mx^{m-1}F - yx^{m-2}F'(y/x)$, $\quad f_y = x^{m-1}F'(y/x)$.

13. $\Phi_x = \Phi_\xi + \Phi_\eta$, $\Phi_t = c(-\Phi_\xi' + \Phi_\eta)$, $\quad \Phi_{xx} = \Phi_{\xi\xi} + 2\Phi_{\xi\eta} + \Phi_{\eta\eta}$,
      $\Phi_{xt} = c(-\Phi_{\xi\xi} + \Phi_{\eta\eta})$, $\quad \Phi_{tt} = c^2(\Phi_{\xi\xi} - 2\Phi_{\xi\eta} + \Phi_{\eta\eta})$.

CHAPTER 5

Exercises

§5.1

1. $V = \displaystyle\iint_{\mathcal{A}} (R^2 - x^2 - y^2)^{1/2}\,dA$, $\quad \mathcal{A}: x^2 + y^2 \leqslant R^2$

2. $\quad V = 2\displaystyle\iint\limits_{\mathscr{A}} (4a^2 - x^2 - y^2)^{1/2}\,\mathrm{d}A, \qquad \mathscr{A}: x^2 + y^2 \leqslant a^2$

§5.2

1. $\quad \tfrac{1}{2}(3e^2 - 4e - 1)$

2. $\quad \tfrac{1}{4}(2 + \sqrt{3})$

3. $\quad 2\pi\{1 - (a + 1)e^{-a}\}$

5. $\quad \tfrac{1}{10}(\pi - \tfrac{16}{15})a^5$

6. $\quad \tfrac{2}{3}\pi R^3; \tfrac{4}{3}\pi a^3(8 - 3\sqrt{3})$

7. $\quad \partial(x, y)/\partial(u, v) = -\tfrac{1}{2}u, \quad \tfrac{1}{2}|\,(c_1^2 - c_2^2)\log(m_2/m_1)\,|$

8. $\quad r = 2a\cos\theta; (2\pi - \tfrac{32}{9})a^3\cot\alpha$

§5.3

1. $\quad V = \tfrac{4}{3}\pi abc$

2. $\quad M = \tfrac{4}{3}\pi R^3\!\left(A + \dfrac{3B}{n + 3}\,R^n\right), \quad I_x = I_y = I_z = \tfrac{8}{15}\pi R^5\left(A + \dfrac{5B}{n + 5}\,R^n\right)$

3. $\quad \displaystyle\int_0^h\!\int_0^{2\pi}\!\int_0^{z\,\tan\alpha} \rho^3\,\mathrm{d}\rho\,\mathrm{d}\phi\,\mathrm{d}z = \tfrac{1}{10}\pi h^5\tan^4\alpha$

4. $\quad r = \tfrac{3}{16}(2 + \sqrt{3})|a, \quad \theta = 0$

§5.4

1. $\quad \tfrac{1}{2}a^2 + b^2 + \dfrac{ab}{2(a^2 - b^2)^{1/2}}\left[b\sinh^{-1}\left\{\dfrac{(a^2 - b^2)^{1/2}}{b}\right\} + 2a\sin^{-1}\left\{\dfrac{(a^2 - b^2)^{1/2}}{a}\right\}\right]$

2. $\quad 438\tfrac{14}{15}, \quad 381\tfrac{1}{3}$

3. $\quad$ (a) $\;8\tfrac{59}{105},\qquad$ (b) $\;10,\qquad$ (c) $\;7\tfrac{5}{6}$

§5.5

1. $\quad \sqrt{2}\pi$

2. $\quad \dfrac{c}{15k^4}\,[\{1 + k^2(a^2 + b^2)\}^{5/2} - (1 + k^2a^2)^{5/2} - (1 + k^2b^2)^{5/2} + 1]$

Problems

1. $\quad \pi ab^2$

2. $\quad \tfrac{2}{3}c^2$

3. $\displaystyle\int_{-1}^{0}\int_{1+y}^{1-y^2}(1-2y)e^{x+y}dx\,dy=\frac{1}{e}$

4. $\frac{1}{4}(\pi-2)$

5. $\partial(u,v)/\partial(x,y)=\dfrac{1}{ab}$, $\displaystyle\iint_{\substack{u^2+v^2\leqslant 1,\\ u\geqslant 0,\,v\geqslant 0}} a^4b^4uv(u^2+v^2)du\,dv=\tfrac{1}{12}a^4b^4$

6. $\bar{x}=\dfrac{1}{A}\displaystyle\iint_{\mathscr{A}}x\,dA=\dfrac{4a}{3(\pi-2)}$, $\bar{y}=\dfrac{1}{A}\displaystyle\iint_{\mathscr{A}}y\,dA=0$

7. $\displaystyle\int_{0}^{1}\int_{x/2}^{x}x^{-1/2}\,dy\,dx+\int_{1}^{2}\int_{x/2}^{1}(2-x)^{-1/2}\,dy\,dx=\tfrac{2}{3}$

8. $M=\frac{1}{3}\pi a^3\sigma(1+3b^4/a^4)$, $I_x=I_y=I_z=\tfrac{4}{45}\pi a^5\sigma(1+5b^6/a^6)$

9. (a) $\frac{1}{32}\pi^2 a^4$,   (b) $\frac{1}{3}\pi h^3\tan^2\alpha$

10. (i) $W_g=6\pi mgb$,   (ii) $-W_R=6\pi R(a^2+b^2)^{1/2}$

11. (a) 16,   (b) $14\frac{1}{5}$,   (c) 16

12. $\frac{1}{3}\pi\{(a^2+1)^{3/2}-1\}$

13. $\pi/\sqrt{2}$

14. $S=\displaystyle\iint_{x^2+y^2\leqslant a^2}\sigma(x,y)\{k^2(x^2+y^2)+1\}^{1/2}dA=\dfrac{2\pi\sigma_0}{3k^2}\{(k^2a^2+1)^{3/2}-1\}$

    $(\sigma=\sigma_0)$

15. (i) $A=a^2\left(\dfrac{\pi}{3}+\dfrac{\sqrt{3}}{2}\right)$,   (ii) $I_y=\tfrac{1}{16}(11\sqrt{3}-4\pi)a^4$

CHAPTER 6

Exercises

§6.1

1. (a) $2\mathbf{i}+3\mathbf{j}-2\mathbf{k}$,   (b) 0,   (c) $5\mathbf{i}-4\mathbf{j}-\mathbf{k}$,   (d) $\sqrt{(14)}$,
   (e) $14(\mathbf{i}+\mathbf{j}+\mathbf{k})$

§6.2

1. $\mathbf{i}+\mathbf{j}(2t-1)+\mathbf{k}\pi\cos\pi t$, $2\mathbf{j}-\mathbf{k}\pi^2\sin\pi t$, $a-\frac{1}{2}b$

§6.3

1. $3\pi\mathbf{i}-\mathbf{j}$, 4π

2. $\dfrac{2x\mathbf{i} + 2y\mathbf{j}}{x^2 + y^2}$,   0, $\dfrac{-2yz\mathbf{i} + 2xz\mathbf{j}}{x^2 + y^2}$,   1,   0 (except at $x = 0, y = 0$), $\dfrac{-2x\mathbf{i} - 2y\mathbf{j}}{x^2 + y^2}$

3. $(145)^{-1/2}(3\mathbf{i} + 6\mathbf{j} + 10\mathbf{k})$,

4.   0, $-2i z - \mathbf{k}x$

§6.4

1. $\displaystyle\iint\limits_{\mathscr{S}} \mathbf{F} \cdot \mathbf{n}\,dS = \frac{4\pi}{3} = \iiint\limits_{\mathscr{R}} \operatorname{div}\mathbf{F}\,dV$

3. $\displaystyle\iiint\limits_{\mathscr{R}} \operatorname{curl}\mathbf{F}\,dV = -\frac{4\pi\mathbf{j}}{3} = -\iint\limits_{\mathscr{S}} \mathbf{F} \times \mathbf{n}\,dS$

4.   Let $\mathscr{R}$ be the interior of a cylinder of unit height based on the plane region $\mathscr{A}$.

§6.5

1. $-\pi$

2. $2z\mathbf{i} - x\mathbf{k}$, $\displaystyle\iint\limits_{\Sigma} \operatorname{curl}\mathbf{F} \cdot \mathbf{n}\,dS = 0 = \oint_{\mathscr{C}} \mathbf{F} \cdot d\mathbf{r}$

3. $\frac{1}{2}x^2 y + \sin yz + e^z + C$

§6.6

1. $\displaystyle\iint\limits_{\mathscr{S}} K \operatorname{grad}\theta \cdot \mathbf{n}\,dS + \iiint\limits_{\mathscr{R}} \dot{\mu}\,dV = \frac{d}{dt}\iiint\limits_{\mathscr{S}} c\theta\,dV,\quad K\nabla^2\theta = c\frac{\partial\theta}{\partial t} - ke^{\beta\theta}$

2. $\displaystyle\iint\limits_{\mathscr{S}} -\nu \operatorname{grad} C \cdot \mathbf{n}\,dS = \left|-\frac{d}{dt}\iiint\limits_{\mathscr{R}} C\,dV\right.$

§6.7

1. $h_u = (\sinh^2 u + \cos^2 v)^{1/2} = h_v,\quad h_\phi = \sqrt{2}\cosh u \cos v$

   $k_u = h_u^{-1}\{(\mathbf{i}\cos\phi + \mathbf{j}\sin\phi)\sinh u \sin v + \mathbf{k}\cosh u \cos v\}$

   $k_v = h_v^{-1}\{(\mathbf{i}\cos\phi + \mathbf{j}\sin\phi)\cosh u \cos v - \mathbf{k}\sinh u \sin v\}$

   $k_\phi = -\mathbf{i}\sin\phi + \mathbf{j}\cos\phi$

2. $\operatorname{div}\mathbf{F} = \sin\phi + \cos\phi = (x + y)/(x^2 + y^2)^{1/2}$

3. $F_r = 0,\quad F_\theta = 0,\quad F_\phi = r^{-1}\sin\theta,\quad \operatorname{div}\mathbf{F} = 0$,

   $\operatorname{curl}\mathbf{F} = 2r^{-2}\mathbf{k}_r \cos\theta,\quad \oint_{\mathscr{C}} \mathbf{F} \cdot d\mathbf{r} = 2\pi\sin^2\theta_0 = \iint\limits_{\Sigma} \operatorname{curl}\mathbf{F} \cdot \mathbf{n}\,dS$

Problems

2. $\quad t = \dfrac{1}{\sqrt{2}}(i + j\cos\eta - k\sin\eta), \quad n = -(j\sin\eta + k\cos\eta),$

$\quad b = \dfrac{1}{\sqrt{2}}(-i + j\cos\eta - k\sin\eta)$

3. (a) $\quad \tfrac{1}{3}(6x + y^2 + 4xy + 2z - 2y),$ (b) $\quad \tfrac{1}{3}(yz + 2xz - 2xy)\sinh xyz$

4. $\quad \left\{ \dfrac{1}{r}i + \left(\dfrac{1}{r} - \dfrac{x}{r^3} \right) r \right\} \cos\left(r + \dfrac{x}{r} \right)$

5. $\quad x^2 - xy, \quad z(2y - x)i + z(2x + y)j + 2xyk$

6. $\quad i(6xy - 9y^2 - 4xz - 12z^2) + j(4yz + 8z^2 - 2x^2 - 3xy)$

$\qquad\qquad\qquad + k(x^2 + 3xz - 3y^2 - 6yz), \quad 0$

8. $\quad \{2s(xi + yj) + c(-yi + xj)\}/(x^2 + y^2) = 2s\rho^{-1}k_\rho + c\rho^{-1}k_\phi$

10. $\quad 4\pi$

11. $\quad 3\tfrac{1}{3}, \quad \tfrac{4}{3}, \quad -2$

12. $\quad 5r^2$

13. (a) $\quad F_x = xg, \quad F_y = yg, \quad F_z = zg, \quad$ where $\quad g = 1 - az(x^2 + y^2 + z^2)^{-1},$

(b) $\quad F_r = r - a\cos\theta, \quad F_\theta = F_\phi = 0,$

$\qquad 3 - 2az(x^2 + y^2 + z^2)^{-1} = 3 - 2ar^{-1}\cos\theta$

14. $\quad h_1 = h_2 = h_3 = 1, \quad k_1 \dfrac{\partial f}{\partial \bar{x}} + k_2 \dfrac{\partial f}{\partial \bar{y}} + k_3 \dfrac{\partial f}{\partial \bar{z}}$

15. $\quad x = \tfrac{1}{2}(\bar{x} - \sqrt{3}\bar{y}), \quad y = \tfrac{1}{2}(\sqrt{3}\bar{x} + \bar{y}), \quad z = \bar{z}$

$\quad k_1 = \tfrac{1}{2}(\bar{k}_1 - \sqrt{3}\bar{k}_2), \quad k_2 = \tfrac{1}{2}(\sqrt{3}\bar{k}_1 + \bar{k}_2), \quad k_3 = \bar{k}_3$

$\quad \bar{x} = \tfrac{1}{2}(x + \sqrt{3}y), \quad \bar{y} = \tfrac{1}{2}(-\sqrt{3}x + y), \quad \bar{z} = z$

$\quad \bar{k}_1 = \tfrac{1}{2}(k_1 + \sqrt{3}k_2), \quad \bar{k}_2 = \tfrac{1}{2}(-\sqrt{3}k_1 + k_2), \quad \bar{k}_3 = k_3$

$\quad F = \tfrac{1}{2}\{(\sqrt{3} - 1)\bar{x} - (\sqrt{3} + 1)\,\bar{y}\}\bar{k}_1 + \tfrac{1}{2}\{-(\sqrt{3} + 1)\bar{x} + (1 - \sqrt{3})\bar{y}\}\bar{k}_2 + \bar{z}\bar{k}_3$

$\quad \text{div } F = 1, \quad \text{curl } F = 0$

CHAPTER 7

Exercises

§7.1

1. (a) Second-order, linear, homogeneous

(b) Second-order, non-linear

    (c)   Second-order, linear, inhomogeneous

    (d)   Second-order, linear, homogeneous

    (e)   Second-order, non-linear

2.   (a) $\theta = A e^{\pm p(kx+t)}$

    (b) $1, x, (A e^{px} + B e^{-px}) e^{p^2 t}, (C \cos px + D \sin px) e^{-p^2 t}$

    (c) $e^{\pm p(x+ct)}, e^{\pm p(x-ct)}, \cos px \cos pct, \cos px \sin pct, \sin px \cos pct,$

          $\sin px \sin pct, (A + Bx)(C + Dt)$

§7.2

5.   (a) $\begin{cases} 0, x + ct < 0, \\ a \sin m(x + ct), x + ct > 0. \end{cases}$ (b) $\begin{cases} 0, x + ct < 0, \\ -a \sin m(x + ct), x + ct > 0 \end{cases}$

                                                                   $x = -\pi/2m$ for $t > \pi/2mc$

§7.4

2. $c\sqrt{5}/2a$ cycles per second

3. $A = 0: y = a/2, B = 0: x = a/2,$ $B = \pm A: y = a - x$ and $y = x$

4. $A = 0: y = a/2$ and $y = 3a/2, B = 0: x = a/2,$

    $B = A: y = a \pm x, B = -A: y = x$ and $y = 2a - x$

§7.5

1. $50°C$

2. $\theta = \sum\limits_{n=1}^{\infty} b_n \sin (n\pi x/a) \exp(-n^2 \pi^2 \kappa t/a^2)$ where $b_n = \dfrac{2\theta_0}{n\pi} \{1 - (-1)^n\}$

    The heat flow is infinite at $t = 0$. It is approximately equal to

    $\dfrac{4K\theta_0}{a} \exp\left(\dfrac{-\pi^2 \kappa t}{a^2}\right)$ when $\dfrac{\kappa t}{a^2}$ exceeds 0.059.

4. $A_n = \dfrac{2}{a} \int_0^a f(x) \cos \dfrac{n\pi x}{a}\, dx$ for $n \geqslant 0$

5. $\theta = c_0 + (c_1 - c_0)(x/a)$

§7.6

1.   (a) $T = 100 - 200(y/b),$ (b) $T = 100x/a,$

    (c) $T = 10 \dfrac{\sinh(3\pi x/b)}{\sinh(3\pi a/b)} \sin(3\pi y/b),$

(d) $T = 20b \sum_{n=1}^{\infty} \dfrac{(-1)^{n+1} \sinh(n\pi x/b)}{n\pi \sinh(n\pi a/b)} \sin(n\pi y/b)$

4.   (a) $T = \tfrac{1}{2}A_0 + \sum_{1}^{\infty} \left(\dfrac{\rho}{a}\right)^n (A_n \cos n\phi + B_n \sin n\phi)$

where $A_n = \dfrac{1}{\pi} \displaystyle\int_{-\pi}^{\pi} f(\phi)\cos n\phi \, d\phi, \quad B_n = \dfrac{1}{\pi} \displaystyle\int_{-\pi}^{\pi} f(\phi)\sin n\phi \, d\phi, \quad n \geqslant 0$

5.   Source of strength $-m$ at $x = 0, y = -d$. Potential in quadrant is

$$-\frac{m}{2}\log\{(x-a)^2 + (y-b)^2\} - \frac{m}{2}\log\{(x-a)^2 + (y+b)^2\}$$

$$-\frac{m}{2}\log\{(x+a)^2 + (y-b)^2\} - \frac{m}{2}\log\{(x+a)^2 + (y+b)^2\}$$

§7.7

2. $T(\rho, z) = 1$ at all points of the cylinder

3. $V = V_0 a/r$

4. $V = \dfrac{bV_b - aV_a}{b - a} - \dfrac{(V_b - V_a)ab}{(b - a)r}$

5. $V = \dfrac{m}{\{x^2 + y^2 + (z - d)^2\}^{1/2}} - \dfrac{m}{\{x^2 + y^2 + (z + d)^2\}^{1/2}}$

§7.9

1. $F = \left(\dfrac{m^2}{b^2} + \dfrac{n^2}{a^2}\right)\pi^2$

Problems

1. $A_n = \dfrac{2}{a} \displaystyle\int_0^a f(x)\cos \dfrac{n\pi x}{a} \, dx.$

$A_0 = \epsilon a/2, \quad A_{2k-1} = 0, \quad A_{2k} = \dfrac{\epsilon a}{k^2 \pi^2}\{(-1)^k - 1\} \quad \text{for } k \geqslant 1.$

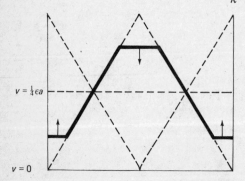

4. $\quad \theta = \frac{1}{2} Hx(a-x) - 2Ha^2 \sum_1^\infty \frac{1-(-1)^n}{n^3 \pi^3} \sin\left(\frac{n\pi x}{a}\right) \exp\left(-\frac{n^2 \pi^2 \kappa t}{a^2}\right)$

CHAPTER 8

Exercises

§8.1

1.   (a) (1),   (b) (4),   (c) (2),   (d) (3),   (e) (3),

    (f) (4)

§8.2

1. $\begin{pmatrix} 7 & 4 \\ -6 & 1 \end{pmatrix}$, $\begin{pmatrix} 1 & -5 \\ 6 & 4 \end{pmatrix}$, $\begin{pmatrix} 17 & -28 \\ 24 & 5 \end{pmatrix}$, $\begin{pmatrix} 6 & 14 \\ -12 & -8 \end{pmatrix}$, $\begin{pmatrix} 4 & 8 \\ -18 & -6 \end{pmatrix}$,

  $\begin{pmatrix} 23 & 7 \\ -14 & 2 \end{pmatrix}$, $\begin{pmatrix} 44 & 16 \\ -68 & 8 \end{pmatrix}$

2. $\begin{pmatrix} 7 & -1 & 5 & -2 \\ 18 & -6 & 9 & -19 \\ 20 & -9 & 5 & 7 \end{pmatrix}$, $\begin{pmatrix} 0 & 3 & 6 & -1 \\ 2 & 11 & -13 & 1 \\ 3 & -8 & 6 & 0 \end{pmatrix}$, $\begin{pmatrix} -3 & 23 & 0 \\ 6 & 0 & 13 \\ 9 & 52 & 6 \end{pmatrix}$,

  $\begin{pmatrix} 28 & -19 & 21 & -11 \\ -5 & -19 & 20 & -15 \\ 6 & 12 & -23 & 13 \\ -7 & 23 & -26 & 17 \end{pmatrix}$

3. $\begin{pmatrix} 5 & 6 & 4 \\ -6 & -4 & -3 \\ 0 & 0 & 1 \end{pmatrix}$, $\begin{pmatrix} 2 & -3 & 2 \\ 6 & -1 & -6 \\ 0 & 0 & 1 \end{pmatrix}$, $\begin{pmatrix} 2 & -6 & -5 \\ 0 & -4 & -9 \\ 0 & 0 & 1 \end{pmatrix}$, $\begin{pmatrix} 4 & 1 & -4 \\ 1 & -4 & 3 \\ -4 & 3 & -2 \end{pmatrix}$,

  $\begin{pmatrix} 21 & -14 & 4 \\ -14 & 13 & -3 \\ 4 & -3 & 1 \end{pmatrix}$

$\mathbf{AC}$ is upper triangular and $\mathbf{A} + \mathbf{A}^T$ and $\mathbf{AA}^T$ are symmetric. Yes

4.   (12), $\begin{pmatrix} 6 & 2 & 4 \\ 12 & 4 & 8 \\ 3 & 1 & 2 \end{pmatrix}$

6.

$$A^2 = \begin{pmatrix} -3 & -2 & -3 \\ -2 & 10 & 1 \\ 2 & 3 & 1 \end{pmatrix}, \quad A^3 = \begin{pmatrix} 3 & -6 & -2 \\ -4 & 33 & 4 \\ 0 & 8 & 5 \end{pmatrix}$$

§8.3

1.   10,   −17,   −27,   287,   −61

2. $(a-b)(b-c)(c-a)$, $(a^2-b^2)(b^2-c^2)(c^2-a^2)$,   0

3.
$$\begin{pmatrix} 4 & 4 & -2 \\ 4 & -8 & -2 \\ 14 & 4 & -10 \end{pmatrix}, \quad \begin{pmatrix} 0 & 15 & -1 \\ 2 & -6 & 0 \\ 10 & 18 & -8 \end{pmatrix}, \quad -8, \ -18, \ 144, \ 144$$

4.   (a) $x = 1$ or $x = -2$,   (b) $x = 8, 2$ or -2

§8.4

1.   (a)
$$\begin{pmatrix} 3 & 2 \\ -1 & 1 \end{pmatrix}, \quad \begin{pmatrix} 3 & -2 \\ 1 & 1 \end{pmatrix}, \quad \begin{pmatrix} 3 & 1 \\ -2 & 1 \end{pmatrix}, \quad \frac{1}{5}\begin{pmatrix} 3 & 1 \\ -2 & 1 \end{pmatrix}$$

(b)
$$\begin{pmatrix} -4 & 2 & 0 \\ 4 & -6 & 0 \\ 0 & 0 & 4 \end{pmatrix}, \quad \begin{pmatrix} -4 & -2 & 0 \\ -4 & -6 & 0 \\ 0 & 0 & 4 \end{pmatrix}, \quad \begin{pmatrix} -4 & -4 & 0 \\ -2 & -6 & 0 \\ 0 & 0 & 4 \end{pmatrix}, \quad \frac{1}{4}\begin{pmatrix} 2 & 2 & 0 \\ 1 & 3 & 0 \\ 0 & 0 & -2 \end{pmatrix}$$

(c)
$$\begin{pmatrix} 3 & -1 & -10 \\ -3 & -7 & 2 \\ -12 & 4 & 16 \end{pmatrix}, \quad \begin{pmatrix} 3 & 1 & -10 \\ 3 & -7 & -2 \\ -12 & -4 & 16 \end{pmatrix}, \quad \begin{pmatrix} 3 & 3 & -12 \\ 1 & -7 & -4 \\ -10 & -2 & 16 \end{pmatrix},$$

$$\frac{1}{24}\begin{pmatrix} -3 & -3 & 12 \\ -1 & 7 & 4 \\ 10 & 2 & -16 \end{pmatrix}$$

(d)
$$\begin{pmatrix} -3 & -4 & 1 \\ -4 & -8 & -4 \\ 1 & -4 & -3 \end{pmatrix}, \quad \begin{pmatrix} -3 & 4 & 1 \\ 4 & -8 & 4 \\ 1 & 4 & -3 \end{pmatrix}, \quad \begin{pmatrix} -3 & 4 & 1 \\ 4 & -8 & 4 \\ 1 & 4 & -3 \end{pmatrix},$$

$$\frac{1}{8}\begin{pmatrix} -3 & 4 & 1 \\ 4 & -8 & 4 \\ 1 & 4 & -3 \end{pmatrix}$$

(e) $\begin{pmatrix} 4 & 6 & 2 \\ 6 & 9 & 3 \\ 2 & 3 & 1 \end{pmatrix}$, $\begin{pmatrix} 4 & -6 & 2 \\ -6 & 9 & -3 \\ 2 & -3 & 1 \end{pmatrix}$, $\begin{pmatrix} 4 & -6 & 2 \\ -6 & 9 & -3 \\ 2 & -3 & 1 \end{pmatrix}$, no inverse

(f) $\begin{pmatrix} -24 & 0 & 0 \\ -12 & 6 & 0 \\ 2 & 5 & -4 \end{pmatrix}$, $\begin{pmatrix} -24 & 0 & 0 \\ 12 & 6 & 0 \\ 2 & -5 & -4 \end{pmatrix}$, $\begin{pmatrix} -24 & 12 & 2 \\ 0 & 6 & -5 \\ 0 & 0 & -4 \end{pmatrix}$,

$\dfrac{1}{24}\begin{pmatrix} 24 & -12 & -2 \\ 0 & -6 & 5 \\ 0 & 0 & 4 \end{pmatrix}$

2. (a) $x_1 = 3/8$, $x_2 = -13/24$, $x_3 = 5/12$

   (b) $x_1 = -1/8$, $x_2 = 9/2$, $x_3 = -13/8$

3. $\dfrac{1}{7}\begin{pmatrix} -7 & 0 & -7 \\ -2 & 2 & -1 \\ 6 & 1 & 3 \end{pmatrix}$

4. $\begin{pmatrix} 1+\sqrt{2} & 0 & \sqrt{2} & 0 \\ 0 & 1 & 0 & 0 \\ \sqrt{2} & 0 & \sqrt{2} & 0 \\ 0 & 0 & 0 & 2-\sqrt{2} \end{pmatrix}$, $\begin{aligned} EAU_B &= -L[(1+\sqrt{2})X_B + \sqrt{2}X_C], \\ EAV_B &= -LY_B, \\ EAU_C &= -L\sqrt{2}(X_B + X_C), \\ EAV_C &= -L(2-\sqrt{2})Y_C \end{aligned}$

§8.5

2. $x_1 = \dfrac{1}{3}\bar{x}_1 - \dfrac{2\sqrt{2}}{3}\bar{x}_2,$

   $x_2 = \dfrac{2}{3}\bar{x}_1 + \dfrac{1}{3\sqrt{2}}\bar{x}_2 + \dfrac{1}{\sqrt{2}}\bar{x}_3,$

   $x_3 = -\dfrac{2}{3}\bar{x}_1 - \dfrac{1}{3\sqrt{2}}\bar{x}_2 + \dfrac{1}{\sqrt{2}}\bar{x}_3,$

   $(-14/3, -8\sqrt{2}/3, \sqrt{2})$

§8.6

1. (a) $\begin{pmatrix} 2 & 1 \\ 1 & 2 \\ 2 & 1 \\ 1 & 2 \end{pmatrix}$, (b) $\begin{pmatrix} 2 & 4 & 2 \\ 2 & 2 & 2 \\ 4 & 2 & 4 \\ 2 & 8 & 2 \\ 6 & 4 & 6 \end{pmatrix}$

2. (a)
$$\frac{1}{4}\begin{pmatrix} 4 & -4 & 0 & 0 & 0 & 0 \\ -1 & 2 & 0 & 0 & 0 & 0 \\ 0 & 0 & 4 & -4 & 0 & 0 \\ 0 & 0 & -1 & 2 & 0 & 0 \\ 0 & 0 & 0 & 0 & 4 & -4 \\ 0 & 0 & 0 & 0 & -1 & 2 \end{pmatrix},$$

(b)
$$\frac{1}{24}\begin{pmatrix} 7 & 2 & -2 & -1 \\ 2 & 7 & -1 & -2 \\ -2 & -1 & 7 & 2 \\ -1 & -2 & 2 & 7 \end{pmatrix}$$

§8.7

1. (a)
$$\begin{pmatrix} 1 & 1 & 0 & \vdots & 1 \\ 0 & 1 & -\tfrac12 & \vdots & \tfrac12 \\ 0 & 0 & 1 & \vdots & 1 \end{pmatrix}$$
  3, 3, consistent
  $x_1 = 0, x_2 = 1, x_3 = 1$

(b)
$$\begin{pmatrix} 1 & -1 & -2 & \vdots & 1 \\ 0 & 1 & 1 & \vdots & 1 \\ 0 & 0 & 0 & \vdots & 0 \end{pmatrix}$$
  2, 2, consistent
  $x_1 = 2 + t, x_2 = 1 - t, x_3 = t$

(c)
$$\begin{pmatrix} 1 & -1 & -2 & \vdots & 1 \\ 0 & 1 & 1 & \vdots & 0 \\ 0 & 0 & 0 & \vdots & 1 \end{pmatrix}$$
  2, 3, inconsistent

(d)
$$\begin{pmatrix} 1 & 1 & 1 & \vdots & 1 \\ 0 & 1 & 2 & \vdots & 3 \end{pmatrix}$$
  2, 2, consistent
  $x_1 = -2 + t, x_2 = 3 - 2t, x_3 = t$

(e)
$$\begin{pmatrix} 1 & 0 & 1 & \vdots & 2 \\ 0 & 1 & 0 & \vdots & 1 \\ 0 & 0 & 1 & \vdots & 1 \\ 0 & 0 & 0 & \vdots & 0 \end{pmatrix}$$
  3, 3, consistent
  $x_1 = 1, x_2 = 1, x_3 = 1$

(f)
$$\begin{pmatrix} 1 & 0 & \tfrac12 & \vdots & 1 \\ 0 & 1 & 0 & \vdots & 1 \\ 0 & 0 & 1 & \vdots & -1 \\ 0 & 0 & 0 & \vdots & 1 \end{pmatrix}$$
  3, 4, inconsistent

(Row echelon forms are not unique)

§8.8

1. (a) No,   (b) $x_1 : x_2 : x_3 = 1 : -1 : 1$,

(c) $x_1 : x_2 : x_3 = 10 : 11 : -3$,   (d) No,

(e) $x_1 : x_2 : x_3 : x_4 = 3 : 6 : -5 : -19$,

(f) $x_1 : x_2 : x_3 = 7 : -2 : -1$

2. (a) $y = A \exp\{\frac{1}{2}(-5 + \sqrt{5})t\} + B \exp\{\frac{1}{2}(-5 - \sqrt{5})t\}$,

$z = \frac{1}{2}(1 + \sqrt{5})A \exp\{\frac{1}{2}(-5 + \sqrt{5})t\} + \frac{1}{2}(1 - \sqrt{5})B \exp\{\frac{1}{2}(-5 - \sqrt{5})t\}$,

(b) $y = 6Ae^{2x} - Be^{-2x} + Ce^x$,

$z = -Ae^{2x} + 6Be^{-2x} + Ee^{-x}$,

(c) $x = Ae^{-t} + Be^{-2t}$,

$y = -Ae^{-t} - Be^{-2t} + Ce^{-3t}$,

$z = \qquad - Be^{-2t} + Ce^{-3t}$

3. $I_1 = A_1 \cos(p_1 t + \epsilon_1) + A_2 \cos(p_2 t + \epsilon_2)$,

$I_2 = B_1 \cos(p_1 t + \epsilon_1) + B_2 \cos(p_2 t + \epsilon_2)$,

where p_1^2, p_2^2 are the roots of

$(L_1 L_2 - M^2)p^4 - (L_1 C_2^{-1} + L_2 C_1^{-1})p^2 + C_1^{-1} C_2^{-1} = 0$,

and

$B_1/A_1 = (-L_1 + C_1^{-1} p_1^{-2})/M, \quad B_2/A_2 = (-L_1 + C_1^{-1} p_2^{-2})/M$

§8.9

1. (a) $4 \pm \sqrt{5}$; $\alpha_1(2 \quad 1 - \sqrt{5})^T$, $\alpha_2(2 \quad 1 + \sqrt{5})^T$

(b) $a \pm ib$; $\alpha_1(1 \quad i)^T$, $\alpha_2(1 \quad -i)^T$

(c) $1, 4, 5$; $\alpha_1(0 \quad 0 \quad 1)^T$, $\alpha_2(1 \quad 0 \quad 0)^T$, $\alpha_3(0 \quad 1 \quad 0)^T$

(d) $1, 1, -1$; $\alpha_1(1 \quad 1 \quad 0)^T + \beta(0 \quad 0 \quad 1)^T$ $(\alpha_1, \beta$ arbitrary), $\alpha_2(1 \quad -1 \quad 0)^T$

(e) $2, 2, -2$; $\alpha_1(0 \quad 1 \quad 1)^T$, $\alpha_2(4 \quad 1 \quad -7)^T$

(f) $1, -1, 2$; $\alpha_1(1 \quad 2 \quad 2)^T$, $\alpha_2(2 \quad -2 \quad 1)^T$, $\alpha_3(2 \quad 1 \quad -2)^T$

(g) $1, e^{i\theta}, e^{-i\theta}$; $\alpha_1(0 \quad 0 \quad 1)^T$, $\alpha_2(1 \quad i \quad 0)^T$, $\alpha_3(1 \quad -i \quad 0)^T$

2. $\alpha_2(1 \quad -1 \quad \sqrt{2})^T$, $\alpha_3(1 \quad 1 \quad 0)^T$

3. (a) $\sqrt{6}/2\pi$; $y_1 = 4A \cos(\sqrt{6}t)$, $y_2 = -A \cos(\sqrt{6}t)$

(b) $1/2\pi$; $y_1 = B \cos t$, $y_2 = B \cos t$

4. (a) $\sqrt{(g/l)}/2\pi$; $\theta_1 = \theta_2 = \theta_3 = A \cos\sqrt{(g/l)}t$

(b) $\{\sqrt{(g/l)} + \sqrt{(k/m)}\}/\pi$; $\theta_1 = -\theta_3 = B \cos\{\sqrt{(g/l)} + \sqrt{(k/m)}\}t$, $\theta_2 = 0$

(c) $\{\sqrt{(g/l)} + 3\sqrt{(k/m)}\}/\pi$; $\theta_1 = \theta_3 = -2\theta_2 = C \cos\{\sqrt{(g/l)} + 3\sqrt{(k/m)}\}t$

Problems

1.   (s = symmetric, a = anti-symmetric, n = neither)

(a) s,   (b) a,   (c) s,   (d) a,   (e) n,

(f) n,   (g) s,   (h) $B + B^T = 0$,   (i) n,

(j) n,   (k) s,   (l) s,   (m) a,   (n) s,

(o) a,   (p) s,   (q) s,   (r) s

3. $x_1 = 4z_1 - 4z_2 - 3z_3,$ $z_1 = \frac{1}{2}(3x_1 - 2x_2 + 3x_3),$

$x_2 = -4z_1 + 3z_2 + 6z_3,$ $z_2 = \frac{1}{5}(4x_1 - 5x_2 + 6x_3),$

$x_3 = -6z_1 + 6z_2 + 7z_3,$ $z_3 = \frac{1}{5}(3x_1 \qquad + 2x_3)$

4. $x_1 = (-\frac{1}{2} - \frac{11}{4}\sqrt{3})y_1 + (-\frac{3}{2} - \sqrt{3})y_2 + (\frac{23}{4} - \frac{1}{2}\sqrt{3})y_3,$

$x_2 = (1 - \sqrt{3})y_1 + (1 + 2\sqrt{3})y_2 + (-1 + \sqrt{3})y_3,$

$x_3 = (\frac{1}{4} + \frac{11}{4}\sqrt{3})y_1 + (-\frac{7}{2} + \frac{1}{2}\sqrt{3})y_2 + (\frac{17}{4} + \frac{1}{4}\sqrt{3})y_3$

5. $\dfrac{1}{3}\begin{pmatrix} -3 & 9 & 0 & -6 \\ 1 & -4 & 2 & 4 \\ -7 & 19 & -5 & -16 \\ -2 & 5 & -1 & -5 \end{pmatrix}, \quad \begin{pmatrix} 1 \\ -1 \\ 3 \\ 2 \end{pmatrix}$

6.   2. $x = \frac{1}{2} + \lambda, \quad y = 6\frac{1}{2} + 3\lambda, \quad z = 2\lambda$

7.   2.   Unique solution $x_1 = \frac{1}{2}, \ x_2 = -2$

8.   First, second and fourth equations are compatible, with solutions

$x_1 = \frac{1}{3}(4\lambda - 3\mu + 8), \quad x_2 = \frac{1}{3}(\lambda - 1), \quad x_3 = \lambda, \quad x_4 = \mu$

9.   No solution if $\beta \neq 1$. If $\beta = 1$, solution is $x_1 = -\frac{1}{2} - \frac{1}{2}\lambda + \frac{3}{2}\mu,$

$x_2 = \frac{5}{6} + \frac{1}{2}\lambda + \frac{5}{6}\mu, \ x_3 = \lambda, \quad x_4 = \mu.$

10.   2, 3. $\alpha(1 \ \ -1 \ \ 0)$

11. $-2, 4, 8.$ $\alpha_1(1 \ \ 0 \ \ -3)^T, \quad \alpha_2(1 \ \ -2 \ \ -3)^T, \quad \alpha_3(1 \ \ 0 \ \ -1)^T;$

$-8, 64, 512,$ same eigenvectors as $\mathbf{A}$;

$-\frac{1}{2}, \frac{1}{4}, \frac{1}{8},$ same eigenvectors as $\mathbf{A}$

12. $3, 4, 5.$ $(\sqrt{\frac{2}{3}} \ \ 1 \ \ \sqrt{\frac{1}{3}})^T$

13. $-3, -1 + i, -1 - i;$ $(-3 : 1 : -6),$ $(1 - i : -1 : 1),$ $(1 + i : -1 : 1)$

14. $\sqrt{2}/2\pi, \quad \omega_1/2\pi, \quad \omega_2/2\pi,$ where $\omega_1^2 = (21 + \sqrt{177})/12,$

$\omega_2^2 = (21 - \sqrt{177})/12$

$(-2 : 0 : 1),$ $(3 : \frac{3}{4} - \frac{1}{4}\sqrt{177} : 2),$ $(3 : \frac{3}{4} + \frac{1}{4}\sqrt{177} : 2)$

15. $\alpha = 2, \quad \sqrt{(2 - \sqrt{2})}/2\pi, \quad \sqrt{(2 + \sqrt{2})}/2\pi, \quad c(1 \ \ \sqrt{2} \ \ 1)^T$

CHAPTER 9

Exercises

§9.2

1. 513 ± 1, 0.002; 513.4 ± 0.2, 0.0005; no significant gain.
   0.885 ± 0.008, 0.009; 0.886 ± 0.007, 0.008; no gain

2. 7.13 ± 0.08, 7.12948 ± 0.00005

3. Using 5 sig. figs., (a) $x_1 = 14.933 \pm 0.00025$, $x_2 = 0.067 \pm 0.00025$,
   (b) $x_1 = 14.933 \pm 0.00025$, $x_2 = 0.066966 \pm 0.000002$

§9.4

2. 1.2134

3. 4.799, 0.512, −0.508

4. $x_{n+1} = \dfrac{1}{N}\left(N + 1 - \dfrac{1}{A}x_n^N\right)x_n$, 1.73205

5. 0.6529

Problems

1. 0.3367

2. 4.236, −0.236

3. $x + x^2 + \frac{1}{3}x^3$, $|x| \leqslant 0.432$; 0.243, −0.219

4. 1.2373

5. $(-0.591, 0.374)$, $(0.949, 1.187)$

6. $x = -0.462$, $y = 2.891$

CHAPTER 10

Exercises

§10.2

1. $x = 1.00$, $y = 2.00$, $z = 3.00$

2. (a) $x = 1.00$, $y = 2.00$
   (b) $x = 1.06$, $y = 4.39$

§10.3

1. $x = 1.06$, $y = 4.39$

2. $x = 1.00, \quad y = 2.00, \quad z = 3.00$

3. $\omega = 1.1, 5$ iterations   and $\omega = 1.4, 10$ iterations

§10.4

1. $\begin{pmatrix} 1.2 & 4.4 & -5.8 \\ -0.2 & -1.4 & 1.8 \\ -0.2 & -0.4 & 0.8 \end{pmatrix}$

2. (a) $\begin{pmatrix} -3.5 & 1.5 \\ 1.5 & -0.5 \end{pmatrix}$ (b) $\begin{pmatrix} -0.273 & 0.636 \\ 0.182 & -0.091 \end{pmatrix}$

3. $\begin{pmatrix} 4.246 & 0.961 & 0.001 & -0.007 \\ 0.961 & 4.020 & 1.001 & 0.002 \\ 0.001 & 1.001 & 3.988 & 0.993 \\ -0.007 & 0.002 & 0.993 & 3.725 \end{pmatrix}$

§10.5

1. (a) $5.3723, \quad (0.4574, 1)T$ (b) $-0.3723, \quad (1, -0.6861)T$

2. 10.7002

Problems

1. $x_1 = 0.46, \quad x_2 = 0.93, \quad x_3 = 0.21, \quad x_4 = 0.56, \quad x_5 = -0.19, \quad x_6 = -0.03$

2. $x = 0.12, \quad y = 0.48, \quad z = 1.10$

3. $x = 1.043, \quad y = 0.971, \quad z = 1.071, \quad w = 0.943$

4. Working with three decimal places gives $x_1 = 14.658$, $x_2 = -57.732$, $x_3 = -30.447$, $x_4 = -15.925$. The solution accurate to three decimal places is $x_1 = 14.429, x_2 = -56.857, x_3 = -30.000, x_4 = -15.714$

5. (a) $\begin{pmatrix} -0.0783 & 0.5391 & -0.1391 & 0.0957 \\ 0.3652 & -0.1826 & -0.0174 & -0.1130 \\ 0.0696 & -0.0348 & 0.2348 & 0.0261 \\ 0.0870 & -0.0435 & 0.0435 & -0.2174 \end{pmatrix}$

    (b) $\begin{pmatrix} 0.0211 & 0.3803 & -0.1127 & 0.0493 \\ 0.3803 & -0.1549 & -0.0282 & -0.1127 \\ -0.1127 & -0.0282 & 0.2676 & 0.0704 \\ 0.0493 & -0.1127 & 0.0704 & -0.2183 \end{pmatrix}$

6. $\mathbf{BZ}^{(i)} = \mathbf{AY}^{(i-1)}$, $\mathbf{Y}^{(i)} = \dfrac{1}{c_i} \mathbf{Z}^{(i)}$, 3.609, $(1, -0.733)T$

CHAPTER 11

Exercises

§11.3

1. (a) 1.1364, (b) 0.7812

2. (i) Everett's formula to 4th diff., 0.4719; to modified 2nd diff., 0.4720,
   (ii) Bessel's formula to 2nd diff., 0.4716; $x = 1.857$

§11.5

1. (i) -0.219, (ii) -0.2227, exact $= -0.2225$

3. $f_1' = (\tfrac{1}{2}h)\{\delta f_{1/2} + \delta f_{3/2} - \tfrac{1}{6}\delta^3 f_{1/2} - \tfrac{1}{6}\delta^3 f_{3/2} + \tfrac{1}{30}(\delta^5 f_{1/2} + \delta^5 f_{3/2}) - \ldots\}$

Problems

1. $f(1.030) = 0.26128$, $x = 1.036446$

2. (a) 25.791, (b) 20.492, (c) 24.54, (d) 9.8787; $x = 3.219$

3. $f(18) = 3.6280$; $\int = 93.279$; $f(25) = 3.9061$; $x = 27.134$ incorporating 3rd differences

4. 2179. Error $= 0(3\Delta^4 f_0/128)$. Round-off errors dominate.

CHAPTER 12

Exercises

§12.4

2. (b) $P(E_1) + P(E_2) + P(E_3) + P(E_4) - P(E_1 \cap E_2) - P(E_1 \cap E_3) - P(E_1 \cap E_4)$
   $\qquad - P(E_2 \cap E_3) - P(E_3 \cap E_4) - P(E_2 \cap E_4) + P(E_2 \cap E_3 \cap E_4)$
   $\qquad + P(E_1 \cap E_3 \cap E_4) + P(E_1 \cap E_2 \cap E_4) + P(E_1 \cap E_2 \cap E_3)$
   $\qquad - P(E_1 \cap E_2 \cap E_3 \cap E_4)$

6. $P(M_1 | D) = 0.258$, $P(M_2 | D) = 0.339$

§12.5

3. $\sigma^2 = \displaystyle\int_{-\infty}^{\infty} (x - x_0)^2 f(x) \mathrm{d}x - (x_0 - \mu)^2$, where $f(x)$ is the p.d.f.

4. 0.72 sq. unit

Problems

1. 'Code' letters a, b, c, ... , z correspond, in order, to 'actual' letters
    M I R V U N K A D W J P F Z O L Y G Q X B S T H E C

3. $\mu = 13.9°C\ (57.0°F)$, $\sigma^2 = 22.4°C^2\ (72.6°F^2)$,   c.v. = 34.1% (15.0%)

4. $P(C_r) = \dfrac{7-r}{28}$, $P(D_s) = \dfrac{1}{28}(1, 1, 2, 2, 3, 3, 4, 3, 3, 2, 2, 1, 1)$ for $s = 0(1)12$,

    $P(E_t) = \dfrac{1}{4}$. The remaining probabilities are: $\dfrac{1}{28}, \dfrac{1}{14}, \dfrac{1}{28}, \dfrac{1}{4}, \dfrac{1}{28}, \dfrac{3}{7}, \dfrac{2}{7}, \dfrac{2}{5}, \dfrac{1}{2}, \dfrac{7}{18}$

5. On average five-sixths of all guesses are wrong. 82

6. 0.265, $1 - (0.95)^{n-1}$

7. $^{n-1}C_{m-1}\,p^{n-m}q^m$ if $n \geqslant m$; 0 otherwise

10. 0.373 (by Bayes's Theorem)

11. $\alpha = \frac{1}{4}$, $\beta = \frac{1}{3}$

12. (a) $\frac{1}{2}r^2 e^{-r}$, $0 \leqslant r < \infty$,   (b) $\dfrac{1}{8\pi\rho}\exp\left\{\left(\dfrac{-3m}{4\pi\rho}\right)^{1/3}\right\}$, $0 \leqslant m < \infty$,

      mean diameter = 6, mean mass = $80\pi\rho$

13. $\left(\dfrac{2}{\pi}\right)^{1/2} e^{-\frac{1}{2}u^2}$, $0 \leqslant u < \infty$, $\left(\dfrac{1}{2\pi v}\right)^{1/2} e^{-\frac{1}{2}v}$, $0 \leqslant v < \infty$

17. $\bar{x} = 1.0$. If X is $Po(1)$ then $P\{X > 2\} = 0.08$

18. (a) 0.995,   (b) 0.0036,   (c) 0.0013;   (a) $1 - (0.995)^{100}$,

      (b) $1 - 0.5(0.995)^{99}$,   (c) $1 - 4950(0.995)^{98}(0.005)^2$.

      Using $\bar{x} = np = 0.5$ gives 0.61, 0.31, 0.08

19. $\bar{x} = 15.96$, $s^2 = 15.2$.   Standardizing, $z = (x - 15.96)/3.90$

Reversals
≤6 7 8 9 10 11 12 13 14 15
Expected Number
2.0 2.0 3.5 5.4 8.6 12.3 15.8 20.5 24.3 25.6

                Reversals
                  16   17   18   19   20   21   22 23 24 25 ≥26
                Expected Number
                  27.4 25.4 24.2 20.2 15.5 12.0 8.3 5.2 3.3 1.9 1.9

20. (a) 0.048,   (b) 0.227,   (c) 0.308;   0.067

21. $\rho(Y_1, Y_2) = \dfrac{k_{11}k_{21} + k_{12}k_{22}}{\{(k_{11}^2 + k_{12}^2)(k_{21}^2 + k_{22}^2)\}^{1/2}}$

Index